ORDINARY DIFFERENTIAL
EQUATIONS *A First Course*

ORDINARY DIFFERENTIAL EQUATIONS

A FIRST COURSE

Fred Brauer and John A. Nohel

University of Wisconsin

W. A. BENJAMIN, INC., *New York · Amsterdam · 1967*

ORDINARY DIFFERENTIAL EQUATIONS: *A First Course*
UNIVERSITY MATHEMATICS SERIES, *Fred Brauer and*
John A. Nohel, Consulting Editors

The manuscript was put into production on March 21, 1967;
this volume was published on August 15, 1967.

This publisher is pleased to acknowledge the assistance of
Sophie Adler who designed the text and cover, and of
Graphic Presentations who produced the illustrations.

W. A. BENJAMIN, INC., *New York, New York 10016*

To Esther and Vera

PREFACE

Differential equations are essential for an understanding of many important physical and mathematical problems. This was first recognized by Newton in the 17th century and used in his study of the motion of particles, including planets. The development of the subject as a branch of modern mathematics came in the 19th and 20th centuries through the pioneering work of a number of mathematicians, notably Birkhoff, Cauchy, Lyapunov, Picard, Poincaré, and Riemann. This theoretical foundation, which has been and is being developed by other mathematicians, has in turn led to interesting new applications and a deeper understanding of complex physical systems.

In this book we use physical problems to motivate the study of differential equations and to explain the need for a theory. We then present methods of solution which are useful for handling problems encountered in simple applications and which will prepare the student for subsequently more difficult theoretical considerations. We have avoided exhaustive descriptions of elementary methods of solutions; at the same time we hope that we have omitted none of the essential ones.

The book is intended as a text for an introductory course for students with no previous experience in differential equations. There is adequate material for courses of various lengths (quarter, semester, or two quarters). By a change in emphasis on the part of the instructor, the material can be taught at several levels either as a regular or an honors course.

In a one-semester sophomore course at the University of Wisconsin for students with no background in linear algebra, taught in two lectures and two discussion sections per week, the authors have covered essentially the first five chapters of this book. Approximately two to two and one-half weeks were spent on each of Chapters 1, 2, and 5, and three and one-half to four weeks were spent on each of Chapters 3 and 4.

Naturally, the needs of a particular group of students or the taste of the instructor may suggest a different choice of topics, and we have provided additional material for this purpose. The following chart indicates the dependence of chapters on one another.

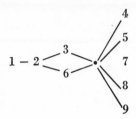

In addition, Bessel functions, covered in Chapter 4, enter in Section 5.6. However, this section could be omitted in a study of Chapter 5. The Gronwall inequality, essential for the study of Chapter 7, is found in Section 6.3, this material being independent of the rest of Chapter 6.

While physical problems are used throughout for motivation and illustration, the treatment is self-contained and does not depend on a knowledge of physics. Likewise, no knowledge of linear algebra is needed in the first five chapters. *However, students who are already familiar with the elements of linear algebra should replace Chapter 3 by Chapter 6.* Except for Section 3.6, all the main results of Chapter 3 are included as special cases of Chapter 6. Thus, a possible sequence for these students is: Chapters 1, 2, 6, Section 3.6, and parts of Chapters 4 and 5. Chapter 7 might well be substituted for parts of Chapters 4 and 5 if the students are more theoretically oriented.

In current applications of differential equations, a significant role is played by high-speed computers. For this reason we have included an introduction to approximate methods of solution suitable for high-speed computation in Chapter 2 and again in more detail in Chapter 8. Students interested primarily in engineering applications might replace parts or all of Chapters 4 and 5 by material in Chapter 8. In addition, these students might profit from an introduction to Laplace transforms in Chapter 9.

Much of the modern theory of differential equations can be explained properly and efficiently only with the aid of linear algebra. As far as the present book is concerned, a knowledge of linear algebra is essential for a proper understanding of Chapter 6 and the last sections of Chapters 7 and 8. We believe that this emphasis is both important and consistent with current and future trends in the mathematical training of engineers, physical scientists, and mathematicians.

The formulation of mathematical models for physical problems is often misunderstood. In our view, a logically reasonable procedure is the following. We start from a concrete physical situation (such as the pendulum), pass to an "idealized" physical model (such as a rod of zero weight, pivot of zero friction, Newton's laws assumed, no air resistance), and then, using the "idealized" physical model, construct a mathematical model. The construction of a mathematical model is often difficult and requires much practice. However, this important aspect of the procedure will not be our main concern. The mathematical model could be as simple as a quadratic equation, or so complex that it would take many pages to describe. The next step is to use mathematical techniques to explore properties of the model, and to answer specific questions. If such questions can be answered, we are then able to compare the mathematical model with physical reality as observed by experiment, thereby testing the validity of the laws assumed in making the physical approximation. The process may be described by Figure 0.1.

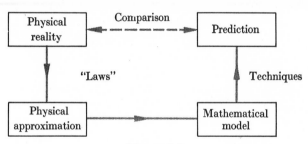

Figure 0.1

The choice of physical laws and approximations and the construction of mathematical models belong more to science than to mathematics. We shall, therefore, concentrate mainly on the techniques used to pass from the mathematical model to the prediction.

It is very important not to confuse the model with reality. A model is most useful when it imitates reality closely, but there will always be aspects of reality which it does not reproduce, and it will always predict events that do not, in fact, occur. The skill of a scientist lies in knowing how far, and in what context, to use a particular mathematical model. One simple illustration may help here. Physicists sometimes speak of light as a wave, and sometimes as a particle. Which is it? The answer is neither, for both are names for specific mathematical models for light. Both successfully predict ("explain") some of the observed behavior of light, but both predict behavior that light does not exhibit. The moral is clear: do not expect to have exactly one correct mathematical model for any aspect of reality.   Newton's "laws of motion" are not the only "correct" ones (for example, at very high velocities, Einstein's laws are closer to reality), nor is Hooke's law the only correct law of elasticity.

Because of the way mathematics is often taught, a student is apt to think of it as merely a collection of techniques, tricks and skills which some professor wishes him to learn.   As his experience grows, the person who does research in other physical sciences will learn that for him mathematics is something entirely different.   He will learn to think of mathematics as a tool which can explain and help him understand various physical phenomena in the physical world.   At the same time, it is very important for the prospective mathematician to become acquainted with those mathematical problems which are closely connected with applications, as many of these problems are of considerable mathematical interest in their own right.   It is our hope that this book will serve these various needs.

Fred Brauer

John A. Nohel

Madison, Wisconsin
April 1967

ACKNOWLEDGMENTS

It would be impossible to acknowledge all the help, direct and indirect, that we have received in the preparation of this book, but certainly the influence of Professors Norman Levinson and Earl Coddington, which dates back to 1950, will be quite apparent. The many discussions that one of us had with Professor Marvin Sledd between 1953 and 1961 about the importance of physical applications in elementary courses have been extremely valuable. The first three chapters grew out of some notes written jointly with our colleague Professor R. Creighton Buck as part of a revised calculus sequence, and his collaboration is acknowledged with pleasure. A preliminary edition of this book has been used in 1966–67, resulting in many helpful comments. We are particularly grateful to Professors H. A. Antosiewicz and Aaron Strauss for detailed reviews of this preliminary edition, as well as to Professors C. C. Conley, J. E. Hall, M. Johnson, B. Noble, and A. D. Ziebur for their helpful suggestions and criticisms. Dr. W. P. Timlake has provided several valuable comments, particularly about Chapter 8. Messrs. D. Appleyard, B. Berndt, D. Ferguson, H. Mullikin, N. Riesenberg, J. Williamson, and R. Witt have also contributed useful suggestions from their teaching of the material and many of the answers to exercises. We are also indebted to the teaching assistants and students at the University of Wisconsin who served as the initial captive audience for us. Finally, it is a pleasure to acknowledge the help of Mrs. Phyllis J. Rickli who has converted almost illegible handwriting into a clean manuscript, and the help of the staff of W. A. Benjamin, Inc., in the construction of this book. Naturally any errors that may remain in spite of all this assistance are our responsibility, and we would appreciate being advised of them.

NOTE TO THE STUDENT

We hope that we have provided you with a readable introduction to the subject of differential equations. May we suggest that a mathematics book is to be read with paper and pencil at hand. There will inevitably be places where you must fill in some details. Scattered throughout the text you will find numerous exercises which are designed to help you to follow the argument and to reach a better understanding of the subject. If you cannot carry out an exercise, assume its validity and continue reading, but remember to fill the gap at the earliest opportunity. The exercises at the ends of sections are intended to give practice in applying the material in the text. The miscellaneous exercises at the end of each chapter are intended to help you review the chapter as a whole, as well as to supplement some of the material in the chapter.

Answers to some exercises, principally those with odd numbers, may be found at the back of the book. If your answers do not agree with ours, recheck your work. If you still do not agree, your answers may be equivalent to ours but written in a different form. Another possibility is that our answers may be incorrect.

CONTENTS

xiii

| Chapter **1** | **INTRODUCTION TO ORDINARY DIFFERENTIAL EQUATIONS** |

Differential equations originated in attempts to explain and understand the motion of particles. Before undertaking a systematic development, we illustrate how differential equations arise by deriving the equations of motion for some typical physical systems. The mass-spring system (considered in Section 1.1) and the pendulum (developed in Section 1.2) lead to differential equations which are prototypes of mathematical models for other important physical systems. We shall use these typical examples to motivate our study of differential equations.

Before turning to the construction of these mathematical models, we recall some aspects of the Newtonian model for the motion of a particle. In this model, it is assumed that a body, called a particle, can be represented as a point having mass. (We shall assume knowledge of the rather difficult concept of mass; for practical purposes, mass can be measured by the weight of the body.) It is assumed that, in the absence of "forces," the motion of the particle is unaccelerated, and therefore is straight-line motion with constant, perhaps zero, velocity (**Newton's first law**). The presence of acceleration is therefore to be interpreted as a sign of the presence of a **force.** This is a vector quantity given by **Newton's second law**: If $\mathbf{F}$* is the force acting on a particle of mass m moving with a velocity $\mathbf{v}$, then

$$\mathbf{F} = \frac{d}{dt}\,(m\mathbf{v})$$

The vector quantity $m\mathbf{v}$ is called the momentum of the particle. If the

---

* Vectors will appear in boldface type throughout.

1

mass is constant, Newton's second law may be written as

$$\mathbf{F} = m\,\frac{d\mathbf{v}}{dt} = m\mathbf{a}$$

where $\mathbf{a}$ is the acceleration vector of the particle, and t is time.

In the Newtonian model, the gravitational force can be shown (experimentally) to be proportional to mass, so that problems involving gravitational forces on particles near the earth's surface can be handled conveniently by assuming that the acceleration g due to gravity is constant.

1.1 The Mass-Spring System

A weight of mass m is suspended from a rigid horizontal support by means of a very light spring (see Figure 1.1). The weight is allowed to

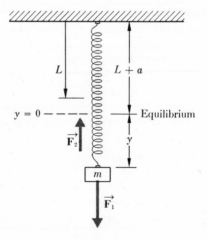

Figure 1.1

move only along a vertical line (no lateral motion in any direction is permitted). The spring has a natural (unstretched) length L when no weight is suspended from it. When the weight is attached, the system has an equilibrium position at which the spring is stretched to a length $L + a$, where a is a positive number. We may set the system in motion by displacing the weight from this equilibrium position by a prescribed amount and releasing it either from rest or with some prescribed initial velocity. Our task is to describe in mathematical terms the motion of the system.

Since the motion is restricted to a vertical line, the position of the weight can be described completely by the displacement y from the equilibrium position (see Figure 1.1).   The mathematical equivalent of the motion of the mass-spring system will then be a function ϕ such that $y = \phi(t)$ describes the position of the weight for each value of $t \geq 0$, where $t = 0$ represents the starting time of the motion.   In order to determine the motion, that is to determine the function ϕ, we must impose additional restrictions on ϕ.   For example, if we displace the weight a distance y_0 and then release it, we would require that $\phi(0) = y_0$.   If we release it from rest at this position, we will also require that $\phi'(0) = 0$.   Experience suggests that with these additional conditions, the motion is completely determined.

In order to obtain a mathematical model for this system, we must use physical principles and simplifying approximations.   The basic tool is Newton's second law.   We first give mathematical expressions for the forces acting on the weight using physical principles and approximations, and then using Newton's second law we obtain an equation which must be satisfied by the function ϕ.   Our assumptions are as follows:

(a) The spring has zero mass.

(b) The weight can be treated as though it were a particle of mass m.

(c) The spring satisfies Hooke's law, which states that the spring exerts a restoring force on the weight toward the equilibrium position; the magnitude of this force is proportional to the amount by which the spring is stretched from its natural length.   The constant of proportionality $k > 0$ is called the spring constant, and a spring obeying Hooke's law is called a linear spring.

(d) There is no air resistance and the only external force is a constant vertical gravitational attraction.

We stress the fact that a different set of physical assumptions would lead to a different mathematical model.   Further, the accuracy of a particular mathematical model in predicting physical phenomena will depend primarily on the reasonableness of the physical assumptions.

Newton's second law is stated above in terms of vectors.   Since in this problem the motion is restricted to a line, the vectors involved are one-dimensional, and vector notation is not needed.   With reference to Figure 1.1, we shall measure the displacement y from equilibrium ($y = 0$) choosing the downward direction as positive.   The force of gravity F_1 in Figure 1.1 is mg, and the restoring force of the spring F_2 is $-k(y + a)$ by

Hooke's law. Observe that Figure 1.1 has been drawn with $y > 0$ so that F_2 is directed upward.

•EXERCISE

1. Sketch the analogue of Figure 1.1 with $y < 0$ and compute the forces F_1 and F_2 in this case.

The total force acting on the weight is

$$F_1 + F_2 = mg - k(y + a)$$

The equilibrium position occurs when this total force is zero. Therefore at equilibrium, $mg - k(0 + a) = 0$ or $a = mg/k$. Thus we can rewrite the total force at any position y of the mass as

$$F_1 + F_2 = mg - k\left(y + \frac{mg}{k}\right) = -ky$$

By Newton's second law,

$$F_1 + F_2 = -ky = \frac{d}{dt}(mv) = m\frac{d^2y}{dt^2}$$

Therefore the motion of the system is specified by the equation

$$\frac{d^2y}{dt^2} + \frac{k}{m}y = 0 \tag{1.1}$$

Equation (1.1) is the mathematical model for the mass-spring system under the assumptions (a), (b), (c), (d). It is a **differential equation** (of the second order). To obtain specific information about a particular motion, we must specify other information. For example, we have already remarked that if we release the weight from rest with an initial displacement y_0, we must impose the pair of **initial conditions**

$$\phi(0) = y_0 \qquad \phi'(0) = 0 \tag{1.2}$$

The mathematical problem is then to find a function ϕ defined for all $t \geq 0$ satisfying the differential equation (1.1), that is $\phi''(t) + (k/m)\phi(t) = 0$

for $t \geq 0$, and the initial condition (1.2). Such a function is called
**a solution of the differential equations (1.1) obeying the initial
conditions (1.2).** We may hope that this solution will give a good
approximation to the actual motion of a real mass-spring system, and
that we can use the solution to predict properties of the motion which can
be measured experimentally.

We can modify the model in several ways by attempting to use physical
laws which are closer to reality. For example, leaving assumptions (a),
(b), (c) intact, we could replace assumption (d) by

(d′) There is air resistance proportional to the velocity in addition to
the gravitational attraction.

In this case, the mathematical model for the mass-spring system will be
the equation

$$\frac{d^2y}{dt^2} + b\frac{dy}{dt} + \frac{k}{m}y = 0 \tag{1.3}$$

together with the initial conditions (1.2), in place of (1.1) and (1.2). The
term $b\,dy/dt$ is the appropriate mathematical translation of the resistance
force of air, where b is a nonnegative constant.

•EXERCISE

2. Derive equation (1.3). [*Hint:* In Figure 1.1 there will now be a force $\mathbf{F}_3$
arising from assumption (d′).]

Another possible model is obtained by replacing (c) by the assumption
that there is a restoring spring force which is not necessarily linear and
leaving assumptions (a), (b), (d) intact. In this case, we replace equation
(1.1) by

$$\frac{d^2y}{dt^2} + g(y) = 0 \tag{1.4}$$

where $g(y)$ is a so-called nonlinear spring term which is positive when y is
positive and negative when y is negative. The precise form of the function g depends on the physical law assumed in place of Hooke's law; we
might have $g(y) = (k_1/m)y + k_2y^3$.

Differential equations such as (1.1), (1.3), or (1.4) describe the "equation of motion" of particular systems. As we shall see, their solutions describe the nature of all the possible motions of the physical system as predicted by each mathematical model. When conditions such as (1.2) are added, we single out one or more special solutions to predict the behavior of the system if the motion starts from some particular state or configuration.

The reader may wish to acquire additional facility in the mathematical formulation of simple physical problems.

•EXERCISES

(In each of the following, assume that the particle is near the earth's surface and that gravity is the only force acting on the particle. The reader will have no difficulty in solving the differential equations obtained.)

3. A particle is released from a height y_0 above the earth's surface ($y = 0$) with initial velocity (velocity at $t = 0$) in the vertical direction of magnitude v_0. Find the height $y(t)$ of the particle above the earth's surface and velocity $v(t) = dy/dt$ as functions of time.

4. A particle is released at an initial position s_0 (distance s is to be considered positive in the downward direction) on a frictionless inclined plane (as shown in Figure 1.2) with an initial velocity v_0. Find its distance $s(t)$, measured along the inclined plane from the top, and its velocity $v(t)$ as functions of time.

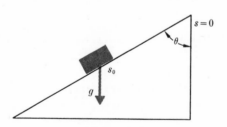

Figure 1.2

5. A projectile is fired from an initial position (x_0, y_0) with an initial velocity of magnitude v_0 at an angle of inclination θ, $0 \leq \theta \leq \pi/2$. Find its horizontal and vertical coordinates $x(t)$ and $y(t)$ as functions of time.

6. In each of the above exercises, discuss factors of actual physical situations which you feel have been neglected and consider their probable effect on the actual behavior of the system. What information do you feel can be obtained from the mathematical models you have constructed? In particular, compare the time it takes for a body released from height h to reach the ground to that time for a projectile fired horizontally with initial velocity v_0.

1.2   The Pendulum Problem

A pendulum is made by attaching a weight of mass m to a very light and rigid rod of length L mounted on a pivot so that the system can swing in a vertical plane.   If we set the weight moving, can we describe the nature of its motion?   For example, can we answer questions such as the following: (1a) How does the nature of the motion depend upon the mass m and the length of the rod L?   (1b) If we hold the weight out an angle θ_0 (see Figure 1.3) and then release it, how will the speed it attains at the bottom of its swing depend upon m, L, and the angle θ_0?   (1c) We know from experience that the weight will swing back approximately to the

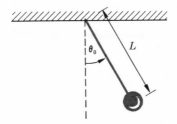

Figure 1.3

original position θ_0.   How long will this take?   How does this period depend upon m, L, and θ_0?   (1d) What happens if we immerse the pendulum in some substance such as water, which will exert a considerable amount of resistance on the moving weight?   How will this affect the nature of the motion?   Will the pendulum eventually come to rest, and, if so, how long will this take?   (1e) Will any of the previous answers change if we move the apparatus to the top of a high mountain or place it in an orbiting satellite?

We have assumed that the rod supporting the weight is perfectly rigid. This means that the position (state) of the pendulum at time t can be described completely by the size of the angle θ (Figure 1.4).   The mathematical equivalent of the "motion" of the pendulum will then be a function ϕ such that $\theta = \phi(t)$ describes the position of the pendulum for each value of $t \geq 0$, where $t = 0$ represents the starting time of the motion. To determine the motion, that is, to determine the function ϕ, we must impose additional restrictions on ϕ.   For example, in the question (1b) posed above, we would require that $\phi(0) = \theta_0$.   If we release the pendulum from rest at that position, we would also require $\phi'(0) = 0$.

We must next apply physical principles to obtain additional restrictions on the function ϕ. Again, the basic tool is **Newton's second law.** In order to apply this to our pendulum problem, we will make a number of

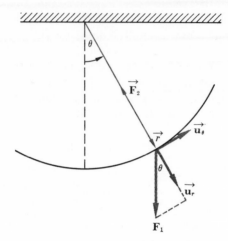

Figure 1.4

simplifying assumptions; this is the step that leads to what we called the **physical approximation** in the Preface (Figure 0.1).

(a) We assume that the rod is rigid, of constant length L, and of zero mass.

(b) We assume that the weight can be treated as though it were a particle of mass m.

(c) We assume that there is no air resistance, that the pivot is without friction, and that the only external force present is a constant vertical gravitational attraction.

At any time t, the gravitational force $\mathbf{F}_1$ has magnitude mg and is directed downward. There is also a force $\mathbf{F}_2$ of tension in the rod of magnitude T directed along the rod toward the pivot. Let $\mathbf{u}_r$ denote a unit vector in the radial direction and let $\mathbf{u}_\theta$ denote a unit vector in the tangential direction, as shown in Figure 1.4. Then $\mathbf{F}_1$ can be expressed as

$$\mathbf{F}_1 = F_r \mathbf{u}_r + F_\theta \mathbf{u}_\theta$$

where F_r, F_θ are the components of $\mathbf{F}_1$ in the radial and tangential directions respectively, $F_r = mg \cos \theta$, $F_\theta = -mg \sin \theta$. Also $\mathbf{F}_2$ can be expressed as

$$\mathbf{F}_2 = -T\mathbf{u}_r$$

where $T > 0$. We recall from calculus that the vectors $\mathbf{u}_r$, $\mathbf{u}_\theta$ satisfy the relations

$$\frac{d\mathbf{u}_r}{d\theta} = \mathbf{u}_\theta \qquad \frac{d\mathbf{u}_\theta}{d\theta} = -\mathbf{u}_r$$

Let $\mathbf{r}$ denote the position vector of the weight, taking the pivot as the origin, so that

$$\mathbf{r} = L\mathbf{u}_r$$

Differentiation, using the chain rule and the above relations, gives

$$\frac{d\mathbf{r}}{dt} = L\frac{d\mathbf{u}_r}{dt} = L\mathbf{u}_\theta \frac{d\theta}{dt}$$

and

$$\frac{d^2\mathbf{r}}{dt^2} = L\mathbf{u}_\theta \frac{d^2\theta}{dt^2} - L\left(\frac{d\theta}{dt}\right)^2 \mathbf{u}_r \tag{1.5}$$

The total force acting on the weight is

$$\mathbf{F}_1 + \mathbf{F}_2 = (mg \cos \theta - T)\mathbf{u}_r - mg \sin \theta \, \mathbf{u}_\theta \tag{1.6}$$

By Newton's second law (since the mass is constant),

$$\mathbf{F}_1 + \mathbf{F}_2 = m\frac{d^2\mathbf{r}}{dt^2}$$

Thus, equating coefficients of $\mathbf{u}_r$, $\mathbf{u}_\theta$ in (1.5) and (1.6) we obtain

$$-mL\left(\frac{d\theta}{dt}\right)^2 = mg \cos \theta - T$$

$$mL\frac{d^2\theta}{dt^2} = -mg \sin \theta$$

Note that the first of these equations contains also the unknown quantity T. However, if the angle θ can be determined from the second equation, then the magnitude of the tension T can be found from the first equation; in fact, $T = mg \cos \theta + mL(d\theta/dt)^2$. Therefore, the motion of the pendulum is completely determined by the second equation which may be written in the form

$$\frac{d^2\theta}{dt^2} + \frac{g}{L} \sin \theta = 0 \tag{1.7}$$

This equation is the mathematical model for this simplified pendulum problem. It is a differential equation (of second order). In deriving this equation we have used only assumptions (a), (b), (c) (p. 8), and we have not yet imposed any additional restrictions. If we wish to be more specific about the questions we ask, we must specify other information. For example, question (1b) (p. 7) asks us to predict the speed of the weight at the bottom of its swing, if we hold the weight out at an angle θ_0 and release it from rest. The last phrase is equivalent to the pair of **initial conditions**

$$\phi(0) = \theta_0 \qquad \phi'(0) = 0 \tag{1.8}$$

Question (1b) can then be restated as:

What is $L\phi'(t)$ when $\theta = 0$?

The **mathematical** problem is then to find a function ϕ, defined for all $t \geq 0$, such that $\theta = \phi(t)$ satisfies the differential equation (1.7), that is,

$$\phi''(t) = -\frac{g}{L} \sin \phi(t) \qquad (t \geq 0)$$

and such that (1.8) also holds. If we can find such a function, we say that we have found a **solution of the differential equation (1.7) obeying the initial conditions (1.8)**. We may then hope that this function ϕ will give a good approximation to the actual motion of a specific pendulum, and that we can use ϕ to predict properties of the pendulum which can be measured experimentally.

We can modify the model in several ways, some motivated by physical intuition and some by mathematical requirements. For example, we could replace assumption (c) (p. 8) by:

(c′) The pendulum encounters resistance, due to the pivot and the sur-
rounding air, which is proportional to the velocity vector,

and leave the remaining assumptions unchanged.
  In this case,

$$\frac{d^2\theta}{dt^2} = -\frac{g}{L}\sin\theta - \frac{k}{m}\frac{d\theta}{dt} \tag{1.9}$$

replaces equation (1.7) as the appropriate mathematical model.   The
last term is the appropriate mathematical translation of the additional
resistance force.   Note that equation (1.9) reduces to (1.7) if $k = 0$.

•EXERCISES

  1. Derive equation (1.9).   [*Hint:* The resistance force is $-kL(d\theta/dt)\mathbf{u}_\theta$.]
  2. What is the magnitude of the tension assuming that θ has been found
from equation (1.9)?

  There are many other possible modifications of the model.   We could,
for example, attempt to imitate nature more closely by allowing the
pendulum rod to be slightly elastic, and let it increase or decrease its
length in accordance with the magnitude of the radial component F_r.
This ought to result in a mathematical model whose predictions come
much closer to agreeing with experiment than either (1.7) or (1.9).   However, it would be such a complicated model that it would be extremely
difficult, at the present state of mathematical knowledge, to extract useful
information from it in a simple way.
  Until research in mathematics makes it possible to develop easier
techniques to work with complicated mathematical models, we must be
content to work with simpler models which are likely to give less accurate
predictions.
  Sometimes, in fact, a complicated model is replaced by a simpler model
that is **mathematically** related to the original one, even though there
may be no physical justification for this step.   Let us reexamine the
differential equation

$$\frac{d^2\theta}{dt^2} = -\frac{g}{L}\sin\theta \tag{1.7}$$

If θ is small, then $\sin\theta$ and θ have almost the same value.   (Consult any
table of trigonometric functions for radian arguments and also recall that

$\lim\limits_{\theta \to 0} \sin \theta/\theta = 1$.)   We might therefore be inclined to replace (1.7) by the equation

$$\frac{d^2\theta}{dt^2} = -\frac{g}{L}\theta \qquad (1.10)$$

and hope that this **new** mathematical model (which, as we shall see, is much easier to solve) is almost as good for some purposes as the model (1.7).   When we analyze these equations, it turns out that (1.7) and (1.10) predict quite different qualitative behavior for pendulums, and that some of the predictions made by (1.10) do not happen at all, but that **both** agree quite well with experiment if we restrict the swing of the pendulum to a rather small arc.   (Incidentally, equations (1.7) and (1.10) also predict things that a "real" pendulum does not do at all; for example, they predict that once a pendulum is set swinging, it will never stop! Equation (1.9) comes closer to reality by at least predicting that the pendulum will slow down.)

1.3   The Need for a Theory

The task of formulating a mathematical model for the motion of a simple pendulum leads to a differential equation; different physical approximations lead to different models (that is, different differential equations). Let us look at just one of these, namely,

$$\frac{d^2\theta}{dt^2} + \frac{g}{L}\sin\theta = 0 \qquad (1.11)$$

Suppose we intend to use this model to answer question (1b) of Section 1.2; we would first have to find a solution $\theta = \phi(t)$ of the equation which satisfies (1.11), and the initial conditions:

$$\phi(0) = \theta_0 \qquad \phi'(0) = 0 \qquad (1.12)$$

It would be disconcerting if there were to be no such solution!   This would seem to mean that there would have to be an internal inconsistency in the set of assumptions that were made about the physical approximation.   Since an actual pendulum certainly moves, this would mean that our model is quite useless, and we would have to construct a new model. Therefore, in order for a model to be useful it must at least have solutions; a very important aspect of mathematical theory has to do with proving that certain classes of differential equations **have** solutions.   For brevity we describe this as the **existence problem.**

This is not the only requirement that is desirable for a useful model. Suppose we displace a pendulum to an angle θ_0 and release it and watch the resulting motion of the pendulum.   Experience suggests that if we could repeat the experiment **exactly,** we would get exactly the same motion.   Described differently, this is the hypothesis of determinism; a particular set of initial conditions must result in exactly one motion. Applied to a differential equation, this means that there should be **exactly one solution for a given set of initial conditions.**   For brevity, we refer to this as the **uniqueness problem.**   For example, if we start an experiment with the pendulum at rest with zero displacement ($\theta_0 = 0$), we know from experience that it will stay at rest.   This motion is described by saying that $\theta \equiv 0$ for all $t \geq 0$.   This means that we would want to be sure that the only solution $\phi(t)$ of the equation (1.11) which obeys $\phi(0) = 0$, $\phi'(0) = 0$, is $\phi(t) \equiv 0$.

There is a third property that experience suggests as a requirement for a satisfactory model.   Experiments cannot in fact be repeated in **exactly** the same way.   However, if all of the initial conditions are **almost** exactly the same, we expect the outcomes to be almost the same.   We therefore desire that the solutions of our mathematical model should also have this property.   Stating this in mathematical language, this says that the solutions of a differential equation ought to depend continuously on the values of the initial conditions.   We refer to this property as **continuity of the solution with respect to initial conditions.**

Thus, a mathematical model of a physical process should have the following three properties:

(a) A solution satisfying the given initial conditions exists.
(b) Each set of initial conditions leads to a unique solution (that is, two solutions that satisfy the same initial conditions are identical).
(c) The solutions depend continuously on the initial conditions.

Mathematicians have shown that wide classes of differential equations obey the requirements (a), (b), (c), even for equations for which there is no possible methods for finding the solutions explicitly.   We will state one of these general results in Section 1.8; it will guarantee, for example, that the various mass-spring and pendulum equations satisfy requirements (a), (b), (c).

•EXERCISE

1. Prove existence, uniqueness, and continuity of the solution ϕ of the equation $y'' = f(t)$, where f is continuous for t in an interval I, such that $\phi(t_0) = y_0$, $\phi'(t_0) = z_0$ for some t_0 in I. [*Hint:* Use the fundamental theorem of the calculus as follows: If ϕ is a solution on some interval I containing t_0, then $\phi'(t) - \phi'(t_0) = \int_{t_0}^{t} \phi''(s)\, ds = \int_{t_0}^{t} f(s)\, ds$, or $\phi'(t) = z_0 + \int_{t_0}^{t} f(s)\, ds$; now integrate again and check the result by direct substitution.]   Note that the solution is a continuous function of (t, t_0, y_0, z_0).

1.4   First-Order Equations

Having seen how physical problems can give rise to differential equations, we now begin a systematic study.   From the mathematical point

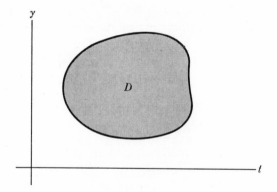

Figure 1.5

of view, a differential equation is an equation involving a function and some of its derivatives from which this function is to be determined, for example, (1.1), (1.7), and (1.10).   Differential equations involving functions of a single variable are called **ordinary differential equations,** while differential equations involving functions of several variables are called **partial differential equations.**   We shall be concerned with the former.

Suppose f is a function that is defined on some region* D in the plane, see Figure 1.5.   Because the independent variable in physical problems is so often time, we label the axes t and y, rather than x and y.   Then, the

---

* We postpone a precise definition of region to p. 23.

first-order differential equation associated with the function f is

$$y' = f(t, y) \tag{1.13}$$

where $'$ denotes differentiation with respect to t.   The reason for calling
(1.13) a first-order differential equation is that the highest-order derivative appearing in (1.13) is the first derivative.   To **solve** (1.13) means to
find an interval I on the t axis (see Figure 1.6) and a function ϕ such that:

(i) $\phi(t)$ and $\phi'(t)$ exist for each t in I.*
(ii) The graph of ϕ lies in the region D, that is, all points $(t, \phi(t))$, for
       t in I, lie in D.
(iii) For each t in I, we have

$$\phi'(t) = f(t, \phi(t)) \tag{1.14}$$

Such a function ϕ is called a solution of (1.13) on the interval I.   For
brevity, we say that $y = \phi(t)$ satisfies (1.13) on the interval I, or that ϕ is

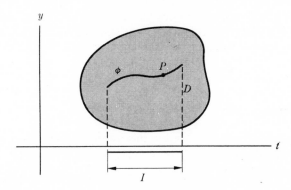

Figure 1.6

a solution of (1.13) on I.   This has an immediate geometric interpretation.   The function f assigns some numerical value $f(t, y)$ to each point
P in D, with coordinates (t, y) (see Figure 1.6).   Then (1.14) merely says
that the tangent to the curve $y = \phi(t)$ has slope $f(t, y)$ at each point P of
its graph.   This simple geometrical interpretation will be used to construct solutions graphically in the next section.

---

* By differentiability of a function at an end point of an interval, we mean the
existence of a one-sided derivative.

In the examples and exercises to follow, we shall employ the notation $\{(t, y) \mid a < t < b, \ c < y < d\}$ to denote the set of points in the plane whose coordinates (t, y) satisfy both inequalities $a < t < b$ and $c < y < d$. Similarly, $\{(t, y) \mid a \leq t \leq b, \ c \leq y \leq d\}$ will denote the set of points whose coordinates (t, y) satisfy both inequalities $a \leq t \leq b$ and $c \leq y \leq d$. Thus for example $\{(t, y) \mid -1 \leq t < 2, 5 \leq y < \infty\}$ denotes the infinite strip in the plane bounded by the lines $t = -1, t = 2, y = 5$, lying above the line $y = 5$, where the lines $t = -1$ and $y = 5$ are included in the set but the line $t = 2$ is not. The reader will have no difficulty in seeing that $\{(t, y) \mid -\infty < t < \infty, \ -\infty < y < \infty\}$ is the entire (t, y) plane, while $\{(t, y) \mid -\infty < t < \infty, 0 < y < \infty\}$ is the upper half-plane excluding the t axis. It should now be clear that $\{t \mid a < t < b\}$ denotes the points on the t axis satisfying the inequality $a < t < b$, that is, the open interval (a, b). For convenience we shall usually write this simply as the interval $a < t < b$. We note also that $\{t \mid -\infty < t < \infty\}$ is the entire t axis while, strictly speaking, the inequality $-\infty < t < \infty$ refers to all real numbers rather than points on the t axis.

Example 1. $y' = 2y$. Here, $f(t, y) = 2y$, for all t and y. We can therefore take the region D to be the whole (t, y) plane. The function $\phi(t) = e^{2t}$ is easily seen to be a solution of $y' = 2y$ on the interval $-\infty < t < \infty$, since (i) and (ii) are satisfied for the choice of I as the interval $-\infty < t < \infty$, and (iii) is satisfied since $\phi'(t) = 2e^{2t} = 2\phi(t)$. Note that the function $\phi(t) = ce^{2t}$ is also a solution for each choice of c.

• EXERCISE

1. Sketch these functions for $c = 0, \pm\frac{1}{2}, \pm 1$.

The differential equation $y' = \alpha y$ has been used as a mathematical model for radioactive decay $(\alpha < 0)$ and population growth $(\alpha > 0)$.

Example 2. $y' = -y^2$. Here, $f(t, y) = -y^2$, and we can again take D to be the whole (t, y) plane. We can check that $\phi(t) = 1/t$ is a solution of the equation on either the interval $-\infty < t < 0$, or on the interval $0 < t < \infty$, but not on an interval such as $-2 < t < 2$. To see this the reader should draw a graph of ϕ on $-\infty < t < 0$ and $0 < t < \infty$, and then verify that the conditions (i), (ii), and (iii) are satisfied on each of these intervals.

• EXERCISES

2. Show that the functions $\phi(t) = 1/(t - c)$ are solutions of the same equation $y' = -y^2$ for each choice of the constant c on a suitably chosen interval. Draw graphs of these solutions for $c = 0, \pm 1, \pm 2$.

3. Consider the differential equation $y' = 2/(t^2 - 1)$ with $f(t, y) = 2/(t^2 - 1)$ defined on each of the domains $D_1 = \{(t, y) \mid -\infty < t < -1, |y| < \infty\}$, $D_2 = \{(t, y) \mid -1 < t < 1, |y| < \infty\}$, and $D_3 = \{(t, y) \mid 1 < t < \infty, |y| < \infty\}$. Verify that

$$\phi(t) = \log\left|\frac{t-1}{t+1}\right|.$$

is a solution of this equation on each of the intervals $-\infty < t < -1$, $-1 < t < 1$, and $1 < t < \infty$. (A graph of ϕ will show why $y = \phi(t)$ is not a solution on an interval such as $-2 < t < 2$.)

4. Consider the differential equation $y' = (y^2 - 1)/2$. Verify that $y = \phi(t) = (1 + ce^t)/(1 - ce^t)$ is a solution of this equation on an appropriate interval I, for any choice of the constant c. [*Hint:* Try this first for specific values of c such as $c = 0$, $c = 1$, $c = -1$.] Draw graphs of ϕ for each choice of c.

1.5   Graphical Solution

The geometric interpretation given in Section 1.4 (p. 15) is the basis for a simple and effective procedure for finding out something about the nature of the solutions of the differential equation

$$y' = f(t, y)$$

where the function f is defined on a region D in the (t, y) plane. We can use a special device to display the values of f in such a fashion that it will be possible to sketch the solutions directly. (Later, we shall see that this crude process is the key to a useful numerical procedure, adaptable to digital computers, for finding approximations to solutions of a differential equation.)

The function f defines a **direction field** or **tangent field** in the region D as follows: At each point P in D with coordinates (t, y), we evaluate $f(t, y)$ and then draw through P a short line segment whose slope is $f(t, y)$. For example, in Figure 1.7 we have constructed part of the direction field defined by the function $f(t, y) = -y$.

As another illustration, we give in Figure 1.8 part of the tangent field corresponding to the function $f(t, y) = y - t$. Note that the function f is constant on each straight line $y = t + k$ (k constant). This fact is helpful in sketching the direction field.

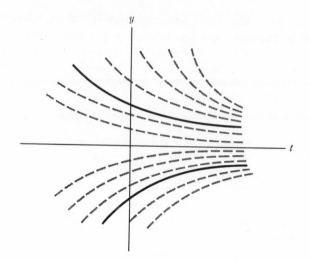

Figure 1.7

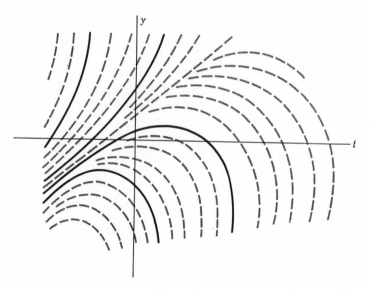

Figure 1.8

How will such a diagram help us find a solution of $y' = f(t, y)$? The answer is that a solution curve $y = \phi(t)$ must be a curve which "flows with" the direction field; that is, at each point on its graph, the function ϕ must be tangent to the corresponding line segment of the direction field. This becomes evident if we superimpose on a direction field the graphs of a number of solutions of the differential equation, as is indicated by the solid curves in Figures 1.7 and 1.8.   In this way we can obtain some useful information about the nature of the solutions of a differential equation by a freehand sketch of curves which obey this simple geometric condition.

•EXERCISES

Construct direction fields for each of the following differential equations, and then sketch several solution curves.

1. $y' = 2y$.
2. $y' = -y^2$.
3. $y' = ty$.
4. $y' = 1 - t^2 - y^2$.
5. $y' = 1 + y^2$.
6. $y' = t^2 + y^2$.

1.6   Initial Conditions

We have seen in Sections 1.1 and 1.2 how physical phenomena may give rise to mathematical models leading to differential equations.   In general, each differential equation will have many solutions, as is suggested by the examples in Section 1.4.   Thus it is necessary to impose additional restrictions, called **initial conditions,** on the equation in order to obtain a unique answer.   For first-order equations of the form $y' = f(t, y)$ a natural additional restriction is to ask that a solution ϕ satisfy a condition such as $\phi(t_0) = y_0$.   Geometrically, this says that we are only interested in solutions of the equation whose graphs pass through the point (t_0, y_0).   Physically, this corresponds to measuring the state of the system described by the differential equation at a time t_0 and predicting the future behavior of the system.

Example 1.   We have seen that each function

$$y = ce^{2t}$$

is a solution of the equation $y' = 2y$.   Suppose we wish to find a solution for which $\phi(1) = 5$.   Imposing this condition on the family of solutions ce^{2t}, we are forced to require that $5 = ce^2$ so that $c = 5e^{-2}$.   Therefore $\phi(t) = 5e^{2(t-1)}$ is a solution, in fact the only solution (see Theorem 1.1 below) passing through the point $(1, 5)$.

Example 2.   Among the solutions

$$y = \frac{1 + ce^t}{1 - ce^t}$$

of the differential equation $y' = \frac{1}{2}(y^2 - 1)$ let us find a solution ϕ which obeys the initial condition $\phi(1) = 5$. If there is such a solution, it must satisfy

$$5 = \frac{1 + ce}{1 - ce}$$

from which we get $5 - 5ce = 1 + ce$, and therefore $c = \frac{2}{3}e^{-1}$. Thus

$$\phi(t) = \frac{1 + \frac{2}{3}e^{t-1}}{1 - \frac{2}{3}e^{t-1}}$$

is the desired solution.

We can also take account of initial conditions in the graphical solution. An initial condition $\phi(t_0) = y_0$ means that our solution curve must pass through the point (t_0, y_0). It is therefore convenient to start from this point and attempt to sketch the desired solution at once.

• **EXERCISES**

1. Find the solutions of the equation $y' = 2y$ (Example 1 above) that pass through the point (a) $(1, 0)$, (b) $(0, 0)$, (c) $(-1, 2)$.

2. Find solutions ϕ of the equation $y' = \frac{1}{2}(y^2 - 1)$ (Example 2 above) that obey the initial condition (a) $\phi(0) = 1$, (b) $\phi(0) = 0$, (c) $\phi(2) = 0$.

3. Using the method of direction fields, sketch a solution of the equation $y' = t + y$ that passes through the point $(0, 0)$.

1.7   Higher-Order Equations

A differential equation may involve derivatives of higher order than the first of the unknown function. This is the case with the physical examples given in Sections 1.1 and 1.2. We now examine such differential equations in more detail.

Let f be a function defined in a region D in three-dimensional space. Then, with this function f we can associate the second-order equation

$$y'' = f(t, y, y') \tag{1.15}$$

A function ϕ is a solution of this equation on an interval I if the following three conditions are satisfied:

(i) $\phi(t)$, $\phi'(t)$, and $\phi''(t)$ exist for each t in I.

(ii) For each t in I, the point $(t, \phi(t), \phi'(t))$ lies in the region D.

(iii) For each t in I, the following identity holds:

$$\phi''(t) = f(t, \phi(t), \phi'(t)) \tag{1.16}$$

As before, we summarize these conditions by saying that ϕ satisfies equation (1.15) on the interval I.

Example 1.   Consider the equation

$$y'' - 2y' + y = 0 \tag{1.17}$$

This has the form (1.15) with $f(t, y, y') = 2y' - y$, and the set D can be taken to be the entire three-dimensional space. We can show that $\phi(t) = e^t$ is a solution of (1.17) for all t, $-\infty < t < \infty$. First, we observe that (i) and (ii) are satisfied; then, we check that ϕ satisfies the equation $\phi''(t) = e^t = 2\phi'(t) - \phi(t)$.

As suggested by the mass-spring system (Section 1.1) and the simple pendulum (Section 1.2), the natural initial conditions for a second-order equation are to prescribe ϕ and ϕ' at an initial time t_0. Physically this prescribes the initial position and initial velocity of the system.

•EXERCISES

1. Show that $\phi(t) = te^t$ is also a solution of (1.17).

2. Show that $Ae^t + Bte^t$ is a solution of (1.17) for each choice of the constants A and B.

3. Show that $\sin 2t$ and $\cos 2t$ are both solutions of $y'' + 4y = 0$, for $-\infty < t < \infty$.

4. Show that $\phi(t) = A \sin 2t + B \cos 2t$ is also a solution of $y'' + 4y = 0$, for each choice of the constants A and B.

5. Using the result of Exercise 4, find a solution ϕ of $y'' + 4y = 0$ that obeys the initial conditions: $\phi(0) = 4$, $\phi'(0) = 2$.

6. Using the result of Exercise 2, find a solution ϕ of $y'' - 2y' + y = 0$ that obeys the initial condition $\phi(0) = 1$, $\phi'(0) = 2$.

Similarly, corresponding to a function f defined in a region D in $(n + 1)$-dimensional space, we can associate the nth-order differential equation

$$y^{(n)} = f(t, y, y', \ldots, y^{(n-1)}) \tag{1.18}$$

where $y^{(k)}$ denotes the kth derivative of y with respect to t. A function ϕ is a solution of this equation on an interval I if the following three conditions are satisfied:

(i) $\phi(t)$, $\phi'(t)$, . . . , $\phi^{(n)}(t)$ exist for each t in I.

(ii) For each t in I, the point $(t, \phi(t), \phi'(t), \ldots, \phi^{(n-1)}(t))$ lies in the region D.

(iii) For each t in I, the following identity holds:

$$\phi^{(n)}(t) = f(t, \phi(t), \phi'(t), \ldots, \phi^{(n-1)}(t)) \tag{1.19}$$

For example, consider the equation

$$y''' + y = 0 \tag{1.20}$$

This has the form (1.18) with $f(t, y, y', y'') = -y$ and the region D can be taken to be the entire four-dimensional space.

•EXERCISES

7. Show that e^{-t} is a solution of (1.20) on $-\infty < t < \infty$.

8. Show that $e^{t/2} \cos \sqrt{3}\, t/2$ are solutions of (1.20) on $-\infty < t < \infty$.

9. Show that $\phi(t) = c_1 e^{-t} + c_2 e^{t/2} \cos \sqrt{3}\, t/2 + c_3 e^{t/2} \sin \sqrt{3}\, t/2$ is a solution of (1.20) for every choice of the constants c_1, c_2, c_3.

10. Determine a solution of (1.20) for which $\phi(0) = 1$, $\phi'(0) = -1$, $\phi''(0) = 0$.

The natural initial conditions for an nth-order equation are to prescribe ϕ, ϕ', . . . , $\phi^{(n-1)}$ at an initial time t_0. This reduces to the special case $n = 2$ discussed above.

1.8 Existence, Uniqueness, and Continuity

It would be desirable, for both physical and mathematical reasons, to have a theory for differential equations which guarantees existence, uniqueness, and continuity of solutions with respect to initial conditions. Moreover, this theory should be applicable to a large number of physical problems. In this section, we shall explain the meaning and application of the basic theorems of this type, without attempting to prove them. The proofs may be found in Chapter 7, or in [5, Chapter 1].

First-Order Equations

In what follows, D will denote a given region in the (t, y) plane. **By a region we will always mean a set of points with the property that given any point (t_0, y_0) in the region it is possible to construct a rectangle centered at (t_0, y_0) which lies entirely in the region** (see Figure 1.9). For our purposes, rectangles are more convenient, but it would be possible to use circles instead. A rectangle centered at (t_0, y_0) is the set $\{(t, y) \mid -a < t - t_0 < a, -b < y - y_0 < b\}$ or, equivalently, $\{(t, y) \mid |t - t_0| < a, |y - y_0| < b\}$, for some $a, b > 0$. The interior of a rectangle or circle, the whole plane, and an infinite strip $\{(t, y) \mid a < t < b, -\infty < y < \infty\}$ are frequently encountered examples of regions. A less obvious example is the interior of a circle with the center removed.

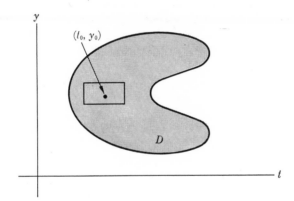

Figure 1.9

The reader should observe that if (t_0, y_0) is on the "boundary" of D, every rectangle centered at (t_0, y_0) contains points which are not in D. (In fact, this statement can be used to give a precise definition of the boundary of D.) In other words, boundary points are not included in D. If (t_0, y_0) is a point of D which lies "close" to the boundary, then the numbers a and b in the definition of a region must necessarily be chosen small.

In what follows, whenever we say that a certain function f is continuous on D we are assuming that it is continuous at all points of D, but we make no assumption concerning its behavior on the boundary. If f is continuous at some boundary points of D as well as in D, then f is still continuous on the region D. In many problems which arise, this is precisely the situation, but the continuity of f at some boundary points is not essential.

• EXERCISES

1. Consider the region $D = \{(t, y) \mid (t - 1)^2 + (y + 2)^2 < 4\}$.
    (a) Construct at least two rectangles centered at the following points which lie entirely in D: $(1, -2)$, $(0, -1)$, $(2, -3)$, $(1, -\frac{1}{10})$.
    (b) Show that the point $(1, 0)$ and $(-1, -2)$ are boundary points.
    (c) Consider the collection of points $\{(t, y) \mid (t - 1)^2 + (y + 2)^2 \leq 4\}$. Is this a region?

2. Which of the following collections of points are regions?
    (a) $\{(t, y) \mid t > 0, -\infty < y < \infty\}$.
    (b) $\{(t, y) \mid -\infty < t < \infty, -2 \leq y < \infty\}$.
    (c) $\{(t, y) \mid 0 < t < 1, -\infty < y < \infty\}$.
    (d) $\{(t, y) \mid -\infty < t < \infty, -\infty < y < \infty\}$.

3. Show that the collection of points $\{(t, y) \mid -1 < t < 1, y = t^2\}$ contains only boundary points.

4. Consider the region $D = \{(t, y) \mid t^2 + y^2 < 1\}$. Are the following functions continuous on D?

    (a) $f(t, y) = \dfrac{1}{1 + t^2 + y^2}$.

    (b) $g(t, y) = \dfrac{1}{1 - t^2 - y^2}$.

We are now ready to state the basic theorem for first-order equations.

Theorem 1.1. *Let f and $\partial f/\partial y$ be continuous functions in a given region D. Let (t_0, y_0) be a given point of D. Then there exists an interval containing t_0 and exactly one solution ϕ, defined on this interval, of the differential equation $y' = f(t, y)$ which passes through (t_0, y_0) (that is, the solution ϕ satisfies the initial condition $\phi(t_0) = y_0$). The solution exists for those values of t for which the points $(t, \phi(t))$ lie in D. Further the solution ϕ is a continuous function, not only of t, but of t_0, y_0 as well (in fact, of the triple (t, t_0, y_0)).*

If the region D is the entire (t, y) plane, then it follows from Theorem 1.1 that every solution exists as long as it remains finite. This obvious remark will be quite useful in showing whether a solution exists for all t. An example will help clarify this point.

Example 1. Consider the differential equation $y' = \alpha y$ (α constant). Here $f(t, y) = \alpha y$ and $(\partial f/\partial y) (t, y) = \alpha$. Both f and $\partial f/\partial y$ are continuous in the whole (t, y) plane. Theorem 1.1 shows that there is a unique solution ϕ of $y' = \alpha y$ through every point (t_0, y_0) in the plane. It is easily verified that $\phi(t) = y_0 e^{\alpha(t-t_0)}$ is a solution of this initial value problem. Therefore $\phi(t) = y_0 e^{\alpha(t-t_0)}$ is the **only** solution. Also, since $|\phi(t)| = |y_0| e^{\alpha(t-t_0)}$ is finite whenever t is finite, all points $(t, \phi(t))$, $-\infty < t < \infty$, lie in D and therefore this solution ϕ exists for $-\infty < t < \infty$.

•EXERCISES

5. Find a solution of $y' = \alpha y$ through $(1, 0)$. Is this the only solution through $(1, 0)$?

6. (a) Show that $-1/t$ is a solution of $y' = y^2$ passing through $(-1, 1)$.

   (b) Show that $\phi(t) = -1/t$ is the only solution of $y' = y^2$ passing through $(-1, 1)$. Be sure to determine an appropriate region D before applying Theorem 1.1.

   (c) What is the largest interval on which $\phi(t) = -1/t$ is a solution of $y' = y^2$ through the point $(-1, 1)$? The reader should observe that Exercise 6 shows that a solution of $y' = f(t, y)$ does not necessarily exist for all t even though f and $\partial f/\partial y$ are continuous in the whole plane.

Example 2. Consider the differential equation $y' + p(t)y = q(t)$, where p and q are given functions, continuous on some interval $a < t < b$. (We may, of course, have p, q continuous on the whole t axis.) Choose t_0 with $a < t_0 < b$ and any y_0. Then we can use Theorem 1.1 to show that there is a **unique** solution ϕ satisfying the initial condition $\phi(t_0) = y_0$, and that this solution exists on $a < t < b$. Since $f(t, y) = -p(t)y + q(t)$ and $\partial f/\partial y \, (t, y) = -p(t)$ are continuous in the region $D = \{(t, y) \mid a < t < b, -\infty < y < \infty\}$, Theorem 1.1 can be applied for every point (t_0, y_0) in D to show the existence of a unique solution. It can also be shown (see Section 2.2) that every solution of this differential equation is bounded by an exponential function which is finite for $a < t < b$. Thus the point $(t, \phi(t))$ remains in D for $a < t < b$, and by Theorem 1.1, the solution ϕ exists on the whole interval $a < t < b$. We shall see in Section 2.2 (p. 41) how to find this solution explicitly. Note, however, that we have obtained a good deal of information about the solution without obtaining an explicit formula for it.

Example 3. Consider the differential equation $y' = 3y^{2/3}$. Here $f(t, y) = 3y^{2/3}$, $\partial f/\partial y = 2y^{-1/3}$. Thus f is continuous in the whole plane and $\partial f/\partial y$ is continuous except on the t axis ($y = 0$). Theorem 1.1 tells us that there is a unique solution through any point (t_0, y_0) with $y_0 \neq 0$, but gives no information about solutions through $(t_0, 0)$. We can easily verify as follows that there is actually an infinite number of solutions through $(t_0, 0)$. The function ϕ_c defined by

$$\phi_c(t) = \begin{cases} 0 & \text{if} \quad -\infty < t \le c \\ (t - c)^3 & \text{if} \quad c \le t < \infty \end{cases}$$

has a continuous derivative for $-\infty < t < \infty$ and is a solution passing through $(t_0, 0)$ for every value of $c > t_0$. In addition to all these solutions, the identically zero function is also a solution (see Figure 1.10). These solutions can be constructed by the method of Section 2.1 (p. 35).

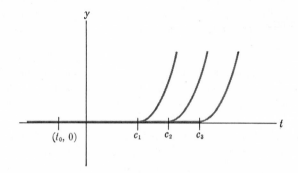

Figure 1.10

This example illustrates that in some cases there may be a solution of the differential equation $y' = f(t, y)$ through (t_0, y_0) even though the hypothesis of Theorem 1.1 is not satisfied. In Example 3, we have existence, but not uniqueness, of solutions through $(t_0, 0)$. Other situations may arise; for example, it can be shown that $\phi(t) \equiv 0$ is the only solution of the differential equation $y' = |y|$ passing through the point $(0, 0)$, in spite of the fact that $\partial f / \partial y$, where $f(t, y) = |y|$, does not exist at $(0, 0)$.

These examples suggest that some or all of the conclusions of Theorem 1.1 may be true even though not all of the hypotheses are satisfied. This is indeed the case; for example, if f is continuous in D, with no assumption on $\partial f / \partial y$, it can be shown that a solution exists but is not necessarily unique. However, in most problems, Theorem 1.1 is applicable and more refined results are not needed.

● **EXERCISES**

7. Does the differential equation $y' = 1 + y^2$ have a unique solution through the point $(0, 0)$?

8.   (a) Does the differential equation $y' = (y^2 - 1)^{1/2}$ have a unique solution through each of the following points?
(i) $(0, 2)$.
(ii) $(1, -5)$.
(b) What can be said about solutions through the point $(0, 1)$?   Note that $\phi(t) \equiv 1$ is a solution.

Second-Order Equations

We have seen that equations of the second order arise naturally in many physical examples.   These are of the form $y'' = g(t, y, y')$, where $g(t, y, z)$ is defined in some region D in the three-dimensional (t, y, z) space.   The concept of a region in three-dimensional space is a natural extension of the two-dimensional situation, with rectangles centered at (t_0, y_0) replaced by rectangular parallelepipeds centered at (t_0, y_0, z_0).   Such a parallelepiped is a set of the form $\{(t, y, z) \mid |t - t_0| < a, |y - y_0| < b, |z - z_0| < c\}$ for some $a, b, c > 0$.

We suspect from the physical examples discussed earlier that in order to obtain a unique solution we should prescribe not only an initial position but also an initial velocity at a time t_0.   In terms of a solution ϕ this means that we prescribe $\phi(t_0)$ and $\phi'(t_0)$.   Keeping in mind the above differences from the first-order case, we can state the following analogue of Theorem 1.1 for second-order equations.

Theorem 1.2.   *Let g, $\partial g/\partial y$, and $\partial g/\partial z$ be continuous in a given region D.   Let (t_0, y_0, z_0) be a given point of D.   Then there exists an interval containing t_0 and exactly one solution ϕ, defined on this interval, of the differential equation $y'' = g(t, y, y')$ which passes through (t_0, y_0, z_0) (that is, the solution ϕ satisfies the initial conditions $\phi(t_0) = y_0$, $\phi'(t_0) = z_0$).   The solution exists for those values of t for which the points $(t, \phi(t), \phi'(t))$ lie in D.   Further, the solution ϕ is a continuous function, not only of t, but of t_0, y_0, z_0 as well (in fact, of the quadruple (t, t_0, y_0, z_0)).*

If the region D is the entire (t, y, z) space, then it follows from Theorem 1.2 that every solution exists for those values of t for which the solution and its derivative remain finite.

Example 4.   Consider the equation $y'' + k_1 y' + k_2 \sin y = 0$, where k_1 and k_2 are constants.   This equation is a model of the motion of a damped simple pendulum with no external forces, and includes equation (1.9) (page 11) as a special case.   It can be written in the form $y'' = g(t, y, y')$ with $g(t, y, z) = -k_1 z - k_2 \sin y$, $\partial g/\partial y = -k_2 \cos y$, $\partial g/\partial z = -k_1$.   Clearly, g, $\partial g/\partial y$, and $\partial g/\partial z$ are continuous for all (t, y, z), no matter what the constants k_1 and k_2 are. Thus Theorem 1.2 shows that given any triple (t_0, y_0, z_0), the differential equation $y'' + k_1 y' + k_2 \sin y = 0$ has a unique solution ϕ with $\phi(t_0) = y_0$, $\phi'(t_0) = z$. Note that here the region D can be taken to be the whole three-dimensional space. It can also be shown that $|\phi(t)|$ and $|\phi'(t)|$ are finite, and that this implies that the solution ϕ exists on $-\infty < t < \infty$. It follows, in particular, that the various models for the simple pendulum discussed in Section 1.2 have these properties.

•EXERCISES

9. Discuss the existence and uniqueness of solutions ϕ of $y'' + ky = 0$ (k constant) with initial conditions $\phi(t_0) = y_0$, $\phi'(t_0) = z_0$.

10. Discuss the existence and uniqueness of solutions ϕ of $y'' + p(t)y' + q(t)y = f(t)$, with initial conditions $\phi(t_0) = y_0$, $\phi'(t_0) = z_0$, where p, q, and f are given functions continuous on some interval $a < t < b$, where $a < t_0 < b$. [*Hint:* See the discussion of Example 2.]

11. (a) Show that $\phi(t) \equiv 0$ is the only solution of $y'' + p(t)y' + q(t)y = 0$ satisfying the initial condition $\phi(0) = \phi'(0) = 0$, if p and q are continuous on some interval containing 0 in its interior.

   (b) Show that if $\psi(t)$ is a solution of $y'' + p(t)y' + q(t)y = 0$ which is tangent to the t axis at some point $(t_1, 0, 0)$, then $\psi(t) \equiv 0$.

12. It is easily verified that $c_1 \cos 2t + c_2 \sin 2t$ is a solution of $y'' + 4y = 0$ on $-\infty < t < \infty$ for every choice of the constants c_1 and c_2.

   (a) Determine c_1 and c_2 so that this solution satisfies the initial conditions

$$\phi\left(\frac{\pi}{4}\right) = 1 \qquad \phi'\left(\frac{\pi}{4}\right) = 2$$

   (b) Write down the solution ϕ satisfying the initial conditions

$$\phi\left(\frac{\pi}{4}\right) = 1 \qquad \phi'\left(\frac{\pi}{4}\right) = 2$$

and prove that this is the only solution satisfying these conditions.

Equations of Higher Order

Finally, there are problems where higher-order equations are encountered. For example, in elasticity theory equations of the fourth order arise naturally. We are interested in equations of order n, of the form $y^{(n)} = h(t, y, y', \ldots, y^{(n-1)})$. We observe that the cases when $n = 1$ and $n = 2$ are the ones we have already discussed. Here h is a function defined in some region D in the $(n + 1)$-dimensional $(t, y_1, y_2, \ldots, y_n)$

space. A "parallelepiped" in $(n + 1)$ dimensions centered at $(t_0, \eta_1, \eta_2, \ldots, \eta_n)$ is a set of the form

$$\{(t, y_1, y_2, \ldots, y_n) \mid |t - t_0| < a, |y_1 - \eta_1| < b_1, \ldots, |y_n - \eta_n| < b_n\}$$

where $a, b_1, \ldots, b_n$ are positive numbers. We have the following analogue of Theorems 1.1 and 1.2.

Theorem 1.3. *Let $h, \partial h/\partial y_1, \ldots, \partial h/\partial y_n$ be continuous in a given region D. Let $(t_0, \eta_1, \ldots, \eta_n)$ be a given point of D. Then there exists an interval containing t_0 and exactly one solution ϕ, defined on this interval, of the differential equation $y^{(n)} = h(t, y, y', \ldots, y^{(n-1)})$ which passes through $(t_0, \eta_1, \ldots, \eta_n)$, (that is, the solution ϕ satisfies the initial conditions $\phi(t_0) = \eta_1, \phi'(t_0) = \eta_2, \ldots, \phi^{(n-1)}(t_0) = \eta_n$). The solution exists for those values of t for which the points $(t, \phi(t), \phi'(t), \ldots, \phi^{(n-1)}(t))$ lie in D. Further, the solution ϕ is a continuous function of the $(n + 2)$ variables $t, t_0, \eta_1, \ldots, \eta_n$.*

•EXERCISES

13. (a) Show that the differential equation $y^{(4)} + 2y'' + 3y = 0$ has a unique solution ϕ satisfying the initial conditions $\phi(1) = 1$, $\phi'(1) = 0$, $\phi''(1) = -1$, $\phi'''(1) = 2$.
    (b) Show that $\psi(t) \equiv 0$ is the unique solution of this equation satisfying the initial conditions $\psi(-1) = \psi'(-1) = \psi''(-1) = \psi'''(-1) = 0$.

14. Show that $\phi(t) \equiv 5$ is the unique solution of $y''' + (y - 5)^2 = 0$ satisfying the initial conditions $\phi(t_0) = 5$, $\phi'(t_0) = \phi''(t_0) = 0$ for any $t_0, -\infty < t_0 < \infty$.

•MISCELLANEOUS EXERCISES

1. Draw the direction field for each of the following differential equations and sketch some solution curves.

(a) $y' = y - t^2$.

(b) $y' = \dfrac{-t}{y}$.

(c) $y' = \dfrac{y}{(t + y)}$.

(d) $y' = \dfrac{t + y}{t - y}$.

(e) $y' = \dfrac{(1 - t^2)y - t}{y}$.

2. Determine the region or regions in the (t, y) plane in which Theorem 1.1 can be applied to obtain existence and uniqueness of real solutions for each of the following differential equations.

(a) $y' = \dfrac{-t}{y}.$

(e) $y' = \dfrac{t+y}{t-y}.$

(b) $y' = \dfrac{y}{2 - t^2 - y^2}.$

(f) $y'^2 + ty' = y = 0.$

(c) $y' = \dfrac{t}{1 + t + y}.$

(g) $y' = \dfrac{y}{1 + t^2 + y^2}.$

(h) $(y')^2 = t^2 - y^2.$

(d) $y' = \dfrac{y}{1 + t^2 + y^2}.$

3.   Determine the region or regions in (t, y, y') space in which Theorem 1.2 can be applied to obtain existence and uniqueness of real solutions for each of the following differential equations.

(a) $y'' = t^2 + y^2 + (y')^2.$

(d) $y'' = \log\left(\dfrac{y'}{y}\right).$

(b) $y'' = \dfrac{y}{4 - (y')^2}.$

(e) $y'' + (\sin t)y' + (\log t)y = 0.$

(f) $y'' + y^2 + y'^2 = 0.$

(c) $y'' = \dfrac{y}{4 - y^2 - (y')^2}.$

4.   Consider the differential equation

$$y' = \begin{cases} 0 & (t \le 0; -\infty < y < \infty) \\ 2y^{1/2} & (t \ge 0; 0 \le y < \infty) \\ y^2 & (t \ge 0; -\infty < y < 0) \end{cases}$$

(a) Show that

$$\phi(t) = \begin{cases} 1 & (t < 0) \\ (t+1)^2 & (t > 0) \end{cases}$$

is a solution on $-\infty < t < \infty$.

(b) Is $\phi(t)$ continuous everywhere?
(c) Is $\phi'(t)$ continuous everywhere?
(d) Can you apply Theorem 1.1 to obtain the existence and uniqueness of solutions through the point $(0, 1)$?   Explain fully.

5.   Consider the differential equation

$$y'' = \begin{cases} y & (t \ge 0; -\infty < y < \infty) \\ 0 & (t < 0; -\infty < y < \infty) \end{cases}$$

(a) Is the function

$$\phi(t) = \begin{cases} 1 & (t < 0) \\ e^t & (t \ge 0) \end{cases}$$

a solution on $-\infty < t < \infty$?

(b) Is $\phi(t)$ continuous everywhere?

(c) Is $\phi'(t)$ continuous everywhere?

(d) Can you apply Theorem 1.2 to obtain the existence of a unique solution ψ such that $\psi(0) = 1$, $\psi' = 1$? Explain fully.

6. Find an equation satisfied by the coordinates of all points (t_0, y_0) with the property that a solution of $y' = f(t, y)$ through (t_0, y_0) has a maximum or minimum at (t_0, y_0). How would you determine whether a solution (t_0, y_0) of this equation is a maximum or minimum of the solution of the differential equation through (t_0, y_0)?

7. Apply Exercise 6 to determine the maxima and minima of solutions of

$$y' = \frac{t + y}{t - y}$$

8. Show that the only solution of

$$y'' + ty' + (1 + t^2)y^2 = 0$$

which touches the t axis at some point $(t_0, 0)$ is the identically zero solution.

9. Find all continuous (not necessarily differentiable) functions $f(t)$ such that

$$[f(t)]^2 - \int_0^t f(s) \, ds \qquad (t \geq 0)$$

Chapter 2 ‖ METHODS OF SOLUTION

The general existence and uniqueness theory of the preceding sections gives us some conditions under which we may expect to have solutions for a particular differential equation satisfying given initial conditions. The next order of business is to learn some methods for finding these solutions. Whenever a uniqueness theorem is applicable, any device for obtaining a solution is legitimate, as long as the function obtained satisfies the equation. This is because the theory tells us that there is at most one solution, and what we have found must therefore be it.

The first method we discuss is quite special, but happens to apply to many of the illustrative problems we gave in Section 1.4 (p. 16). The second method, treated in Section 2.2, will be of more general usefulness. These two methods will enable us to solve many of the simpler types of first-order equations. They will not, in general, apply to the more complicated cases that arise when more accurate models are used. For this reason, we devote some time to a discussion of methods for finding approximate solutions, both with and without the use of a high speed digital computer.

2.1 Variables Separable

We shall say that a differential equation of first order

$$y' = f(t, y)$$

has **variables separable** if the function f can be written in the form

$$f(t, y) = g(t)h(y) \tag{2.1}$$

32

The reason for the name is that the differential equation can be written as

$$\frac{y'}{h(y)} = g(t)$$

provided, of course, that $h(y) \neq 0$. For example, $y' = y^2$ and $y' = y/(1 + t^2)$ are both of this type, while $y' = \sin t - 2ty$ is not.

Before explaining the technique for the general case, we will work out a simple case.

Example 1.

$$y' = y^2 \tag{2.2}$$

Since $f(t, y) = y^2$, $\partial f/\partial y \ (t, y) = 2y$ are continuous in the whole (t, y) plane, we know from Theorem 1.1 (p. 24) that through any point (t_0, y_0) there passes exactly one solution ϕ. This function must satisfy the equation

$$\phi' = \{\phi(t)\}^2$$

on some interval I containing t_0. Assuming that $\phi(t) \neq 0$ for all t in the interval I (and hence that $y_0 \neq 0$), we would have to have

$$\frac{\phi'(t)}{\{\phi(t)\}^2} = 1$$

If we integrate this equation from t_0 to t, we obtain

$$\int_{t_0}^{t} \frac{\phi'(s)}{\{\phi(s)\}^2}\, ds = \int_{t_0}^{t} 1\, ds$$

The substitution $u = \phi(s)$ yields $\int_{\phi(t_0)}^{\phi(t)} du/u^2 = t - t_0$, and therefore, by the fundamental theorem of calculus,

$$-\frac{1}{u}\bigg|_{\phi(t_0)}^{\phi(t)} = -\frac{1}{\phi(t)} + \frac{1}{\phi(t_0)} = t - t_0$$

Since our solution ϕ is to pass through the point (t_0, y_0), we must have $\phi(t_0) = y_0$. Hence,

$$-\frac{1}{\phi(t)} + \frac{1}{y_0} = t - t_0 \qquad (y_0 \neq 0)$$

or, solving for $\phi(t)$,

$$\phi(t) = \frac{y_0}{1 - y_0(t - t_0)} \qquad (y_0 \neq 0) \tag{2.3}$$

We have thus shown that if ϕ is a solution of the equation (2.2) which is never zero, then ϕ has the form (2.3). It remains to be shown that the function ϕ defined by (2.3) actually satisfies the equation (2.2) on some interval.

•EXERCISES

1. Show that the function ϕ defined by (2.3) satisfies equation (2.2) on a suitable interval I and $\phi(t_0) = y_0$.

2. What is the domain of definition of the function ϕ in (2.3)?

3. Let J be the domain of definition of the function ϕ in (2.3). Does J coincide with the interval I in Exercise 1?

In the discussion above, we assumed from the start that $y_0 \neq 0$, and in fact that $\phi(t) \neq 0$ for all choices of t in the interval I. It is therefore not surprising that the solution (2.3) never assumes the value 0 for any choice of t. Does this mean that there is **no** solution of (2.2) through the point $(t_0, 0)$? This would certainly contradict Theorem 1.1. The answer is simple; we have overlooked the fact that $\phi(t) \equiv 0$ is also a solution of (2.2), and that this indeed does satisfy the initial condition $\phi(t_0) = 0$. Including the zero solution with the solutions given by (2.3), we have shown by actual construction that for every initial point (t_0, y_0), there is a solution ϕ through this point. What has happened in this example is quite common; a "general" method may not succeed in producing all of the solutions of a differential equation, and for certain exceptional initial conditions other methods may have to be used. Notice that the function ϕ as given by (2.3) is well defined for $y_0 = 0$. In fact, it happens that the zero solution is obtainable from (2.3) by taking $y_0 = 0$.

We mentioned in Section 1.3 (p. 13) that solutions of differential equations ought to depend continuously on the initial conditions. This property holds for the solutions of the equation (2.2). If we fix a time interval I, say $a \leq t \leq b$, then slight changes in either t_0 or y_0 will cause only slight changes in the value of ϕ as given by (2.3). This continuity is evident from the graphs of the solutions.

•EXERCISES

4. The graphs of the functions ϕ defined by (2.3) above are all hyperbolas. Draw the solution curves $y = \phi(t)$ passing through the points $(0, \frac{1}{2})$, $(0, 1)$, $(0, 2)$, $(0, -1)$, $(0, -2)$.   Observe how these curves compare with the "special" solution $\phi(t) \equiv 0$.

5. Use the method explained above to find the solution of the equation $y' = 3y^{2/3}$ passing through (t_0, y_0).   Give a complete discussion of the various cases.   Note that $y_0 \neq 0$ and $y_0 = 0$ again must be treated separately, and that $\phi(t) \equiv 0$ is again a solution.   However, this time the hypotheses of Theorem 1.1 are not satisfied in the case $y_0 = 0$ (why?), and in fact we do **not** have uniqueness.   For example, $\phi(t) \equiv 0$ is a solution through the origin $(0, 0)$, and so is

$$\phi_c(t) = \begin{cases} 0 & -\infty < t \leq c \\ (t - c)^3 & c \leq t < \infty \end{cases}$$

for any $c \geq 0$.   (Verify!)   Sketch the graphs of these solutions.

6. Carry out a similar investigation for the equation $y' = 2y^{1/2}$.

Let us apply the same technique to the general case of **variables separable.**   Suppose we have

$$y' = g(t)h(y) = f(t, y) \tag{2.4}$$

where g is continuous on some interval $a < t < b$ and h and h' are continuous on some interval $c < y < d$.   The functions $f(t, y) = g(t)h(y)$ and $(\partial f/\partial y)\,(t, y) = g(t)h'(y)$ are continuous on the rectangle $D = \{(t, y) \mid a < t < b, c < y < d\}$ (see Figure 2.1).   Theorem 1.1 tells us that equa-

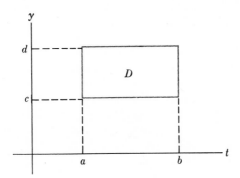

Figure 2.1

tion (2.4) has a unique solution $y = \phi(t)$ passing through any initial point (t_0, y_0) in the rectangle D, existing on some interval I containing t_0. We must therefore have $\phi'(t) = g(t)h(\phi(t))$ for every t on I. If we exclude for the moment the possibility that $h(\phi(t)) = 0$ on I, we can write

$$\frac{\phi'(t)}{h(\phi(t))} = g(t)$$

and therefore

$$\int_{t_0}^{t} \frac{\phi'(s) \, ds}{h(\phi(s))} = \int_{t_0}^{t} g(s) \, ds$$

for every t on I. Putting $u = \phi(s)$ and using the initial condition $\phi(t_0) = y_0$, we obtain

$$\int_{y_0}^{\phi(t)} \frac{du}{h(u)} = \int_{t_0}^{t} g(s) \, ds \qquad (2.5)$$

This equation defines the solution ϕ implicitly. As Example 1 above and Examples 2 and 3 below show, it may be possible to solve the resulting equation for $\phi(t)$, thus obtaining an explicit solution of (2.4). This may, however, present technical difficulties.

• EXERCISE

7. (a) Look up the statement of the implicit function theorem for solving an equation of the form $F(t, y) = 0$ for y in terms of t near a given point (t_0, y_0) for which $F(t_0, y_0) = 0$.

(b) Apply the implicit function theorem to the equation (2.5) and determine conditions which permit you to solve (2.5) for $\phi(t)$ near the point (t_0, y_0).

What happens if there are values of t where $h(\phi(t)) = 0$? In particular, suppose that $h(y_0) = 0$. Then, it is easy to see that the constant function $y = y_0$ satisfies equation (2.4) and must therefore be the unique solution ϕ satisfying the initial condition $\phi(t_0) = y_0$.

Example 2. Solve the initial value problem

$$y' = ty^3, \quad (t_0, y_0) = (0, 1)$$

In the notation of (2.4) $g(t) = t$, $h(y) = y^3$. Since $g(t)$ is continuous for all t, and since $h(y)$ and $h'(y) = 3y^2$ are continuous for all y, Theorem 1.1 (p. 24) tells us that this problem has a unique solution ϕ which satisfies

$\phi'(t) = t\{\phi(t)\}^3$.   If $\phi(t) \neq 0$ we have $\phi'(t)/\{\phi(t)\}^3 = t$, and therefore, using $t_0 = 0$,

$$\int_0^t \frac{\phi'(s)}{\{\phi(s)\}^3} \, ds = \int_s^t s \, ds$$

Since $\phi(0) = y_0 = 1$

$$\int_0^t \frac{\phi'(s)}{\{\phi(s)\}^3} \, ds = \int_1^{\phi(t)} \frac{1}{u^3} \, du = -\frac{1}{2u^2}\bigg|_1^{\phi(t)} = -\frac{1}{2\{\phi(t)\}^2} + \frac{1}{2}$$

Also $\int_0^t s \, ds = t^2/2$.   Therefore $\phi(t)$ is defined implicitly by the equation (which corresponds to (2.5) above):

$$-\frac{1}{\{\phi(t)\}^2} + 1 = t^2$$

In this example this gives $\{\phi(t)\}^2 = (1 - t^2)^{-1}$ and finally, since $\phi(0) > 0$, $\phi(t) = (1 - t^2)^{-1/2}$, $(-1 < t < 1)$.   We readily verify that $\phi(0) = 1$ and that $\phi(t) = (1 - t^2)^{-1/2}$ satisfies the differential equation $y' = ty^3$ on $-1 < t < 1$; notice that $\phi(t)$ is never zero for $-1 < t < 1$.

•EXERCISES

8. In the solution in the example above, we found that $\{\phi(t)\}^2 = (1 - t^2)^{-1}$. Why could ϕ not be given by $\phi(t) = -(1 - t^2)^{-1/2}$?

9. Can you suggest an initial point (t_0, y_0) for which $\phi(t) = -(1 - t^2)^{-1/2}$ would have been the correct choice?

10. What is the rectangle D in this example?

11. Why is the solution obtained only valid for $-1 < t < 1$?

12. Try this method for the initial point $(a, 0)$ and the same equation.

13. Try this method for the initial point $(1, 2)$ and the same equation.

Example 3.   Consider again the differential equation $y' = ty^3$, but this time with an arbitrary initial point (t_0, y_0), $y_0 > 0$ (why do we require $y_0 > 0$?); then, proceeding as in Example 2, we obtain

$$\int_{t_0}^t \frac{\phi'(s)}{\{\phi(s)\}^3} \, ds = \int_{y_0}^{\phi(t)} \frac{1}{u^3} \, du = \int_{t_0}^t s \, ds$$

which yields

$$-\frac{1}{\{\phi(t)\}^2} + \frac{1}{y_0^2} = t^2 - t_0^2$$

If we let $1/y_0{}^2 + t_0{}^2 = c^2$ $(c > 0)$, this becomes $\phi(t) = (c^2 - t^2)^{-1/2}$ $(|t| < c)$. It is easily verified that this is a solution of the differential equation $y' = ty^3$ on the interval $-c < t < c$ for every choice of the constant $c > 0$, that is, for every initial point (t_0, y_0) with $y_0 > 0$. If $y_0 = 0$, the corresponding solution is $\phi(t) \equiv 0$, which is not obtainable from the expression $\phi(t) = (c^2 - t^2)^{-1/2}$ for any choice of c.

• **EXERCISES**

14. Sketch the solutions found in the above example corresponding to $c = 1$, $c = 2$, $c = 5$. Be sure to indicate the appropriate intervals.

15. Solve the above example for an arbitrary initial point (t_0, y_0) with $y_0 < 0$.

In each of the following problems, find solutions through the given initial point. Decide, if you can, whether the solution obtained is unique; be sure to specify the interval in which your solution is valid.

16. $y' = t^2 y$ $(5, 1)$.   21. $y' = \dfrac{y - y^2}{t + t^2}$ $(2, 1)$.

17. $y' = t^2 y$ $(1, 0)$.   22. $y' = \dfrac{e^{t-y}}{(1 + e^t)}$ $(0, 1)$.

18. $y' = \dfrac{t}{y}$ (t_0, y_0), $y_0 > 0$.   23. $y' = t^2 y^2 - 4t^2$ $(5, -2)$.

19. $y' = \dfrac{t}{y}$ (t_0, y_0), $y_0 < 0$.   24. $y' = t^2 y^2 - 4t^2$ (t_0, y_0).

20. $y' = \dfrac{y - y^2}{t + t^2}$ (t_0, y_0), $t_0 \neq 0$, -1; $y_0 \neq 0, 1$.

25. Consider the solution ϕ of the differential equation $y' = t^2 + y^2$ passing through the point $(0, 1)$. Show that the curve $y = \phi(t)$ has a vertical asymptote for a value $t = t_0$ with $\pi/4 \leq t_0 \leq 1$. [*Hints:* To see that $t_0 \leq 1$, observe that ϕ satisfies the differential inequality $\phi'(t) \geq [\phi(t)]^2$. Integrate this inequality using $\phi(0) = 1$ to obtain $\phi(t) \geq 1/(1 - t)$. To see that $t_0 \geq \pi/4$ observe that ϕ also satisfies the differential inequality $\phi'(t) \leq 1 + [\phi(t)]^2$ for $0 \leq t \leq 1$, and proceed in a similar fashion.]

2.2   Linear Equations of the First Order

We will now consider another type of first-order equation for which there is a general procedure for finding solutions. The equation $y' = f(t, y)$ will be called **linear** if $f(t, y)$ is a linear function of y. This means that the equation can be written in the form

$$y' + p(t)y = q(t) \tag{2.6}$$

Examples are $y' + y \cos t = \sin t$, $y' + 3ty = e^{-t}$, or $(1 + t^2)y' + ty = \cos t$. More generally, a linear equation is written in the form

$$a_0(t)y' + a_1(t)y = b(t) \tag{2.7}$$

If $a_0(t) \neq 0$, this can be reduced to (2.6) by division by $a_0(t)$. If $a_0(t_0) = 0$ for some t_0, then neither our existence theory nor our method of solution

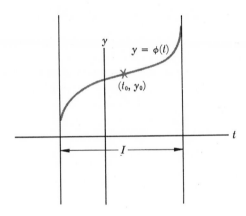

Figure 2.2

is applicable to (2.7) on any interval containing t_0. We will return to a discussion of the case $a_0(t_0) = 0$ in Chapter 4. Here, we exclude this possibility by requiring $a_0(t) \neq 0$ for all t under consideration.

If p and q are continuous on an interval I, then the hypotheses of the fundamental existence and uniqueness theorem (Theorem 1.1, p. 24) are satisfied for (2.6) in the vertical strip $S = \{(t, y) \mid t \text{ in } I, -\infty < y < \infty\}$ (see Figure 2.2). Through any point (t_0, y_0) with t_0 in the interval I there passes exactly one solution ϕ of (2.6), and it will be shown that this solution exists on the **whole** interval I. We shall do this by finding an explicit expression for ϕ which is defined and remains finite for all t in I. (See the remark following Theorem 1.1, p. 24.)

We first work with some examples, which will suggest the approach to the general problem.

Example 1. $y' + 2ty = 0$ with initial point $(0, y_0)$.   Here the strip S of Figure 2.2 is the whole (t, y) plane.   This equation has variables separable, and we can use the method of the previous section to obtain the solution $\phi_0(t) = y_0e^{-t^2}$, for $-\infty < t < \infty$, if $y_0 \neq 0$.   If $y_0 = 0$, we obtain the solution $\phi_0(t) \equiv 0$, which, incidentally, is also included in the formula $\phi_0(t) = y_0e^{-t^2}$.

Another way to express the fact that the solution $\phi_0(t)$ is $y_0e^{-t^2}$ is to write

$$e^{t^2}\phi_0(t) = y_0$$

If we differentiate this relation we obtain

$$0 = \frac{d}{dt}[e^{t^2}\phi_0(t)] = \phi_0'(t)e^{t^2} + 2te^{t^2}\phi_0(t) = e^{t^2}[\phi_0'(t) + 2t\phi_0(t)]$$

Since $e^{t^2} \neq 0$, this says that ϕ_0 is a solution of $y' + 2ty = 0$.   What we learned from this is that if ϕ_0 is a solution and if we multiply both sides of the equation $\phi_0'(t) + 2t\phi_0(t) = 0$ by e^{t^2} we obtain on the left side, the

* derivative of $e^{t^2}\phi_0(t)$.   Since this derivative is zero, it follows that $e^{t^2}\phi_0(t)$ is a constant; in fact, the initial condition $\phi_0(0) = y_0$ tells us that this constant has the value y_0.   This procedure of multiplying the differential equation by a suitable function (in this case e^{t^2}) gives us another way of finding the solution ϕ_0.   While these remarks may appear to be a waste of time in this example, they will be useful for the solution of the next example.

Example 2. $y' + 2ty = \sin t$, initial point $(0, y_0)$.   If $\phi(t)$ is a solution, so that $\phi'(t) + 2t\phi(t) = \sin t$, we can make the left side of the equation the derivative of $e^{t^2}\phi(t)$ by multiplying by e^{t^2}, as we have seen in Example 1.   If we multiply the whole equation through by e^{t^2}, we obtain $d/dt\,[e^{t^2}\phi(t)] = e^{t^2} \sin t$.   But now we can integrate, obtaining

$$e^{t^2}\phi(t) - \phi(0) = \int_0^t e^{s^2} \sin s \, ds \quad \text{or} \quad _* \quad e^{t^2}\phi(t) = y_0 + \int_0^t e^{s^2} \sin s \, ds$$

and this gives $\phi(t) = y_0e^{-t^2} + e^{-t^2}\int_0^t e^{s^2} \sin s \, ds$ for $-\infty < t < \infty$.   The integral $\int_0^t e^{s^2} \sin s \, ds$ cannot be evaluated in terms of elementary functions, but nevertheless it defines a differentiable function, whose value for $t = 0$ is zero and whose derivative is $e^{t^2} \sin t$.   We now check our result by substituting this expression for ϕ in the differential equation $y' + 2ty = \sin t$ and we obtain, using the product rule and the fundamental theorem of calculus,

$$\phi'(t) = -2te^{-t^2}y_0 + e^{-t^2}\frac{d}{dt}\int_0^t e^{s^2}\sin s\, ds - 2te^{-t^2}\int_0^t e^{s^2}\sin s\, ds$$

$$= -2te^{-t^2}y_0 + \sin t - 2te^{-t^2}\int_0^t e^{s_2}\sin s\, ds = -2t\phi(t) + \sin t$$

This shows that ϕ is actually a solution of the differential equation. Observe that ϕ is the sum of two terms, one of which is the solution ϕ_0 in Example 1.

Now let us try to use the method developed in these examples to solve (2.6). We begin by considering the simpler equation

$$y' + p(t)y = 0 \tag{2.8}$$

which has variables separable and is easily solved. If we define $P(t) = \int_{t_0}^t p(s)\, ds$, the solution ϕ_0 passing through (t_0, y_0) is given by $\phi_0(t) = y_0 e^{-P(t)}$. We can write this as $e^{P(t)}\phi_0(t) = y_0$ and differentiate, using $P'(t) = p(t)$, to obtain

$$\frac{d}{dt}[e^{P(t)}\phi_0(t)] = e^{P(t)}\phi_0'(t) + P'(t)e^{P(t)}\phi_0(t) = e^{P(t)}[\phi_0'(t) + p(t)\phi_0(t)] = 0$$

This is just what we need to find the solution ϕ of the full equation (2.6) passing through (t_0, y_0). For, if we multiply both sides of the equation $\phi'(t) + p(t)\phi(t) = q(t)$ by $e^{P(t)}$, we obtain $d/dt\,[e^{P(t)}\phi(t)] = e^{P(t)}q(t)$. Now we can integrate from t_0 to t, obtaining

$$e^{P(t)}\phi(t) - e^{P(t_0)}\phi(t_0) = \int_{t_0}^t e^{P(s)}q(s)\, ds$$

or, using $P(t_0) = 0$ and $\phi(t_0) = y_0$,

$$\phi(t) = y_0 e^{-P(t)} + e^{-P(t)}\int_{t_0}^t e^{P(s)}q(s)\, ds \tag{2.9}$$

We must now verify that the function defined by (2.9) is a solution of (2.6).

• **EXERCISE**

1. Verify that (2.9) does satisfy both the differential equation and the initial condition.

Combining this exercise with Theorem 1.1 (p. 24), we see that (2.9) is the **unique** solution of equation (2.6) passing through the point (t_0, y_0).

Observe that the expression for ϕ is the sum of two terms, the solution of (2.8) through (t_0, y_0) and the solution of (2.6) through $(t_0, 0)$. The expression is defined and remains finite so long as $p(t)$ and $q(t)$ are continuous, and this implies, as remarked earlier, that the solution ϕ exists on the whole interval on which $p(t)$ and $q(t)$ are continuous.

While (2.9) is a formula for the solution, it is easier to use the method of solution which gave (2.9) than to memorize the formula. The formula is more complicated than it appears since $P(t) = \int_{t_0}^{t} p(s) \, ds$.

• EXERCISES

2. Find the solution of $t^2 y' + 2ty = 1$ passing through $(1, 0)$. On what interval is the solution valid?

3. Find the solution of $y' + 2y = e^t$ passing through $(0, 1)$.

4. Find the solution of $y' + py = q$ passing through (t_0, y_0), where p and q are constants.

5. Find the solution of the equation $y' + a(t)y = b(t)y^k$ (Bernoulli equation), through (t_0, y_0), where k is a constant, $k \neq 1$. [*Hint:* Make the change of dependent variable $z = y^{1-k}$.]

6. The current y in an electrical circuit involving a resistance R, and inductance L, and an applied voltage $E \sin wt$ connected in series, where R, L, E, and w are positive constants, is governed by the differential equation $Ly' + Ry = E \sin wt$. Find the solution ϕ with $\phi(0) = 0$, and show that it can be written in the form

$$\phi(t) = \frac{EwL}{R^2 + w^2 L^2} e^{-Rt/L} + \frac{E}{(R^2 + w^2 L^2)^{1/2}} \sin (wt - \alpha)$$

where α is an angle defined by

$$\cos \alpha = \frac{R}{(R^2 + w^2 L^2)^{1/2}}, \quad \sin \alpha = \frac{wL}{(R^2 + w^2 L^2)^{1/2}}$$

Note that the solution for the current is the sum of two terms; the first is called the transient solution which approaches zero as $t \to +\infty$ and the second term is called the steady state solution.

7. Discuss the behavior of all solutions of the differential equation

$$y' = \lambda y$$

as $t \to +\infty$ for each of the cases $\lambda > 0$, $\lambda = 0$, $\lambda < 0$.

8. Discuss the behavior of all solutions as $t \to +\infty$ of each of the following differential equations:

(a) $y' = -2y + e^{-t}$.

(b) $y' = -2y + e^{t}$.

(c) $y' = -2y + 1$.

(d) $y' = -2y + 1/(1 + t^2)$. [*Hint:* Use l'Hospital's Rule to evaluate the limit.]

(e) $y' = -2y + f(t)$

where $f(t)$ is a continuous function for which $\lim\limits_{t \to +\infty} f(t) = 0$.

2.3 Second-Order Equations Solvable by First-Order Methods

A small class of differential equations of the second order can be reduced, by a change of the dependent variable, to a differential equation of the first order. If the transformed first-order equation has variables separable or is linear, then it may be solved by the methods of Sections 2.1 or 2.2. From this, it is possible to obtain a solution of the original second-order equation. This solution may of course be difficult or impossible to evaluate explicitly.

First, consider the equation

$$y'' = g(t, y') \tag{2.10}$$

where g does not depend explicitly on y, and g satisfies the conditions of the basic existence and uniqueness theorem (Theorem 1.2, p. 27). Make the change of variable $y' = p$, so that $y'' = p'$, and (2.10) becomes $p' = g(t, p)$. This is a first-order differential equation. If we can solve for p as a function of t, we can then integrate to obtain a solution ϕ of (2.10). If (2.10) is accompanied by initial conditions $\phi(t_0) = y_0$, $\phi'(t_0) = z_0$, we can find the solution ψ of $p' = g(t, p)$ subject to the initial condition $\psi(t_0) = z_0$, and then take ϕ to be the indefinite integral of $\psi(t)$ satisfying $\phi(t_0) = y_0$, that is, $\phi(t) = y_0 + \int_{t_0}^{t} \psi(s) \, ds$.

Example 1. Find the solution ϕ of $y'' + 2y' = t$ which satisfies the initial conditions $\phi(0) = 1$, $\phi'(0) = 0$. Theorem 1.2 guarantees the existence of a unique solution $\phi(t)$ for $-\infty < t < \infty$. The substitution $y' = p$ gives $p' + 2p = t$. We must find the solution ψ of this equation with $\psi(0) = 0$. This is a linear first-order equation and we can use the method of Section 2.2 to obtain

$$\psi'(t)e^{2t} + 2\psi(t)e^{2t} = te^{2t}$$

and then

$$\frac{d}{dt}\{\psi(t)e^{2t}\} = te^{2t}$$

and

$$\psi(t)e^{2t} - \psi(0)e^0 = \int_0^t se^{2s}\,ds = \frac{t}{2}e^{2t} - \frac{1}{4}e^{2t} + \frac{1}{4}$$

Since $\psi(0) = 0$, this gives the solution for ψ:

$$\psi(t) = \frac{t}{2} - \frac{1}{4} + \frac{1}{4}e^{-2t}$$

Since we had $\phi'(t) = \psi(t)$ with $\phi(0) = 1$, we get

$$\phi(t) = 1 + \int_0^t \left(\frac{s}{2} - \frac{1}{4} + \frac{1}{4}e^{-2s}\right)ds = \frac{9}{8} + \frac{t^2}{4} - \frac{1}{4}t - \frac{1}{8}e^{-2t}$$

Next, consider an equation which can be written as

$$y'' = h(y, y') \tag{2.11}$$

where h satisfies the hypotheses of Theorem 1.2. The following special device for transforming (2.11) into a pair of first-order equations to which our present methods apply was probably first used by Newton.

Let ϕ be the unique solution of (2.11) such that $\phi(0) = y_0$, $\phi'(0) = z_0$. Let us set $\phi'(t) = p(t)$, so that $\phi''(t) = p'(t)$ and (2.11) becomes $p'(t) = h(\phi(t), p(t))$. To solve this equation, we resort to the following trick. Assuming we have found the solution ϕ of (2.11), suppose we can solve the equation $y = \phi(t)$ for t in terms of y, say $t = s(y)$. Let $y' = \phi'(t) = p(t) = p(s(y)) = q(y)$. Then, by the chain rule

$$\phi''(t) = p'(t) = \frac{dq}{dy}\phi'(t) = \frac{dq}{dy}p(t) = \frac{dq}{dy}q(y)$$

But

$$\phi''(t) = h(\phi(t), p(t)) = h(y, q(y))$$

and therefore (2.11) is equivalent to the pair of equations

$$q(y) \frac{dq}{dy} = h(y, q(y))$$
$$y' = q(y) \tag{2.12}$$

To construct the solution ϕ of (2.11) satisfying the initial conditions $\phi(0) = y_0$, $\phi'(0) = z_0$, we begin by finding the solution $\psi(y)$ of the first equation of (2.12) satisfying the initial condition $\psi(y_0) = z_0$, corresponding to $z_0 = p(0) = q(y_0)$ and identifying ψ with q.   This cannot always be done, unless the first equation in (2.12) has variables separable or is linear. The careful reader will note that the case when $q = 0$ may lead to difficulties.   If $z_0 = 0$, then it can happen that $q \equiv 0$ is a solution of the first equation in (2.12), which in turn gives $\phi(t) \equiv y_0$ as the unique solution of (2.11).   If $q \equiv 0$ is not a solution of the first equation in (2.12), we proceed by ignoring the fact that (2.12) is meaningless for $q = 0$.   We use the function ψ determined from the first equation in the second equation of (2.12) in place of q and determine ϕ as that solution of the separable equation $y' = \psi(y)$ which satisfies the initial condition $\phi(0) = y_0$.   Having found the function ϕ, we verify by direct substitution that it is a solution of (2.11) satisfying the initial conditions.   Thus, by Theorem 1.2 (p. 27), we have found the unique solution of the problem.

Example 2.   The equation of motion for the simple pendulum, considered in Chapter 1, is

$$\frac{d^2\theta}{dt^2} = -\frac{g}{L} \sin \theta \tag{2.13}$$

Let us attempt to find a solution ϕ obeying $\phi(0) = \theta_0$, $\phi'(0) = 0$, and answer some of the questions raised in Section 1.2 (p. 7).   We put $d\theta/dt = p(t) = q(\theta)$ and (2.13) becomes

$$q \frac{dq}{d\theta} = -\frac{g}{L} \sin \theta \quad \text{and} \quad \frac{d\theta}{dt} = q(\theta)$$

We must find the solution ψ of the first of these equations such that $\psi(\phi(0)) = \phi'(0)$ or $\psi(\theta_0) = 0$.   Note that this equation has no meaning for $q = 0$. Separation of variables gives

$$\int_0^{\psi(\theta)} v \, dv = -\frac{g}{L} \int_{\theta_0}^{\theta} \sin u \, du$$

or

$$\frac{1}{2} [\psi(\theta)]^2 = \frac{g}{L} (\cos \theta - \cos \theta_0)$$

Therefore, the solution $\phi(t)$ satisfies the equation

$$|\psi(\theta)| = |\phi'(t)| = \left(\frac{2g}{L}\right)^{1/2} (\cos \phi(t) - \cos \theta_0)^{1/2}$$

which determines the angular speed of the pendulum at any position. For example, at the bottom of its swing, $\theta = 0$, and the angular speed there is

$$|\phi'(t)|_{\theta=0} = \omega = \left(\frac{2g}{L}\right)^{1/2} (1 - \cos \theta_0)^{1/2} = 2 \left(\frac{g}{L}\right)^{1/2} \sin \left(\frac{\theta_0}{2}\right)$$

● **EXERCISES**

1. Repeat the discussion above for the simplified model of the pendulum whose differential equation is

$$\frac{d^2\theta}{dt^2} = -\frac{g}{L} \theta$$

to obtain as solutions

$$|\phi'(t)| = \left(\frac{g}{L}\right)^{1/2} (\theta_0^2 - [\phi(t)]^2)^{1/2}$$

and

$$\omega = |\phi'(t)| \Big|_{\theta=0} = \left(\frac{g}{L}\right)^{1/2} \theta_0$$

2. Show that when $\theta_0 = \pi/2$, the answers for ω obtained from these two different models differ by fifteen percent.

If we are dealing with a portion of the swing of the pendulum where $\phi'(t) \geq 0$ (or $\phi'(t) \leq 0$), then we can proceed with either model to solve for $\theta = \phi(t)$.   For the first model, we have

$$\phi'(t) = \left(\frac{2g}{L}\right)^{1/2} (\cos \phi(t) - \cos \theta_0)^{1/2}$$

By separation of variables, we find $\theta = \phi(t)$ where $\phi(0) = \theta_0$, and

$$\int_{\theta_0}^{\phi(t)} \frac{d\theta}{(\cos \theta - \cos \theta_0)^{1/2}} = \int_0^t \left(\frac{2g}{L}\right)^{1/2} dt = \left(\frac{2g}{L}\right)^{1/2} t \qquad (2.14)$$

The improper integral on the left exists but cannot be evaluated in terms of elementary functions.   However, it can be estimated numerically to give a value of $\phi(t)$ for each t.

•EXERCISES

3. Verify that the function ϕ defined implicitly by (2.14) satisfies the equation (2.13).   Note that there is still a difficulty for $\phi(t) = \theta_0$.

4. Repeat this procedure with the simplified model of Exercise 1 (p. 46) to find $\phi(t)$ subject to the initial conditions $\phi(0) = \theta_0$, $\phi'(0) = 0$.   [*Hint:* $\int(1 - x^2)^{1/2}\, dx = \arcsin(x) + C$.   The   answer   is $\phi(t) = \theta_0 \cos (g/L)^{1/2}t$. The simplicity of this solution and the ease with which it is obtained is the reason the simplified model is often used.   We will find an even easier way to obtain this solution in Chapter 3.]

Example 3.   Rocket Flight.   The force of gravity is not constant, but depends upon the distance from the center of mass of the earth (and to some degree upon local rock densities).   In dealing with large distances, it is a reasonable approximation for some purposes to assume that the force of gravity on an object of mass m outside the earth's atmosphere is given by $F = kmx^{-2}$ where k is a constant and x is the distance from the object to the center of the earth, which is assumed spherical.   During the initial "powered flight" period of a rocket, the laws of motion are rather complicated.   After "burn out," things are much simpler since the rocket is merely coasting, with its velocity being decreased by the effects of earth's gravity.   We can therefore ask the following questions (we assume that the rocket moves directly away from the earth):

(a) Knowing the height and velocity of the rocket at burn out, can we find how high it will go before beginning to fall back to earth?
(b) Can we determine what velocity it must have at "burn out" in order to continue rising indefinitely?

We assume that the burn out height is essentially the radius of the earth R.   Let x be the distance from the rocket to the center of the earth. From Newton's law of gravitation we see that the differential equation for the motion is $x'' = -k/x^2$, where k is chosen so that at the surface of the earth $(x = R)$ the acceleration is g.   The initial conditions are that at $t = 0$, $x = R$ and $dx/dt = V =$ velocity at burn out.   If we put $v = x'$, $w(x) = v(x(t))$, and $x''(t) = w(x)\, dw/dt$, we can reduce the problem to one which can be solved by separation of variables.

• EXERCISE

5. (a) Solve the equation of motion of the rocket and use the initial conditions to find

$$w^2 = V^2 - 2gR + \frac{2gR^2}{x}$$

(b) Show that if $V^2 < 2gR$, the maximum height reached by the rocket is given by

$$x = \frac{2gR^2}{2gR - V^2}$$

(c) Discuss what seems to happen if $V^2 = 2gR$.
(d) Discuss what seems to happen if $V^2 > 2gR$.
(e) If $g = 32$ ft/sec^2 and $R = 4000$ miles, calculate the "escape velocity" in miles per hour.

2.4   Geometry of First-Order Equations

While we have not proved it here, all first-order equations can be solved, at least in theory, in terms of integrals.   However, these are often hard to evaluate and to interpret.   Therefore, it is difficult to draw any conclusions about how solutions behave and this, after all, is the important matter.   We can often get some idea about this **without** solving the equation by exploiting the notion of direction field more than was done in Section 1.5 (p. 17).   We illustrate by considering an example.

Example 1.   Consider the differential equation $y' = y^2$, and for the present let us ignore the fact that we have already solved this equation in Example 1, Section 2.1 (p. 33).   From Theorem 1.1 (page 24) we know that through each point (t_0, y_0) of the (t, y) plane there passes a unique solution ϕ.   However, we do not know on how large an interval, both for $t \geq t_0$ and for $t \leq t_0$, this solution exists.   We see, using the geometric interpretation of solution, that the slope of the solution at the initial point is $y_0^2 > 0$ if $y_0 \neq 0$.   Therefore the values of the function $\phi(t)$ increase for $t \geq t_0$ and decrease for $t \leq t_0$ (that is, as we move to the left from t_0); see Figure 2.3.   For values of $t > t_0$ and near t_0, it is clear that because $\phi(t)$ increases as t does, so does the slope $\phi'(t) = [\phi(t)]^2$, and consequently the solution will increase more rapidly as t increases.   It might therefore be expected in the case $y_0 > 0$ not only that $\phi(t) \to +\infty$ as t increases but also that this might happen as t approaches some finite value $t_1 > t_0$.

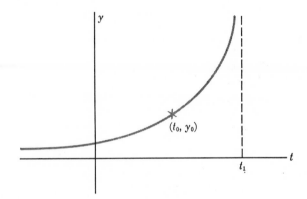

Figure 2.3

(This does in fact happen, as we see by looking at the explicit solution, equation (2.3), p. 34.)

For values of $t < t_0$, the solution ϕ decreases as we move to the left and when $\phi(t)$ becomes less than 1, the slope $[\phi(t)]^2$ becomes smaller.   Therefore the solution $\phi(t)$ decreases less rapidly as t increases.   However, the solution ϕ can never cross the t axis; for by uniqueness if it did ϕ would be identically zero, contradicting the assumption $y_0 > 0$.   Therefore we would expect the solution ϕ to exist for all $t < t_0$ and $\lim\limits_{t \to -\infty} \phi(t) = 0$.

Examination of the explicit solution, equation 2.3 (p. 34) shows that this is indeed the case.

Now consider the case $y_0 < 0$.   Again, the initial slope is $y_0^2 > 0$, and the solution ϕ increases for $t \geq t_0$ and decreases for $t \leq t_0$ (that is, as we move to the left from t_0); see Figure 2.4.   For values of $t > t_0$, $\phi(t)$ will continue to increase but more slowly as $|\phi(t)|$ becomes smaller.   As the solution ϕ cannot cross the t axis (why?), we would expect ϕ to exist for all $t > t_0$ and that $\lim\limits_{t \to +\infty} \phi(t) = 0$ in the case $y_0 < 0$. For $t < t_0$ the solution will become more negative and approach $-\infty$; this in fact happens for a finite value $t_1 < t_0$ as can be seen from the explicit solution (2.3) (p. 34).

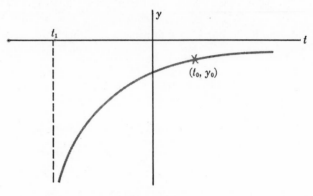

Figure 2.4

● **EXERCISES**

1. For a fixed $y_0 > 0$, vary t_0 and use the argument given above to sketch the solution curves in the (t, y) plane. Repeat for a fixed $y_0 < 0$. What happens if $y_0 = 0$?

2. By a similar analysis sketch the solution curves of the differential equation $y' = -y^2$.

3. Sketch the solution curves of the differential equations $y' = y$ and $y' = -y$.

4. Sketch the solution curves of the differential equation $y' = t^2 + y^2$.

5. Sketch the solution curves of the differential equation $y' = 1/(t^2 + y^2)$.

2.5   A Numerical Method

We have seen in Example 2, Section 2.2 (page 40) that the differential equation

$$y' + 2ty = \sin t$$

subject to the initial condition $\phi(0) = y_0$ can be "solved" for $y = \phi(t)$. The result is $\phi(t) = e^{-t^2}y_0 + e^{-t^2}\int_0^t e^{s^2} \sin s \, ds$. However, if we want the numerical value of $\phi(1)$, this "solution" is not very useful since it gives

$$\phi(1) = e^{-1}y_0 + e^{-1}\int_0^1 e^{s^2} \sin s \, ds$$

and the integral $\int_0^1 e^{s^2} \sin s \, ds$ cannot be evaluated exactly. Of course, we can approximate the integral by the trapezoidal rule or Simpson's rule, and obtain a numerical value which approximates $\phi(1)$.

Another difficulty, more serious than this one, arises in the simple pendulum model, for which we found in Example 2, Section 2.3 (p. 47) that the displacement $\phi(t)$ is defined by solving the following equation for ϕ:

$$\left(\frac{L}{2g}\right)^{1/2} \int_{\theta_0}^{\phi(t)} \frac{d\theta}{(\cos \phi(t) - \cos \theta_0)^{1/2}} = t$$

It is not possible to evaluate the integral on the left side of this equation in terms of elementary functions. A numerical approximation for the integral is impractical since the upper limit of integration is variable. Even if a numerical approximation could be obtained, we would still have the problem of solving for the implicitly defined function ϕ. Also, the integral is improper, which adds to the difficulties.

In fact, in practical problems, the most common situation is that no usable expression for the solution can be found at all, even though it can be shown that there is a unique solution. When we meet such difficulties we must often resort to the use of numerical approximations from the start. In this section, we shall develop one approximation method, and we shall indicate some of its refinements which are frequently used on electronic computers in Chapter 8.

Let us consider the solution of the first-order differential equation

$$y' = f(t, y) \tag{2.15}$$

through the point (t_0, y_0). We assume that f satisfies the assumptions of the existence and uniqueness theorem (Theorem 1.1, p. 24) in some rectangle $R = \{(t, y) \mid |t - t_0| < a, |y - y_0| < b\}$. Then the theorem assures us that there is a unique solution ϕ of this problem existing on some interval $|t - t_0| < \alpha$, where $\alpha \leq a$. We wish to find a numerical approximation for the number $\phi(t_0 + T)$, where T is specified and $|T| < \alpha$ (see Figure 2.5). We shall do this by a construction which makes use of the geometric interpretation of the solution suggested in Section 1.5 (p. 17). To be specific, we suppose that $t_0 + T$ is to the right of t_0, $0 < T \le \alpha$, and divide the interval $[t_0, t_0 + T]$ into n subintervals by specifying intermediate points $t_0 < t_1 < t_2 < \cdots < t_n = t_0 + T$. In practice, these points are usually equally spaced, but this is not necessary. Now start at (t_0, y_0). We know that the curve $y = \phi(t)$ passes through the point (t_0, y_0) and that its derivative at (t_0, y_0) is $f(t_0, y_0)$. Since we do not know $\phi(t)$, we cannot follow it to t_1. Instead, we pretend that the solution is a straight line L_0 with slope $f(t_0, y_0)$, and we follow this line to t_1. The

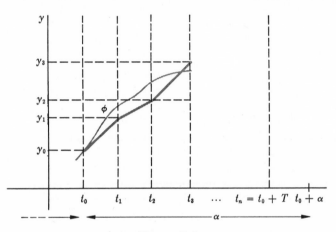

Figure 2.5

premise, of course, is that if t_1 is close enough to t_0, the error made by following the straight line segment instead of the solution (called the truncation error) is not too large. We know from analytic geometry that the equation of the straight line L_0 through (t_0, y_0) with the slope $m_0 = f(t_0, y_0)$ is $y = y_0 + (t - t_0)f(t_0, y_0)$. We compute y_1, an approximation for $\phi(t_1)$, by substituting $t = t_1$ in the equation of L_0. This gives

$$y_1 = y_0 + (t_1 - t_0)f(t_0, y_0) = y_0 + m_0(t_1 - t_0)$$

We now **pretend** that the solution $y = \phi(t)$ passes through (t_1, y_1). If it did, its tangent at (t_1, y_1) would have slope $m_1 = f(t_1, y_1)$. Let L_1 be the straight line through (t_1, y_1) with slope m_1. We know that the equation of L_1 is $y = y_1 + (t - t_1)f(t_1, y_1)$. We now proceed along the straight line L_1 and compute our approximation y_2 to $\phi(t_2)$ by substituting

$t = t_2$ in the equation of L_1.   This gives

$$y_2 = y_1 + (t_2 - t_1)f(t_1, y_1)$$

In general, of course, y_1 is not likely to be $\phi(t_1)$, and $\phi'(t_1)$ is not necessarily m_1.   Thus we are retaining the error made in the first stage and possibly compounding it by using the wrong slope.   For the moment, let us not worry about this error.   We can continue the process until, at the nth stage, we obtain an approximation y_n for $\phi(T)$.

This construction, which is called an iterative procedure, can also be expressed analytically as follows.   Having computed the approximations y_i $(i = 1, 2, \ldots, k)$, we compute y_{k+1} from the formula:

$$y_{k+1} = y_k + (t_{k+1} - t_k)f(t_k, y_k) \tag{2.16}$$

This relation is an example of a difference equation.   If we denote by $\psi(t)$ the "approximate" solution constructed by this method, then

$$\psi(t) = y_k + (t - t_k)f(t_k, y_k)$$

on the interval $t_k < t \leq t_{k+1}$, for $k = 0, 1, \ldots, n - 1$.   The graph of ψ is the "polygonal curve" in Figure 2.5.   It can be regarded as the solution of the difference equation (2.16), and the method amounts to approximating the differential equation (2.15) by the difference equation (2.16).

If $t_0 + T$ is to the left of t_0, the same procedure can be used, with the obvious modification that we go to the left along each line segment.   In practice, the interval $[t_0, t_0 + T]$ is usually divided into subintervals of equal length h, so that $h = T/n$.   The formula (2.16) then becomes

$$y_{k+1} = y_k + hf(t_k, y_k)$$

This technique of approximating solutions is called the **Euler method** or the **Cauchy polygon method**.   It is suitable for high speed computation; in practice, the methods most often used are refinements of the Euler method.

Example 1.   Let ϕ be the solution of $y' = y$ passing through $(0, 1)$. Compute $\phi(1)$ using equally spaced mesh points with $h = 0.1$.

Here $f(t, y) = y$ and the iterative formula for y_{k+1} becomes

$$y_{k+1} = y_k + hy_k = (1 + h)y_k = (1.1)y_k \qquad (k = 0, 1, \ldots, 9)$$

and we can tabulate our results as follows:

k	t_k	y_k	$y_{k+1} = 1.1y_k$
0	0.0	1.000	1.100
1	0.1	1.100	1.210
2	0.2	1.210	1.331
3	0.3	1.331	1.464
4	0.4	1.464	1.610
5	0.5	1.610	1.771
6	0.6	1.771	1.948
7	0.7	1.948	2.143
8	0.8	2.143	2.357
9	0.9	2.357	2.593
10	1.0	2.593	

The exact solution is given by $\phi(t) = e^t$, and thus $\phi(1) = e$. We have obtained the approximation 2.593 for e. Note that we have actually calculated $(1 + 1/n)^n$ with $n = 10$.

●**EXERCISE**

1. Use the same procedure with $h = 0.05$ to see how much better the approximation becomes.

In Exercise 1, we are calculating $(1 + 1/n)^n$ with $n = 20$. Since $\lim_{n \to \infty} (1 + 1/n)^n = e$, it is clear that we can approximate e as accurately as desired by using the Euler method with sufficiently small h and obtaining the approximation $(1 + h)^{1/h}$ or $(1 + 1/n)^n$ with $n = 1/h$.

A numerical approximation is useless unless there is some way to estimate the error of the method. What is actually needed is an error bound —a maximum possible value for the error.

In the example, we rounded off all entries to three decimal places. This introduces an error at each stage, called the **round-off error,** which may accumulate from step to step. It can be shown that we can decrease the round-off error at each stage by keeping more decimal places.

There is another error in the Euler method, called the truncation error, caused by the use of straight lines to approximate the solution curves. We must be careful to distinguish between the **local truncation error,** which is the error that would be introduced in going from the value y_k at t_k to the value y_{k+1} at t_{k+1} if y_k were exact, and the **cumulative trunca-**

tion error, which is the actual error in the value of $\phi(t_0 + T)$ caused by the approximation.   The reader should note that the cumulative truncation error is not simply the sum of all the local truncation errors.   Since there may be an error already present in y_k, there may be an additional error in y_{k+1} caused by using the wrong slope at t_k, as well as the wrong value of the solution.

As an example, let us calculate the local truncation error of the Euler method.   The differential equation

$$y' = f(t, y)$$

has $\phi(t)$ as its exact solution.   This means that

$$\phi'(t) = f(t, \phi(t)) \qquad (t_0 \leq t \leq t_0 + \alpha)$$

Now, $\phi(t_k)$ is the exact value at t_k, $\phi(t_{k+1})$ is the **exact** value at t_{k+1}, and

$$\phi(t_{k+1}) - \phi(t_k) = \int_{t_k}^{t_{k+1}} \phi'(t)\, dt = \int_{t_k}^{t_{k+1}} f(t, \phi(t))\, dt$$

Thus the **exact** value at t_{k+1} is given by

$$\phi(t_{k+1}) = \phi(t_k) + \int_{t_k}^{t_{k+1}} t(t, \phi(t))\, dt \tag{2.17}$$

The formula for the **approximate** value y_{k+1} at t_{k+1} is

$$y_{k+1} = y_k + (t_{k+1} - t_k)f(t_k, y_k) \tag{2.18}$$

In this formula, y_k is the approximate value at t_k.   The local truncation error T_k is defined as $|\phi(t_{k+1}) - y_{k+1}|$ under the assumption that $\phi(t_k) = y_k$, that is, that the approximate value at t_k is exact.   By subtracting (2.18) from (2.17) we see that

$$T_k = \left| \int_{t_k}^{t_{k+1}} f(t, \phi(t))\, dt - (t_{k+1} - t_k)f(t_k, y_k) \right|$$

For convenience of notation, set $f(t, \phi(t)) = F(t)$.   Then

$$T_k = \left| \int_{t_k}^{t_{k+1}} F(t)\, dt - (t_{k+1} - t_k)F(t_k) \right|$$

We can use the **mean value theorem** to get an upper bound for the error.   We have

$$F(t) - F(t_k) = (t - t_k)F'(s_k)$$

where s_k is some point between t_k and t.   From this, we obtain

$$\int_{t_k}^{t_{k+1}} F(t) \, dt = \int_{t_k}^{t_{k+1}} \{F(t_k) + (t - t_k)F'(s_k)\} \, dt$$
$$= (t_{k+1} - t_k)F(t_k) + \int_{t_k}^{t_{k+1}} (t - t_k)F'(s_k) \, dt$$

and we find that the local truncation error is given by

$$T_k = \left| \int_{t_k}^{t_{k+1}} (t - t_k)F'(s_k) \, dt \right|$$

Suppose that $M = \max\limits_{t_0 \leq t \leq t_0 + T} |F'(t)|$.   Since

$$F'(t) = \frac{\partial f}{\partial t}(t, \phi(t)) + \frac{\partial f}{\partial y}(t, \phi(t))\phi'(t) = \frac{\partial f}{\partial t}(t, \phi(t)) + \frac{\partial f}{\partial y}(t, \phi(t))f(t, \phi(t))$$

if f, $\partial f/\partial t$, and $\partial f/\partial y$ are bounded on the rectangle R, a bound for the number M can be calculated explicitly from the expression

$$M \leq \max_{R} \left| \frac{\partial f}{\partial t}(t, y) \right| + \max_{R} \left| \frac{\partial f}{\partial y}(t, y) \right| \max_{R} |f(t, y)|$$

where the maxima are all taken over the rectangle R.   Note that this expression does not depend on the particular (unknown) solution ϕ. Then we have

$$T_k \leq M \int_{t_k}^{t_{k+1}} (t - t_k) \, dt = \frac{M}{2} (t_{k+1} - t_k)^2$$

In the standard case of **equal subdivisions**, $t_{k+1} - t_k = h$, and we have shown that the local truncation error of Euler's method is at most $\frac{1}{2}Mh^2$.

If the cumulative truncation error were the sum of all the local truncation errors, then, since there are $N = T/h$ steps, this error would be at most

$$\frac{1}{2} Mh^2 \cdot N = \frac{1}{2} TMh$$

It can be shown (see for example Section 8.1) that although this reasoning is invalid, the cumulative truncation error is in fact no greater than a constant multiplied by h. This shows that we can reduce the cumulative truncation error by making the value of h smaller (that is, by increasing the number of subdivisions).

The bound obtained here for the truncation error is usually far larger than the actual error which occurs when the method is applied to a specific problem. This is a common phenomenon in numerical analysis.

The method we have used to estimate the truncation error suggests an obvious refinement—use a more sophisticated approximation for the integral, such as the trapezoidal rule or Simpson's rule. In fact, the use of Simpson's rule leads to an approximation method known as Milne's method (see for example Section 8.3) which is widely used for computation. It has a cumulative truncation error no greater than a constant multiplied by h^4.

The fact that the truncation error involves a positive power of h implies that for small values of h, we obtain a high degree of accuracy. Roughly speaking, the higher the power of h, the more accurate the method. It would be possible to devise very complicated approximation procedures with truncation errors no greater than a constant times h^{17}, but it is more effective and faster on a computer to use a relatively simple formula, and a very small value of h.

The method we have discussed can be adapted to second-order differential equations, but the adaptation involves some complications that we shall not discuss here.

•EXERCISES

2. Use the Euler method to estimate $\phi(1)$, where ϕ is the solution of $y' = t + y$ passing through $(0, 0)$. Use equal spacing with $h = t_{k+1} - t_k = 0.1$. Also calculate $\phi(1)$ exactly by solving the equation, and compare the results.

3. Repeat Exercise 2 for the differential equation $y' + 2ty = \sin t$ with initial condition $\phi(0) = 0$. Note that you will need to use tables to find $\sin 0.1$, $\sin 0.2$, etc., and that you will not be able to compare your answer with the exact solution of the equation.

4. Use the Euler method to estimate the value of $\phi(1)$ where ϕ is the solution of

$$\frac{dy}{dt} = 2ty + 1 - 2t^2$$

passing through $(0, 0)$. Use equal spacing with $h = 0.1$.

•MISCELLANEOUS EXERCISES

1. For each of the following differential equations, verify whether the existence theorem (Theorem 1.1, p. 24) is applicable, and find the solution through the given initial point.   In each case, give the interval on which the solution exists.

(a) $y' = 1 + y^2$ $(-\pi/4, 0)$ (g) $y' = t - 3y$ $(0, 0)$

(b) $ty' + y = e^t$ $(1, 1)$ (h) $y' = -2t(y - t^2)$ $(0, 0)$

(c) $y' = 7y^3 \cos t$ $(1, 0)$

(d) $ty' + 2y = t^2 - t + 1$ $(1, \frac{1}{2})$ (i) $y' = \dfrac{y^2}{1 - t}$ $\left(-1, \dfrac{1}{\log 2}\right)$

(e) $y' = \tan t \tan y$ $(0, \pi/6)$ (j) $y' + 3y = e^{2t}$ $(0, 1)$

(f) $y' = ty^2$ $(0, -2)$ (k) $y' + 3y = e^{-3t}$ $(0, 1)$

                                            (l) $y' = 2t(1 - y^2)^{1/2}$ $(0, 1)$

2. By solving the differential equation

$$y' = 1 + y^2$$

show that no solution through the origin exists for $-\infty < t < \infty$.

3. Find the solution of each of the following differential equations through the point $(0, a)$, where a is a given constant.

(a) $(t + 1)(y' + y) = e^t$.

(b) $y' - y = 2te^{2t}$.

(c) $y(t) = \int_0^t y(s) \, ds + t + a$.   [*Hint:* Differentiate the equation.]

(d) $y' - y \tan t = 1$.

4. Find the solution ϕ of each of the following differential equations satisfying the given initial conditions.

(a) $y'' = y$ $\phi(0) = 1,\ \phi'(0) = -1$.

(b) $y'' = y' + 1$ $\phi(1) = 0,\ \phi'(1) = -1$.

(c) $y'' = \frac{4}{3}y'y^3$ $\phi(0) = 1,\ \phi'(0) = \frac{1}{3}$.

5. Consider the differential equation

$$y'' + (y^2 - 1)y' + y = 0$$

(van der Pol equation), which occurs in the theory of vacuum tube circuits.

(a) Show that the change of variable $y' = v$ transforms this to the form $dv/dy = (-y/v) - (y^2 - 1)$.

(b) Sketch the direction field and a few solution curves of the equation obtained in part (a).   (See [1], pp. 156–158.)

6. (a) Use the Euler method with $h = 0.1$ to approximate the value of $\phi(0.3)$, where ϕ is the solution of $y' = t^2 + y^2$ such that $\phi(0) = 1$.

(b) Repeat part (a), but with $h = 0.05$.

7. Consider the differential equation

$$y' = f(y)$$

where $f(y)$ is a continuous positive function for $y > 0$ and $f(0) = 0$. By solving explicitly, show that if $\int_\epsilon^{y_0} du/f(u)$ diverges as $\epsilon \to 0+$, then there is a unique solution through the point $(0, y_0)$. This solution is strictly positive and tends to 0 as $t \to -\infty$. If $\int_\epsilon^{y_0} du/f(u)$ converges as $\epsilon \to 0+$, then there is an infinite number of solutions through the point $(0, y_0)$. Give some examples of functions $f(u)$ and sketch the corresponding solution curves. [*Hint:* While Theorem 1.1 is not applicable, the method of separation of variables may be used. The result follows from the inverse function theorem.]

8. (a) Show, by constructing it, that the equation

$$y' + y = f(t)$$

has a unique solution bounded for $-\infty < t < \infty$, where $|f(t)| \leq M$, and f is continuous for $-\infty < t < \infty$. [*Hint:* Consider the solution ϕ_A with $\phi_A(-A) = 0$, where $A > 0$, and let $A \to \infty$; $\phi(t) = \lim_{A\to\omega} \phi_A(t)$.]

(b) If the function $f(t)$ is periodic of period 2π (that is, if $f(t + 2\pi) = f(t)$ for $-\infty < t < \infty$), show that the solution obtained in part (a) is periodic. [*Hint:* Show by a suitable change of the variable of integration that the solution ϕ obtained in part (a) satisfies $\phi(t + 2\pi) = \phi(t)$ for every t.]

9. Given the differential equation

$$y' + a(t)y = f(t)$$

where $a(t)$ and $f(t)$ are continuous, where $a(t) \geq c > 0$, and $\lim_{t\to\infty} f(t) = 0$, show that every solution tends to zero as $t \to \infty$.

10. Let a be a positive constant and let $\lim_{t\to0+} f(t) = b$. Show that the equation

$$ty' + ay = f(t)$$

has a unique solution which is bounded as $t \to 0+$ and find the limit of this solution as $t \to 0+$.

11. Given a family of curves $f(x, y) = c$ in the (x, y) plane, a family of curves $g(x, y) = c$ is said to form a set of orthogonal trajectories of the first family if every intersection of a curve in the first family with a curve in the second family is at right angles. Find the orthogonal trajectories of each of the following families of curves.

(a) $x^2 + y^2 = c$.   (c) $y^2 = 4cx$.
(b) $y = ce^{-2x}$.   (d) $2x^2 + y^2 = c^2$.

[*Hint* (for part (a)): Show that for every curve in the given family $dy/dx = -x/y$. Therefore, for every orthogonal trajectory, $dy/dx = y/x$.]

12. Find all curves such that the trapezoid bounded by the coordinate axes, the tangent line at an arbitrary point, and the vertical line through the point has the constant area $3a^2$.

(The reader is warned that some of the following problems are difficult. They are concerned with the transition from physical models to mathematical models, and, therefore, are not part of the study of differential equations, strictly speaking.)

13. The law of radioactive decay says that the rate of decay of a substance is proportional at each instant to the amount of substance present. If the half-life of a substance is 30 days (that is, if half of the substance has decayed after 30 days), how long will it take until 99 percent of the substance has decayed?

14. Newton's law of cooling says that the rate of change of temperatures of a cooling body is proportional to the difference of temperature between the body and its surroundings. If a body cools from 100°C to 60°C in surroundings at 20°C in 10 minutes, how long will it take for the body to cool to 25°C?

15. Assume that the number of monkeys on a tropical island depends on the rate of reproduction and on the available banana supply. Suppose that the birth rate is $k\phi(t)$, where k is a given positive constant (that is, if $\phi(t)$ is the number of monkeys on the island at time t, then approximately $kh\phi(t)$ monkeys are born between time t and time $t + h$). Also, suppose that the death rate, due to starvation and other phenomena, is $k[\phi(t)]^2 - k(A - 1)\phi(t)$, where A is a given constant, with $A > 2$. Find the number of monkeys on the island at time t, if there were 2 monkeys at time $t = 0$. Does this number tend to a limit as $t \to \infty$? [*Hint:* Show that $\phi'(t) = k\phi(t)(A - \phi(t))$, and solve, noting that since $\phi'(t) > 0$ if $\phi(t) < A$ and $\phi'(t) = 0$ if $\phi(t) = A$ you have $A - \phi(t) \geq 0$ for all t.]

16. A tank contains 10 liters of water to which is being added a salt solution containing 0.3 kilograms of salt per liter. This salt solution is being poured in at the rate of 2 liters per minute and being thoroughly mixed, and then the mixture is drained off at the same rate (2 liters per minute). How much salt is in the flask after five minutes? [*Hint:* Let $\phi(t)$ be the amount of salt in the tank at the end of t minutes. Then between t and $(t + h)$ minutes, approximately $2 \times 0.3 \times h = 0.6h$ kilograms of salt enter the tank, and approximately $2 \times \phi(t) \times \frac{1}{10} \times h = 0.2h\phi(t)$ kilograms of salt leave the tank. Thus $\phi(t + h) - \phi(t) \approx 0.6h - 0.2h\phi(t)$; dividing by h and letting $h \to 0$ we have $\phi'(t) + 0.2\phi(t) = 0.6$. Also $\phi(0) = 0$.]

17. A tank contains 100 liters of water and 10 kilograms of salt, thoroughly mixed. Pure water is added at the rate of 5 liters per minute, and the mixture is poured off at the same rate. How much salt is left in the tank after one hour? Assume complete and instantaneous mixing.

18. A small solid sphere of density γ (pounds per cubic foot) falls from rest under the influence of gravity into a large reservoir of liquid whose surface is h feet below the point at which the sphere is released (see Figure 2.6). The density of the liquid is $k\gamma$, where $k > 1$.

If the frictional resistance of the liquid to the motion of the sphere is proportional to the velocity of the sphere (the constant of proportionality being p), determine the maximum depth to which the sphere sinks.

Assume that the reservoir is deep so that the sphere does not strike the bottom. Neglect air friction. Make the approximation that the sphere is either entirely in air or entirely in the liquid and that the instant of entry coincides with the time when the center of mass of the sphere passes through the free surface of the liquid.

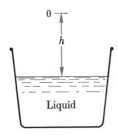

Figure 2.6

Recall that a submerged body is buoyed up by a force equal to the weight of the liquid displaced. If the mass of liquid displaced is w lb, then this force is wg.

19. A small sphere weighing 0.1 pounds is projected vertically upward with an initial velocity of 1500 feet per second from a height of 1000 feet above the earth's surface. It is subsequently acted upon only by gravity and by air friction. The resistive force of air friction (in pounds) is 10^{-7} times the square of the velocity (feet per second). Assuming that the acceleration of gravity has the constant value 32 feet per second per second, draw a graph showing the altitude of the sphere as a function of time from the instant of release until the instant of contact with the earth.

20. A steel sphere is projected vertically upward from the earth's surface with a positive initial velocity v_0. Does it take the sphere longer to reach its maximum height or to fall back to the earth from that height?

Assume that the acceleration of gravity (g) is constant, that the air is still, and that the retarding force of air friction is proportional to the velocity of the sphere relative to the air through which it moves. Call the constant of proportionality p.

If you claim that one time is longer than the other, give a mathematical justification of your claim (not an intuitive physical argument).

21. When lying on its side on a smooth horizontal plane, a helical spring is L inches long (see Figure 2.7). The spring is a "linear spring" in the sense that the amount it is compressed by an axial force is proportional to the force applied. The constant of proportionality, which is called the "spring constant," is K (pounds per inch), and the total weight of the spring is m pounds.

When the spring is stood on end, it shortens due to its own weight. If x represents the distance (inches) measured positively downward from the upper end of the up-ended spring, and if $w(x)$ is the weight of that portion of the spring above a section x units from the top, then the function $w(x)$ is a solution of the differential equation

$$\frac{dw}{dx} = \frac{L}{1 - w/KL} \qquad w(0) = 0$$

Solve this initial value problem for the function $w(x)$.

Let L' represent the axial length of the up-ended spring. Noting that $w(L') = m$, find L'. How much did the spring shorten when up-ended?

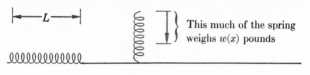

Figure 2.7

If $\rho(x)$ is the weight per unit length of the up-ended spring, then

$$\rho(x) = \frac{dw}{dx}$$

For what value of x does the maximum value ρ_{max} of $\rho(x)$ occur? Determine ρ_{max}. What is the ratio of ρ_{max} to $\rho_{average}$?

22. The circuit shown in Figure 2.8 consists of a battery in series with a fixed inductance and a variable resistor. The resistance R increases linearly with time according to the relation $R = kt$, where k is a positive constant.

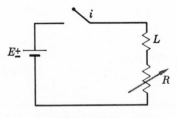

Figure 2.8

The current i is zero before the switch is closed at $t = 0$. For $t \geq 0$ the differential equation

$$E = iR + L\frac{di}{dt}$$

applies, where E and L are constants and $R = kt$.

Show that a solution ϕ of this equation valid for $t \geq 0$ and satisfying the initial condition $\phi(0) = 0$ is

$$\phi(t) = \frac{E}{L} \exp\left[-\frac{kt^2}{2L} \right] \int_0^t \exp\left[\frac{kx^2}{2L} \right] dx$$

Show also that

$$\lim_{t \to \infty} \phi(t) = 0$$

Is this relation a physically reasonable result? Why? If $E = 100$ volts, if $k = 5.0$ ohms per second, and if the current reaches its maximum value when $t = 2$ seconds, determine the value of i_{max}.

Chapter 3

LINEAR DIFFERENTIAL EQUATIONS

3.1 Introduction

In this chapter we will study linear differential equations. We will concentrate on second-order equations of the form

$$a_0(t)y'' + a_1(t)y' + a_2(t)y = f(t) \tag{3.1}$$

where a_0, a_1, a_2, f are given functions continuous on some interval I; the interval I may be open, closed, or open at one end and closed at the other. We shall see that all the results concerning (3.1) can readily be extended to linear equations of order higher than 2.

Equations of the form (3.1) occur in many applications. For example, the simplest (and least accurate) mathematical model for the simple pendulum is of the form of equation (3.1) with $a_0(t) \equiv 1$, $a_1(t) \equiv 0$, $a_2(t) = g/L$, $f(t) \equiv 0$ (see equation (1.10), p. 12). Many physical problems, such as the motion of a pendulum, a "mass spring" system, and the oscillations in the shaft of an electric motor, have equations such as (3.1) as their crudest mathematical models. By this we mean that in most instances the mathematical model may well be more complicated; for example, in the case of the simple pendulum, the derivation originally led to a nonlinear differential equation (equation (1.7), p. 10). In such cases one naturally tries to see whether the relevant equation may be simplified in such a way that the new approximating equation can actually be solved. This process usually involves "linearizing" the equation. In the case of the pendulum equation (1.7) we accomplish this by replacing $\sin \theta$ by θ to obtain equation (1.10). Naturally we hope that for "small oscillations" this approximation is good enough to predict the nature of the motion.

It certainly is not obvious at this stage that the linearized equation will be any simpler to handle than the original one. However, experience will show that linear equations are relatively easy to handle, while nonlinear ones present serious difficulties.

If one linearizes a problem (for the simple pendulum this means replacing sin θ by θ) the following question arises naturally: How good an approximation does the linearized equation actually produce? For the pendulum we would like to prove that in some sense the motions of the linear and nonlinear models are close to one another when $|\theta|$ is "small." While we cannot hope to answer such questions at this stage, the material presented here constitutes an essential first step in this direction.

Before beginning the study of the general theory of equation (3.1), we recall that we already know something about this equation. Namely, as a direct application of our fundamental existence and uniqueness theorem for second-order equations (Theorem 1.2, p. 27; see also Exercise 10, Section 1.8, p. 28), we can state the following result:

Theorem 3.1. *Let a_0, a_1, a_2, f be functions continuous on some interval I and let $a_0(t) \neq 0$ for all t in I. Then for each t_0 in I, there exists one and only one solution $\phi(t)$ of equation (3.1) satisfying arbitrary prescribed initial conditions $\phi(t_0) = y_0$, $\phi'(t_0) = z_0$. This solution $\phi(t)$ exists on the interval I.*

We may say this in another way. For a linear second-order differential equation a solution with a given initial displacement and slope exists and is unique as long as the coefficients are continuous and the coefficient of the leading term ($a_0(t)$ in (3.1)) is not zero.

Example 1. Consider

$$a_0(t)y'' + a_1(t)y' + a_2(t)y = 0 \tag{3.2}$$

where a_0, a_1, a_2 are continuous on some interval I and $a_0(t) \neq 0$ on I. Then it is readily verified that the function ϕ, defined by $\phi(t) = 0$ for all t in I, is a solution of equation (3.2) on I. Therefore by Theorem 3.1 (here $f(t) \equiv 0$), $\phi(t) = 0$ is the **only solution** of equation (3.2) on I **satisfying the initial conditions** $\phi(t_0) = 0$, $\phi'(t_0) = 0$, for any point t_0 in I.

●**EXERCISE**

1. Show that if solutions ϕ of equation (3.2) are represented as curves in the (t, y) plane, **no** solution of (3.2) except $\phi \equiv 0$ can be tangent to the t axis at any point of I.

Example 2.   Consider $ty'' + (\cos t)y' + [1 - 1/(t + 1)]y = 2t$. Discuss existence and uniqueness of solutions.

Here $a_0(t) = t$, $a_1(t) = \cos t$, $a_2(t) = 1 - 1/(t + 1)$, $f(t) = 2t$ are continuous for all t except $a_2(t)$, which is discontinuous at $t = -1$; also $a_0(0) = 0$. Thus we must distinguish three cases for the initial time t_0: *Case (i)* $t_0 < -1$; *Case (ii)* $-1 < t_0 < 0$; *Case (iii)* $t_0 > 0$. We do not take $t_0 = 0$ or $t_0 = -1$ (why?). In case (i) by Theorem 3.1 given any $t_0 < -1$, there exists one and only one solution ϕ of the given equation satisfying the initial conditions $\phi(t_0) = y_0$, $\phi'(t_0) = z_0$, where y_0, z_0 are arbitrary given real numbers; this solution ϕ exists on the interval $-\infty < t < -1$.

•EXERCISES

2. Discuss in a similar way the existence and uniqueness problem for cases (ii) and (iii) of the equation in Example 2.

3. Discuss the existence and uniqueness problem for real solutions of the equation

$$(1 + t)y'' + 2ty' + (\log t)y = \cos t$$

4. Do the same for the equation

$$a_0 y'' + a_1 y' + a_2 y = f(t)$$

where a_0, a_1, a_2 are **constants** and $f(t)$ is continuous on $-\infty < t < \infty$.

3.2   Linearity

To develop the theory of linear differential equations, such as (3.1), it is convenient to introduce the **operator** L defined by the relation

$$L(y)(t) = a_0(t)y''(t) + a_1(t)y'(t) + a_2(t)y(t) \tag{3.3}$$

which we denote briefly by $L(y)$, where $L(y) = a_0 y'' + a_1 y' + a_2 y$. Here, we think of $L(y)(t)$ as the value of the function $L(y)$ at the point t. Noticing that $L(y)$ is precisely the left-hand side of equation (3.1), we may write the equation simply as

$$L(y) = f \tag{3.4}$$

where it is understood that all functions are functions of t.

An operator is, roughly speaking, a function applied to functions. In the present case, the operator L is a rule which assigns to each twice differentiable function y on some interval I the function $L(y)$, where $L(y)(t) = a_0(t)y''(t) + a_1(t)y'(t) + a_2(t)y(t)$.

The operator L is a particular example of a class of operators called linear operators: **An operator T defined on a collection S of functions is said to be linear if and only if for any two functions y_1 and y_2 in the collection S and for any constants c_1 and c_2 one has**

$$T(c_1y_1 + c_2y_2) = c_1T(y_1) + c_2T(y_2)$$

It is easy to verify that our operator L defined by (3.3) is linear. To see this, let S be the collection of twice differentiable functions defined on the interval I. Then if y_1 and y_2 are any two functions in S and c_1 and c_2 are any two constants, $L(c_1y_1 + c_2y_2) = a_0(c_1y_1 + c_2y_2)'' + a_1(c_1y_1 + c_2y_2)' + a_2(c_1y_1 + c_2y_2) = c_1L(y_1) + c_2L(y_2)$ by elementary facts about differentiation (which ones?).

• EXERCISES

1. Show that the operator T defined by $T(y)(t) = \int_a^t y(s)\,ds$, for any function y continuous on $a \leq t \leq b$, is a linear operator.

2. Give other examples of linear operators.

3. Show that the operator T defined by $T(y) = (y')^2$, for any function y differentiable on some interval I, is not linear.

We shall need some more terminology before proceeding to the theory of linear differential equations. If the function $f \not\equiv 0$ on I, we will say that (3.4) is **nonhomogeneous** (with nonhomogeneous term f). With every nonhomogeneous linear differential equation of the form (3.4) we associate the **homogeneous** (or reduced) linear differential equation

$$L(y) = 0 \tag{3.5}$$

obtained from (3.4) by replacing f by the zero function.

We now give two basic properties of solutions of linear differential equations; these are immediate consequences of the linearity of the operator L, and do not necessarily hold if L fails to be linear.

(i) *If ϕ_1 and ϕ_2 are any two solutions of the homogeneous linear differential equation $L(y) = 0$ on some interval I, then for any constants c_1 and c_2 the function $c_1\phi_1 + c_2\phi_2$ (called a linear combination of ϕ_1 and ϕ_2) is also a solution of $L(y) = 0$ on I.* To see this we merely compute: $L(c_1\phi_1 + c_2\phi_2) = $

$c_1L(\phi_1) + c_2L(\phi_2)$, by the linearity of L. Since ϕ_1 and ϕ_2 are solutions of (3.5) on I, $L(\phi_1) = L(\phi_2) = 0$ for every t on I, and therefore $c_1\phi_1 + c_2\phi_2$ is a solution of (3.5) on I.

• EXERCISE

4. Use mathematical induction and the above result to establish the analogue of property (i) for m solutions $\phi_1(t)$, . . . , $\phi_m(t)$ of (3.5).

This result is usually expressed by saying that any linear combination of solutions of (3.5) is again a solution of (3.5). It is sometimes called **the principle of superposition** of solutions. Our object in the next section will be to show that the problem of solving the equation (3.5) can be reduced to the problem of finding certain special solutions of (3.5) and obtaining all other solutions as linear combinations of these special solutions.

Example 1. Since $\sin t$ and $\cos t$ are solutions of the equation $y'' + y = 0$ on any interval I (as can be checked by direct substitution), and since this is a linear homogeneous differential equation, the linear combination of solutions $(1/\sqrt{2}) \sin t - (1/\sqrt{2}) \cos t = \sin t \cos \pi/4 - \cos t \sin \pi/4 = \sin (t - \pi/4)$ is also a solution on I. This can be verified by direct substitution, or we can apply our general result, with $\phi_1(t) = \sin t$, $\phi_2(t) = \cos t$, $c_1 = (1/\sqrt{2})$, $c_2 = -(1/\sqrt{2})$.

Another important consequence of the linearity of the operator L is the following:

(ii) *If ϕ and ψ are any two solutions of the nonhomogeneous linear differential equation $L(y) = f$ on some interval I, then $\phi - \psi$ is a solution of the corresponding homogeneous equation $L(y) = 0$.* To see this, we merely compute $L(\phi - \psi)$. By the linearity of L we have $L(\phi - \psi) = L(\phi) - L(\psi)$, for t in I. But ϕ and ψ are solutions of (3.4) on I. Therefore, $L(\phi - \psi) = f - f = 0$ for t in I, which proves the result.

This result shows that it is only necessary to find one solution of the equation (3.4), **provided** one knows all solutions of (3.5). This is because every other solution of the nonhomogeneous equation (3.4) differs from the known one by some solution of the homogeneous equation (3.5).

• EXERCISES

5. If u is a solution of $L(y) = 0$ and if v is a solution of $L(y) = f$ on some interval I, show that $u + v$ is a solution of $L(y) = f$ on I.

6. Suppose f can be written as the sum of m functions $f_1, \ldots, f_m$; that is, $f(t) = f_1(t) + f_2(t) + \cdots + f_m(t)$, for t on some interval I. Suppose that u_1 is a solution of the linear equation $L(y) = f_1$, u_2 is a solution of the linear equation $L(y) = f_2$, and in general u_i is a solution of the linear equation $L(y) = f_i$ on I for $i = 1, \ldots, m$. Show that the function $u = u_1 + u_2 + \cdots + u_m$ is a solution of $L(y) = f$ on I. (This result, also called **the principle of superposition,** enables us to decompose the problem of solving $L(y) = f$ into simpler problems in certain cases.)

Before closing this section we repeat that the only property of the operator L used above is linearity. Therefore our results are much more general than appears to be the case. In particular, if we define the linear differential operator L_n of order n by the relation

$$L_n(y)(t) = a_0(t)y^{(n)}(t) + a_1(t)y^{(n-1)}(t) + \cdots + a_{n-1}(t)y'(t) + a_n(t)y(t)$$

where y is any function which is n times differentiable on some interval I, and the functions a_j $(j = 0, 1, \ldots, n)$ are continuous on I, $a_0(t) \neq 0$ on I, then all results stated in Section 3.2 hold.

•EXERCISES

7. Formulate the analogue of Theorem 3.1 for the equation $L_n(y) = f$ for $n = 1, 3, 4$, and n an arbitrary positive integer.

8. Formulate and verify the analogues of the linearity properties (i) and (ii) for the equation $L_n(y) = f$ for $n = 1, 3, 4$, and n an arbitrary positive integer.

3.3   Linear Homogeneous Equations

In this section we go far beyond the result established above, that any linear combination of solutions of the linear homogeneous differential equation $L(y) = 0$ is again a solution of $L(y) = 0$. We will show that **every** solution of $L(y) = 0$ is a linear combination of certain special solutions. Then in Section 3.8 we will show how to use these special solutions to find every solution of the nonhomogeneous equation $L(y) = f$, using the linearity property (ii) established in the previous section.

Before we can do this we need the important concept of linear dependence.

Definition. *We say that m functions $g_1, g_2, \ldots, g_m$ are linearly dependent on an interval I if and only if there exist constants $b_1, b_2, \ldots, b_m$,* *not all zero, such that*

$$b_1g_1(t) + b_2g_2(t) + \cdots + b_mg_m(t) = 0$$

for every t on I.   We say further that the m functions are linearly independent on I if they are not linearly dependent on I.

Example 1.   The functions $\sin^2 t$, $\cos^2 t$, 1 are linearly dependent on any interval since $\sin^2 t + \cos^2 t - 1 \equiv 0$ for every t.   In the above definition we have used $g_1(t) = \sin^2 t$, $g_2(t) = \cos^2 t$, $g_3(t) = 1$, $b_1 = b_2 = 1$, $b_3 = -1$.

Example 2.   The functions e^{r_1t}, e^{r_2t}, where r_1, r_2 are real constants, are linearly independent on any interval I, provided $r_1 \neq r_2$.   To see this, suppose that e^{r_1t} and e^{r_2t} ($r_1 \neq r_2$) are linearly dependent on I.   Then, in accordance with the definition, there exist constants b_1, b_2, not both zero, such that $b_1e^{r_1t} + b_2e^{r_2t} = 0$ for all t on I.   Multiplying by e^{-r_1t} we obtain $b_1 + b_2e^{(r_2-r_1)t} = 0$ for all t on I, and by differentiation $b_2(r_2 - r_1)e^{(r_2-r_1)t} = 0$ for all t on I.   Since $r_1 \neq r_2$ and since $e^{(r_2-r_1)t}$ is never zero, this implies that b_2 must be zero.   But then $b_1e^{r_1t} + b_2e^{r_2t} = 0$ for all t on I implies that $b_1e^{r_1t} = 0$ for all t on I, and hence b_1 must also be zero.   This contradicts the assumption that b_1 and b_2 are not both zero and proves the linear independence of e^{r_1t} and e^{r_2t}.

More generally, we have the following result which will be useful on several occasions.

Lemma 3.1.   *The n functions*

$$e^{r_1t}, te^{r_1t}, \ldots, t^{k_1-1}e^{r_1t},$$
$$e^{r_2t}, te^{r_2t}, \ldots, t^{k_2-1}r^{r_2t},$$
$$\cdots \qquad \cdots \qquad \cdots$$
$$e^{r_it}, te^{r_it}, \ldots, t^{k_i-1}e^{r_it}$$
$$\cdots \qquad \cdots \qquad \cdots$$
$$e^{r_st}, te^{r_st}, \ldots, t^{k_s-1}e^{r_st},$$

where $k_1 + k_2 + \cdots + k_s = n$ and where $r_1, r_2, \ldots, r_s$ are distinct numbers, are linearly independent on every interval I.

Proof. The proof is an extension of the argument used in Example 2 above. While the idea is very simple, the proof is somewhat complicated in detail. (Note that Example 2 is the special case $n = 2$, $k_1 = k_2 = 1$.) Suppose the n functions are linearly dependent on some interval I. Then there exist n constants a_{ij}, $i = 1, 2, \ldots, s$, $j = 0, 1, \ldots, k_i - 1$, not all zero, such that

$$a_{10}e^{r_1t} + a_{11}te^{r_1t} + \cdots + a_{1,k_1-1}t^{k_1-1}e^{r_1t} + a_{20}e^{r_2t} + a_{21}te^{r_2t} + \cdots$$
$$+ a_{2,k_2-1}t^{k_2-1}e^{r_2t} + \cdots + a_{s0}e^{r_st} + a_{s1}te^{r_st} + \cdots + a_{s,k_s-1}t^{k_s-1}e^{r_st} = 0$$

or, more compactly,

$$\sum_{i=1}^{s} (a_{i0}e^{r_it} + a_{i1}te^{r_it} + \cdots + a_{i,k_i-1}t^{k_i-1}e^{r_it}) = 0$$

for all t in I. We may define the polynomials

$$P_i(t) = a_{i0} + a_{i1}t + \cdots + a_{i,k_i-1}t^{k_i-1} \qquad (i = 1, \ldots, s)$$

to write this condition in the form

$$P_1(t)e^{r_1t} + P_2(t)e^{r_2t} + \cdots + P_s(t)e^{r_st} = 0 \tag{3.6}$$

for all t in I. Since, by assumption, the constants a_{ij} are not all zero, at least one of the polynomials $P_i(t)$ is not identically zero. It is convenient to assume that $P_s(t) \not\equiv 0$; we can always arrange this by a suitable labeling of the numbers $r_1, r_2, \ldots, r_s$. Now we divide the equation (3.6) by e^{r_1t} and differentiate at most k_1 times until the first term drops out. Note that all terms in (3.6) can be differentiated as often as we wish. Then we have an equation of the form

$$Q_2(t)e^{(r_2-r_1)t} + Q_3(t)e^{(r_3-r_1)t} + \cdots + Q_s(t)e^{(r_s-r_1)t} = 0 \tag{3.7}$$

for every t in I. The term $Q_i(t)e^{(r_i-r_1)t}$ in (3.7) is obtained by differentiating $P_i(t)e^{(r_i-r_1)t}$ $(i = 2, \ldots, s)$, as often as necessary to remove the first term $P_1(t)$. Note that differentiation of a polynomial multiplied by an exponential gives a polynomial **of the same degree** multiplied by the same exponential (think of the rule for differentiation of products). Thus the polynomial Q_s in (3.7) has the same degree as P_s, and does not vanish identically. We continue this procedure, dividing by the exponential in the first term and then differentiating often enough to remove the first term, until we are left with only one term.   Then we have an equation of the form

$$R_s(t)e^{(r_s-r_{s-1})t} \equiv 0$$

in which the polynomial R_s has the same degree as P_s, and does not vanish identically.   However, the exponential term in this equation does not vanish, and we have a contradiction.   This shows that all the constants a_{ij} must be zero, and therefore that the n given functions are linearly independent on I. ∎

• **EXERCISES**

1. Establish the linear independence of the following sets of functions on the intervals indicated.
   (a) $\sin t$, $\cos t$ on any interval I.
   (b) e^{r_1t}, e^{r_2t}, e^{r_3t} on any interval if r_1, r_2, r_3 are all different.
   (c) e^{r_1t}, te^{r_1t} on any interval I.
   (d) 1, t, t^2, t^3 on any interval I.
   (e) t^2, $t|t|$ on $-1 \leq t \leq 1$, but **not** on $0 \leq t \leq 1$.
   (f) The functions $f_1(t), f_2(t)$ on $-1 < t < 1$, where

$$f_1(t) = \sum_{n=0}^{\infty} t^{2n} \qquad f_2(t) = \sum_{n=0}^{\infty} (-1)^n t^{2n+1}$$

2. Prove that the functions f, g are linearly dependent on I if and only if there exists a constant c such that either $f(t) = cg(t)$ or $g(t) = cf(t)$ for every t in I.

The above discussion of linear dependence and independence of functions has not been, up to this point, related to the differential equation $L(y) = 0$.   Before continuing, the student should review Theorem 3.1 and the notion of linearity as given in this chapter.   Using these we now establish one of the key results of this theory of linear differential equations.

Theorem 3.2.   *Let a_0, a_1, a_2 be functions continuous on some interval I and let $a_0(t) \neq 0$ for all t on I.   Then the differential equation*

$$L(y) = a_0(t)y'' + a_1(t)y' + a_2(t)y = 0 \tag{3.5}$$

has two linearly independent solutions ϕ_1, ϕ_2 on I.   Moreover, if ϕ is any solution of (3.5) on I, then it is possible to find a unique pair of constants

c_1, c_2 *such that for every t on I*

$$\phi(t) = c_1\phi_1(t) + c_2\phi_2(t)$$

Proof. Let t_0 be any point of the interval I. By Theorem 3.1 (p. 65) there exists a unique solution ϕ_1 on I of (3.5) satisfying the special initial conditions $\phi_1(t_0) = 1$, $\phi_1'(t_0) = 0$. Similarly, there exists on I a unique solution ϕ_2 of (3.5) such that $\phi_2(t_0) = 0$, $\phi_2'(t_0) = 1$. We select these particular solutions because it will be easy to prove that they are linearly independent on I. The reader will see later that many other choices are possible.

We claim first that these solutions ϕ_1 and ϕ_2 are linearly independent on I. Suppose they are linearly dependent on I. Then there exist constants b_1, b_2 not both zero such that

$$b_1\phi_1(t) + b_2\phi_2(t) = 0 \tag{3.8}$$

for every t on I. Since ϕ_1, ϕ_2 are solutions of $L(y) = 0$ on I, they are differentiable on I and hence from (3.8) we have also

$$b_1\phi_1'(t) + b_2\phi_2'(t) = 0 \tag{3.9}$$

for every t on I. In particular, for $t = t_0$ in (3.8) and (3.9), we obtain respectively

$$b_1 \cdot 1 + b_2 \cdot 0 = 0$$
$$b_1 \cdot 0 + b_2 \cdot 1 = 0$$

and we therefore conclude that $b_1 = b_2 = 0$ which contradicts the assumption that the solutions ϕ_1, ϕ_2 are linearly dependent on I and therefore proves their linear independence on I.

To complete the proof of the theorem, let ϕ be any solution of $L(y) = 0$ on I and calculate $\phi(t_0) = \alpha$, $\phi'(t_0) = \beta$. (That is, we evalute $\phi(t)$ and $\phi'(t)$ at $t = t_0$ and call the values at t_0, α and β, respectively.) If there are to exist constants c_1 and c_2 such that $\phi(t) = c_1\phi_1(t) + c_2\phi_2(t)$ for all t in I, this relation must hold in particular at t_0, and we must have

$$\alpha = \phi(t_0) = c_1\phi_1(t_0) + c_2\phi_2(t_0) = c_1 \cdot 1 + c_2 \cdot 0 = c_1$$
$$\beta = \phi'(t_0) = c_1\phi_1'(t_0) + c_2\phi_2'(t_0) = c_1 \cdot 0 + c_2 \cdot 1 = c_2$$

Define the function ψ by the relation $\psi(t) = \alpha\phi_1(t) + \beta\phi_2(t)$ for t in I. Clearly (by the linearity property (i), p. 67), ψ is a solution of $L(y) = 0$

on I; moreover,

$$\psi(t_0) = \alpha\phi_1(t_0) + \beta\phi_2(t_0) = \alpha \cdot 1 + \beta \cdot 0 = \alpha$$
$$\psi'(t_0) = \alpha\phi_1'(t_0) + \beta\phi_2'(t_0) = \alpha \cdot 0 + \beta \cdot 1 = \beta$$

Therefore ϕ and ψ are both solutions of $L(y) = 0$ on I which satisfy the same pair of initial conditions at t_0. Since, by Theorem 3.1 (p. 65), there is only one such solution, we conclude that $\phi(t) = \psi(t) = \alpha\phi_1(t) + \beta\phi_2(t)$ on I, which completes the proof. $\blacksquare$

• EXERCISES

3. Why are the constants c_1, c_2 in the statement of the theorem unique?

4. Carry out the proof of Theorem 3.2 by using the solutions ψ_1 and ψ_2 of (3.5) on I satisfying the initial conditions $\psi_1(t_0) = 2$, $\psi_1'(t_0) = -1$ and $\psi_2(t_0) = -1$, $\psi_2'(t_0) = 1$ in place of the solutions ϕ_1 and ϕ_2. [*Hint:* Begin by showing that the solutions ψ_1, ψ_2 of (3.5) are linearly independent on I.]

Example 3.   Find that solution ϕ of $y'' + y = 0$ such that $\phi(0) = 1$, $\phi'(0) = -1$.

It is easily shown that $\cos t$ and $\sin t$ are linearly independent solutions of $y'' + y = 0$ on any interval I. To find the desired solution we apply Theorem 3.2, letting $\phi_1(t) = \cos t$, $\phi_2(t) = \sin t$, and observing that $\phi_1(0) = 1$, $\phi_1'(0) = 0$, $\phi_2(0) = 0$, $\phi_2'(0) = 1$ as in the above proof. By Theorem 3.2 we know that there exist unique constants c_1, c_2 such that $\phi(t) = c_1 \cos t + c_2 \sin t$; as we saw in the proof we may determine c_1 and c_2 by imposing the initial conditions. Thus we obtain

$$\phi(0) = 1 = c_1 \cdot 1 + c_2 \cdot 0$$
$$\phi'(0) = -1 = -c_1 \cdot 0 + c_2 \cdot 1$$

Therefore $c_1 = 1$, $c_2 = -1$ and the desired solution ϕ is $\phi(t) = \cos t - \sin t$.

• EXERCISES

5. State and prove a theorem analogous to Theorem 3.2 for the linear third-order differential equation:

$$L_3(y) = a_0(t)y''' + a_1(t)y'' + a_2(t)y' + a_3(t)y = 0$$

where a_0, a_1, a_2, a_3 are continuous on some interval I and $a_0(t) \neq 0$ on I. [*Hint:* For any t_0 on I let ϕ_1 be that solution of $L_3(y) = 0$ for which $\phi_1(t_0) = 1$, $\phi_1'(t_0) = 0$, $\phi_1''(t_0) = 0$, let ϕ_2 be that solution of $L_3(y) = 0$ for which $\phi_2(t_0) = 0$, $\phi_2'(t_0) = 1$, $\phi_2''(t_0) = 0$, let ϕ_3 be that solution of $L_3(y) = 0$ for which $\phi_3(t_0) = 0$, $\phi_3'(t_0) = 0$, $\phi_3''(t_0) = 1$ and now proceed as in the proof of Theorem 3.2.]

6. State the analogous result for the linear nth-order differential equation

$$L_n(y) = a_0(t)y^{(n)} + a_1(t)y^{(n-1)} + \cdots + a_{n-1}(t)y' + a_n(t)y = 0$$

In practice it is undesirable to restrict ourselves to solutions ϕ_1, ϕ_2 which satisfy special initial conditions such as $\phi_1(t_0) = 1$, $\phi_1'(t_0) = 0$, $\phi_2(t_0) = 0$, $\phi_2'(t_0) = 1$ at some t_0 on I. We shall show shortly that instead of the special solutions ϕ_1, ϕ_2 used, **any** two linearly independent solutions of $L(y) = 0$ on I will serve the purpose just as well. To do this it is convenient to introduce the concept of the Wronskian, which, as we shall see, also serves another objective.

Definition. *Let f_1, f_2, be any two differentiable functions on some interval I. Then the determinant*

$$W(f_1, f_2) = \begin{vmatrix} f_1 & f_2 \\ f_1' & f_2' \end{vmatrix} = f_1 f_2' - f_1' f_2$$

is called the Wronskian of f_1 and f_2. Its value at any t in I will be denoted by $W(f_1, f_2)(t)$. More generally, if $f_1, \ldots, f_n$ are n functions which are $n - 1$ times differentiable on I, then the nth-order determinant

$$W(f_1, \ldots, f_n) = \begin{vmatrix} f_1 & f_2 & \cdots & f_n \\ f_1' & f_2' & \cdots & f_n' \\ \cdot & \cdot & & \cdot \\ \cdot & \cdot & & \cdot \\ \cdot & \cdot & & \cdot \\ f_1^{(n-1)} & f_2^{(n-1)} & \cdots & f_n^{(n-1)} \end{vmatrix}$$

is called the Wronskian of $f_1, \ldots, f_n$.

• **EXERCISE**

7. Evaluate the Wronskian of the following functions
   (a) $f_1(t) = \sin t$, $f_2(t) = \cos t$, $(-\infty < t < \infty)$.
   (b) $f_1(t) = e^t$, $f_2(t) = e^{-t}$, $(-\infty < t < \infty)$.
   (c) $f_1(t) = t^2$, $f_2(t) = t|t|$, $(-\infty < t < \infty)$.
   (d) $f_1(t) = 1$, $f_2(t) = 1$, $f_3(t) = t^2$, $(-\infty < t < \infty)$.

The Wronskian of two solutions of $L(y) = 0$ on I provides us with the following simple test of their linear independence.

Theorem 3.3. *Let a_0, a_1, a_2 be given functions continuous on some interval I, and let $a_0(t) \neq 0$ for all t on I. Then two solutions ϕ_1, ϕ_2 of*

$$L(y) = a_0(t)y'' + a_1(t)y' + a_2(t)y = 0 \tag{3.5}$$

are linearly independent on I if and only if $W(\phi_1, \phi_2)(t) \neq 0$ for all t on I.

Before proving this result we give an illustration.

Example 4. The functions $\phi_1(t) = \cos t$, $\phi_2(t) = \sin t$ are solutions of $y'' + y = 0$ on $-\infty < t < \infty$. To test their linear independence we compute their Wronskian

$$W(\cos t, \sin t) = \begin{vmatrix} \cos t & \sin t \\ -\sin t & \cos t \end{vmatrix} \equiv 1 \qquad (-\infty < t < \infty)$$

Therefore, by Theorem 3.3, $\phi_1(t) = \cos t$, $\phi_2(t) = \sin t$ are linearly independent solutions of $y'' + y = 0$ on $-\infty < t < \infty$. Of course, we already know this result from having applied the definition of linear independence directly. However, when dealing with solutions of a linear homogeneous equation of the form (3.5), the theorem is often easier to use than the definition.

WARNING. Do not apply Theorem 3.3 when the functions being tested for linear independence are **not known** to be solutions of a linear homogeneous equation of the form (3.5). To see why, consider the functions $f_1(t) = t^2$, $f_2(t) = t|t|$ and take for I the interval $-1 \leq t \leq 1$. Then as we saw in Exercise 7(c), the functions f_1, f_2 are linearly independent on I and yet $W(f_1, f_2)(t) = 0$ for every t on $-1 \leq t \leq 1$.

Proof of Theorem 3.3. The proof consists of two parts. Suppose first that the solutions $\phi_1(t)$, $\phi_2(t)$ of $L(y) = 0$ are such that $W(\phi_1, \phi_2)(t) \neq 0$ for all t on I and yet ϕ_1, ϕ_2 are linearly dependent on I. Then by the definition of linear dependence there exist constants b_1, b_2 not both zero such that

$$b_1\phi_1(t) + b_2\phi_2(t) = 0 \qquad \text{for all } t \text{ on } I \tag{3.10}$$

and also

$$b_1\phi_1'(t) + b_2\phi_2'(t) = 0 \qquad \text{for all } t \text{ on } I \text{ (why?)} \tag{3.11}$$

For each fixed t on I, equations (3.10) and (3.11) are linear homogeneous algebraic equations satisfied by b_1 and b_2, and the determinant of their coefficients is precisely $W(\phi_1, \phi_2)(t)$. Since, by assumption, $W(\phi_1, \phi_2)(t) \neq 0$ at any t on I, it follows from the theory of linear homogeneous systems of algebraic equations (see Appendix 1) that $b_1 = b_2 = 0$, which contradicts the assumed linear dependence of the solutions ϕ_1, ϕ_2 of (3.5) on I. This shows that if the Wronskian of two solutions of (3.5) is different from zero on I, then these solutions are linearly independent on I.

To prove the second part of the theorem, assume that the solutions ϕ_1, ϕ_2 of $L(y) = 0$ are linearly independent on I and assume that there is at least one $\hat{t}$ on I such that $W(\phi_1, \phi_2)(\hat{t}) = 0$. (If there is no such $\hat{t}$ there is nothing to prove!) Now look again at the algebraic system (3.10), (3.11) for $t = \hat{t}$. It follows, again from the theory of linear homogeneous systems of algebraic equations (see Appendix 1), that because $W(\phi_1, \phi_2)(\hat{t}) = 0$, the system of algebraic equations

$$b_1\phi_1(\hat{t}) + b_2\phi_2(\hat{t}) = 0$$
$$b_1\phi_1'(\hat{t}) + b_2\phi_2'(\hat{t}) = 0 \tag{3.12}$$

has at least one solution b_1, b_2, where b_1 and b_2 are not both zero. To complete the proof define the function $\psi(t) = b_1\phi_1(t) + b_2\phi_2(t)$, where b_1, b_2 are taken as any solution of (3.12). First observe that ψ is a solution of (3.5) (why?). Because of (3.12) the solution ψ satisfies the initial conditions $\psi(\hat{t}) = 0$, $\psi'(\hat{t}) = 0$. Therefore, by Theorem 3.1 and the discussion which follows it (p. 65), $\psi(t) = 0$ for every t on I. This means that we have found constants b_1, b_2 not both zero such that $b_1\phi_1(t) + b_2\phi_1(t) = 0$ for every t on I. This contradicts the assumed linear independence of the solutions ϕ_1, ϕ_2 on I. Therefore the assumption $W(\phi_1, \phi_2)(\hat{t}) = 0$ is false; that is, no such $\hat{t}$ exists and $W(\phi_1, \phi_2)(t) \neq 0$ for every t in I. This completes the proof of Theorem 3.3. ∎

•EXERCISES

8. Show that e^{2t}, e^{-2t} are linearly independent solutions of $y'' - 4y = 0$ on $-\infty < t < \infty$.

9. Show that $e^{-t/2} \cos \sqrt{3}\, t/2$, $e^{-t/2} \sin \sqrt{3}\, t/2$ are linearly independent solutions of $y'' + y' + y = 0$ on $-\infty < t < \infty$.

10. Show that e^{-t}, te^{-t} are linearly independent solutions of $y'' + 2y' + y = 0$ on $-\infty < t < \infty$.

11. Show that $\sin t^2$, $\cos t^2$ are linearly independent solutions of $ty'' + y' + 4t^3 y = 0$ on $0 < t < \infty$ or $-\infty < t < 0$. Show that $W(\sin t^2, \cos t^2)(0) = 0$. Why does this fact not contradict Theorem 3.3?

12. (a) Let ϕ_1, ϕ_2 be any two solutions, on some interval I, of $L(y) = a_0(t)y'' + a_1(t)y' + a_2(t)y = 0$ where a_0, a_1, a_2 are continuous on I and $a_0(t) \neq 0$ on I. Show that the Wronskian $W(\phi_1, \phi_2)(t)$ satisfies the first-order linear differential equation

$$W' = -\frac{a_1(t)}{a_0(t)} W \qquad (t \text{ on } I) \tag{*}$$

[*Hint:*

$$W'(\phi_1, \phi_2)(t) = \begin{vmatrix} \phi_1(t) & \phi_2(t) \\ \phi_1'(t) & \phi_2'(t) \end{vmatrix}' = (\phi_1\phi_2' - \phi_1'\phi_2)' = \phi_1\phi_2'' - \phi_1''\phi_2$$

Now use the fact that ϕ_1, ϕ_2 are solutions of $L(y) = 0$ on I to replace ϕ_1'' and ϕ_2'' by terms involving ϕ_1, ϕ_1', ϕ_2, ϕ_2'. If you then collect terms you should get (*).]

(b) By solving (*), derive **Abel's formula:**

$$W(\phi_1, \phi_2)(t) = W(\phi_1, \phi_2)(t_0) \exp\left(-\int_{t_0}^{t} \frac{a_1(s)}{a_0(s)} \, ds \right)$$

for t_0, t on I. This establishes the following result, which follows from looking at Abel's formula, and noting that the exponential term is never zero.

Theorem 3.4. *Let the hypothesis of Theorem 3.3 be satisfied on some interval I. Let ϕ_1, ϕ_2 be any two solutions of $L(y) = 0$ on I. Then their Wronskian $W(\phi_1, \phi_2)(t)$ is either zero for every t on I, or it is different from zero for every t on I.*

•EXERCISES

13. State the analogue of Theorem 3.3 for the linear third-order differential equation

$$L_3(y) = a_0(t)y''' + a_1(t)y'' + a_2(t)y' + a_3(t)y = 0$$

14. Show that e^t, $\cos t$, $\sin t$ are linearly independent solutions on $-\infty < t < \infty$ of the differential equation $y''' - y'' + y' - y = 0$.

15. Theorem 3.4 established in Exercise 12(b) above, combined with Theorem 3.3 provides a convenient method for testing solutions of linear differential equations for linear independence on some interval. For, according to these results it is enough to evaluate the Wronskian at some con-

veniently chosen point.   Thus, for example, show that

$$\phi_1(t) = 1 + \sum_{m=1}^{\infty} \frac{t^{3m}}{2 \cdot 3 \cdot 5 \cdot 6 \cdots (3m-1)(3m)}$$

$$\phi_2(t) = t + \sum_{m=1}^{\infty} \frac{t^{3m+1}}{3 \cdot 4 \cdot 6 \cdot 7 \cdots (3m)(3m+1)}$$

are linearly independent solutions of $y'' - ty = 0$ on the interval $-\infty < t < \infty$.   (Here you may assume that it has already been shown that ϕ_1 and ϕ_2 are solutions of $y'' - ty = 0$, but how could you verify this?)

Recall that the linearity of L implies that any linear combination of solutions of $L(y) = 0$, is again a solution.   We have raised the question: "Can every solution of $L(y) = 0$ be generated in this manner?"   We answered this partially in Theorem 3.2 using a particular pair of linearly independent solutions.   With the help of Theorem 3.3 we can now answer the question completely.

Theorem 3.5.   *Let a_0, a_1, a_2 be functions continuous on some interval I, and let $a_0(t) \neq 0$ for all t in I.   If ϕ_1 and ϕ_2 are any two linearly independent solutions of*

$$L(y) = a_0(t)y'' + a_1(t)y' + a_2(t)y = 0 \tag{3.5}$$

on I (not necessarily the two special solutions ϕ_1, ϕ_2 of Theorem 3.2), then every solution ϕ of (3.5) on I can be written in the form

$$\phi(t) = c_1\phi_1(t) + c_2\phi_2(t) \qquad t \text{ in } I \tag{3.13}$$

for some unique choice of constants c_1, c_2.

From a practical point of view, the theorem tells us that knowledge (possibly by guessing) of any two linearly independent solutions ϕ_1, ϕ_2 of (3.5) on I enables us to express every solution of (3.5) on I by means of formula (3.13) by choosing the constants c_1, c_2 suitably.   For this reason, we call the function defined by (3.13) **the general solution** of (3.5) on I, and we sometimes say that the linearly independent solutions form a **fundamental set.**

Proof of Theorem 3.5.   Let ϕ be any solution of (3.5) on I and let t_0 be any point in I.   Compute $\phi(t_0) = \alpha$, $\phi'(t_0) = \beta$.   Because ϕ_1 and ϕ_2 are linearly independent solutions of (3.5), Theorem 3.3 tells us that

$W(\phi_1, \phi_2)(t) \neq 0$ for all t on I; in particular $W(\phi_1, \phi_2)(t_0) \neq 0$. If the representation (3.13) holds for all t in I, it will have to hold at $t = t_0$. To see if this is possible, we impose the conditions $\phi(t_0) = \alpha$, $\phi'(t_0) = \beta$ and obtain the system of algebraic equations

$$c_1\phi_1(t_0) + c_2\phi_2(t_0) = \alpha$$
$$c_1\phi_1'(t_0) + c_2\phi_2'(t_0) = \beta$$

with determinant of coefficients $W(\phi_1, \phi_2)(t_0) \neq 0$. Therefore by the theory of linear nonhomogeneous systems of algebraic equations (see Appendix 1) this algebraic system can be solved uniquely for c_1, c_2, and we obtain

$$c_1 = \frac{\alpha\phi_2'(t_0) - \beta\phi_2(t_0)}{W(\phi_1, \phi_2)(t_0)} \qquad c_2 = \frac{\beta\phi_1(t_0) - \alpha\phi_1'(t_0)}{W(\phi_1, \phi_2)(t_0)} \tag{3.14}$$

This choice of c_1, c_2 makes (3.13) hold at $t = t_0$. To see whether this choice of c_1, c_2 does the job for all t in I, we define the function

$$\psi(t) = c_1\phi_1(t) + c_2\phi_2(t)$$

where c_1, c_2 are the numbers given by (3.14). We observe that $\psi(t)$ (as well as $\phi(t), \phi_1(t), \phi_2(t)$) is a solution of (3.5) on I. To complete the proof we need only show that $\psi(t) = \phi(t)$ for every t in I. But using (3.14) we see that

$$\psi(t_0) = \alpha = \phi(t_0) \text{ and } \psi'(t_0) = \beta = \phi'(t_0)$$

Therefore ϕ and ψ are both solutions of (3.5) on I and they satisfy the same initial conditions at $t = t_0$. By uniqueness (Theorem 3.1, p. 65) ϕ and ψ are identical and this establishes Theorem 3.5. The theorem extends to linear equations of higher order in an obvious way. ∎

REMARK (for students acquainted with linear algebra). The theory developed in Sections 3.2 and 3.3 shows that the solutions of a linear homogeneous differential equation $L(y) = 0$ with continuous coefficients on some interval I and with nonvanishing leading coefficient on I, form a vector space V over the real or complex numbers (see property (i), p. 67). Theorem 3.2 shows that the dimension of V is 2 if L is a linear differential operator of order 2 by exhibiting a basis for V consisting of the special linearly independent solutions ϕ_1 and ϕ_2 constructed in the theorem. Theorem 3.5 shows that any two linearly independent solutions of (3.5) also form a basis for V, provided the order of L is 2. We can derive this more simply using knowledge of linear algebra. Once we know, by Theorem 3.2, that V has dimension 2, it follows immediately that any two linearly independent vectors in V (that is, solutions) span V. The analogue of Theorem 3.2 for a homogeneous linear differential equation of order n shows that for such an equation the vector space of solutions has dimension n. For a more general discussion of this topic we refer the reader to Chapter 6.

Example 5. The functions e^{2t}, e^{-2t} are solutions of $y'' - 4y = 0$ for all t (why?). They are linearly independent solutions of $L(y) = y'' - 4y = 0$ on $-\infty < t < \infty$ (why?). Therefore, by Theorem 3.5 every solution ϕ of $y'' - 4y = 0$ on $-\infty < t < \infty$ can be written in the form

$$\phi(t) = c_1 e^{2t} + c_2 e^{-2t}$$

for some unique choice of the constants c_1, c_2. This is called the general solution of $y'' - 4y = 0$ on $-\infty < t < \infty$. For example, to find that solution of $y'' - 4y = 0$ on $-\infty < t < \infty$ for which $\phi(0) = 1$, $\phi'(0) = 0$, we see from $\phi(t) = c_1 e^{2t} + c_2 e^{-2t}$ that c_1 and c_2 must satisfy the equations

$$c_1 + c_2 = 1$$
$$2c_1 - 2c_2 = 0$$

or $c_1 = c_2 = \frac{1}{2}$. Thus $\phi(t) = (e^{2t} + e^{-2t})/2 = \cosh 2t$. The reader should note that Theorem 3.2 alone does not supply enough information to solve this problem.

•EXERCISES

16. In each of the following find that solution ϕ of the given differential satisfying the initial conditions specified. Also find the general solution in each case.

    (a) $y'' - 4y = 0$, $\phi(0) = 2$, $\phi'(0) = -1$ (see Exercise 8, p. 77).
    (b) $y'' + y' + y = 0$, $\phi(0) = 1$, $\phi'(0) = 3$ (see Exercise 9, p. 77).
    (c) $y'' + y' + y = 0$, $\phi(10) = 0$, $\phi'(10) = 0$.
    (d) $y'' + 2y' + y = 0$, $\phi(1) = -1$, $\phi'(1) = 1$ (see Exercise 10, p. 77).
    (e) $y'' - ty = 0$, $\phi(0) = 0$, $\phi'(0) = 2$ (see Exercise 15, p. 78).
    (f) $y''' - y'' + y' - y = 0$, $\phi(0) = 2$, $\phi'(0) = -1$, $\phi''(0) = 1$ (see Exercise 14, p. 78).

17. Show that for any constant $\alpha > 0$, $\sin \alpha t$ and $\cos \alpha t$ are linearly independent solutions on $-\infty < t < \infty$ of $y'' + \alpha^2 y = 0$. What is the general solution? Find all solutions which pass through the point $((\pi/4\alpha), 5)$. Which one of these has slope α at the point $((\pi/4\alpha), 5)$? Which has slope $-\alpha$ at the point $((\pi/4\alpha), 5)$? Letting ϕ_1 and ϕ_2 represent the solutions of slope α and $-\alpha$ respectively at the point $((\pi/4\alpha), 5)$, decide whether ϕ_1 and ϕ_2 are linearly independent on $-\infty < t < \infty$.

3.4   Solution of Linear Homogeneous Differential Equations of Second Order with Constant Coefficients

In this section we will learn, with the aid of the theory just developed, how to solve the linear second-order equation $L(y) = 0$ in certain special cases. We will be guided by the fact that in order to find all solutions of $L(y) = 0$, we merely need to find two linearly independent solutions and then apply Theorem 3.5. Subsequently, we will study linear homogeneous equations of higher order. We will begin with the simplest case of constant coefficients and then consider in the following sections several more complicated cases of variable coefficients. We note that in the general case of continuous coefficients a solution of $L(y) = 0$ will exist but cannot necessarily be found in terms of elementary functions. Fortunately, large numbers of interesting physical problems lead to mathematical models which, when simplified sufficiently, fall into categories which we can handle easily.

An important example of a model leading to an equation of the form

$$L(y) = y'' + py' + qy = 0 \qquad (-\infty < t < \infty)$$

where p and q are real nonnegative constants, is the crudest model of damped oscillations (see equation (1.3), p. 5, and also equation (1.9), p. 11, with $\sin \theta$ replaced by θ). Another important model is a linear electrical circuit consisting of a capacitance C, a resistance R, and an inductance L connected in series. It can be shown that the potential difference (voltage) $v(t)$ across the capacitance can be reasonably described by the equation

$$v'' + \frac{R}{L} v' + \frac{1}{LC} v = 0$$

Properties of these models will be discussed in future exercises.

We first solve the linear differential equation

$$L(y) = a_0 y'' + a_1 y' + a_2 y = 0 \qquad (-\infty < t < \infty)$$

where a_0, a_1, a_2 are real constants, $a_0 \neq 0$. Thus we may as well divide through by a_0 and assume that the equation has the form

$$L(y) = y'' + py' + qy = 0 \qquad (-\infty < t < \infty) \tag{3.15}$$

where p and q are real constants, not necessarily positive.   Our task is to find two linearly independent solutions of (3.15).   Recall that for the first-order equation $y' + ry = 0$, where r is a constant, e^{-rt} is a solution. In Section 2.1 (p. 35), we found this solution by separation of variables. However, we could also find it as follows: If for some constant z, e^{zt} is to be a solution of $y' + ry = 0$, then we must have $(e^{zt})' + re^{zt} = 0$ or $(z + r)e^{zt} = 0$.   Since $e^{zt} \neq 0$, we see that e^{zt} can be a solution of $y' + ry = 0$ only if $z = -r$ which gives e^{-rt} as a candidate for a solution. Direct verification shows that it is.

Let us try to find a solution of (3.15) of the form e^{zt} on $-\infty < t < \infty$. Then we must have $L(e^{zt}) = 0$.   But $L(e^{zt}) = (e^{zt})'' + p(e^{zt})' + qe^{zt} = (z^2 + pz + q)e^{zt}$.   Therefore e^{zt} can be a solution of $L(y) = 0$ on $-\infty < t < \infty$ only if

$$(z^2 + pz + q)e^{zt} = 0$$

or, since $e^{zt} \neq 0$, only if z is a root of the quadratic equation

$$z^2 + pz + q = 0 \tag{3.16}$$

Equation (3.16) is called the **characteristic equation** or **auxiliary equation** associated with (3.15), and $z^2 + pz + q$ is called the **characteristic polynomial** associated with (3.15).   The quadratic equation (3.16) has the roots

$$z_1 = \frac{-p + (p^2 - 4q)^{1/2}}{2} \qquad z_2 = \frac{-p - (p^2 - 4q)^{1/2}}{2}$$

●**EXERCISE**

1. Verify that $e^{z_1 t}$, $e^{z_2 t}$ are solutions of (3.15).

Now we have two possibilities:

(i) if $p^2 \neq 4q$ the roots z_1 and z_2 are distinct,
(ii) if $p^2 = 4q$, $z_1 = z_2$.

In case (i) this means that $e^{z_1 t}$ and $e^{z_2 t}$ $(z_1 \neq z_2)$ are two distinct solutions of the differential equation (3.15) on $-\infty < t < \infty$.   The only question which remains is: Are these solutions linearly independent on $-\infty < t < \infty$?   They are, as was shown directly in Example 2, Section 3.3, p. 70.   Alternatively, since $e^{z_1 t}$, $e^{z_2 t}$ are solutions of (3.15), we can establish their linear independence by Theorem 3.3 (p. 76) using the

Wronskian.   We have

$$W(e^{z_1t}, e^{z_2t}) = \begin{vmatrix} e^{z_1t} & e^{z_2t} \\ z_1 e^{z_1t} & z_2 e^{z_2t} \end{vmatrix} = (z_2 - z_1)e^{(z_1+z_2)t} \qquad (-\infty < t < \infty)$$

Since $z_1 \neq z_2$, $W(e^{z_1t}, e^{z_2t}) \neq 0$ and Theorem 3.3 gives the desired linear independence.   Therefore, in case (i), by Theorem 3.5 (p. 79), every solution ϕ of equation (3.15) has the form

$$\phi(t) = c_1 e^{z_1t} + c_2 e^{z_2t} \qquad (-\infty < t < \infty) \tag{3.17}$$

for some unique choice of the constants c_1, c_2; (3.17) is called **the general solution** of (3.15), as explained in the remarks following Theorem 3.5 (p. 79).

Example 1.   Find the general solution of $y'' - 9y = 0$.   By the method just given, the characteristic equation (3.16) is $z^2 - 9 = 0$, which has the roots $z_1 = 3$, $z_2 = -3$.   Since $z_1 \neq z_2$, the solutions e^{3t}, e^{-3t} are linearly independent on $-\infty < t < \infty$ and therefore the general solution of $y'' - 9y = 0$ is $\phi(t) = c_1 e^{-3t} + c_2 e^{-3t}$, where c_1, c_2 are arbitrary constants.

• EXERCISES

2. Find the general solution of each of the following equations, and then the solution ϕ satisfying the given initial conditions:
   (a) $y'' - y = 0$, $\phi(0) = 0$, $\phi'(0) = 1$.
   (b) $y'' - 5y' + 6y = 0$, $\phi(0) = 0$, $\phi'(0) = 1$.
   (c) $y''' - 6y'' + 11y' - 6y = 0$, $\phi(0) = \phi'(0) = 0$, $\phi''(0) = 1$.

3. In the equation (3.15) for damped oscillations (that is, $p, q > 0$), find values of p and q such that the roots of the characteristic equation are real and distinct.   For such values, discuss the asymptotic behavior (behavior as $t \to +\infty$) of the solutions by computing $\lim\limits_{t \to +\infty} \phi(t)$, where $\phi(t)$ is any solution of (3.15).

The careful reader may have noticed that in case (i), the roots z_1, z_2 will be real and distinct if $p^2 > 4q$, and will be complex conjugate (hence distinct) if $p^2 < 4q$.   For example, the differential equation

$$y'' + y' + y = 0$$

has the characteristic equation $z^2 + z + 1 = 0$, and its roots are

$$z_1 = \frac{-1 + \sqrt{3}\,i}{2} \qquad z_2 = \frac{-1 - \sqrt{3}\,i}{2}$$

Therefore,

$$\exp\left[\frac{-1 + \sqrt{3}\,i}{2}t\right] \quad \text{and} \quad \exp\left[\frac{-1 - \sqrt{3}\,i}{2}t\right]$$

should be, and in fact are, solutions.   However, these functions are **complex-valued functions of the real variable** t, **and up to this point all functions considered have been real.**   The reader unfamiliar with complex-valued functions of a real variable is advised to read Appendix 2 before proceeding.

In view of the theory of complex-valued functions of a real variable discussed in Appendix 2, every definition and theorem given for real solutions of the real equation

$$L(y) = a_0(t)y'' + a_1(t)y' + a_2(t)y = b(t)$$

where a_0, a_1, a_2, b are real functions defined on some interval I, holds for complex-valued solutions of this equation.   This remains true even if a_0, a_1, a_2, b are complex functions.   This specifically applies to existence and uniqueness of such solutions, and linear dependence and independence of such solutions (including the Wronskian test).   There is no change needed in any of the statements and their proofs; it is only necessary to bear in mind that the functions which enter each discussion may be complex-valued.

• EXERCISES

   4. Show that the functions

$$\exp\left[\frac{-1 + \sqrt{3}\,i}{2}t\right] \quad \text{and} \quad \exp\left[\frac{-1 - \sqrt{3}\,i}{2}t\right]$$

satisfy the differential equation $y'' + y' + y = 0$ for all real t.

   5. Reprove Theorem 3.2 (p. 72) in the case that the coefficients $a_0(t)$, $a_1(t)$, $a_2(t)$ are continuous complex-valued functions on an interval I and t is real.

We now present a result on complex-valued solutions of **real** linear differential equations which is of great importance in applications.   Note that this result is not restricted to equations with constant coefficients.

   Theorem 3.6.   *Let ϕ be a complex-valued solution of the differential equation*

$$L(y) = a_0(t)y'' + a_1(t)y' + a_2(t)y = 0$$

on some interval I, where a_0, a_1, a_2 are given real functions on I.   Then the
real functions $u = \Re\phi$, $v = \Im\phi$ are themselves (real) solutions of $L(y) = 0$
on I.

Proof.   Since ϕ is a solution of $L(y) = 0$ on I, we have

$$a_0(t)\phi''(t) + a_1(t)\phi'(t) + a_2(t)\phi(t) = 0$$

for every t on I.   (The fact that ϕ may be complex valued does not change
anything.)   Since $\phi = u + iv$, we have, from the definition of derivative
$\phi'(t) = u'(t) + iv'(t)$, $\phi''(t) = u''(t) + iv''(t)$.   Therefore,

$$a_0(t)[u''(t) + iv''(t)] + a_1(t)[u'(t) + iv'(t)] + a_2(t)[u(t) + iv(t)] = 0$$

Separating the left-hand side into real and imaginary parts we obtain
(remember that a_0, a_1, a_2 are real) for all t on I:

$$a_0(t)u''(t) + a_1(t)u'(t) + a_2(t)u(t)$$
$$+ i[a_0(t)v''(t) + a_1(t)v'(t) + a_2(t)v(t)] = 0$$

(*Note:* This also shows that $L(\phi) = L(u) + iL(v)$; this is true in general if
L is a linear differential operator with real coefficients.)   Since the last
relation holds for every t on I and since a complex number is zero if and
only if both its real and imaginary parts are zero, we have, for all t in I:

$$L(u) = a_0(t)u''(t) + a_1(t)u'(t) + a_2(t)u(t) = 0$$

and

$$L(v) = a_0(t)v''(t) + a_1(t)v'(t) + a_2(t)v(t) = 0$$

which shows that $u = \Re\phi$ and $v = \Im\phi$ are both solutions of $L(y) = 0$ on
I and completes the proof. ∎

● **EXERCISE**

6. Let ϕ be a solution on some interval I of the differential equation

$$L(y) = a_0(t)y'' + a_1(t)y' + a_2(t)y = b(t)$$

where a_0, a_1, a_2 are real and b is complex.   Show that $u = \Re\phi$ satisfies the
equation $L(y) = \Re b$ and prove an analogous result for $v = \Im\phi$.

Example 2. We have seen that

$$\phi_1(t) = \exp\left[\frac{-1 + \sqrt{3}\,i}{2}t\right] \quad \text{and} \quad \phi_2(t) = \exp\left[\frac{-1 - \sqrt{3}\,i}{2}t\right]$$

are both (complex-valued) solutions of $y'' + y' + y = 0$ on $-\infty < t < \infty$. They are linearly independent on $-\infty < t < \infty$; for by Theorem 3.3 (p. 76) interpreted for complex-valued solutions

$$W(\phi_1, \phi_2)(t) = -\sqrt{3}\,ie^{-t} \neq 0 \qquad (-\infty < t < \infty)$$

Therefore, by Theorem 3.5 (p. 79), interpreted for complex-valued solutions, every solution ϕ (possibly complex valued) of $y'' + y' + y = 0$ on $-\infty < t < \infty$ has the form $\phi(t) = c_1\phi_1(t) + c_2\phi_2(t)$ for some unique choice of the (possibly complex) constants c_1, c_2. By Theorem 3.6 (p. 85) (applicable because the coefficients are real) the real functions $u_1(t) = \Re\phi_1(t) = \exp[-t/2]\cos(\sqrt{3}/2)t$ and $v_1(t) = \Im\phi_1(t) = \exp[-t/2]\sin(\sqrt{3}/2)t$ are also solutions of $y'' + y' + y = 0$ for $-\infty < t < \infty$. The same statement applies to $u_2(t) = \Re\phi_2(t) = \exp[-t/2]\cos(\sqrt{3}/2)t$ and $v_2(t) = \Im\phi_2(t) = -\exp[-t/2]\sin(\sqrt{3}/2)t$. The reader can easily check that $W(u_1, v_1)(t) \neq 0$ on $-\infty < t < \infty$. Therefore, by Theorem 3.5 again, every solution ϕ of $y'' + y' + y = 0$ on $-\infty < t < \infty$ has the form

$$\phi(t) = a_1 \exp\left[-\frac{t}{2}\right]\cos\frac{\sqrt{3}}{2}t + a_2 \exp\left[-\frac{t}{2}\right]\sin\frac{\sqrt{3}}{2}t$$

for some unique choice of the (possibly complex) constants a_1, a_2. Starting with the complex form of the solution ϕ we may also arrive at the "real form" as follows. Using Euler's formula (see Appendix 3) and collecting terms, we have

$$\begin{aligned}
\phi(t) &= c_1\phi_1(t) + c_2\phi_2(t) \\
&= c_1 \exp\left[-\frac{t}{2}\right]\left(\cos\frac{\sqrt{3}}{2}t + i\sin\frac{\sqrt{3}}{2}t\right) \\
&\quad + c_2 \exp\left[-\frac{t}{2}\right]\left(\cos\frac{\sqrt{3}}{2}t - i\sin\frac{\sqrt{3}}{2}t\right) \\
&= (c_1 + c_2)\exp\left[-\frac{t}{2}\right]\cos\frac{\sqrt{3}}{2}t + i(c_1 - c_2)\exp\left[-\frac{t}{2}\right]\sin\frac{\sqrt{3}}{2}t
\end{aligned}$$

If we now define $a_1 = c_1 + c_2$, $a_2 = i(c_1 - c_2)$, we obtain the desired form. It is clear from this that the solution $\phi(t)$ of the equation $y'' + y' + y = 0$ will be real if and only if $c_2 = \overline{c_1}$ (the complex conjugate of c_1). In this case, of course, a_1 and a_2 are both real.

We now return to the general equation (3.15), page 82, where p and q are real constants and summarize what we have learned up to this point.

Theorem 3.7. *Every solution ϕ of the differential equation*

$$y'' + py' + qy = 0 \tag{3.15}$$

where p, q are real constants with $p^2 \neq 4q$ is defined on $-\infty < t < \infty$ and has the form

$$\phi(t) = c_1 e^{z_1 t} + c_2 e^{z_2 t} \qquad (-\infty < t < \infty) \tag{3.17}$$

The numbers z_1, z_2 are the distinct roots of the characteristic equation

$$z^2 + pz + q = 0 \tag{3.16}$$

and c_1, c_2 are constants. If $p^2 > 4q$, z_1 and z_2 are real and distinct. If $p^2 < 4q$ the roots z_1, z_2 are complex conjugates. In this case if $z_1 = \alpha + i\beta$ (α, β real) the solution ϕ may be expressed in the form

$$\phi(t) = e^{\alpha t}(a_1 \cos \beta t + a_2 \sin \beta t) \tag{3.18}$$

where a_1, $a_2 =$ are constants. If ϕ is real, a_1 and a_2 are real.

We have already proved all of Theorem 3.7 except for equation (3.18). To prove (3.18), we proceed exactly as in Exercise 5 above; namely, we know from Theorem 3.6 that $e^{\alpha t} \cos \beta t$, $e^{\alpha t} \sin \beta t$ are solutions of $y'' + py' + qy = 0$, where $\alpha + i\beta$ is a root of $z^2 + pz + q = 0$. Since these solutions are linearly independent on $-\infty < t < \infty$, formula (3.18) is a direct consequence of Theorem 3.5. ∎

•EXERCISES

7. Show that $e^{\alpha t} \cos \beta t$, $e^{\alpha t} \sin \beta t$ are linearly independent solutions on $-\infty < t < \infty$ of (3.15) when $p^2 < 4q$.

8. Proceeding as in Example 2, show that a_1, a_2 in (3.18) are given in terms of c_1 and c_2 by the formulas $a_1 = c_1 + c_2$, $a_2 = i(c_1 - c_2)$.

9. Find the solution ϕ satisfying the initial conditions $\phi(0) = \phi'(0) = 1$ of each of the following differential equations:

(a) $y'' + y = 0$. (c) $y'' + 4y = 0$.

(b) $y'' - 4y' + 13y = 0$. (d) $y'' + 2y' + 2y = 0$.

10. In equation (3.15) with p, q nonnegative, find conditions on the constants which lead to complex roots of the characteristic equation and investigate the behavior of the solutions for various choices of these constants as $t \to +\infty$.

We now turn to the case of equal roots of the characteristic equation. In case (ii), $p^2 = 4q$, and the characteristic equation

$$z^2 + pz + q = 0$$

has the double root $z = -p/2$ and therefore $\exp[(-p/2)t]$ is a solution of

$$y'' + py' + qy = 0 \tag{3.15}$$

on $-\infty < t < \infty$ if $p^2 = 4q$. The theory tells us that in all cases, (3.15) should have two linearly independent solutions. **We now employ a useful trick** to find (guess) a second linearly independent solution. Knowing that $\exp[(-p/2)t]$ is a solution of (3.15), we try to determine a nonconstant function w such that

$$\psi(t) = \exp\left(-\frac{p}{2}t\right)w(t) \tag{3.19}$$

will also be a solution of (3.15). Now ψ will be a solution of (3.15) on $-\infty < t < \infty$ if and only if

$$\psi''(t) + p\psi'(t) + q\psi(t) = 0$$

or equivalently, using (3.19), if and only if

$$\exp\left(-\frac{p}{2}t\right)w''(t) - p\exp\left(-\frac{p}{2}t\right)w'(t) + \frac{p^2}{4}\exp\left(-\frac{p}{2}t\right)w(t)$$
$$+ p\left[-\frac{p}{2}\exp\left(-\frac{p}{2}t\right)w(t) + \exp\left(-\frac{p}{2}t\right)w'(t)\right]$$
$$+ q\exp\left(-\frac{p}{2}t\right)w(t) = 0$$

or

$$\exp\left(-\frac{p}{2}t\right)\left[w''(t) + \left(q - \frac{p^2}{4}\right)w(t)\right] = 0 \qquad (-\infty < t < \infty)$$

Since $q = p^2/4$, w must satisfy the equation $\exp[(-p/2)t]w''(t) = 0$. But $\exp[(-p/2)t] \neq 0$, and so (3.19) will be a solution of (3.15) only if w is determined such that $w''(t) = 0$ ($-\infty < t < \infty$). Thus $w(t) = c_1 + c_2 t$ where c_1, c_2 are constants. We therefore have $\psi(t) = (c_1 + c_2 t)$ $\exp[(-p/2)t]$ as a candidate for the solution of (3.15). **Direct substitution shows that it is.** Now $\exp[(-p/2)t]$ is a solution of $y'' + py' + qy = 0$ if $p^2 = 4q$, and $t \exp[(-p/2)t]$ is another solution on $-\infty < t < \infty$ (verify!). Since they are linearly independent solutions on $-\infty < t < \infty$ (verify!), Theorem 3.5 tells us that we have proved the following result.

Theorem 3.8. *Let p and q be constant such that $p^2 = 4q$. Then every solution ϕ on $-\infty < t < \infty$ of*

$$y'' + py' + qy = 0 \tag{3.15}$$

has the form

$$\phi(t) = (c_1 + c_2 t) \exp\left[-\frac{p}{2}t\right] \qquad (-\infty < t < \infty)$$

where c_1 and c_2 are constants.

There is an alternative and instructive way to establish the fact that if $p^2 = 4q$, then $t \exp[(-p/2)t]$ is also a solution of (3.15). We give this method because it is useful for solving higher-order equations. We know that $\exp[(-p/2)t]$ is a solution of $L(y) = y'' + py' + (p^2/4)y = 0$. This means that

$$L(e^{zt})\Big|_{z=-p/2} = e^{zt}\left(z^2 + pz + \frac{p^2}{4}\right)\Big|_{z=-p/2} = 0$$

Since

$$\frac{\partial}{\partial z}(L(e^{zt})) = \frac{\partial}{\partial z}\left(e^{zt}\left(z^2 + pz + \frac{p^2}{4}\right)\right) = te^{zt}\left(z^2 + pz + \frac{p^2}{4}\right) + e^{zt}(2z + p)$$

we see by substituting $z = -p/2$ that also

$$\frac{\partial}{\partial z}(L(e^{zt}))\Big|_{z=-p/2} = 0$$

Notice that $2z + p$ is the derivative of $z^2 + pz + p^2/2$ and both of these vanish at the double root $z = -p/2$. (This is a general result about multiple roots—see Appendix 3.) As the reader may verify,

$$\frac{\partial}{\partial z}\left(\frac{\partial e^{zt}}{\partial t}\right) = \frac{\partial}{\partial t}\left(\frac{\partial e^{zt}}{\partial z}\right) \qquad \frac{\partial}{\partial z}\left(\frac{\partial^2 e^{zt}}{\partial t^2}\right) = \frac{\partial^2}{\partial t^2}\left(\frac{\partial e^{zt}}{\partial z}\right)$$

so that $(\partial/\partial z(L(e^{zt}))) = L(\partial/\partial z(e^{zt}))$. Therefore

$$L\left(\frac{\partial}{\partial z}\,e^{zt}\right)\bigg|_{z=-p/2} = L(te^{zt})\bigg|_{z=-p/2} = 0$$

This shows that $te^{(-p/2(t))}$ is also a solution of $y'' + py' + qy = 0$ if $q = p^2/4$.

● **EXERCISES**

11. Find the general solution of each of the following equations. If the equation is real, express the solution in real form. Note that Theorem 3.8 is true if p and q are complex, and thus equations with complex coefficients can be solved.

(a) $y'' + 9y = 0$.
(b) $y'' - 5y' + 6y = 0$.
(c) $y'' + 10y' + 25y = 0$.
(d) $y'' + 2iy' + y = 0$.
(e) $4y'' - y = 0$.
(f) $y'' + 5y' + 10y = 0$.
(g) $\epsilon y'' + 2y' + y = 0$ $\quad (0 < \epsilon < 1)$.
(h) $4y'' + 4y' + y = 0$.

12. In equation (3.15) with $p^2 = 4q$, investigate the behavior of the solutions as $t \to +\infty$ for various values of the constants.

13. Recall the *Definition: A function f is said to be bounded on some interval I if and only if there exists a constant $M > 0$ such that $|f(t)| \le M$ for all t on I.* For example, $\sin t$, $\cos t$ are bounded on any interval, $1/t$ is bounded on $[1, 2]$ but not on $(0, \infty)$, e^{-t} is bounded on $[-5, \infty)$ but not on $(-\infty, -5]$.

(a) *Determine* which differential equations in Exercise 10 have **all** their solutions bounded on $[0, \infty)$.
(b) Repeat part (a) for the interval $(-\infty, \infty)$.

The Phase Plane

Let ϕ be a real solution on $0 \le t < \infty$ of the linear second-order differential equation $L(y) = 0$, where L has real constant coefficients. Let $y_1 = \phi(t)$, $y_2 = \phi'(t)$, where we now think of t as a parameter, ranging over the interval $0 \le t < \infty$. It is of interest to examine the graph of the curve Γ, called a **positive semiorbit,** given parametrically by the equations $y_1 = \phi(t)$, $y_2 = \phi'(t)$ in the (y_1, y_2) plane (called the **phase plane**). For example, for the equation $y'' + y = 0$, we may consider the solution $y_1 = \phi(t) = c_1 \cos t + c_2 \sin t$, so that $y_2 = \phi'(t) = -c_1 \sin t + c_2 \cos t$, $0 \leq t < \infty$, for each choice of the real constants c_1, c_2. It is clear that $y_1{}^2 + y_2{}^2 = c_1{}^2 + c_2{}^2$, in particular $y_1 = 0$, $y_2 = 0$ if $c_1 = c_2 = 0$, and hence each positive semiorbit $y_1 = \phi(t)$, $y_2 = \phi'(t)$ $(0 \leq t < \infty)$, is a circle in the phase plane with center at the origin. The arrow (Figure 3.1)

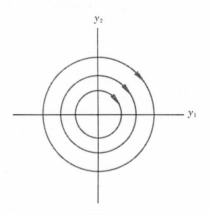

Figure 3.1

represents the direction of motion along each curve in the phase plane as t increases. Notice that through each point in the phase plane there passes one and only one semiorbit. (This is not hard to prove using the uniqueness property, Theorem 3.1 p. 65.) We notice also that the above example, though not too difficult to handle, would be even more transparent if we observe that the solution

$$\phi(t) = c_1 \cos t + c_2 \sin t$$

with c_1, c_2 not both zero, can be expressed in still another form, namely,

$$\phi(t) = A \sin (t + \alpha)$$

where $A = (c_1{}^2 + c_2{}^2)^{1/2}$ is called the **amplitude,** and $\alpha = \arcsin$ $(c_1/(c_1{}^2 + c_2{}^2)^{1/2})$ is called the **phase shift.** It is now obvious that $\phi'(t) = A \cos (t + \alpha)$ and therefore the curve $y_1 = \phi(t)$, $y_2 = \phi'(t)$, $0 \leq t < \infty$ in the (y_1, y_2) plane is a circle of radius A centered at the origin.

•**EXERCISES**

14. Establish the above formulas for A, α. [*Hint:* Assuming c_1, c_2 are not both zero,

$$c_1 \cos t + c_2 \sin t = (c_1{}^2 + c_2{}^2)^{1/2} \left[\frac{c_1}{(c_1{}^2 + c_2{}^2)^{1/2}} \cos t + \frac{c_2}{(c_1{}^2 + c_2{}^2)^{1/2}} \sin t \right]$$

15. (a) Write the general solution of the equation $y'' + 2y = 0$ in the "amplitude-phase shift form."
   (b) Determine the amplitude, period, phase shift of that solution ϕ of $y'' + 9y = 0$ which satisfies $\phi(0) = 1$, $\phi'(0) = 2$.
   (c) Sketch and identify several typical positive semiorbits (that is, let $0 \leq t < \infty$) of the equation $y'' + 9y = 0$ in the phase plane. What happens if we let t range on the interval $-\infty < t \leq 0$ (negative semiorbit)? Indicate the direction of the motion along each curve as t increases.

16. Sketch a few typical positive semiorbits in the phase plane for each of the following differential equations. Consider also the negative semiorbits. Indicate the direction of the motion along each curve as t increases.
   (a) $y'' + 2y' + 2y = 0$.
   (b) $y'' - y = 0$.

17. Suppose we had a pendulum for which a crude mathematical model would give rise either to the equation in Exercise 15(a) or 16(a) above. Can you give a physical interpretation of the semiorbits in the phase plane in each case?

18. Consider two solutions $\phi(t) = c_1 \cos t + c_2 \sin t$ and $\psi(t) = d_1 \cos t + d_2 \sin t$ of the equation $y'' + y = 0$, where $c_1{}^2 + c_2{}^2 = d_1{}^2 + d_2{}^2$. Show that these solutions both give rise to the same positive semiorbit in the phase plane.

Exercise 18 shows that although only one orbit passes through each point of the phase plane, each orbit corresponds to many solutions with different phase shifts.

3.5   Linear Homogeneous Equations of Arbitrary Order with Constant Coefficients

We can easily generalize the results of Section 3.4 for second-order linear differential equations with constant coefficients to equations of arbitrary order. Consider the linear homogeneous equation of order n

with constant coefficients

$$L_n(y) = y^{(n)} + a_1 y^{(n-1)} + \cdots + a_{n-1} y' + a_n y = 0 \qquad (3.20)$$

and look for a solution of the form e^{zt} as before.   Note that the equation (3.20) reduces to (3.15) when $n = 2$, with $a_1 = p$, $a_2 = q$. Since $L_n(e^{zt}) = p_n(z)e^{zt}$, where

$$p_n(z) = z^n + a_1 z^{n-1} + \cdots + a_{n-1} z + a_n$$

is a polynomial of degree n, called the **characteristic polynomial,** we see that the analogues of Theorems 3.7 and 3.8 (although rather more involved) may be stated as follows:

Theorem 3.9.   *Let z_1, z_2, . . . , z_s, where $s \leq n$ be the distinct roots of the characteristic equation* (of degree n)

$$p_n(z) = z^n + a_1 z^{n-1} + \cdots + a_{n-1} z + a_n = 0$$

and suppose the root z_i has multiplicity m_i, $i = 1$, . . . , s, $(m_1 + m_2 + \cdots + m_s = n)$.   Then the n functions

$$e^{z_1 t}, \ t e^{z_1 t}, \ \ldots , \ t^{m_1 - 1} e^{z_1 t}$$
$$e^{z_2 t}, \ t e^{z_2 t}, \ \ldots , \ t^{m_2 - 1} e^{z_2 t}$$
$$\cdot$$
$$\cdot$$
$$\cdot$$
$$e^{z_s t}, \ t e^{z_s t}, \ \ldots , \ t^{m_s - 1} e^{z_s t}$$

are (i) *solutions of $L_n(y) = 0$ on $-\infty < t < \infty$, and* (ii) *linearly independent on $-\infty < t < \infty$.*

Hence by Theorem 3.5 interpreted for nth-order equations every solution ϕ of $L_n(y) = 0$ on any interval can be expressed as some unique linear combination of these linearly independent solutions.   Of course, Theorem 3.6 holds without change for higher-order equations, and if the coefficients a_1, . . . , a_n are real each solution of $L_n(y) = 0$ can be expressed in real form exactly as before.

We do not prove Theorem 3.9 except to remark that if z_i, $1 \leq z_i \leq s$ is a root of multiplicity m_i of the polynomial equation $p_n(z) = 0$, then

$$p_n(z_i) = 0, \ p_n'(z_i) = 0, \ \ldots \ , \ p_n^{(m_i - 1)}(z_i) = 0$$

but $p_n^{(m_i)}(z_i) \neq 0$ (see Appendix 3).   This observation enables us to prove the result much as was done in the second-order case.   The linear independence of these solutions has been proved in Lemma 3.1 (p. 70).

Example 1.   Find the general solution of the equation $y^{(4)} + 16y = 0$. Since this equation has order 4, is homogeneous, and has constant coefficients, Theorem 3.9 is applicable.   The characteristic equation is $z^4 + 16 = 0$.   To solve this equation, we write

$$z^4 = -16 = 16e^{i(\pi + 2n\pi)} \qquad (n = 0, \pm 1, \pm 2, \ldots)$$

or, letting $z = re^{i\theta}$,

$$r^4 e^{4i\theta} = 16e^{i(\pi + 2n\pi)} \qquad (n = 0, \pm 1, \pm 2, \ldots)$$

Hence $r^4 = 16$ and $\theta = \pi/4 + (n/2)\pi$ $(n = 0, \pm 1, \pm 2, \ldots)$, and the only distinct roots are $z_1 = 2 \exp [i(\pi/4)] = \sqrt{2}\,(1 + i)$, $z_2 = 2 \exp [3i(\pi/4)] = \sqrt{2}\,(-1 + i)$, $z_3 = 2 \exp [-i(\pi/4)] = \sqrt{2}\,(1 - i)$, $z_4 = 2 \exp [-3i(\pi/4)] = \sqrt{2}\,(-1 - i)$, corresponding to $n = 0$, $n = 1$, $n = -1$, $n = -2$, respectively.   It is clear that the choices $n = +2$, $\pm 3, \ldots$, lead us back to one of the roots z_1, z_2, z_3, z_4 already listed. Thus every solution ϕ of the equation $y^{(4)} + 16y = 0$ has by Theorem 3.9 (here $n = 4$, $m_1 = m_2 = m_3 = m_4 = 1$) the form .

$$\phi(t) = c_1 \exp [\sqrt{2}\,(1 + i)t] + c_2 \exp [\sqrt{2}\,(1 - i)t] \\ + c_3 \exp [\sqrt{2}\,(-1 + i)t] + c_4 \exp [\sqrt{2}\,(-1 - i)t]$$

for some unique choice of the constants c_1, c_2, c_3, c_4.   This may be written in the real form

$$\phi(t) = \exp [\sqrt{2}\,t](a_1 \cos \sqrt{2}\,t + a_2 \sin \sqrt{2}\,t) \\ + \exp [-\sqrt{2}\,t](a_3 \cos \sqrt{2}\,t + a_4 \sin \sqrt{2}\,t)$$

for some unique choice of constants a_1, a_2, a_3, a_4.

Example 2.   Find the general solution of the equation $y''' + 3y'' + 3y' + y = 0$.   Again Theorem 3.9 is applicable and the characteristic equation is $z^3 + 3z^2 + 3z + 1 = (z + 1)^3 = 0$.   Thus $z = -1$ is a triple root and e^{-t}, te^{-t}, t^2e^{-t} are by Theorem 3.9 linearly independent solutions on $-\infty < t < \infty$. Hence every solution ϕ has the form

$$\phi(t) = e^{-t}(c_1 + c_2 t + c_3 t^2)$$

for some unique choice of the constants c_1, c_2, c_3.

•EXERCISES

1. Find the general solutions of the following differential equations.
   (a) $y''' = 27y = 0$.   (d) $y^{(4)} + 5y'' + 4y = 0$.
   (b) $y^{(4)} - 16y = 0$.   (e) $y^{(6)} + y = 0$.
   (c) $y^{(4)} + 2y'' + y = 0$.

2. Find that solution ϕ of $y^{(4)} + 16y = 0$ for which $\phi(0) = 1$, $\phi'(0) = 0$, $\phi''(0) = 0$, $\phi'''(0) = 0$. (See Example 1 above.)

3. Given the equation $y^{(4)} + \lambda y = 0$, where λ is a constant, find the general solution (in real form) in each case: (a) $\lambda = 0$, (b) $\lambda > 0$, (c) $\lambda < 0$.

4. Which of the equations in Exercise 1 have the property that (a) all their solutions tend to zero at $t \to +\infty$, (b) all their solutions are bounded on $0 \le t < \infty$, (c) all their solutions are bounded on $-\infty < t < \infty$?

In closing this section we emphasize that the methods of solution which we have developed are only applicable when the coefficients are constant and the equation is linear! The analogue of the phase plane ($n = 2$) is n-dimensional phase space and again solutions ϕ of equation (3.20) can be pictured as curves in this space. However, we shall not pursue this topic further at this point.

3.6   A Special Linear Equation with Variable Coefficients (The Euler Equation)

We consider the linear equation of order n

$$t^n y^{(n)} + a_1 t^{n-1} y^{(n-1)} + a_2 t^{n-2} y^{(n-2)} + \cdots + a_{n-1} t y' + a_n y = 0 \quad (3.21)$$

where $a_1, \ldots, a_n$ are constants. The theory of Sections 3.1, 3.2, 3.3 applies on any interval I which does not include $t = 0$ (why?) but Sections 3.4 and 3.5 do not apply at all. However, equation (3.21) can be transformed to a linear homogeneous differential equation of order n with constant coefficients by the change of variable $|t| = e^s$. The resulting equation can then be solved by applying Theorem 3.9. We illustrate this for the case $n = 2$ by considering

$$t^2 y'' + a_1 t y' + a_2 y = 0 \tag{3.22}$$

We consider first the case $t > 0$, so that the change of variable is $t = e^s$. Moreover, let $w(s) = y(e^s) = y(t)$. Then by the chain rule, using $s = \log t$,

$$\frac{dy}{dt} = \frac{dw}{ds}\frac{ds}{dt} = \frac{1}{t}\frac{dw}{ds}$$

and

$$\frac{d^2y}{dt^2} = \left(-\frac{1}{t^2}\right)\frac{dw}{ds} + \frac{1}{t}\frac{d}{dt}\left(\frac{dw}{ds}\right) = -\frac{1}{t^2}\frac{dw}{ds} + \frac{1}{t}\frac{d^2w}{ds^2}\left(\frac{ds}{dt}\right) = \frac{1}{t^2}\left(\frac{d^2w}{ds^2} - \frac{dw}{ds}\right)$$

Substituting in (3.22) we obtain, for $t > 0$,

$$\frac{d^2w}{ds^2} + (a_1 - 1)\frac{dw}{ds} + a_2w = 0 \tag{3.23}$$

•EXERCISE

1. Show that the change of variable $|t| = e^s$ also transforms (3.22) to (3.23) for $t < 0$.

Now equation (3.23) has the general solution $c_1e^{z_1s} + c_2e^{z_2s}$ if z_1, z_2 are distinct roots of the quadratic equation

$$z^2 + (a_1 - 1)z + a_2 = 0 \tag{3.24}$$

and it has the general solution $(c_1 + c_2s)e^{z_1s}$ if z_1 is a double root of equation (3.24). Thus employing the change of variable $|t| = e^s$ again we see that every solution ϕ of equation (3.22) has one of the forms

$$\phi(t) = c_1|t|^{z_1} + c_2|t|^{z_2} \qquad \text{or} \qquad \phi(t) = (c_1 + c_2 \log|t|)|t|^{z_1}$$

according as z_1, z_2 are distinct or equal roots of the auxiliary equation (3.24). This solution is valid on any interval which does not contain $t = 0$. Incidentally, if z is a complex number, $|t|^z$ means $e^{z \log|t|}$; thus if $z = \alpha + i\beta$ (α, β real),

$$|t|^z = e^{(\alpha+i\beta)\log|t|} = |t|^\alpha[\cos(\beta \log|t|) + i\sin(\beta \log|t|)]$$

We shall meet the Euler equation again in Section 4.5, where it will serve as the simplest example of an equation with a regular singular point.

•**EXERCISES**

2. Find the general solution of each of the following equations, valid for $t \neq 0$.

(a) $t^2 y'' + 2ty' - 6y = 0$.

(b) $t^2 y'' + ty' + 4y = 0$.

(c) $2t^2 y'' + ty' - y = 0$.

(d) $t^2 y'' - (2 + i)ty' + 3iy = 0$.

(e) $t^3 y''' + 2t^2 y'' - ty' + y = 0$.

3.* (a) For $t \neq 0$ show directly that $|t|^z$ is a solution of the differential equation (3.22) if and only if z is a root of the algebraic equation $z^2 + (a_1 - 1)z + a_2 = 0$.   [*Hint:* Take $t > 0$ and form $L(y) = t^2 y'' + a_1 ty' + a_2 y$.   Then take the case $t < 0$.]

(b) Show that the solutions $|t|^{z_1}$, $|t|^{z_2}$ ($z_1 \neq z_2$) of equation (3.22) are linearly independent on any interval I which does not contain $t = 0$, where z_1, z_2 are roots of the algebraic equation $z^2 + (a_1 - 1)z + a_2 = 0$.

4. Find the general solution of the equation

$$(t - t_0)^n y^n + a_1(t - t_0)^{n-1} y^{(n-1)} + \cdots + a_{n-1}(t - t_0)y^2 + a_n y = 0$$

[*Hint:* Show how to find n solutions, and then use an argument analogous to Lemma 3.1 (p. 70) to prove that these solutions are linearly independent.]

3.7   Reduction of Order

The methods of Sections 3.4 and 3.5 do not apply to linear equations with variable coefficients.   Thus even though our theory tells us that there are two linearly independent solutions of a second-order linear homogeneous equation, it may not be possible to find them.   Sometimes it is possible to guess or by some other means find one solution ϕ_1 on some interval I of the linear equation

$$L(y) = a_0(t)y'' + a_1(t)y' + a_2(t)y = 0$$

where a_0, a_1, a_2 are continuous on I and $a_0(t) \neq 0$ on I.   Then the same trick which led to Theorem 3.8 (p. 90) in the case of constant coefficients with equal roots of the auxiliary equation will enable us to find a second, linearly independent solution of $L(y) = 0$ on I by reducing the problem to one of solving a first-order equation.

---

* The reader who intends to study Chapter 4 should not omit this exercise.

Assuming that we know a solution ϕ_1, we let $\phi_2(t) = w(t)\phi_1(t)$ and try to find a nonconstant function w so that $L(\phi_2) = 0$ for every t on I. (Why should w be nonconstant?) Since

$$\phi_2' = w'\phi_1 + w\phi_1' \qquad \phi_2'' = w''\phi_1 + 2w'\phi_1' + w\phi_1''$$

we see that

$$L(\phi_2) = a_0\phi_1 w'' + (2a_0\phi_1' + a_1\phi_1)w' + wL(\phi_1)$$

But $L(\phi_1) = 0$, since ϕ_1 is a solution of $L(y) = 0$. Therefore, $L(\phi_2) = 0$ for all t on I if and only if w satisfies the equation

$$a_0(t)\phi_1(t)w'' + (2a_0(t)\phi_1'(t) + a_1(t)\phi_1(t))w' = 0 \tag{3.25}$$

for all t on I. **Note that** (3.25) **is a first-order linear equation in** w', and is readily solved as follows. Let $w' = v$ and assume that $\phi_1 \neq 0$; then (3.25) becomes

$$v' + \left(2\frac{\phi_1'}{\phi_1} + \frac{a_1}{a_0}\right)v = 0$$

Separating variables we obtain the solution

$$v(t) = \frac{1}{\phi_1{}^2(t)} \exp\left[-\int_{t_0}^t \frac{a_1(s)}{a_0(s)}\,ds\right]$$

Then for t_0, t in I,

$$w(t) = \int_{t_0}^t \frac{1}{\phi_1{}^2(\sigma)} \exp\left[-\int_{t_0}^\sigma \frac{a_1(s)}{a_0(s)}\,ds\right] d\sigma$$

and

$$\phi_2(t) = \phi_1(t) \int_{t_0}^t \frac{1}{\phi_1{}^2(\sigma)} \exp\left[-\int_{t_0}^\sigma \frac{a_1(s)}{a_0(s)}\,ds\right] d\sigma \tag{3.26}$$

The reader should verify by direct substitution that $L(\phi_2) = 0$. This leads us to the following result.

Theorem 3.10. *If ϕ_1 is a solution of $L(y) = 0$ on I, where a_0, a_1, a_2 are continuous on I and $a_0(t) \neq 0$ on I, and if $\phi_1(t) \neq 0$, then the function ϕ_2 given by* (3.26) *is also a solution of $L(y) = 0$ on I. Moreover, the solutions ϕ_1, ϕ_2 are linearly independent on I; hence every solution ϕ of $L(y) = 0$ on I has the form $\phi = c_1\phi_1 + c_2\phi_2$ for some unique choice of c_2, c_2.*

We have only to prove the linear independence of the solutions ϕ_1, ϕ_2 on *I*. This is done by computing $W(\phi_1, \phi_2)$ and using Theorem 3.3 (p. 76).

● **EXERCISE**

1. Carry out the proof of linear independence of ϕ_1, ϕ_2 on *I*.

Example 1.   One solution of $y'' + ty' - y = 0$ is $\phi_1(t) = t$. Find a second linearly independent solution ϕ_2. We could, of course, apply formula (3.26). Rather than try to remember such a complicated formula, we proceed directly by putting $\phi_2 = tw$ and forming $L(\phi_2) = L(tw)$. Since $\phi_2' = tw' + w$ and $\phi_2'' = tw'' + 2w'$ we have $L(\phi_2) = tw'' + 2w' + t^2w'$. Thus $L(\phi_2) = 0$ if and only if $v = w'$ satisfies

$$tv' + (2 + t^2)v = 0$$

Thus, for $t \neq 0$, $v(t) = (e^{-t^2/2}/t^2)$, $w(t) = \int_{t_0}^{t}(e^{-s^2/2}/s^2) \ ds$, $(t_0 \neq 0)$, and $\phi_2(t) = t\int_{t_0}^{t}(e^{-s^2/2}/s^2) \ ds$, $(t_0 \neq 0, \ t \neq 0)$. To establish the linear independence of ϕ_1 and ϕ_2, we form their Wronskian

$$W(\phi_1, \phi_2)(t) = \begin{vmatrix} t & t\int_{t_0}^{t}\dfrac{e^{-s^2/2}}{s^2} \ ds \\ 1 & \dfrac{e^{-t^2/2}}{t} + \int_{t_0}^{t}\dfrac{e^{-s^2/2}}{s^2} \ ds \end{vmatrix} = e^{-t^2/2} \qquad (t \neq 0)$$

Since this Wronskian is different from zero, ϕ_1 and ϕ_2 are linearly independent on any interval not containing the origin.

● **EXERCISE**

2. Given one solution ϕ_1, in each case find a second linearly independent solution ϕ_2 on the interval indicated.

(a) $y'' - \dfrac{2}{t^2y} = 0$ $\qquad\qquad$ $\phi_1(t) = t^2$ $\quad (0 < t < \infty)$.

(b) $y'' - 4ty' + (4t^2 - 2)y = 0$ $\quad$ $\phi_1(t) = e^{t^2}$ $\quad (-\infty < t < \infty)$.

(c) $(1 - t^2)y'' - 2ty' + 2y = 0$ $\quad$ $\phi_1(t) = t$ $\qquad (0 < t < 1)$.

(d) $ty'' - (t + 1)y' + y = 0$ $\qquad$ $\phi_1(t) = e^t$ $\quad (t > 0)$.

In general if $\phi_1, \ldots, \phi_k$, where $k < n$, are k linearly independent solutions on some interval *I* of the linear equation of *n*th-order

$$L_n(y) = a_0(t)y^{(n)} + a_1(t)y^{(n-1)} + \cdots + a_{n-1}(t)y' + a_n(t)y = 0$$

where $a_0, a_1, \ldots, a_n$ are continuous on I and $a_0(t) \neq 0$ on I, it is possible to reduce the problem successively to a linear equation of order $n - k$. We illustrate this with the following exercises.

•EXERCISES

3. Suppose ϕ_1, ϕ_2 are linearly independent solutions on an interval I of the differential equation

$$L_3(y) = y''' + a_1(t)y'' + a_2(t)y' + a_3(t)y = 0$$

(we are taking $a_0(t) \equiv 1$).
   (a) Let $\phi = w\phi_1$ and compute the linear equation of order two which must be satisfied by w' in order that $L_3(\phi) = 0$.
   (b) Show that $(\phi_2/\phi_1)'$ is a solution of the equation of order two found in part (a).
   (c) Use the result of part (b) to reduce the second-order equation to one which is linear and of first order.

4. Two solutions of

$$t^3 y''' - 3ty' + 3y = 0 \qquad (t > 0)$$

are $\phi_1(t) = t$, $\phi_2(t) = t^3$. Use this and Exercise 3 to find the form of every solution of the given equation for $t > 0$.

3.8   Linear Nonhomogeneous Equations

We now turn to the nonhomogeneous second-order linear equation

$$L(y) = a_0(t)y'' + a_1(t)y' + a_2(t)y = f(t) \tag{3.27}$$

and, more generally, the nth-order linear equation

$$L_n(y) = a_0(t)y^{(n)} + a_1(t)y^{(n-1)} + \cdots + a_n(t)y = f(t) \tag{3.28}$$

where throughout $a_0, a_1, \ldots, a_n$, and f are given functions continuous on some interval I, and $a_0(t) \neq 0$ on I. In physical problems having (3.27) or (3.28) for a mathematical model, the nonhomogeneous term $f(t)$ represents an external force acting on the system. For example, if the damped linear mass-spring system considered in Section 1.1 (p. 5) is subjected to a given periodic external force $A \cos \omega t$, then the equation of motion (1.3) (p. 5) is replaced by

$$y'' + by' + \frac{k}{m} y = \frac{A}{m} \cos \omega t \tag{3.29}$$

Initial conditions are imposed as before. We remark that the equation for the current in an electrical circuit having resistance, inductance, and capacitance in series and a periodic impressed voltage also has the form (3.29) under the appropriate physical assumptions.

The entire development is based on the following fundamental result:

Theorem 3.11.   *Suppose ψ_p is some particular solution of $L(y) = f$ on I, and suppose that ϕ_1, ϕ_2 are two linearly independent solutions of $L(y) = 0$ on I. Then every solution ψ of $L(y) = f$ on I has the form*

$$\psi = c_1\phi_1 + c_2\phi_2 + \psi_p \tag{3.30}$$

where c_1, c_2 are constants which can be determined uniquely.

Since every solution of (3.27) has the form (3.30) we refer to (3.30) as **the general solution** of (3.27). According to Theorem 3.11, to find any solution of (3.27), we need only find two linearly independent solutions ϕ_1, ϕ_2 of $L(y) = 0$ and some particular solution ψ_p of $L(y) = f$, and then use the given initial conditions to determine c_1 and c_2.

Proof of Theorem 3.11.   Since ψ_p is a solution of (3.27) on I, we have $L(\psi_p) = f$ for all t on I. Since ψ is also to be a solution of (3.27) on I we have, using the linearity of L (p. 67),

$$L(\psi - \psi_p) = L(\psi) - L(\psi_p) = f - f = 0$$

This shows that $\psi - \psi_p$ is a solution of the homogeneous equation $L(y) = 0$ on I. (The reader will recall that this much of the proof was already established in Section 3.1 (p. 68).) Therefore, by Theorem 3.5 (p. 79), there exist unique constants c_1, c_2 such that

$$\psi - \psi_p = c_1\phi_1 + c_2\phi_2 \qquad \text{for all } t \text{ on } I$$

which completes the proof. ∎

The nth-order linear nonhomogeneous equation (3.28) can be treated in the same way, and Theorem 3.11 has the following analogue.

Theorem 3.12.   *Suppose ψ_p is some particular solution of $L_n(y) = f$ on I, and suppose that ϕ_1, ϕ_2, . . . , ϕ_n are n linearly independent solutions of*

$L_n(y) = 0$ on I.   Then every solution ψ of $L_n(y) = f$ on I has the form

$$\psi = c_1\phi_1 + c_2\phi_2 + \cdots + c_n\phi_n + \psi_p$$

where $c_1, c_2, \ldots, c_n$ are constants which can be determined uniquely.

• EXERCISES

1. Prove Theorem 3.12.

2. Compare Theorem 3.12 in the case $n = 1$ with the results of Section 2.2 (p. 41).

We will now study some methods for finding a particular solution of the equation $L(y) = f$ or $L_n(y) = f$.

The Method of Variation of Constants

This method for finding a particular solution is applicable whenever one knows the general solution of the associated homogeneous equation $L(y) = 0$ on I.

Let ϕ_1, ϕ_2 be two linearly independent solutions of $L(y) = 0$ on I. (These may either be given to us or in some instances we can find them by one of the methods already studied.)   The method consists of finding functions u_1, u_2 such that the function

$$\psi_p = u_1\phi_1 + u_2\phi_2 \tag{3.31}$$

will satisfy the equation $L(y) = f$ for all t on I.   It is remarkable that such a simple device will work, because when u_1 and u_2 are constants the function (3.31) satisfies $L(y) = 0$ and thus cannot be a solution of $L(y) = f$ for $f \neq 0$.   It is of course not obvious that such functions u_1, u_2 can be found.   We first argue in reverse; suppose we have found functions u_1, u_2 such that (3.31) satisfies $L(y) = f$ on I.   Then we have, for all t on I

$$(u_1\phi_1 + u_2\phi_2)' = u_1\phi_1' + u_2\phi_2' + u_1'\phi_1 + u_2'\phi_2,$$
$$(u_1\phi_1 + u_2\phi_2)'' = u_1\phi_1'' + u_2\phi_2'' + 2u_1'\phi_1' + 2u_2'\phi_2' + u_1''\phi_1 + u_2''\phi_2$$

and using $L(\phi_1) = L(\phi_2) = 0$ we obtain

$$\begin{aligned}
L(u_1\phi_1 + u_2\phi_2) &= u_1 L(\phi_1) + u_2 L(\phi_2) + a_0(\phi_1 u_1'' + \phi_2 u_2'') \\
&\quad + 2a_0(\phi_1' u_1' + \phi_2' u_2') + a_1(\phi_1 u_1' + \phi_2 u_2') \\
&= a_0[(\phi_1 u_1'' + \phi_2 u_2'') + 2(\phi_1' u_1' + \phi_2' u_2')] \\
&\quad + a_1(\phi_1 u_1' + \phi_2 u_2') = f
\end{aligned}$$

for all t on I. We would now like to obtain two relations from which to determine the two functions u_1, u_2. Examining the last relation we see that if $\phi_1 u_1' + \phi_2 u_2' = 0$ for all t on I then also $(\phi_1 u_1' + \phi_2 u_2')' = 0$ for all t on I. But $(\phi_1 u_1' + \phi_2 u_2')' = \phi_1 u_1'' + \phi_2 u_2'' + \phi_1' u_1' + \phi_2' u_2'$. Therefore, if we assume

$$\phi_1 u_1' + \phi_2 u_2' = 0 \tag{3.32}$$

for all t on I, then the requirement

$$a_0[(\phi_1 u_1'' + \phi_2 u_2'') + 2(\phi_1' u_1' + \phi_2' u_2')] + a_1(\phi_1 u_1' + \phi_2 u_2') = f$$

implies, on using (3.32) and the equation obtained by differentiating (3.32), that we must also have

$$\phi_1' u_1' + \phi_2' u_2' = \frac{f}{a_0} \tag{3.33}$$

for all t on I. Thus the assumption of the existence of a solution of the form (3.31) of the equation $L(y) = f$ has led us to the two equations (3.32), (3.33) from which we hope to determine u_1', u_2' and then the functions u_1, u_2. But now reversing the argument we see that **if we can find two functions** u_1, u_2 **to satisfy equations** (3.32), (3.33), then indeed $\psi_p = u_1 \phi_1 + u_2 \phi_2$ will satisfy $L(y) = f$ on I.

To find a particular solution of the equation $L(y) = f$, we may therefore concentrate on equations (3.32), (3.33). These are linear algebraic equations for the quantities u_1', u_2' and the determinant of their coefficients is $W(\phi_1, \phi_2)$. Since the solutions ϕ_1, ϕ_2 of $L(y) = 0$ are by hypothesis linearly independent on I, it follows that $W(\phi_1, \phi_2)(t) \neq 0$ for all t on I (Theorem 3.3, p. 76) and the system $((3.32), (3.33))$ of equations can therefore be always solved (in fact uniquely) for the quantities u_1', u_2'. By Cramer's rule (Appendix 1), the solution of the algebraic equations (3.32), (3.33) is

$$u_1' = \frac{-f\phi_2}{a_0 W(\phi_1, \phi_2)} \qquad u_2' = \frac{f\phi_1}{a_0 W(\phi_1, \phi_2)} \qquad (t \text{ on } I)$$

Thus a possible choice for u_1, u_2 is

$$u_1(t) = -\int_{t_0}^{t} \frac{f(s)\phi_2(s)}{a_0(s) W(\phi_1, \phi_2)(s)} \, ds \qquad u_2(t) = \int_{t_0}^{t} \frac{f(s)\phi_1(s)}{a_0(s) W(\phi_1, \phi_2)(s)} \, ds$$

for any t_0, t on I, and substituting in (3.31) we find that

$$\psi_p(t) = \int_{t_0}^t \frac{f(s)[\phi_2(t)\phi_1(s) - \phi_1(t)\phi_2(s)]}{a_0(s)W(\phi_1, \phi_2)(s)} \, ds \tag{3.34}$$

is a solution of $L(y) = f$ on I as is verified by direct substitution. The equation (3.34) is usually called the **variation of constants formula.** The reason for this name is clear from the method. Although the condition expressed by the equation (3.32) is artificial, the fact that we can solve the problem using it justifies it, and this is actually the essence of the method. This method of finding a particular solution of $L(y) = f$ can be used whenever the coefficients a_0, a_1, a_2 in L and the function f are continuous on I and $a_0 \neq 0$ on I, and whenever one knows the general solution of the associated homogeneous equation. It is not restricted to equations with constant coefficients.

• **EXERCISE**

3. Show by direct substitution that the function ψ_p given by (3.34) satisfies $L(y) = f$ on I. [*Hint:* Write ψ_p in the form

$$\psi_p(t) = \phi_2(t) \int_{t_0}^t \frac{f(s)\phi_1(s)}{a_0(s)W(\phi_1, \phi_2)(s)} \, ds - \phi_1(t) \int_{t_0}^t \frac{f(s)\phi_2(s)}{a_0(s)W(\phi_1, \phi_2)(s)} \, ds$$

before beginning the differentiation.]

Example 1. Find the general solution of the equation

$$y'' + y = \tan t \qquad \left(-\frac{\pi}{2} < t < \frac{\pi}{2}\right)$$

Since $\phi_1(t) = \cos t$, $\phi_2(t) = \sin t$ are linearly independent solutions of $y'' + y = 0$ on any interval, they are linearly independent on $-\pi/2 < t < \pi/2$, in fact

$$W(\phi_1, \phi_2)(t) = \begin{vmatrix} \cos t & \sin t \\ -\sin t & \cos t \end{vmatrix} \equiv 1$$

By what we have just seen $\psi_p = u_1 \cos t + u_2 \sin t$ will be a solution of $y'' + y = \tan t$ on $-\pi/2 < t < \pi/2$ if and only if the functions u_1 and u_2 are such that u_1', u_2' satisfy equations ((3.32), (3.33)), that is, if and only if

$$\begin{cases} u_1' \cos t + u_2' \sin t = 0 \\ -u_1' \sin t + u_2' \cos t = \tan t \end{cases} \qquad \left(-\frac{\pi}{2} < t < \frac{\pi}{2}\right)$$

Thus

$$u_1'(t) = -\tan t \sin t = -\frac{\sin^2 t}{\cos t} = -\frac{1 - \cos^2 t}{\cos t} = \cos t - \sec t$$

$$u_2'(t) = \cos t \tan t = \sin t \qquad \left(-\frac{\pi}{2} < t < \frac{\pi}{2}\right)$$

and we may take

$$u_1(t) = \int_0^t (\cos t - \sec t)\, dt \qquad u_2(t) = \int_0^t \sin t\, dt$$

or

$$u_1(t) = \sin t - \log|\sec t + \tan t| \qquad u_2(t) = -\cos t$$

$$\left(-\frac{\pi}{2} < t < \frac{\pi}{2}\right)$$

Therefore, by Theorem 3.11 every solution of $y'' + y = \tan t$ on $-\pi/2 < t < \pi/2$ has the form

$$\psi(t) = c_1 \cos t + c_2 \sin t - \cos t \log|\sec t + \tan t|$$

for some unique choice of the constants c_1 and c_2.

• EXERCISES

4. Find the general solution of each of the following differential equations.
   (a) $y'' + y = \sec t$ $(-\pi/2 < t < \pi/2)$.
   (b) $y'' + 4y' + 4y = \cos 2t$.
   (c) $y'' + 4y = f(t)$, where f is any continuous function on some interval I.
   (d) $y'' - 4y' + 4y = 3e^{-t} + 2t^2 + \sin t$.
   (e) $t^2 y'' + t y' + y = t^3$ $(t > 0)$.
   (f) $y'' + (1/4t^2)y = f(t)$, $(t > 0)$, f continuous, given that $\phi_1(t) = \sqrt{t}$ is a solution.

5. If ϕ is a solution of the equation $y'' + k^2 y = f(t)$, where k is a real constant different from zero and f is continuous for $0 \le t < \infty$, show that c_1 and c_2 can be chosen so that

$$\phi(t) = c_1 \cos kt + \frac{c_2}{k} \sin kt + \frac{1}{k}\int_0^t \sin k(t-s)f(s)\, ds$$

for $0 \le t < \infty$.   (Use $\cos kt$ and $\sin kt/k$ as a fundamental set of solutions of the homogeneous equation.)   Find an analogous formula in the case $k = 0$.

6. Given the equation

$$y'' + 5y' + 4y = f(t)$$

Use the variation of constants formula and Theorem 3.11 to prove that:
  (a) If f is bounded on $0 \leq t < \infty$ (that is, there exists a constant $M \geq 0$ such that $|f(t)| \leq M$ on $0 \leq t < \infty$), then every solution of $y'' + 5y' + 4y = f(t)$ is bounded on $0 \leq t < \infty$.
  (b) If also $f(t) \to 0$ as $t \to \infty$ then every solution ϕ of $y'' + 5y' + 4y = f(t)$ satisfies $\phi(t) \to 0$ as $t \to \infty$.

7. Can you formulate Exercise 5 for the general equation

$$y'' + a_1 y' + a_2 y = f(t) \qquad a_1, a_2 \text{ constant}$$

with a_1, a_2 suitably restricted?

  The method of variation of constants and Theorem 3.11 are applicable to the nth-order equation $L_n(y) = f$ with coefficients $a_0, a_1, \ldots, a_n, f$ continuous and $a_0(t) \neq 0$ on some interval I provided one knows n linearly independent solutions $\phi_1, \phi_2, \ldots, \phi_n$ of the homogeneous equation $L_n(y) = 0$ on I. Using the second-order case for motivation we try to find n functions $u_1, u_2, \ldots, u_n$, not all constant, so that

$$\psi_p = u_1 \phi_1 + u_2 \phi_2 + \cdots + u_n \phi_n$$

will be a solution of $L_n(y) = f$ on I. If (see the second-order case) $u_1' \phi_1 + u_2' \phi_2 + \cdots + u_n' \phi_n = 0$ on I, then $\psi_p' = u_1 \phi_1' + \cdots + u_n \phi_n'$ on I and if $u_1' \phi_1' + \cdots + u_n' \phi_n' = 0$ on I, then $\psi_p'' = u_1 \phi_1'' + \cdots + u_n \phi_n''$. Continuing in this manner we find that if $u_1', u_2', \ldots, u_n'$ are chosen to satisfy the system of linear algebraic equations on I

$$
\begin{cases}
u_1' \phi_1 + u_2' \phi_2 + \cdots + u_n' \phi_n = 0 \\
u_1' \phi_1' + u_2' \phi_2' + \cdots + u_n' \phi_n' = 0 \\
\quad \cdot \\
\quad \cdot \\
\quad \cdot \\
u_1' \phi_1^{(n-2)} + u_2' \phi_2^{(n-2)} + \cdots + u_n' \phi_n^{(n-2)} = 0 \\
u_1' \phi_1^{(n-1)} + u_2' \phi_2^{(n-1)} + \cdots + u_n' \phi_n^{(n-1)} = \dfrac{f}{a_0}
\end{cases}
\tag{3.35}
$$

then the function

$$\psi_p = u_1 \phi_1 + u_2 \phi_2 + \cdots + u_n \phi_n$$

will satisfy $L_n(y) = f$ on I.

• EXERCISE

8. Verify this last statement for the case $n = 3$.

Thus the entire problem is reduced to solving the algebraic system (3.35). Since its determinant of coefficients is $W(\phi_1, \phi_2, \ldots, \phi_n)$, and since the solutions $\phi_1, \ldots, \phi_n$ of $L_n(y) = 0$ on I are linearly independent on I, $W(\phi_1, \ldots, \phi_n)(t) \neq 0$ for t on I (see Exercise 13, p. 78, interpreted for nth order equations), and (3.35) always has a unique solution for the quantities $u_1', \ldots, u_n'$ on I. In fact, letting $W_j(t)$ be the n by n determinant having the same elements as $W(\phi_1, \ldots, \phi_n)(t)$ except with $(0, 0, \ldots, 1)$ as its jth column; we see that Cramer's rule (Appendix 1) gives

$$u_j'(t) = \frac{W_j(t)}{W(\phi_1, \ldots, \phi_n)} \frac{f(t)}{a_0(t)} \qquad (j = 1, \ldots, n)$$

The u_j are obtained by integration, so that

$$\psi_p(t) = \sum_{j=1}^{n} \phi_j(t) \int_{t_0}^{t} \frac{W_j(s)}{W(\phi_1, \ldots, \phi_n)(s)} \frac{f(s)}{a_0(s)} \, ds$$

where t_0 and t are any two points of I. Application of Theorem 3.12 now yields all solutions of $L_n(y) = f$ on I.

• **EXERCISE**

9. Find all solutions of the differential equation
   (a) $y''' - 8y = e^{2t}$.
   (b) $y^{(4)} + 16y = f(t)$, f continuous on $-\infty < t < \infty$.

The Method of Judicious Guessing (also known as the method of undetermined coefficients or the annihilator method)

It is clear from the above discussion that the method of variation of constants always yields a solution of the nonhomogeneous linear equation if one knows the general solution of the homogeneous equation regardless of whether the equation has constant or variable coefficients. However, there is a quicker way to solve the equation $L_n(y) = f$ **provided L_n has constant coefficients and provided f has a rather special form.** We shall study the general equation of order n here because it is no more difficult than the second-order equation. We shall assume that f is defined on $-\infty < t < \infty$ and has at most a finite number of linearly independent derivatives. This is equivalent to assuming that f must satisfy some homogeneous linear differential equation with constant coefficients. (Why? Think of the definition of linear dependence of the functions $f, f', \ldots, f^{(m)}$ for some $m \geq 1$.) **Therefore, it must in** fact be assumed that $f(t)$ is a linear combination of terms of the form

$$t^k e^{mt}$$

where $k \geq 0$ is an integer and m is a real or complex number including possibly zero. By the principle of superposition, Section 3.2 (see Exercise 6, p. 69) we may as well assume that $f(t)$ consists of only one term of the form

$$f(t) = ct^k e^{mt}$$

where c is a constant. (Why?) **Before we proceed we stress again that the method we are about to explore further only works under the special conditions stated above. If these conditions are not satisfied, the method of variation of constants is applicable.**

For simplicity of exposition let us first assume that $f(t) = ce^{mt}$ where m is a real or complex number, possibly zero, and let us consider $L_n(y) = ce^{mt}$, where $L_n(y) = y^{(n)} + a_1 y^{(n-1)} + \cdots + a_{n-1} y' + a_n y$. Our task is to find a particular solution ψ_p of $L_n(y) = ce^{mt}$ and then to apply Theorem 3.12 to find all solutions. By an elementary calculation (see Section 3.4, p. 83)

$$L_n(e^{zt}) = p_n(z) e^{zt}$$

where $p_n(z)$ is the characteristic polynomial

$$p_n(z) = z^n + a_1 z^{n-1} + \cdots + a_{n-1} z + a_n$$

We therefore try as a solution of the equation $L_n(y) = ce^{mt}$ the function $\psi_p(t) = (c/p_n(m)) e^{mt}$ provided m is not a root of $p_n(z) = 0$ (that is, provided $p_n(m) \neq 0$). Indeed, if $p_n(m) \neq 0$ we have by the linearity of L_n

$$L_n(\psi_p) = L_n\left(\frac{c}{p_n(m)} e^{mt}\right) = \frac{c}{p_n(m)} L_n(e^{mt})$$

$$= \frac{c}{p_n(m)} \cdot p_n(m) e^{mt} = ce^{mt}$$

Note that the assumption that m is not a root of $p_n(z) = 0$ is equivalent to the assumption that e^{mt} is not a solution of $L_n(y) = 0$. In practice we could try as a solution $\psi_p(t) = Ae^{mt}$, A a constant (undetermined coefficient) to be determined; then in order to have $L_n(Ae^{mt}) = ce^{mt}$, we must have $L_n(Ae^{mt}) = Ap_n(m)e^{mt} = ce^{mt}$ and therefore $A = (c/p_n(m))$, if $p_n(m) \neq 0$. Having a particular solution, we then apply Theorem 3.12 to find all solutions.

Example 2. $y'' - 9y = e^t$.
Here we try $\psi_p = Ae^t$. Then $\psi_p'' - 9\psi_p = Ae^t - 9Ae^t = -8Ae^t$. Then $\psi_p'' - 9\psi_p = e^t$ if and only if $-8A = 1$ or $A = -\frac{1}{8}$. Thus $\psi_p = -\frac{1}{8}e^t$ and by Theorem 3.11 every solution has the form $\psi = c_1e^{3t} + c_2e^{-3t} - \frac{1}{8}e^t$.

Example 3. $y'' - 9y = \sin 2t$.
Since $\sin 2t = \text{Im } e^{2it}$, we consider first $y'' - 9y = e^{2it}$ and try $\psi_p = Ae^{2it}$. Then $\psi_p' = 2iAe^{2it}$, $\psi_p'' = -4Ae^{2it}$. Thus $\psi_p'' - 9\psi_p = (-4A - 9A)e^{2it} = e^{2it}$ if and only if $A = -\frac{1}{13}$. Therefore $\psi_p = (-\frac{1}{13})e^{2it}$. By Theorem 3.6 (p. 85), $(-\frac{1}{13}) \sin 2t$ is a particular solution of $y'' - 9y = \sin 2t$ and the general solution has the form $\psi(t) = c_1e^{3t} + c_2e^{-3t} - (\frac{1}{13}) \sin 2t$.

Returning to the equation $L_n(y) = ce^{mt}$, let us now suppose that e^{mt} is a solution of $L_n(y) = 0$ but te^{mt} is not; this is equivalent to assuming that m is a simple root of the algebraic equation $p_n(z) = 0$. This means that $p_n(m) = 0$, but $p_n'(m) \neq 0$ (see Appendix 3). We have

$$L_n(e^{zt}) = p_n(z)e^{zt}$$

Since $(\partial/\partial z)L_n(e^{zt}) = p_n'(z)e^{zt} + p_n(z)e^{zt}$, and since $(\partial/\partial z)L_n(e^{zt}) = L_n(\partial e^{zt}/\partial z) = L_n(te^{zt})$ we see that $L_n(te^{zt}) = p_n'(z)e^{zt} + te^{zt}p_n(z)$. (Compare with the case of equal roots in Section 3.4, p. 90.) Therefore, $L_n(te^{mt}) = p_n'(m)e^{mt}$, which suggests that if m is a simple root of $p_n(z) = 0$, the equation $L_n(y) = ce^{mt}$ has a particular solution of the form

$$\psi_p = Ate^{mt}$$

for some constant A. Indeed, we see that $\psi_p = (c/p_n'(m))te^{mt}$. Of course, in practice we simply would assume a solution of the form Ate^{mt}, substitute and determine A.

Example 4.   Find a particular solution of $y'' - 9y = e^{3t}$. We observe that e^{3t} is a solution of $y'' - 9y = 0$, but te^{3t} is not and therefore we guess a particular solution of the form $\psi_p(t) = Ate^{3t}$. Then

$$\psi_p'(t) = 3Ate^{3t} + Ae^{3t}$$
$$\psi_p''(t) = 9Ate^{3t} + 6Ae^{3t}$$

Therefore, $\psi_p''(t) - 9\psi_p(t) = 6Ae^{3t} = e^{3t}$ if and only if $A = \frac{1}{6}$. Thus $\psi_p(t) = (t/6)e^{3t}$ is a particular solution of $y'' - 9y = e^{3t}$.

Similarly **if m is a double root of** $p_n(z) = 0$, then $p_n(m) = p_n'(m) = 0$, but $p_n''(m) \neq 0$. This implies that e^{mt}, te^{mt} are solutions of $L_n(y) = 0$, but t^2e^{mt} is not, and this in turn suggests assuming a solution of $L_n(y) = e^{mt}$ of the form $\psi_p = At^2e^{mt}$ for some constant A. As before, one determines A by direct substitution.

In general, if m is a k-fold root of $p_n(z) = 0$ $(k \leq n)$, then $p_n(m) = p_n'(m) = \cdots = p_n^{(k-1)}(m) = 0$, but $p^{(k)}(m) \neq 0$. This implies that e^{mt}, $te^{mt}, \ldots, t^{k-1}e^{mt}$ are solutions of $L_n(y) = 0$ but t^ke^{mt} is not. Thus in this case one would "judiciously guess" a solution ψ_p of $L_n(y) = e^{mt}$ of the form $\psi_p = At^ke^{mt}$ and substitute to determine the constant A.

We turn now to the more general equation $L_n(y) = ct^ke^{mt}$, k a positive integer, c a constant. A straightforward but tedious calculation shows that

$$L(t^ke^{mt}) = p_n(m)t^ke^{mt} + p_n'(m)kt^{k-1}e^{mt} + k(k-1)t^{k-2}p_n''(m)e^{mt} + \cdots$$

where there are at most a total of $k + 1$ nonzero terms. Therefore when guessing the form of a particular solution it is clear that we cannot now merely try $\psi_p(t) = At^ke^{mt}$, but must include terms t^je^{mt} $(j = 0, 1, \ldots, k)$ which will serve to cancel out the terms we get in the above calculation. Thus we try $\psi_p(t) = A_1e^{mt} + A_2te^{mt} + \cdots + A_{k+1}t^ke^{mt}$ and find the A_j's by substitution.

Example 5.   Consider the equation $y'' - 9y = t^3e^t$.
Here $k = 3$, $m = 1$ (and $m = 1$ is not a root of $m^2 - 9 = 0$). In this case we try $\psi_p(t) = A_1t^3e^t + A_2t^2e^t + A_3te^t + A_4e^t$, where the constants A_1, A_2, A_3, A_4 are determined by direct substitution.

●**EXERCISE**

10. Find the general solution of $y'' - 9y = t^3e^t$.

As in the case $k = 0$ considered previously, additional complications arise if now one or more of the functions e^{mt}, $te^{mt}, \ldots, t^ke^{mt}$ is a solution of the homogeneous equation $L_n(y) = 0$. The "judicious guess" based on the above considerations is to multiply each one of these functions by **the lowest power** of t, say t^j, such that none of the resulting functions is a solution of the homogeneous equation $L_n(y) = 0$; then assume a solution of the form $\psi_p(t) = A_1t^je^{mt} + A_2t^{j+1}e^{mt} + \cdots + A_{k+1}t^{k+j}e^{mt}$, and determine the constants $A_1, A_2, \ldots, A_{k+1}$ by direct substitution in the equation

$$L_n(y) = ct^k e^{mt}.$$

Example 6.   Consider the equation $y'' - 9y = t^3 e^{-3t}$.

Here e^{-3t} is a solution of $y'' - 9y = 0$, but te^{-3t} is not. Therefore, to find ψ_p we try $\psi_p(t) = A_1 te^{-3t} + A_2 t^2 e^{-3t} + A_3 t^3 e^{-3t} + A_4 t^4 e^{-3t}$. (Note there is no point in including also a term $A_0 e^{-3t}$ since e^{-3t} is a solution of the nonhomogeneous equation.)

•EXERCISES

11. Find the general solution of the equation $y'' - 9y = t^3 e^{-3t}$.

12. Examine the problems in Exercises 4 and 9 which were done by variation of constants and decide which ones could be done by the method of judicious guessing and which ones could not. Carry out the details of those that could.

13. Find the general solution of each of the following:
   (a) $y'' + 4y = \sin 2t$.
   (b) $y'' - 4y = 2e^{-2t}$.
   (c) $y''' + 3y'' + 3y' + y = t^2 - e^{-t}$.
   (d) $y'' - 4y = te^t$.
   (e) $y'' - 4y = te^{2t}$.
   (f) $y'' - 4y = t^2 e^{2t}$.

14. Consider the equation $y'' + k^2 y = 2k \sin kt$, and show that all solutions are **unbounded as** $t \to \infty$. This phenomenon will always occur if the non-homogeneous term is a sine or cosine function which is a solution of the homogeneous equation (physically speaking if the "applied" frequency is a "natural" frequency of the system).

3.9   Resonance

Consider the undamped mass-spring system with a given periodic external force. The equation of motion is (3.29) with $a = 0$. For convenience, we write this equation in the form

$$y'' + k_0^2 y = A \cos kt \tag{3.36}$$

We call k_0 the natural frequency of the system and k the applied frequency. We can solve the equation (3.36) by the method of judicious guessing. If $k \neq k_0$, a particular solution is given by

$$\psi_p(t) = \frac{A}{k_0^2 - k^2} \cos kt \tag{3.37}$$

•**EXERCISE**

 1. Verify the particular solution (3.37) of the equation (3.36) with $k \neq k_0$.

Observe that if the applied frequency k is close to the natural frequency k_0, then the particular solution given by (3.37) represents an oscillation with large amplitude.   If we think of k_0 as fixed and let, in (3.37), the applied frequency k approach k_0, then the amplitude of the oscillation becomes unbounded.   This phenomenon is called **resonance**.   If $k = k_0$, a particular solution cannot be obtained from (3.37).   However, returning to (3.36) with $k = k_0$, we obtain a particular solution

$$Y_p(t) = \frac{A}{2k_0} t \sin k_0 t$$

of the equation $y'' + k_0^2 y = A \cos k_0 t$.

•**EXERCISE**

 2. Find the above particular solution.   (See also Exercise 14, Section 3.8 (p. 112).)

Thus we see that in the case of resonance, the amplitude of the particular solution (often called a forced oscillation) is not constant, but is an unbounded function of t.   This phenomenon predicted by the model (3.36) does not occur in a real physical system because of the presence of friction, which causes damped oscillations rather than periodic solutions in the homogeneous case.   In the presence of friction the equation (3.36) is replaced by

$$y'' + ay' + k_0^2 y = A \cos kt \qquad (a > 0) \tag{3.38}$$

•**EXERCISES**

 3. Find a particular solution of the equation (3.38).

 4. Show that as k approaches k_0, the amplitude of the particular solution found in Exercise 3 increases, but remains bounded if $a > 0$.

The situation described in Exercise 4 is of practical importance in tuning radio circuits, where the object is to adjust the applied frequency to resonance, thereby maximizing the amplitude.   In other situations, the object is to avoid resonance.

•MISCELLANEOUS EXERCISES

1. For each of the following differential equations determine the largest intervals on which a unique solution is certain to exist as an application of Theorem 3.1.   In each problem it is assumed that you are given initial conditions of the form $\phi(t_0) = y_0$, $\phi'(t_0) = z_0$.

(a) $ty'' + y = t^2$.

(b) $t^2(t - 3)y'' + y' = 0$.

(c) $y'' + \sqrt{t}\, y = 0$.

(d) $(1 + t^2)y'' - y' + ty = \cos t$.

(e) $e'y'' - \sin ty' + y = t^3$.

(f) $y'' - \log |t|y = 0$.

2. Decide which of the following sets of functions are linearly dependent and which are linearly independent on the given interval.   Justify your answer in each case.

(a) $\phi_1(t) = e^t$, $\phi_2(t) = e^{t+1}$ $(-\infty < t < \infty)$.

(b) $\phi_1(t) = e^{2t}$, $\phi_2(t) = e^t$ $(-\infty < t < \infty)$.

(c) $\phi_1(t) = \sqrt{t}$, $\phi_2(t) = t$ $(0 < t < \infty)$.

(d) $\phi_1(t) = 1$, $\phi_2(t) = e^t$, $\phi_3(t) = e^{-t}$ $(-\infty < t < \infty)$.

(e) $\phi_1(t) = t^2$, $\phi_2(t) = t^2 \sin t$ $(-1 \le t \le 1)$.

(f) $\phi_1(t) = 1$, $\phi_2(t) = \begin{cases} 0 & (t \le 0) \\ t & (t > 0) \end{cases}$, $\phi_3(t) = \begin{cases} 0 & (t \le 0) \\ t^2 & (t > 0) \end{cases}$, $(-\infty < t \le -1)$.

(g) $\phi_1(t) = 1$, $\phi_2(t) = \begin{cases} 0 & (t \le 0) \\ t & (t > 0) \end{cases}$, $\phi_3(t) = \begin{cases} 0 & (t \le 0) \\ t^2 & (t > 0) \end{cases}$, $(-\infty < t < \infty)$.

(h) $\phi_1(t) = t^2$, $\phi_2(t) = t^4$, $\phi_3(t) = t^6$, $\phi_4(t) = t^{10}$ $(-1 \le t \le 1)$.

3. (a) Let ϕ_1 and ϕ_2 be solutions of $L(y) = y'' - 4ty' + (4t^2 - 2)y = 0$ on the interval $-\infty < t < \infty$, satisfying the initial conditions $\phi_1(1) = 1$, $\phi_1'(1) = \frac{1}{3}$, $\phi_2(1) = 3$, $\phi_2'(1) = 1$.   Are these solutions linearly independent on $-\infty < t < \infty$?   Justify your answer.

(b) Show that $\psi_1(t) = e^{t^2}$ is a solution of the equation $L(y) = 0$ and find a second linearly independent solution on $-\infty < t < \infty$.

(c) Find the solutions ϕ_1 and ϕ_2 in part (a).

4. Given that the equation

$$ty'' - (2t + 1)y' + 2y = 0   (t > 0)$$

has a solution of the form e^{ct} for some c, find the general solution.   [*Hint:* First find what c must be.]

5. In each of the following, let $\phi_1(t)$ and $\phi_2(t)$ be solutions of the differential equation

$$L(y) = y'' + p(t)y' + q(t)y = 0$$

on some interval I.

(a) If $\phi_1(t_0) = \phi_2(t_0) = 0$ for some t_0 in I, show that ϕ_1 and ϕ_2 cannot form a fundamental set of solutions on I.

(b) If ϕ_1 and ϕ_2 both have a maximum or a minimum at some point t_1 in I, show that ϕ_1 and ϕ_2 cannot form a fundamental set of solutions on I.

(c) Let ϕ_1 and ϕ_2 form a fundamental set of solutions on I which both have an inflection point at some point t_2 in I. Show that $p(t_2) = q(t_2) = 0$.

(d) Let ϕ_1 and ϕ_2 form a fundamental set of solutions on I. Show that $\psi_1 = \phi_1 + \phi_2$, $\psi_2 = \phi_1 - 2\phi_2$ also form a fundamental set of solutions on I.

6. Find the general solution of each of the following differential equations.

(a) $y'' + y = \operatorname{cosec} t \cot t$ $(0 < t < \pi)$.

(b) $t^2y'' + ty' + 4y = \sin \log |t|$.

(c) $t^3y''' - 3t^2y'' + 6ty' - 6y = 0$.

(d) $y'' - 6y' + 9y = e^t$.

(e) $y'' - 6y' + 9y = t^2e^{3t}$.

(f) $t^2y'' - 3ty' + 4y = \log |t|$.

(g) $y^{(8)} + 8y^{(4)} + 16y = 0$.

(h) $t^2y'' + ty' - 2iy = 0$.

(i) $y^{(4)} - 2y'' + y = e^t + \sin t$.

(j) $y''' + y' = \tan t$ $(0 < t < \pi/2)$.

(k) $y^{(4)} + y = g(t)$ g continuous.

(l) $y'' + y = h(t)$, where

$$h(t) = t \quad (0 \le t \le \pi) \qquad h(t) = \pi \cos(\pi - t) \quad (\pi < t \le 2\pi)$$

and h is periodic with period 2π.

7. (a) One solution of the equation

$$L(y) = t^2y'' + ty' + (t^2 - \tfrac{1}{4})y = 0 \qquad (t > 0)$$

is $t^{-1/2} \sin t$. Find the general solution of the equation $L(y) = 3t^{1/2} \sin t$ $(t > 0)$.

(b) Repeat part (a) for the equation

$$2ty'' + (1 - 4t)y' + (2t - 1)y = e^t$$

given that e^t is one solution of the homogeneous equation.

8. Make the change of variable $y = u(t)v(t)$ in the equation

$$y'' + p(t)y' + q(t)y = 0$$

and choose the function $v(t)$ to make the coefficient of u' in the resulting equation for u equal to zero. Show that the equation for u then becomes

$$u'' - \tfrac{1}{4}\{[p(t)]^2 + 2p'(t) - 4q(t)\}u = 0$$

9. Apply the change of variable suggested in Exercise 8 to the equation

$$t^2 y'' + t y' + (t^2 - n^2) y = 0$$

and find the resulting equation.

10. (a) Show that the change of variable $y = u'/q(t)u$ reduces the nonlinear first-order equation

$$y' + p(t)y + q(t)y^2 = r(t)$$

known as the Riccati equation, to the second-order linear equation

$$u'' + \left[p(t) - \frac{q'(t)}{q(t)} \right] u' - r(t)q(t)u = 0$$

(b) Apply this procedure to solve the equation

$$t^2 y' + t y + t^2 y^2 = 1$$

11. A 50-gram mass can stretch a spring 2 cm under its own weight. If the spring satisfies Hooke's law and there is no friction or external force, determine the frequency with which the mass will oscillate. That is, assume that the hypotheses (a), (b), (c), (d) of Section 1.1 (p. 3) are satisfied. [*Hint:* The spring constant is determined from the information in the first sentence. Note also that $g = 980$.]

12. If the mass–spring system in Exercise 11 is oscillating with an amplitude of 5 cm, find the maximum velocity. [*Hint:* Consider the initial conditions $\phi(0) = 5$, $\phi'(0) = 0$.]

13. Suppose the mass–spring system in Exercise 11 is at rest in an equilibrium position at time $t = 0$, and a force $500 \cos 2t$ is applied. For what value of t will the displacement first equal one centimeter?

14. A spring is stretched 15 cm by an 8 kg weight. Suppose a 4-kg weight is attached to the spring and released 30 cm below the point of equilibrium with an initial velocity of 180 cm per second directed downward. Determine the motion of the system, assuming that the hypotheses (a), (b), (c), (d) of Section 1.1 (p. 3) are satisfied.

15. Determine the motion of the system in Exercise 14, but assuming hypothesis (d') (p. 5) in place of (d), with air resistance 1000 dynes when the velocity is one centimeter per second. (Note that $g = 980$.)

16. Consider the mass–spring system of Exercise 14, but with an additional external force $5 \cos 2t$. Determine the motion.

17. A body of mass m falls from rest from a height h above the surface of the earth. Assume that the only forces acting on the body are the force of gravity and a force of air resistance which is c times the velocity of the body. Find

the motion of the body, and show that its velocity approaches the limit mg/c as $t \rightarrow \infty$.

18. The bob of a simple pendulum of length 2 feet is displaced so that the pendulum makes an angle of 5° with the vertical and released.
    (a) Find the angle θ which the pendulum makes with the vertical as a function of time.
    (b) Determine the frequency of the vibration.
    (c) Calculate the distance traveled by the pendulum bob during one period.
    (d) Find the velocity and acceleration of the bob at the centre of its path. (Assume that the motion is governed by equation (1.10), p. 12.)

19. A simple pendulum of unit mass vibrates in a medium in which the damping is proportional to velocity. If the pendulum bob passes through the equilibrium position $\theta = 0$ at $t = 0$ with velocity v_0, show that the angle θ is given by

$$\theta(t) = \frac{v_0}{\omega} e^{-kt/2} \sin \omega t$$

where $\omega = (g/L - k^{2/4})^{1/2}$, k is the damping constant, and L is the length of the pendulum. Find k if the distance traveled during one complete vibration is half the distance traveled during the previous vibration. Use the linearized version of equation (1.9), p. 11.

20. The current I in amperes in an electrical circuit with resistance R ohms, inductance L henrys, and capacitance C farads in series is governed by the equation

$$LI'' + RI' + \frac{1}{C}I = E'(t)$$

where $E(t)$ is the applied voltage. Suppose the applied voltage is a constant E_0.
    (a) Show that the current decreases exponentially if $CR^2 > 4L$.
    (b) Find the current if $CR^2 = 4L$ and $I(0) = 0$, $I'(0) = E_0/L$.
    (c) Find the current if $CR^2 < 4L$ and $I(0) = 0$, $I'(0) = E_0/L$.

21. Consider the circuit of Exercise 20. Find the current if

$$E(t) = \begin{cases} 0 & t \leq 0 \\ E_0 \sin \alpha t & t > 0 \end{cases}$$

assuming $I(0) = 0$, $I'(0) = 0$.

22. Find the current in an electrical circuit with inductance and capacitance, but no resistance, and an applied voltage $E(t)$ given by

$$E(t) = \begin{cases} t \sin \frac{\pi}{2} t & (0 \leq t \leq 1) \\ 1 & (t > 1) \end{cases}$$

with $I(0) = 0$, $I'(0) = 0$.

23. Show that the solutions of the differential equation

$$y'' + py' + qy = 0$$

(p and q positive constants) are oscillations with amplitudes which decrease exponentially when $p^2 < 4q$ (light damping) and decrease exponentially without oscillating if $p^2 > 4q$ (over damping). How do they behave if $p^2 = 4q$ (critical damping)?

24. Determine a particular solution of the differential equation

$$y'' + py' + qy = A \cos kt$$

of the form $\phi(t) = B \cos (kt - \alpha)$. Show that the amplitude of the oscillation B is a maximum if $k = (\dot{q} - p^2/2)^{1/2}$ (called the resonant frequency) provided $p^2 < 4q$. What happens in the case $p^2 \geq 4q$? Show that at resonance the amplitude of the oscillation is inversely proportional to the damping p.

25. Consider the differential equation

$$my'' + ky = f(t)$$

where

$$f(t) = \begin{cases} F_0/\epsilon & (0 \leq t \leq \epsilon) \\ 0 & (t > \epsilon) \end{cases}$$

Find the solution $\phi(t)$ such that $\phi(0) = 0$, $\phi'(0) = 0$. Is ϕ a solution in the sense of Theorem 1.2 (p. 27)? Give a physical interpretation of this problem and its solution, thinking of ϵ as a small positive constant. Discuss the behavior of the solution as $\epsilon \to 0$; does $\lim_{\epsilon \to 0+} \phi'(t)$ exist for all t?

26. A sphere of radius R floating half submerged in a liquid is set into vibration. If y is the vertical displacement of the diametral plane of the sphere from the equilibrium position, show that

$$y'' = -\frac{3g}{2}\left[\frac{y}{R} - \frac{1}{3}\left(\frac{y}{R}\right)^3\right]$$

Show that for small vibrations (neglecting the nonlinear term) the sphere vibrates with frequency $1/2\pi(3g/2R)^{1/2}$.

Chapter 4 | SERIES SOLUTIONS OF LINEAR DIFFERENTIAL EQUATIONS

4.1 Introduction

In many mathematical and physical problems, we are led to differential equations which cannot be solved in closed form. (By a solution in closed form we mean a solution expressed in terms of elementary functions, that is, polynomials, rational functions, exponentials, logarithms, trigonometric functions, etc.) For many such differential equations it is possible to prove that the solution can be expanded in a power series, and to calculate the coefficients of this power series. The purpose of this chapter is to give an exposition of these methods of solution. While most of the chapter is devoted to linear differential equations, we start with a very simple method which is applicable to some nonlinear equations. It is, however, usually cumbersome to apply unless one needs only the first few terms of the series solution.

Example 1. We begin by returning to the differential equation

$$y'' = - \sin y - y' \tag{4.1}$$

which represents a possible model for a damped pendulum (see Section 1.2, p. 11), and which cannot be solved in terms of elementary functions. Let us try to find the solution ϕ of (4.1) which satisfies the initial conditions

$$\phi(0) = \frac{\pi}{4} \qquad \phi'(0) = 0 \tag{4.2}$$

From Theorem 1.2 (p. 27), we know that the equation (4.1) has a unique solution satisfying the initial conditions (4.2). Moreover, it can be shown that this solution can be expanded in a convergent power series in powers of t about $t = 0$.* **Assuming this fact, how can we find the coefficients of this power series?** Recall first that if ϕ can be expanded in a power series about $t = 0$, then ϕ must have derivatives of all orders at $t = 0$ and ϕ has the Taylor series expansion

$$\phi(t) = \phi(0) + \phi'(0)t + \frac{\phi''(0)}{2!}\,t^2 + \cdots + \frac{\phi^{(n)}(0)}{n!}\,t^n + \cdots$$

where the series on the right side converges to $\phi(t)$ in some interval $|t| < r$. Thus we need only evaluate the solution and its derivatives at $t = 0$ in order to find the expansion (assuming that there is one).

From (4.2) we already know that the function ϕ must satisfy $\phi(0) = \pi/4$, $\phi'(0) = 0$. In terms of the graph of ϕ, this means that we know that $y = \phi(t)$ passes through the point $(0, \pi/4)$ with slope 0. Since ϕ is a solution of (4.1), we know that

$$\phi''(t) = -\sin\phi(t) - \phi'(t) \qquad (t \geq 0) \tag{4.3}$$

In particular, we can set $t = 0$ in (4.3), and find $\phi''(0) = -\sin\phi(0) - \phi'(0) = -\sin(\pi/4) - 0 = -\sqrt{2}/2$. Since $\phi''(0)$ is negative, this tells us that the graph of ϕ is concave downward near $t = 0$, and the value $-\sqrt{2}/2$ would enable us to compute its curvature there (see Figure 4.1). How can we find the values of the higher derivatives of ϕ at the origin?

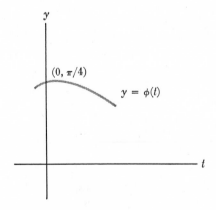

Figure 4.1

---

* This follows from an extension of Theorem 4.1 (p. 129) below to nonlinear equations, but will not be studied here.

Differentiating the identity (4.3), we obtain

$$\phi^{(3)}(t) = -[\cos \phi(t)]\phi'(t) - \phi''(t) \qquad (t \geq 0) \tag{4.4}$$

Therefore $\phi^{(3)}(0) = -[\cos (\pi/4)](0) - (-\sqrt{2}/2) = \sqrt{2}/2$. Here it should be noticed that we need the value of $\phi''(0)$ that we found just above. In exactly the same way, we can differentiate (4.4), and obtain

$$\phi^{(4)}(t) = [\sin \phi(t)][\phi'(t)]^2 - [\cos \phi(t)]\phi''(t) - \phi^{(3)}(t)$$

and therefore $\phi^{(4)}(0) = (\sqrt{2}/2)(0)^2 - (\sqrt{2}/2)(-\sqrt{2}/2) - \sqrt{2}/2 = (1 - \sqrt{2})/2$. Continuing this procedure, we could determine the values of **all** the derivatives of ϕ at the point $t = 0$. Therefore, the expansion of the solution ϕ begins with the terms

$$\phi(t) = \pi/4 - \frac{\sqrt{2}}{2}\frac{t^2}{2!} + \frac{\sqrt{2}}{2}\frac{t^3}{3!} + \frac{1 - \sqrt{2}}{2}\frac{t^4}{4!} + \cdots$$

•EXERCISES

1. Continuing with Example 1, find the numerical values of $\phi^{(5)}(0)$ and $\phi^{(6)}(0)$.

2. Let ψ be the (unique) solution of (4.1) that obeys the initial conditions $\psi(0) = 0$, $\psi'(0) = 1$. Find the values of the first four derivatives of ψ at $t = 0$ and write down the first few terms of the power series expansion of ψ about $t = 0$, assuming that it has one.

3. Consider the first-order differential equation $y' = t^2 + y^3$. If ϕ is the solution satisfying the initial condition $\phi(1) = 0$, find the values of $\phi'(1)$, $\phi''(1)$, $\phi^{(3)}(1)$, and $\phi^{(4)}(1)$. Also, write down the first few terms of the power series expansion of ϕ about $t = 1$, assuming that it has.one.

4. Consider the solution ϕ of the first-order equation $y' + y = 0$ such that $\phi(0) = 1$. Use the above method to find the power series expansion, if there is one, of ϕ. Can you sum this series and verify that the sum represents a solution?

5. Repeat Exercise 4 for the solution ϕ of the differential equation $y'' + y = 0$ such that $\phi(0) = 1$, $\phi'(0) = 1$.

While the above procedure can sometimes be used, it presents several difficulties. As Example 1 above shows, each successive derivative is usually more difficult to evaluate. Unless one can compute a formula for $\phi^{(n)}(0)$ for every n, it is impossible to verify the convergence of the resulting series and thereby justify the method. This also is demonstrated by Example 1. Another difficulty that can arise is illustrated by the following example.

Example 2. Consider the differential equation $y' = f(t)$, where f is defined by

$$f(t) = \begin{cases} \exp(-1/t^2) & (t \neq 0) \\ 0 & (t = 0) \end{cases}$$

The function f has derivatives of all orders at the origin and $f^{(n)}(0) = 0$ $(n = 0, 1, 2, \ldots)$. If ϕ is the solution of $y' = f(t)$ such that $\phi(0) = 0$, and if ϕ can be expanded in a convergent power series about $t = 0$, then every coefficient in this power series must be zero, and ϕ must be the zero function. However, the zero function does not satisfy the differential equation.

We will study systematically methods of obtaining power series solutions which avoid the difficulties illustrated by these examples. **We will limit ourselves to linear equations.** We propose to concentrate on second-order equations since they are of the greatest interest for physical applications and since they exhibit most of the important phenomena.

4.2 Review of Power Series

Every power series $\Sigma_{n=0}^{\infty} c_n t^n$ has a radius of convergence $R \geq 0$. (If $R = 0$, the facts stated below are meaningless.) The numbers c_n as well as t can be real or complex. The following properties hold:

(i) The series $\Sigma_{n=0}^{\infty} c_n t^n$ converges absolutely for $|t| < R$.

(ii) If we let $f(t) = \Sigma_{n=0}^{\infty} c_n t^n$ for $|t| < R$, then f is a continuous function and f has derivatives of all orders for $|t| < R$. Its derivative f' is the sum of the power series $\Sigma_{n=0}^{\infty} n c_n t^{n-1}$, and the differentiated series also has radius of convergence R. More generally, for any $k \geq 1$,

$$f^{(k)}(t) = \sum_{n=k}^{\infty} n(n-1) \cdots (n-k+1) c_n t^{n-k} \qquad \text{for } |t| < R$$

(iii) If a and b are in the interval of convergence, then $\int_a^b f(s)\, ds = \Sigma_{n=0}^{\infty} c_n \int_a^b s^n\, ds$. In particular $\int_0^t f(s)\, ds = \Sigma_{n=0}^{\infty} c_n \int_0^t s^n\, ds = \Sigma_{n=0}^{\infty} \dfrac{c_n}{n+1} t^{n+1}$, which is a power series also having radius of convergence R.

(iv) Identity theorem for power series: If $\tilde{\Sigma}_{n=0}^{\infty} d_n t^n$ is another power series with radius of convergence $\tilde{R} > 0$, and if $\Sigma_{n=0}^{\infty} d_n t^n = \Sigma_{n=0}^{\infty} c_n t^n$ on some interval in which both series converge, then $d_n = c_n$ for all n.   **In particular, if the sum of a power series is zero for all t in some interval, then every coefficient in the power series must be zero.**

(v) Convergent power series can be added by adding corresponding terms.   More precisely, if $f(t) = \Sigma_{n=0}^{\infty} c_n t^n$ and $g(t) = \Sigma_{n=0}^{\infty} d_n t^n$, then $f(t) + g(t) = \Sigma_{n=0}^{\infty} (c_n + d_n) t^n$, wherever the power series for f and g both converge.

(vi) Convergent power series can be multiplied by multiplying individual terms and grouping terms containing the same power of t. Specifically, if $f(t) = \Sigma_{n=0}^{\infty} c_n t^n$ and $g(t) = \Sigma_{n=0}^{\infty} d_n t^n$, then $f(t) g(t) = \Sigma_{n=0}^{\infty} p_n t^n$, where $p_n = c_n d_0 + c_{n-1} d_1 + \cdots + c_0 d_n$.   The series $\Sigma_{n=0}^{\infty} p_n t^n$ converges for all values of t for which the power series for f and g both converge.

We remark that properties (i)–(vi) hold equally well for power series of the form $\Sigma_{n=0}^{\infty} c_n (t - a)^n$, with the interval of convergence $|t - a| < R$. To simplify the notation we introduce the following terminology.

Definition.   *A function f defined on an interval containing the point $t = a$ is said to be analytic at $t = a$ if f can be expanded in a Taylor series $f(t) = \Sigma_{n=0}^{\infty} c_n (t - a)^n$ with a positive radius of convergence.*

Note that if f is expanded in such a power series, the coefficients are given by $c_k = f^{(k)}(a)/k!$, as can be verified by using property (ii) and then setting $t = a$.

•EXERCISE

1. Determine the values of t, if any, at which the following functions **fail** to be analytic: $\sin t$, $1/t$, $1/(t - 7)$, $1/(t^2 + 1)$, $(t - 2)/(5t + 4)(t - 3)$.

The ratio test is a useful and simple method of determining the radius of convergence of a power series.

Ratio Test

Consider the power series $\Sigma_{n=0}^{\infty} c_n (t - a)^n$.   If $\lim_{n \to \infty} |c_{n+1}/c_n|$ exists and has the value ρ, then the power series has radius of convergence $R = 1/\rho$ if $\rho \neq 0$, and $R = \infty$ if $\rho = 0$, and the power series converges absolutely for $|t - a| < R$.

We remind the reader that the end points of the interval of convergence must be investigated separately.

Another useful method of estimating the radius of convergence of the power series $\Sigma_{n=0}^{\infty} c_n (t - a)^n$ is the following.

Comparison Test

If there exist constants $C_n \geq 0$ such that $|c_n| < C_n$ for $n = 0, 1, 2, \ldots$, and if $\Sigma_{n=0}^{\infty} C_n (t - a)^n$ converges for $|t - a| < R$, then $\Sigma_{n=0}^{\infty} c_n (t - a)^n$ also converges at least for $|t - a| < R$.

We will make frequent use of the following fact about analytic functions whose power series begins with different powers of $(t - a)$. We state the result for two functions, but the extension to any number of functions is obvious.

Lemma 4.1. *Let f and g be functions analytic at the point a, given by the power series*

$$f(t) = \sum_{n=p}^{\infty} c_n (t - a)^n \qquad g(t) = \sum_{n=q}^{\infty} d_n (t - a)^n$$

respectively. Suppose $p < q$ and $c_p \neq 0$, $d_q \neq 0$. (This ensures that the series for f begins with a term in $(t - a)^p$ and the series for g begins with a term in $(t - a)^q$.) Then the functions f and g are linearly independent on every interval I on which both their series expansions converge.

Proof. Suppose f and g are linearly dependent on I. Then there exist constants A and B, not both zero, such that

$$Af(t) + Bg(t) = A \sum_{n=p}^{\infty} c_n (t - a)^n + B \sum_{n=q}^{\infty} d_n (t - a)^n = 0$$

for every t in I. Using property (v), we may add these power series term-by-term. The resulting power series has the lowest order term $Ac_p (t - a)^p$ (since $p < q$). Using property (iv), we conclude that $A = 0$. But then

$$B \sum_{n=q}^{\infty} d_n (t - a)^n = 0$$

for every t in I, which implies $B = 0$, again by property (iv). Thus $A = B = 0$, which contradicts the hypothesis of linear dependence, and completes the proof. ∎

4.3   Second-Order Linear Equations with Analytic Coefficients

Before presenting a general theorem we study a specific problem.

Example 1.   Suppose we wish to find the solution ϕ of the differential equation

$$y'' - ty = 0 \qquad\qquad (4.5)$$

satisfying the initial conditions $\phi(0) = a$, $\phi'(0) = b$. The existence and uniqueness theorem for linear equations (Theorem 3.1, p. 65) tells us that this problem has a unique solution ϕ which exists for all t. However, no method of solution that we have studied will yield this solution in closed form. (We must ask the reader to accept this fact.)

The power series method begins with the assumption that the solution ϕ is analytic at $t = 0$. (If the initial conditions were given at $t = t_0$, we would begin by assuming that ϕ is analytic at $t = t_0$.) This assumption means that $\phi(t)$ can be expanded in a power series

$$\phi(t) = c_0 + c_1 t + \cdots + c_k t^k + \cdots = \sum_{k=0}^{\infty} c_k t^k \qquad (4.6)$$

which converges in some interval $|t| < A$, where the constant A is positive and to be determined. Our object is to determine the coefficients c_k in this power series so that ϕ satisfies the equation (4.5) and the initial conditions $\phi(0) = a$, $\phi'(0) = b$.

If the power series (4.6) represents a solution of (4.5), we must be able to differentiate it twice. Proceeding formally (that is, without worrying about convergence) for the present, we obtain

$$\phi'(t) = c_1 + 2c_2 t + \cdots + k c_k t^{k-1} + \cdots = \sum_{k=1}^{\infty} k c_k t^{k-1}$$

$$\phi''(t) = 2c_2 + 3 \cdot 2c_3 t + \cdots + k(k-1)c_k t^{k-2} + \cdots$$

$$= \sum_{k=2}^{\infty} k(k-1)c_k t^{k-2} \qquad (4.7)$$

Also,

$$t\phi(t) = c_0 t + c_1 t^2 + \cdots + c_k t^{k+1} + \cdots = \sum_{k=0}^{\infty} c_k t^{k+1} \qquad (4.8)$$

Using (4.7) and (4.8), we obtain

$$\begin{aligned}
\phi''(t) - t\phi(t) &= [2c_2 + 3 \cdot 2c_3 t + \cdots + k(k-1)c_k t^{k-2} + \cdots] \\
&\quad - [c_0 t + c_1 t^2 + \cdots + c_k t^{k+1} + \cdots] \\
&= 2c_2 + (3 \cdot 2c_3 - c_0)t + \cdots \\
&\qquad\qquad\qquad + \{k(k-1)c_k - c_{k-3}\}t^{k-2} + \cdots \\
&= 2c_2 + \sum_{k=3}^{\infty} \{k(k-1)c_k - c_{k-3}\}t^{k-2}
\end{aligned}$$

Before proceeding, we note that it is not necessary to write out the calculations as explicitly as we have done above. From (4.7) and (4.8) again, we have

$$\phi''(t) - t\phi(t) = \sum_{k=2}^{\infty} k(k-1)c_k t^{k-2} - \sum_{k=0}^{\infty} c_k t^{k+1} \tag{4.9}$$

To combine these series, we observe that the first one begins with a constant term while the second one begins with the term $c_0 t$. Therefore, we separate the constant term from the first series. We must also rewrite one of the two series in such a way that the general terms of both series contain the same power of t. To do this with the second series, we let $k + 1 = n - 2$, or $k = n - 3$. Then the second series is $\sum_{k=0}^{\infty} c_k t^{k+1} = \sum_{n=3}^{\infty} c_{n-3} t^{n-2}$. We also observe that the particular letter used for the index of summation is of no importance, and we may use k in place of n again if we wish. We rewrite (4.9) as

$$\begin{aligned}
\phi''(t) - t\phi(t) &= 2c_2 + \sum_{k=3}^{\infty} k(k-1)c_k t^{k-2} - \sum_{k=3}^{\infty} c_{k-3} t^{k-2} \\
&= 2c_2 + \sum_{k=3}^{\infty} \{k(k-1)c_k - c_{k-3}\}t^{k-2}
\end{aligned} \tag{4.10}$$

which is the same result as that obtained before.

Assuming that the operations which led to (4.10) are justified, we see that ϕ, represented by the series (4.6), is a solution of the differential equation (4.5) if and only if the c_k satisfy the relation

$$2c_2 + \sum_{k=3}^{\infty} \{k(k-1)c_k - c_{k-3}\}t^{k-2} = 0 \tag{4.11}$$

By the identity theorem for power series (property (iv), Section 4.2, p. 123), the coefficient of each power of t in (4.11) must vanish.   Therefore

$$2c_2 = 0 \qquad k(k-1)c_k - c_{k-3} = 0 \qquad (k = 3, 4, \ldots) \qquad (4.12)$$

Relations such as (4.12) are said to determine the coefficients c_n **recursively.**   Solving these in succession, we find

$$c_2 = 0 \qquad c_3 = \frac{1}{2 \cdot 3} c_0 \qquad c_4 = \frac{1}{3 \cdot 4} c_1 \qquad c_5 = \frac{1}{4 \cdot 5} c_2$$

$$c_6 = \frac{1}{5 \cdot 6} c_3 = \frac{1}{2 \cdot 3} \frac{1}{5 \cdot 6} c_0, \qquad c_7 = \frac{1}{6 \cdot 7} c_4 = \frac{1}{3 \cdot 4} \frac{1}{6 \cdot 7} c_1 \cdots$$

In general, we can describe the solution by the following formulas:

$$c_2 = 0 \qquad c_3 = \frac{1}{3!} c_0 \qquad\qquad\qquad c_4 = \frac{2}{4!} c_1$$

$$c_5 = 0 \qquad c_6 = \frac{(1)(4)}{6!} c_0 \qquad\qquad\qquad c_7 = \frac{(2)(5)}{7!} c_1$$

$$. \qquad\qquad . \qquad\qquad\qquad\qquad\qquad .$$
$$. \qquad\qquad . \qquad\qquad\qquad\qquad\qquad .$$
$$. \qquad\qquad . \qquad\qquad\qquad\qquad\qquad .$$

$$c_{3m+2} = 0 \; c_{3m} = \frac{(1)(4) \cdots (3m-2)}{(3m)!} c_0 \quad c_{3m+1} = \frac{(2)(5)(8) \cdots (3m-1)}{(3m+1)!} c_1$$

$$. \qquad\qquad . \qquad\qquad\qquad\qquad\qquad .$$
$$. \qquad\qquad . \qquad\qquad\qquad\qquad\qquad .$$
$$. \qquad\qquad . \qquad\qquad\qquad\qquad\qquad .$$

Thus all coefficients can be expressed in terms of c_0 and c_1; these in turn can be determined from the initial conditions.   If the solution ϕ of (4.5) is to satisfy the initial conditions $\phi(0) = a$, $\phi'(0) = b$, we find that $c_0 = a$, $c_1 = b$, and, therefore, a candidate for the solution is

$$\phi(t) = a \left[1 + \sum_{m=1}^{\infty} \frac{(1)(4) \cdots (3m-2)}{(3m)!} t^{3m} \right]$$

$$+ b \left[t + \sum_{m=1}^{\infty} \frac{(2)(5) \cdots (3m-1)}{(3m+1)!} t^{3m+1} \right] \qquad (4.13)$$

provided the above procedure can be justified.

● **EXERCISES**

1. Use mathematical induction to establish the formulas for c_{3m}, c_{3m+1}, and c_{3m+2} above.

2. Show how (4.13) is obtained from the formulas of Exercise 1.

3. Use the ratio test to prove that each infinite series in (4.13) converges for $|t| < \infty$.

Using the convergence of the series established in Exercise 3, we now observe that all the formal calculations beginning with (4.6) and leading to the solution (4.13) are fully justified for $-\infty < t < \infty$ by applying the properties of power series given in Section 4.2. Moreover, the solutions ϕ_1, ϕ_2 represented by the power series

$$\phi_1(t) = 1 + \sum_{m=1}^{\infty} \frac{(1)(4) \cdots (3m - 2)}{(3m)!} t^{3m}$$

$$\phi_2(t) = t + \sum_{m=1}^{\infty} \frac{(2)(5) \cdots (3m - 1)}{(3m + 1)!} t^{3m+1}$$

are linearly independent by Lemma 4.1 (p. 124). Therefore, if a and b are considered as arbitrary constants, the general solution of the equation (4.5) is given by $a\phi_1(t) + b\phi_2(t)$.

While the series in (4.13) converge for all t, only a small number of terms is needed to give a good approximation to the solution for small values of t. This is of practical importance in obtaining numerical approximations of solutions. For large values of t (say, $t = 10$) the series converges too slowly to be of practical value. In this case, however, the method of asymptotic expansions and numerical techniques are available which make use of the values computed from the power series for small t. Some of these techniques will be discussed in Section 4.11 and Chapter 8.

● **EXERCISES**

Employing the method used in solving the equation (4.5), find the solution ϕ of each of the following initial value problems.

4. $y'' + y = 0$, $\phi(0) = a$, $\phi'(0) = b$. (Write the solution in closed form if you recognize the resulting series.)

5. $y'' - ty' + y = 0$, $\phi(0) = 1$, $\phi'(0) = 0$.

6. $y'' - 2ty' + 2ny = 0$ (n an even integer, $n = 2m$), $\phi(0) = (-1)^m (2m)!/m!$, $\phi'(0) = 0$.

7. $y'' - 2ty' + 2ny = 0$ (n an odd integer, $n = 2m + 1$), $\phi(0) = 0$, $\phi'(0) = 2(-1)^m(2m + 1)!/m!$.

The solutions of Exercises 6 and 7 are called the Hermite polynomials.

• **EXERCISE**

8. For which values of α does the equation $y'' - 2ty' + \alpha y = 0$ have solutions which are polynomials in t? [*Hint:* Assume a power series solution and determine a condition on α which causes the series to terminate.]

The above examples suggest that second-order linear equations with analytic coefficients can be solved by power series. The reader should observe that in equation (4.5) as well as in all the equations considered in the exercises the coefficients are polynomials in t, hence analytic at every point, in particular at $t = 0$ where the initial conditions are imposed. In fact, the following theorem, which will be proved in Section 4.4, is true.

Theorem 4.1.   *Consider the differential equation*

$$y'' + p(t)y' + q(t)y = f(t)$$

If p, q, and f are analytic at t_0, then there is a unique solution ϕ satisfying the initial conditions $\phi(t_0) = a$, $\phi'(t_0) = b$. This solution is analytic at $t = t_0$ and its expansion $\phi(t) = \displaystyle\sum_{k=0}^{\infty} c_k(t - t_0)^k$ converges for at least those values of t for which the power series expansions of p, q, and f in powers of $(t - t_0)$ converge. The coefficients c_k may be determined recursively by direct substitution.

We remark that Theorem 4.1, as well as all other considerations in this chapter hold without change for the case when the independent variable t is complex; the proofs of the results are more meaningful in the complex domain.

The reader is warned that differential equations must be put in the form given above (with leading coefficient 1) before the theorem can be applied.

Example 2.   (Legendre equation.)   Consider the equation $(1 - t^2)y'' - 2ty' + \alpha(\alpha + 1)y = 0$, where α is a given constant. We wish to determine whether this differential equation has a series solution about $t = 0$. To apply the theorem, we must divide the equation by $1 - t^2$, and write it as

$$y'' - \frac{2t}{1 - t^2} y' + \frac{\alpha(\alpha + 1)}{1 - t^2} y = 0$$

which is certainly justified if $t \neq \pm 1$. Then

$$t_0 = 0 \qquad p(t) = -\frac{2t}{1 - t^2} \qquad q(t) = \frac{\alpha(\alpha + 1)}{1 - t^2} \qquad f(t) = 0$$

and p and q can be expanded in power series valid for $|t| < 1$.

$$p(t) = -\frac{2t}{1 - t^2} = -2t(1 + t^2 + t^4 + \cdots) = -2t \sum_{k=0}^{\infty} t^{2k}$$

$$q(t) = \frac{\alpha(\alpha + 1)}{1 - t^2} = \alpha(\alpha + 1)(1 + t^2 + t^4 + \cdots) = \alpha(\alpha + 1) \sum_{k=0}^{\infty} t^{2k}$$

Theorem 4.1 tells us that the Legendre equation has a unique analytic solution ϕ satisfying any pair of initial conditions $\phi(0) = a$, $\phi'(0) = b$, and the power series expansion of ϕ converges at least for $|t| < 1$.

•EXERCISES

9. Compute the first 5 terms of the series expansion of ϕ if the initial conditions are $\phi(0) = 1$, $\phi'(0) = 0$. Can you guess the general term? Show that if α is an even nonnegative integer, $\alpha = 2m$, then ϕ is a polynomial of degree $2m$. Compute this polynomial for $m = 0, 1, 2, 3$.

10. Repeat Exercise 9 for initial conditions $\phi(0) = 0$, $\phi'(0) = 1$. Show that if α is an odd positive integer $\alpha = 2m + 1$, then ϕ is a polynomial of degree $(2m + 1)$. Compute this polynomial for $m = 0, 1, 2$.

Note that although Theorem 4.1 tells us that the series expansion of ϕ converges for $|t| < 1$, it may actually converge on a larger interval. This is illustrated in Exercises 6–10 where the solution turns out to be a polynomial.

Exercises 9 and 10 above show that for each nonnegative integer n, the Legendre equation $(1 - t^2)y'' - 2ty' + n(n + 1)y = 0$ has a solution which is a **polynomial** of degree n. If this polynomial is multiplied by a suitable constant to make its value for $t = 1$ equal to 1, the resulting solution (why is it a solution?) is called the Legendre polynomial of degree n, written $P_n(t)$.

•EXERCISES

11. Compute the first 5 Legendre polynomials.

12. Show that $\int_{-1}^{1} P_0(t)P_1(t)\, dt = 0$, $\int_{-1}^{1} P_0(t)P_2(t)\, dt = 0$, $\int_{-1}^{1} P_1(t)P_2(t)\, dt = 0$.

13. Compute $\int_{-1}^{1}[P_0(t)]^2\, dt$, $\int_{-1}^{1}[P_1(t)]^2\, dt$, $\int_{-1}^{1}[P_2(t)]^2\, dt$.

It can be shown that in general $\int_{-1}^{1} P_m(t)P_n(t)\, dt = 0$ if $m \neq n$, and $\int_{-1}^{1}[P_n(t)]^2\, dt = 2/(2n + 1)$ $(n = 0, 1, 2, \ldots)$. The Legendre polynomials and their properties play an important role in many physical problems having spherical symmetry, including problems of potential theory and heat transfer.

•EXERCISES

14. Consider the Legendre equation with α an even integer, $\alpha = 2m$, namely, $(1 - t^2)y'' - 2ty' + 2m(2m + 1)y = 0$. In Exercise 9 above, the solution ϕ with $\phi(0) = 1$, $\phi'(0) = 0$ was found to be a polynomial of degree $2m$. Find a second linearly independent solution valid in a neighborhood of $t = 0$.

15. Show that the second solution found in Exercise 14 in the form of a power series converges for $|t| < 1$ but diverges for $t = \pm 1$.

16. Consider the Legendre equation with α an odd integer, $\alpha = 2m + 1$, namely, $(1 - t^2)y'' - 2ty' + (2m + 1)(2m + 2)y = 0$. In Exercise 10 above, the solution ϕ with $\phi(0) = 0$, $\phi'(0) = 1$ was found to be a polynomial of degree $2m + 1$. Find a second linearly independent solution valid in a neighborhood of $t = 0$.

17. Show that the second solution found in Exercise 16 in the form of a power series converges for $|t| < 1$ but diverges for $t = \pm 1$.

These exercises show that the Legendre polynomials are the only bounded solutions of the Legendre equation on $-1 \leq t \leq 1$ when α is an integer. In fact, if α is not an integer, it is easily shown that no solution of the Legendre equation is bounded on $-1 \leq t \leq 1$.

In applying Theorem 4.1 to a specific equation, we divide through by the coefficient of y'' before applying the theorem. However, to solve the equation it is usually easier to return to the original form to calculate the series solution. For example, to find a series solution of $(1 + t^2)y'' + y = 0$, we substitute $\phi(t) = \sum_{k=0}^{\infty} c_k t^k$ into this equation to give

$$(1 + t^2) \sum_{k=2}^{\infty} k(k - 1)c_k t^{k-2} + \sum_{k=0}^{\infty} c_k t^k = 0$$

carry out the multiplication, and proceed as usual.

• **EXERCISES**

18. Apply Theorem 4.1 to each of the following differential equations and initial conditions when applicable, but do not solve the equation. In each case give the interval of convergence of the series solution ϕ guaranteed by Theorem 4.1.

(a) $(1 + t^2)y'' + y = 0$ $\phi(0) = 1 \quad \phi'(0) = 2.$

(b) $(1 - t^2)y'' + y = 0$ $\phi(1) = 1 \quad \phi'(1) = 0.$

(c) $(\sin t)y'' + (\cos t)y' + y = 0$ $\phi\left(\dfrac{\pi}{2}\right) = a \quad \phi'\left(\dfrac{\pi}{2}\right) = b.$

(d) $(\sin t)y'' + (\cos t)y' + y = 0$ $\phi(\pi) = a \quad \phi'(\pi) = b.$

19. Solve the initial value problem given in Exercise 18(a).

20. Solve the initial value problem given in 18(c).

We remark that for the equation of order n

$$y^{(n)} + p_1(t)y^{(n-1)} + \cdots + p_{n-1}(t)y' + p_n(t)y = f(t)$$

where the functions $p_1, \ldots, p_n$, and f are analytic at $t = t_0$, there is an exact analogue to Theorem 4.1 which asserts the existence of a unique solution ϕ analytic at $t = t_0$ satisfying prescribed initial conditions.

• **EXERCISES**

21. State the analogue of Theorem 4.1 for the equation of order n.

22. Find the solution ϕ of the differential equation $y^{(3)} + ty' - y = 0$ such that $\phi(0) = 0$, $\phi'(0) = 1$, $\phi''(0) = 0$.

4.4   Proof of Theorem on Solutions in Power Series

In this section we shall prove Theorem 4.1 in the special case $f(t) \equiv 0$. This is the case which commonly arises; we shall make some remarks on the nonhomogeneous problem after the completion of the proof. The proof is constructive, in the sense that it shows us how to proceed to find a power series solution for any given second-order linear equation with analytic coefficients, and is based on the useful method of majorants.

Thus we consider the differential equation

$$y'' + p(t)y' + q(t)y = 0 \tag{4.14}$$

and we seek the solution ϕ satisfying the initial conditions

$$\phi(t_0) = a \qquad \phi'(t_0) = b \tag{4.15}$$

We assume that p and q are analytic at t_0.   This means that we can write

$$p(t) = \sum_{k=0}^{\infty} p_k(t - t_0)^k \qquad q(t) = \sum_{k=0}^{\infty} q_k(t - t_0)^k$$

with both series converging in some interval $|t - t_0| < A$, where $A > 0$. The object is to see whether the solution ϕ of (4.14), (4.15), whose existence is guaranteed by Theorem 3.1 (p. 65), is analytic at t_0; that is, whether it is possible to write $\phi(t) = \sum_{k=0}^{\infty} c_k(t - t_0)^k$, with the series converging in some interval $|t - t_0| < B$, where $B > 0$.

Assuming for the moment that the solution ϕ is analytic at $t = t_0$, we can write, for $|t - t_0| < B$,

$$\phi'(t) = \sum_{k=1}^{\infty} kc_k(t - t_0)^{k-1} \qquad \phi''(t) = \sum_{k=2}^{\infty} k(k - 1)c_k(t - t_0)^{k-2}$$

Substituting the series for p, q, ϕ, ϕ', and ϕ'' into equation (4.14), we obtain

$$\phi''(t) + p(t)\phi'(t) + q(t)\phi(t)$$
$$= \sum_{k=2}^{\infty} k(k - 1)c_k(t - t_0)^{k-2} + \sum_{k=0}^{\infty} p_k(t - t_0)^k \cdot \sum_{k=1}^{\infty} kc_k(t - t_0)^{k-1}$$
$$+ \sum_{k=0}^{\infty} q_k(t - t_0)^k \cdot \sum_{k=0}^{\infty} c_k(t - t_0)^k = 0$$

Shifting indices in the first two terms, we obtain

$$\phi''(t) + p(t)\phi'(t) + q(t)\phi(t) = \sum_{k=0}^{\infty} (k + 2)(k + 1)c_{k+2}(t - t_0)^k$$
$$+ \sum_{k=0}^{\infty} p_k(t - t_0)^k \cdot \sum_{k=0}^{\infty} (k + 1)c_{k+1}(t - t_0)^k$$
$$+ \sum_{k=0}^{\infty} q_k(t - t_0)^k \cdot \sum_{k=0}^{\infty} c_k(t - t_0)^k = 0$$

Carrying out the multiplication and addition of these power series (properties (v) and (vi), p. 123) and grouping terms in the same power of $(t - t_0)$, we obtain

$$\sum_{k=0}^{\infty} [(k+2)(k+1)c_{k+2} + (k+1)p_0c_{k+1} + kp_1c_k + \cdots + p_kc_1$$
$$+ q_0c_k + q_1c_{k-1} + \cdots + q_kc_0](t-t_0)^k = 0 \quad (4.16)$$

We remark that if the power series for p and q converge for $|t - t_0| < A$ and if the power series for ϕ converges for $|t - t_0| < B$, then the power series in (4.16) actually converges for $|t - t_0| < C$ where $C = \min(A, B) > 0$. By the identity theorem for analytic functions, the coefficient of every power of $(t - t_0)$ in (4.16) must be zero; this gives the following recursive system of equations for the coefficients c_k.

$$\begin{cases} 2 \cdot 1c_2 + p_0c_1 + q_0c_0 = 0 \\ 3 \cdot 2c_3 + 2p_0c_2 + p_1c_1 + q_0c_1 + q_1c_0 = 0 \\ 4 \cdot 3c_4 + 3p_0c_3 + 2p_1c_2 + p_2c_1 + q_0c_2 + q_1c_1 + q_2c_0 = 0 \\ \qquad \cdot \\ \qquad \cdot \\ \qquad \cdot \\ (k+2)(k+1)c_{k+2} + \sum_{m=0}^{\infty} [(m+1)p_{k-m}c_{m+1} + q_{k-m}c_m] = 0 \\ \qquad \cdot \\ \qquad \cdot \\ \qquad \cdot \end{cases} \quad (4.17)$$

We can solve these in succession. The first equation gives c_2 as a linear combination of c_0 and c_1. The second equation gives c_3 as a linear combination of c_0, c_1, and c_2; since c_2 has already been expressed as a linear combination of c_0 and c_1, this means that c_3 is a linear combination of c_0 and c_1, and so on. By induction, the equation expressing the fact that the coefficient of $(t - t_0)^k$ is zero gives c_{k+2} as a linear combination of $c_0, c_1, \ldots, c_{k+1}$, with the coefficients in this linear combination depending on the given coefficients $p_0, p_1, \ldots, p_k, q_0, q_1, \ldots, q_k$. Our method of successive solution shows then that c_{k+2} is actually a linear combination of c_0 and c_1. We can write $c_{k+2} = d_{k+2}c_0 + e_{k+2}c_1$ $(k = 0, 1, 2, \ldots)$, where d_{k+2}, e_{k+2} can be calculated successively from (4.17) and depend on $p_0, p_1, \ldots, p_k, q_0, q_1, \ldots, q_k$. Thus we have found the coefficients in the power series for ϕ, and we can write

$$\phi(t) = c_0 + c_1(t - t_0) + \sum_{k=2}^{\infty} (d_kc_0 + e_kc_1)(t - t_0)^k$$
$$= c_0 \left[1 + \sum_{k=2}^{\infty} d_k(t - t_0)^k \right] + c_1 \left[(t - t_0) + \sum_{k=2}^{\infty} e_k(t - t_0)^k \right] \quad (4.18)$$

Now c_0 and c_1 can be determined from the initial conditions. In fact, $c_0 = \phi(t_0) = a$, $c_1 = \phi'(t_0) = b$. Thus we have shown that if the solution ϕ is analytic at t_0, then it must have the form (4.18), where the coefficients are computed successively with the aid of the system of equations (4.17). The reader should notice that it is not at all obvious that the series (4.18) which represents the solution ϕ converges, or what its radius of convergence is. To complete the proof of Theorem 4.1, we will show that the series (4.18) has a positive radius of convergence B, and in fact that $B \geq A$. Once this has been done, all the operations which led from the differential equation (4.14) to the formal solution (4.18) are readily justified by using properties of power series just as in the examples in the previous section. Incidentally, once we have established the convergence of the solution (4.18), we should note that we can write $\phi(t) = c_0\phi_1(t) + c_1\phi_2(t)$, where $\phi_1(t) = 1 + \Sigma_{k=2}^{\infty}d_k(t - t_0)^k$, $\phi_2(t) = (t - t_0) + \Sigma_{k=2}^{\infty}e_k(t - t_0)^k$. Since the series for ϕ_1 and ϕ_2 begin with different powers of $(t - t_0)$, the functions ϕ_1 and ϕ_2 are linearly independent by Lemma 4.1 (p. 124), and we have expressed the solution ϕ of (4.14) as a linear combination of the linearly independent solutions ϕ_1 and ϕ_2. Thus $\phi(t)$ in (4.18) is the general solution of (4.14). We shall show that the series $\Sigma_{k=0}^{\infty}c_k(t - t_0)^k$ converges for $|t - t_0| < A$ by constructing a **majorant series** which converges for $|t - t_0| < A$.

To establish the convergence of the series solution (4.18), we shall need to make use of the following fact about power series, known as Cauchy's inequality: **If $\Sigma_{k=0}^{\infty}a_k(t - t_0)^k$ converges in $|t - t_0| < R$, then for every r, $0 < r < R$, there is a constant $M > 0$ such that $|a_k|r^k \leq M$ $(k = 0, 1, 2, \ldots)$.** This follows immediately from the fact that if $\Sigma_{k=0}^{\infty}a_k r^k$ converges, then $\lim_{k \to \infty} |a_k r^k| = 0$, and therefore $|a_k|r^k$ is bounded; that is, there exists a constant $M > 0$, independent of k, such that $|a_k|r^k \leq M$ $(k = 0, 1, 2, \ldots)$.

The coefficients c_k are determined by the equations (4.17) which may be written as

$$(k + 2)(k + 1)c_{k+2} = - \sum_{m=0}^{k} [(m + 1)p_{k-m}c_{m+1} + q_{k-m}c_m] \qquad (k = 0, 1, 2, \ldots) \quad (4.19)$$

Since the series $\Sigma_{j=0}^{\infty}p_j(t - t_0)^j$, $\Sigma_{j=0}^{\infty}q_j(t - t_0)^j$ converge in $|t - t_0| < A$, corresponding to every positive number $r < A$ there is a constant $M > 0$ such that

$$|p_j|r^j \leq M \qquad |q_j|r^j \leq M \qquad (j = 0, 1, 2, \ldots) \quad (4.20)$$

Using (4.20) in (4.19), we obtain,

$$(k + 2)(k + 1)|c_{k+2}| \leq \frac{M}{r^k} \sum_{m=0}^{k} [(m + 1)|c_{m+1}| + |c_m|]r^m$$

$$\leq \frac{M}{r^k} \sum_{m=0}^{k} [(m + 1)|c_{m+1}| + |c_m|]r^m + M|c_{k+1}|r \quad (4.21)$$

where the positive term $M|c_{k+1}|r$ added on the right side of (4.21) only increases this side of the inequality and is needed in what follows. Now we define $C_0 = |c_0|$, $C_1 = |c_1|$, and for $k = 0, 1, 2, \ldots$, we define C_k recursively by

$$(k + 2)(k + 1)C_{k+2} = \frac{M}{r^k} \sum_{m=0}^{k} [(m + 1)C_{m+1} + C_m]r^m + MC_{k+1}r \quad (4.22)$$

Comparison of (4.22) with (4.21) shows that $0 \leq |c_k| \leq C_k$ ($k = 0, 1, 2, \ldots$).

• **EXERCISE**

1. Use induction to show that $0 \leq |c_k| \leq C_k$.

Replacing k by $(k - 1)$ in (4.22), we obtain

$$(k + 1)kC_{k+1} = \frac{M}{r^{k-1}} \sum_{m=0}^{k-1} [(m + 1)C_{m+1} + C_m]r^m + MC_k r \quad (4.23)$$

Using (4.22),

$$\frac{M}{r^k} \sum_{m=0}^{k} [(m + 1)C_{m+1} + C_m]r^m = (k + 2)(k + 1)C_{k+2} - MrC_{k+1}$$

On the other hand, from (4.23)

$$\frac{M}{r^k} \sum_{m=0}^{k} [(m + 1)C_{m+1} + C_m]r^m = \frac{1}{r} \frac{M}{r^{k-1}} \sum_{m=0}^{k-1} [(m + 1)C_{m+1} + C_m]r^m$$

$$+ M(k + 1)C_{k+1} + MC_k$$

$$= \frac{1}{r}(k + 1)kC_{k+1} - MC_k + M(k + 1)C_{k+1} + MC_k$$

Combining these, we obtain

$$(k + 2)(k + 1)C_{k+2} = \left[\frac{-(k + 1)k}{r} + M(k + 1) + Mr \right] C_{k+1}$$

and therefore

$$\frac{C_{k+2}}{C_{k+1}} = \frac{(k + 1)k + M(k + 1)r + Mr^2}{r(k + 2)(k + 1)}$$

Since $\lim_{k \to \infty} C_{k+2}/C_{k+1} = 1/r$, the ratio test shows that the majorant series $\sum_{k=0}^{\infty} C_k(t - t_0)^k$ converges in $|t - t_0| < r$. This implies, by the comparison test, that $\sum_{k=0}^{\infty} c_k(t - t_0)^k$ also converges in $|t - t_0| < r$. Since this is true for every $r < A$, the series $\sum_{k=0}^{\infty} c_k(t - t_0)^k$ converges in $|t - t_0| < A$, and the proof is complete. $\blacksquare$

In the nonhomogeneous case,

$$y'' + p(t)y' + q(t)y = f(t)$$

let

$$f(t) = \sum_{k=0}^{\infty} f_k(t - t_0)^k$$

It is easy to see that the coefficients c_k in the series solution $\sum_{k=0}^{\infty} c_k(t - t_0)^k$ are now determined by the equations

$$2 \cdot 1c_2 + p_0c_1 + q_0c_0 = f_0$$
$$3 \cdot 2c_3 + 2p_0c_2 + p_1c_1 + q_0c_1 + q_1c_0 = f_1$$

$$(k + 2)(k + 1)c_{k+2} + \sum_{m=0}^{k} [(m + 1)p_{k-m}c_{m+1} + q_{k-m}c_m] = f_k$$

in place of equation (4.17).

•EXERCISES

2. Derive the above set of equations for the coefficients c_k in the nonhomogeneous case. [*Hint:* Give a development which parallels (4.14)–(4.17) in this case.]

3. Show that the c_k in Exercise 2 can be determined recursively from the above system.

It is possible to establish the convergence of the formal series solution obtained in this manner either by an extension of the methods for the homogeneous case, or by use of the variation of constants formula (p. 105).

4.5   Singular Points of Linear Differential Equations

Many differential equations which arise in applications, the so-called equations of mathematical physics, fail to satisfy the hypotheses of Theorem 4.1.   For such equations the power series method developed in Sections 4.3 and 4.4 can be modified.   We propose to study these modifications systematically for a broad class of such equations.   As has been our custom, we shall concentrate on equations of the second order.   To see what we may expect, we consider first the familiar second-order Euler equation (see equation (3.22), p. 96).

$$(t - t_0)^2 y'' + (t - t_0)a_1 y' + a_2 y = 0 \tag{4.24}$$

where a_1 and a_2 are constants.   The Euler equation serves as a simple but useful prototype of the general situation which will be explained in detail below.   We recall from our previous work that equation (4.24) has at least one solution of the form $|t - t_0|^{z_1}$ and a second linearly independent solution of the form either $|t - t_0|^{z_2}$ or $|t - t_0|^{z_1} \log |t - t_0|$, according as the algebraic equation

$$z^2 + (a_1 - 1)z + a_2 = 0 \tag{4.25}$$

has unequal roots z_1, z_2 or a double root z_1.   We notice immediately that Theorem 4.1 cannot be applied to the equation (4.24) in a neighborhood of the point $t = t_0$ because the functions $p(t) = a_1/(t - t_0)$, $q(t) = a_2/(t - t_0)^2$ are not analytic at $t = t_0$.   However, in a neighborhood of any point $t_1 \neq t_0$, Theorem 4.1 is applicable.

•EXERCISE

1. Deduce the existence of a unique analytic solution ϕ of (4.24) which satisfies the initial conditions $\phi(t_1) = y_0$, $\phi'(t_1) = z_0$, where $t_1 \neq t_0$.   [*Hint:*

show that Theorem 4.1 can be applied; note that

$$\frac{1}{t - t_0} = \frac{1}{t_1 - t_0 + t - t_1} = \frac{1}{t_1 - t_0}\bigg/1 + \frac{t - t_1}{t_1 - t_0}$$

$$= \frac{1}{t_1 - t_0}\left[1 - \left(\frac{t - t_1}{t_1 - t_0}\right) + \cdots\right], \qquad \left|\frac{t - t_1}{t_1 - t_0}\right| < 1$$

and similarly for $1/(t - t_0)^2$.]

We notice also that although Theorem 4.1 cannot be applied to equation (4.24) to deduce the existence of a solution analytic at $t = t_0$, it may happen that a solution analytic at $t = t_0$ does exist (for example, if z_1 or z_2 or both are distinct nonnegative integers, either the solution $(t - t_0)^{z_1}$ or $(t - t_0)^{z_2}$ or both are analytic at $t = t_0$).

•EXERCISES

2. Make up an example of a differential equation of the form (4.24) (with $t_0 = 0$ if you wish) which has at least one solution analytic at t_0, and another example for which every solution is analytic at t_0.

3. Discuss the form of the general solution of the equation

$$(t - t_0)^4 y^{(4)} + (t - t_0)^3 a_1 y^{(3)} + (t - t_0)^2 a_2 y'' + (t - t_0)a_3 y' + a_4 y = 0$$

in a neighborhood of $t = t_0$, and also in a neighborhood of $t = t_1 \neq t_0$, where a_1, a_2, a_3, a_4 are constants. [*Hint:* Use the result of Exercise 4, Section 3.6, p. 98.]

For the Euler equation, we see that the behavior of solutions when t is near t_0 and when t is near $t_1 \neq t_0$ is quite different. Every solution is analytic at $t_1 \neq t_0$ but not necessarily at t_0. This suggests that the point $t = t_0$ plays a special role here. The point $t = t_0$ will be called a singular point of the equation

$$a_0(t)y'' + a_1(t)y' + a_2(t)y = 0 \tag{4.26}$$

where a_0, a_1, a_2 are given functions analytic at t_0, if $a_0(t_0) = 0$ but a_1 and a_2 are not both zero at t_0. (If $a_0(t_0) = a_1(t_0) = a_2(t_0) = 0$, then we can divide the equation (4.26) by a suitable power of $(t - t_0)$ so that at least one of the coefficients is different from zero at t_0.) More generally, $t = t_0$ is a singular point of the equation

$$a_0(t)y^{(n)} + a_1(t)y^{(n-1)} + \cdots + a_{n-1}(t)y' + a_n(t)y = 0 \tag{4.27}$$

if $a_0, a_1, \ldots, a_n$ are analytic at t_0 and $a_0(t_0) = 0$ but $a_1, a_2, \ldots, a_n$ are not all zero at t_0.

We shall see that the behavior of solutions of the equation (4.26) or (4.27) near the singular point t_0 depends very much on how rapidly $a_0(t)$ approaches zero as $t \to t_0$. For this reason, we distinguish two different types of singular points and we make the following classification.

Definition.   *The point t_0 is called a regular singular point of the equation (4.26) if it is a singular point and if*

$$p(t) = \frac{a_1(t)}{a_0(t)} \qquad q(t) = \frac{a_2(t)}{a_0(t)}$$

have the property that $(t - t_0)p(t)$ and $(t - t_0)^2 q(t)$ are both analytic at t_0. More generally, the point t_0 is called a regular singular point of the equation (4.27) if it is a singular point and if

$$p_1(t) = \frac{a_1(t)}{a_0(t)} \quad p_2(t) = \frac{a_2(t)}{a_0(t)}, \quad \ldots, \quad p_n(t) = \frac{a_n(t)}{a_0(t)}$$

have the property that $(t - t_0)p_1(t)$, $(t - t_0)^2 p_2(t)$, $\ldots$, $(t - t_0)^n p_n(t)$ are all analytic at t_0.

Examples

1. The Euler equation (4.24) is perhaps the simplest example of an equation which has a regular singular point at $t = t_0$ because t_0 is a singular point and $p(t) = a_1/(t - t_0)$, $q(t) = a_2/(t - t_0)^2$ have the property that $(t - t_0)p(t) = a_1$, $(t - t_0)^2 q(t) = a_2$ are analytic everywhere, in particular at t_0.

2. The equation $t^2 y'' + (\frac{3}{2})t y' + t y = 0$ has $t = 0$ as a regular singular point because $p(t) = 3/2t$, $q(t) = 1/t$ have the property that $tp(t) = \frac{3}{2}$, $t^2 q(t) = t$ are both analytic everywhere, in particular at $t = 0$.

3. The equation $(t - 1)^3 y'' + 2(t - 1)^2 y' \doteq 7ty = 0$ does not have a regular singular point at $t = 1$ because $p(t) = 2/(t - 1)$, $q(t) = -7t/(t - 1)^3$ do **not** have the property that $(t - 1)p(t) = 2$, $(t - 1)^2 q(t) = -7t/(t - 1)$ are both analytic at $t = 1$.

If a singular point $t = t_0$ for equation (4.26) or (4.27) (such as $t = 1$ in Example 3 above) is not regular, then we say that t_0 is an **irregular singular point**. On the other hand, points $t = t_0$ which are not singular points of an equation (4.26) or (4.27) with coefficients analytic at t_0 are called **ordinary points** (or regular points). Thus in Examples 1, 2, 3 above the points $t = t_0$, $t = 0$, $t = 1$ respectively are singular points, and all other finite values of t are ordinary points. The points $t = t_0$ in Example 1 and $t = 0$ in Example 2 are regular singular points, while the point $t = 1$ in Example 3 is an irregular singular point. Theorem 4.1 describes completely the behavior of solutions in a neighborhood of an ordinary point; our next task is to discuss the behavior of solutions in a neighborhood of a singular point. As we shall see, it is considerably easier to do this for regular singular points than for irregular singular points, and we shall begin with the study of the former. Naturally it is essential that, given a differential equation of the form (4.26) or (4.27), we first locate and classify its singular points.

•EXERCISES

Locate and classify all the singular points for finite values of t of each of the following differential equations.

4. $t^2 y'' + y' = 0$.

5. $(1 - t^2)y'' - 2ty' + \alpha(\alpha + 1)y = 0$ (Legendre equation).

6. $t^2 y'' + ty' + (\alpha^2 - t^2)y = 0$ (Bessel equation).

7. $t(1 - t^2)y'' + 2(t - 1)y' - 5ty = 0$.

8. $t^3 y'' + 5t \sin ty' + 7ty = 0$.

9. $t^2 y'' + \dfrac{2t}{1 + t} y' + 2y = 0$.

10. $t(1 - t)y'' + [c - (a + b + 1)t]y' - aby = 0$ (hypergeometric equation, with a, b, c constants).

11. $ty^{(4)} + \dfrac{7}{(2 + t)^2} y'' - (\sin t)y = 0$.

12. $t^4(1 - t^2)^3 y^{(3)} + 5t^5(1 + t)y'' - 2t^2(1 - t^2)y' + y = 0$.

4.6   Solutions about a Regular Singular Point—Examples

It follows immediately from the definition given in Section 4.5 that the equation

$$a_0(t)y'' + a_1(t)y' + a_2(t)y = 0 \tag{4.26}$$

has a regular singular point at $t = t_0$ if and only if (4.26) can be written in the form

$$(t - t_0)^2 y'' + (t - t_0)\alpha(t)y' + \beta(t)y = 0 \tag{4.28}$$

where $\alpha(t) = (t - t_0)a_1(t)/a_0(t)$ and $\beta(t) = (t - t_0)^2 a_2(t)/a_0(t)$ are analytic at t_0, with at least one of the three numbers $\alpha(t_0)$, $\beta(t_0)$, $\beta'(t_0)$ different from zero. (If all three of these numbers are zero, then (4.28) has $(t - t_0)^2$ as a factor and $t = t_0$ is only apparently a singular point. If we divide (4.28) by $(t - t_0)^2$, the resulting equation will have an ordinary point at $t = t_0$.) Notice that the Euler equation (4.24), p. 138, is of the form (4.28) with $\alpha(t)$ and $\beta(t)$ constant functions.

• **EXERCISE**

1. Show that the equation (4.27) (p. 139) has a regular singular point at $t = t_0$ if and only if the equation can be written in the form

$$(t - t_0)^n y^{(n)} + (t - t_0)^{n-1}\alpha_1(t)y^{(n-1)} + \cdots$$
$$+ (t - t_0)\alpha_{n-1}(t)y' + a_n(t)y = 0 \quad (4.29)$$

with $\alpha_1, \alpha_2, \ldots, \alpha_n$ analytic at t_0.

In order to simplify the discussion, it is convenient to make a preliminary transformation. The change of independent variable $t = x + t_0$ enables us to transfer the singular point t_0 in (4.28) (or (4.29)) to the origin without changing the form of the equation in any essential way. Namely, if $t_0 \neq 0$, we let $\bar{\alpha}(x) = \alpha(t_0 + x)$, $\bar{\beta}(x) = \beta(t_0 + x)$. Then $\bar{\alpha}$ and $\bar{\beta}$ are analytic at $x = 0$ since α and β are analytic at $t = t_0$. We also let $\bar{y}(x) = y(t_0 + x)$. The chain rule gives

$$\frac{d\bar{y}}{dx} = y'(t_0 + x) \qquad \frac{d^2\bar{y}}{dx^2} = y''(t_0 + x)$$

and therefore (4.28) becomes

$$x^2 \frac{d^2\bar{y}}{dx^2} + x\bar{\alpha}(x)\frac{d\bar{y}}{dx} + \bar{\beta}(x)\bar{y} = 0 \tag{4.30}$$

This is of the same form as (4.28), but with $x = 0$ a regular singular point. Conversely, if $\bar{y}(x)$ is a solution of (4.30), the function $y(t) = \bar{y}(t - t_0)$ is a solution of (4.28). Thus (4.28) with a regular singular point at $t = t_0 \neq 0$ and (4.30) with a regular singular point at $x = 0$ are equivalent. The same transformation $t = x + t_0$ may, of course, also be applied to (4.29). We will therefore assume that such a preliminary simplification has already been made, and we will consider the equation

$$t^2 y'' + t\alpha(t)y' + \beta(t)y = 0 \tag{4.31}$$

where α and β are given functions analytic at $t = 0$ and having power series expansions

$$\alpha(t) = \sum_{k=0}^{\infty} \alpha_k t^k \qquad \beta(t) = \sum_{k=0}^{\infty} \beta_k t^k$$

which converge in some interval $|t| < r$ $(r > 0)$, and such that the numbers $\alpha_0, \beta_0, \beta_1$ are not all zero. Thus $t = 0$ is a regular singular point for (4.31). Every statement about the equation (4.31) can, of course, readily be changed to apply to (4.28) by means of the above change of variable.

•EXERCISES

Make the appropriate change of independent variable in each of the following equations to transfer each singular point to the origin, and find the transformed equation with singular point at the origin.

2. $(1 - t)y'' + 2ty' + 3y = 0$.
3. $(1 - t^2)y'' - 2ty' + \alpha(\alpha + 1)y = 0$ (Legendre equation).
4. $t(1 - t)y'' + [c - (a + b + 1)t]y' - aby = 0$ (hypergeometric equation).

Before proceeding with a general theory, let us consider three specific equations.

Example 1.   The equation $2ty'' + y' + ty = 0$ has a regular singular point at $t = 0$. We wish to find an expression for the general solution valid in a neighborhood of $t = 0$. The reader should recall that it suffices to find two linearly independent solutions (Theorem 3.5, p. 79). This equation may be written as

$$t^2y'' + \frac{1}{2} ty' + \frac{1}{2} t^2y = 0 \tag{4.32}$$

which is of the form (4.31) with $\alpha(t) = \frac{1}{2}$, $\beta(t) = \frac{1}{2}t^2$. Since α and β are both analytic at $t = 0$, $t = 0$ is a regular singular point. If α and β were both constants, then (4.32) would be an Euler equation and would have at least one solution of the form $|t|^z$. To take into account the fact that in this example β is not a constant, we try to find a solution of the form $|t|^z \sum_{k=0}^{\infty} c_k t^k$ $(c_0 \neq 0)$, where the constants z, c_k are determined by substitution into the differential equation (4.32), and where the series $\sum_{k=0}^{\infty} c_k t^k$ converges on some interval about $t = 0$. Note that we cannot deduce the existence or uniqueness of any solution with initial conditions prescribed at $t = 0$ from Theorem 3.1 (why not?), let alone a solution of the above form. Since $t = 0$ is a singular point for (4.32), we separate the cases $t > 0$ and $t < 0$. We consider first the case $t > 0$ and try as a solution the function $\phi(t) = t^z \Sigma_{k=0}^{\infty} c_k t^k = \Sigma_{k=0}^{\infty} c_k t^{z+k}$, which for $t > 0$ has

$$\phi'(t) = \sum_{k=0}^{\infty} c_k(z + k)t^{z+k-1} \qquad \phi''(t) = \sum_{k=0}^{\infty} c_k(z + k)(z + k - 1)t^{z+k-2}$$

We postpone any justification of the differentiation for the moment. Substitution into (4.32) gives, for those $t > 0$ for which these series converge absolutely (see Section 4.3 (p. 126), for a similar argument):

$$t^2\phi''(t) + \frac{1}{2}t\phi'(t) + \frac{1}{2}t^2\phi(t)$$

$$= \sum_{k=0}^{\infty} c_k(z + k)(z + k - 1)t^{z+k} + \frac{1}{2}\sum_{k=0}^{\infty} c_k(z + k)t^{z+k} + \frac{1}{2}\sum_{k=0}^{\infty} c_k t^{z+k+2}$$

$$* = \sum_{k=0}^{\infty} c_k \left[(z + k)(z + k - 1) + \frac{1}{2}(z + k) \right] t^{z+k} + \frac{1}{2}\sum_{m=2}^{\infty} c_{m-2} t^{z+m}$$

$$= c_0 z \left(z - \frac{1}{2} \right) t^z + c_1(z + 1) \left(z + \frac{1}{2} \right) t^{z+1}$$

$$+ \sum_{k=0}^{\infty} \left[(z + k) \left(z + k - \frac{1}{2} \right) c_k + \frac{1}{2} c_{k-2} \right] t^{z+k}$$

Writing $f(z) = z(z - \frac{1}{2})$, we can write this last relation (for $t > 0$) as

$$t^2\phi''(t) + \frac{1}{2}t\phi'(t) + \frac{1}{2}t^2\phi(t)$$

$$= t^z \left[c_0 f(z) + c_1 f(z + 1)t + \sum_{k=2}^{\infty} \left\{ f(z + k)c_k + \frac{1}{2} c_{k-2} \right\} t^k \right] \quad (4.33)$$

Therefore the equation (4.32) can be satisfied by the function $\phi(t) = t^z \Sigma_{k=0}^{\infty} c_k t^k$ for $t > 0$ only if the coefficient of every power of t in the right

---

* The reader is reminded about shifting indices in series (p. 126).

side of (4.33) vanishes.   Since we assumed $c_0 \neq 0$, we must therefore have

$$f(z) = 0, \quad c_1 f(z+1) = 0, \quad f(z+1)c_k + \frac{1}{2}c_{k-2} = 0 \quad (k = 2, 3, 4, \ldots)$$

The function $f(z)$ is a polynomial, called the **indicial polynomial**.   For a second-order differential equation with a regular singular point at $t = 0$ this polynomial is always quadratic, as we shall see in Section 4.7.   In the present example, $f(z) = z(z - \frac{1}{2})$ and thus the relation $f(z) = 0$ is satisfied if $z = \frac{1}{2}$ or if $z = 0$.   Taking first the case $z = \frac{1}{2}$, we must next choose $c_1 = 0$ to satisfy the relation $c_1 f(z+1) = 0$, since $f(\frac{3}{2}) \neq 0$. Then we must calculate the coefficients c_k $(k \geq 2)$ from the relations $f(\frac{1}{2} + k)c_k + \frac{1}{2}c_{k-2} = 0$ $(k = 2, 3, 4, \ldots)$.   Since $f(\frac{1}{2} + k) = (k + \frac{1}{2})k \neq 0$ for $k = 2, 3, 4, \ldots$, we can write these relations as

$$c_k = \frac{-1}{2k(k + \frac{1}{2})} c_{k-2} \qquad (k = 2, 3, 4, \ldots)$$

Now we can express all the coefficients in terms of c_0, which remains arbitrary.   We obtain

$$c_1 = 0, \quad c_3 = 0, \ldots, c_{2m-1} = 0, \ldots$$

$$c_2 = -\frac{c_0}{2 \cdot 5}, \quad c_4 = -\frac{c_2}{4 \cdot 9} = \frac{c_0}{2 \cdot 4 \cdot 5 \cdot 9}, \ldots$$

$$c_{2m} = (-1)^m \frac{c_0}{2 \cdot 4 \cdot 6 \cdots 2m \cdot 5 \cdot 9 \cdots (4m+1)}, \ldots$$

• **EXERCISE**

5. Verify the formula for c_{2m} by induction.

Substituting these quantities into the assumed form of the solution $\phi(t) = t^z \sum_{k=0}^{\infty} c_k t^k$, we obtain as **one candidate for a solution** of the equation (4.32) for $t > 0$ the function

$$\phi_1(t) = t^{1/2}\left[1 + \sum_{m=1}^{\infty} \frac{(-1)^m}{2 \cdot 4 \cdots (2m) \cdot 5 \cdot 9 \cdots (4m+1)} t^{2m}\right]$$

We have chosen the arbitrary constant c_0 as 1, since it is merely a factor multiplying the whole series.   Similarly, taking the root $z = 0$ of the indicial equation $f(z) = 0$ we find that c_0 is arbitrary, $c_1 = 0$, and $f(k)c_k +$

$\frac{1}{2}c_{k-2} = 0$ for $k = 2, 3, \ldots$.   Since $f(k) = k(k - \frac{1}{2}) \neq 0$ for $k = 2, 3, \ldots$, we can write these relations as

$$c_k = -\frac{1}{2k(k - \frac{1}{2})} c_{k-2} \qquad (k = 2, 3, 4, \ldots)$$

and we find

$$c_2 = -\frac{c_0}{2 \cdot 3}, \quad c_3 = 0, \quad c_4 = -\frac{c_2}{4 \cdot 7} = \frac{c_0}{2 \cdot 3 \cdot 4 \cdot 7}, \cdots,$$

$$c_{2m-1} = 0, \quad c_{2m} = (-1)^m \frac{c_0}{2 \cdot 4 \cdots \cdots (2m) \cdot 3 \cdot 7 \cdots \cdots (4m - 1)}, \cdots$$

Again taking $c_0 = 1$ we obtain as a second candidate for a solution of (4.32) for $t > 0$ the function

$$\phi_2(t) = 1 + \sum_{m=1}^{\infty} \frac{(-1)^m}{2 \cdot 4 \cdots \cdots (2m) \cdot 3 \cdot 7 \cdots \cdots (4m - 1)} t^{2m}$$

The approach now is to prove that the candidates ϕ_1 and ϕ_2 are in fact solutions of (4.32) in some interval $0 < t < a$ and that ϕ_1 and ϕ_2 are linearly independent on this interval.   Before doing this we observe that, assuming the convergence of the relevant series in some interval, the above calculations are all valid for $t < 0$ if t^z is replaced by $|t|^z = e^{z \log |t|}$.

●**EXERCISE**

6. Verify this last statement by calculating $\phi_1(t)$ for $t < 0$.

We thus have, for those $t \neq 0$ for which the series converge absolutely,

$$\phi_1(t) = |t|^{1/2} \left[1 + \sum_{m=1}^{\infty} \frac{(-1)^m}{2 \cdot 4 \cdots \cdots (2m) \cdot 5 \cdot 9 \cdots \cdots (4m + 1)} t^{2m} \right]$$

$$\phi_2(t) = 1 + \sum_{m=1}^{\infty} \frac{(-1)^m}{2 \cdot 4 \cdots \cdots (2m) \cdot 3 \cdot 7 \cdots \cdots (4m + 1)} t^{2m}$$

$$(4.34)$$

as candidates for solutions of (4.32).   Next, we apply the ratio test to the series for $\phi_1(t)$.   We let

$$U_m(t) = \frac{(-1)^m}{2 \cdot 4 \cdots \cdots (2m) \cdot 5 \cdot 9 \cdots \cdots (4m + 1)} t^{2m}$$

Then

$$\left| \frac{U_{m+1}(t)}{U_m(t)} \right| = \frac{t^2}{(2m+2)(4m+5)} \to 0 \qquad (m \to \infty)$$

and thus by the ratio test the series

$$1 + \sum_{m=0}^{\infty} \frac{(-1)^m t^{2m}}{2 \cdot 4 \cdots \cdots (2m) \cdot 5 \cdot 9 \cdots \cdots (4m+1)}$$

converges absolutely for $-\infty < t < \infty$.

• EXERCISE

7. Show that the series for $\phi_2(t)$ also converges for $-\infty < t < \infty$.

Now, because of the relevant properties of power series (Section 4.2, p. 122), it is clear that all of the calculations which lead from the assumption of the solution of the form $|t|^z \sum_{k=0}^{\infty} c_k t^k$ to the two candidates for solutions ϕ_1, ϕ_2 given by (4.34) are fully justified for $-\infty < t < 0$ and for $0 < t < \infty$. The value $t = 0$ must be omitted because the differential equation (4.32) has no meaning at the singular point $t = 0$.

• EXERCISE

8. Show that the solutions ϕ_1 and ϕ_2 given by (4.34) are linearly independent on $-\infty < t < 0$ and $0 < t < \infty$, and hence on any interval not containing $t = 0$. [*Hint:* Modify the argument of Lemma 4.1 (p. 124) to fit the present situation.]

Using the result of Exercise 8, we see that the general solution of (4.32) on any interval which does not contain the origin is $a_1\phi_1(t) + a_2\phi_2(t)$, where a_1 and a_2 are arbitrary constants.

• EXERCISE

9. Use the technique of Example 1 to find the general solution of the equation $ty'' + (\tfrac{3}{2})y' + y = 0$, and determine the interval of validity of this solution.

In Example 1, the assumption that the given equation has a solution of the form $|t|^z \sum_{k=0}^{\infty} c_k t^k$ leads to a quadratic equation in z, called the **indicial equation.** Each root of the indicial equation leads to a solution of the differential equation, and the two solutions obtained are linearly independent. As the next example shows, the indicial equation may have equal roots, making the search for two linearly independent solutions considerably more difficult.

Example 2. Consider the differential equation $ty'' + y' + y = 0$, which may be written as

$$t^2 y'' + ty' + ty = 0 \qquad (4.35)$$

Clearly $t = 0$ is a regular singular point and (4.35) is of the form (4.31) with $\alpha(t) = 1$, $\beta(t) = t$. Assuming again the existence of a solution of the form $\phi(t) = |t|^z \sum_{k=0}^{\infty} c_k t^k$ ($c_0 \neq 0$) on some interval (excluding the origin), we consider the case $t > 0$. Proceeding as in Example 1, completely formally at first, we have

$$t^2 \phi''(t) + t\phi'(t) + t\phi(t) = \sum_{k=0}^{\infty} (k+z)(k+z-1)c_k t^{k+z}$$

$$+ \sum_{k=0}^{\infty} (k+z)c_k t^{k+z} + \sum_{k=0}^{\infty} c_k t^{k+z+1}$$

$$= z^2 c_0 t^z + \sum_{k=1}^{\infty} [(k+z)^2 c_k + c_{k-1}]t^{k+z}$$

$$= t^z \left[f(z)c_0 + \sum_{k=1}^{\infty} \{f(k+z)c_k + c_{k-1}\}t^k \right]$$

where $f(z) = z^2$. Thus, since (4.35) can have a solution of the assumed form only if the coefficient of every power of t in this expression vanishes, we must have $f(z) = 0$ and

$$f(k+z)c_k + c_{k-1} = 0 \qquad (k = 1, 2, \ldots)$$

The indicial polynomial in this example is $f(z) = z^2$, quadratic as in Example 1, but the indicial equation has a double root $z = 0$. Since $f(k+z) \neq 0$ for $k = 1, 2, \ldots$, we can solve for the coefficients c_k from the recursive equations $c_k = -c_{k-1}/k^2$ $(k = 1, 2, \ldots)$.

•EXERCISES

10. Determine the coefficients c_k and complete the derivation of the solution of the assumed form as in Example 1.

11. Determine the interval of validity of this solution.   (Notice that we can see directly from the recursion formulas, **without finding the coefficients,** that $|c_{k+1}t^{k+1}/c_k t^k| = t/(k+1)^2 \to 0$ as $k \to \infty$.)

Note that although the differential equation (4.35) makes no sense at the singular point $t = 0$, the function defined by the series $\Sigma_{k=0}^{\infty} c_k t^k$ in this case is well defined at the singular point $t = 0$.   This remark is important in applications (see especially Section 4.9).   The same remark applies to the solution $\phi_2(t)$ of Example 1 (p. 143).

We see that in this example, because the indicial equation has a double root, there is only one solution of the form $|t|^z \Sigma_{k=0}^{\infty} c_k t^k$.   Since the differential equation (4.35) is of the second order, it must have two linearly independent solutions, though not necessarily both of the same form. We postpone to Section 4.8 the finding of a second, linearly independent solution.

From Examples 1 and 2, we might suspect that whenever the indicial equation corresponding to a regular singular point at the origin has distinct roots, the differential equation has two linearly independent solutions of the form $|t|^z \Sigma_{k=0}^{\infty} c_k t^k$, one corresponding to each root of the indicial equation.   However, the following example shows that this is not always the case.

Example 3.   The equation $ty'' + ty' - y = 0$, which may be written as

$$t^2 y'' + t^2 y' - ty = 0 \tag{4.36}$$

has $t = 0$ as a regular singular point, since it is of the form (4.31) with $\alpha(t) = t$, $\beta(t) = -t$.   In seeking a solution of the form $\phi(t) = |t|^z \Sigma_{k=0}^{\infty} c_k t^k$ ($c_0 \neq 0$), we first restrict ourselves to the case $t > 0$, and we find exactly as before

$$t^2 \phi''(t) + t^2 \phi'(t) - t\phi(t)$$

$$= \sum_{k=0}^{\infty} (k+z)(k+z-1)c_k t^{k+z} + \sum_{k=0}^{\infty} (k+z)c_k t^{k+z+1} - \sum_{k=0}^{\infty} c_k t^{k+z+1}$$

$$= \sum_{k=0}^{\infty} (k+z)(k+z-1)c_k t^{k+z} + \sum_{k=0}^{\infty} (k+z-1)c_k t^{k+z+1}$$

$$= z(z-1)c_0 t^z + \sum_{k=1}^{\infty} [(k+z)(k+z-1)c_k + (k+z-2)c_{k-1}]t^{k+z}$$

$$= t^z \left[f(z)c_0 + \sum_{k=1}^{\infty} \{f(k+z)c_k + (k+z-2)c_{k-1}\}t^k \right]$$

where $f(z) = z(z - 1)$. As in Examples 1 and 2, $\phi(t)$ can be a solution of (4.36) only if z is a root of the indicial equation $f(z) = 0$, that is, only if $z = 0$ or $z = 1$, and

$$f(k + z)c_k + (k + z - 2)c_{k-1} = 0 \qquad (k = 1, 2, \ldots) \qquad (4.37)$$

Taking $z = 1$, we have $f(k + 1) = k(k + 1) \neq 0$ $(k = 1, 2, \ldots)$, and so $c_k = -(k - 1)c_{k-1}/k(k + 1)$ $(k = 1, 2, \ldots)$. This gives $c_k = 0$ $(k = 1, 2, \ldots)$, and, taking $c_0 = 1$, we obtain the solution $\phi_1(t) = |t|$ $(t \neq 0)$.* There is obviously no difficulty about convergence.

To see if there is a second solution of the assumed form, we consider the root $z = 0$ of the indicial equation. Now the recursion formulas (4.37) become

$$k(k - 1)c_k + (k - 2)c_{k-1} = 0 \qquad (k = 1, 2, \ldots)$$

Taking $k = 1$, we see that c_1 must be determined from the relation $0 \cdot c_1 - c_0 = 0$. Since $c_0 \neq 0$, this is impossible, and there can be no solution of the assumed form corresponding to the root $z = 0$. As in Example 2, a second, linearly independent, solution of a different form may be found by a method to be studied in Section 4.8.

•EXERCISES

12. Find a formula for a second, linearly independent, solution of the equation (4.36) by the method of Section 3.7 (p. 99).

Using the methods of the examples studied in this section, find as many linearly independent solutions of the form $|t|^z \sum_{k=0}^{\infty} c_k t^k$ $(c_0 \neq 0)$ as possible for each of the following differential equations. Also find the interval of validity of each such solution.

13. $2t^2 y'' + 4t(1 + t)y' + 2y = 0$.
14. $t^2 y'' + 4ty' + 2(1 + 2t)y = 0$.
15. $t^2 y'' + t(1 + t)y' - y = 0$.
16. $t^2 y'' + (t^2 - \frac{7}{36})y = 0$.
17. $t^3 y'' + ty' = y = 0$.

---

* We could have guessed this solution from a careful inspection of (4.36).

4.7 Solutions about a Regular Singular Point—Theorem

The examples of Section 4.6 suggest that for any linear second-order differential equation with a regular singular point at the origin there is at least one solution of the form $|t|^z u(t)$, where $u(t)$ is analytic at $t = 0$. Indeed, let the equation be

$$L(y) = t^2 y'' + t\alpha(t)y' + \beta(t)y = 0 \tag{4.31}$$

where $\alpha(t) = \Sigma_{k=0}^{\infty} \alpha_k t^k$, $\beta(t) = \Sigma_{k=0}^{\infty} \beta_k t^k$ for $|t| < r$ and not all the numbers α_0, β_0, β_1 are zero (see Section 4.6, p. 143). We consider first the case $t > 0$, and we will show by the same formal procedure used in the examples of Section 4.6 that (4.31) has at least one solution of the form $\phi(t) = t^z \Sigma_{k=0}^{\infty} c_k t^k$ $(c_0 \neq 0)$, which might be called a **generalized power series**, whose coefficients c_k may be computed recursively. It is also true (see Theorem 4.2 below) that this series expansion is a valid representation of a solution on the "punctured" interval $0 < |t| < r$ (that is, the interval $-r < t < r$ with the center $t = 0$ removed). The proof of this last statement parallels the proof of the corresponding statement in Theorem 4.1 (p. 129) for an ordinary point, and is carried out below.

Assuming the existence of a solution of the desired form on some punctured interval $0 < |t| < A$ $(A \leq r)$, we have, for $0 < t < A$,

$$\phi'(t) = \sum_{k=0}^{\infty} (k + z)c_k t^{z+k-1} \qquad \phi''(t) = \sum_{k=0}^{\infty} (k + z)(k + z - 1)c_k t^{z+k-2}$$

and therefore, using the rule for multiplying power series (property (vi), Section 4.2 (p. 123)),

$$\beta(t)\phi(t) = \left(\sum_{k=0}^{\infty} \beta_k t^k \right)\left(\sum_{k=0}^{\infty} c_k t^{k+z} \right) = \sum_{k=0}^{\infty} \left(\sum_{j=0}^{k} \beta_{k-j}c_j \right) t^{z+k}$$

$$t\alpha(t)\phi'(t) = t\left(\sum_{k=0}^{\infty} \alpha_k t^k \right)\left(\sum_{k=0}^{\infty} (k + z)c_k t^{k+z-1} \right)$$

$$= \sum_{k=0}^{\infty} \left(\sum_{j=0}^{k} \alpha_{k-j}(j + z)c_j \right) t^{z+k}$$

$$t^2\phi''(t) = \sum_{k=0}^{\infty} (k + z)(k + z - 1)c_k t^{k+z}$$

Therefore $\phi(t)$ can be a solution of $0 < t < A$ only if on this interval

$$L(\phi(t)) = t^2 \sum_{k=0}^{\infty} \left[(k+z)(k+z-1)c_k + \sum_{j=0}^{k} (j+z)c_j\alpha_{k-j} + \sum_{j=0}^{k} \beta_{k-j}c_j \right] t^k$$

$$= t^z \left\{ (z(z-1) + \alpha_0 z + \beta_0)c_0 + \sum_{k=1}^{\infty} \left[(k+z)(k+z-1)c_k \right. \right.$$

$$\left. \left. + \sum_{j=0}^{k-1} ((j+z)\alpha_{k-j} + \beta_{k-j})c_j \right] t^k \right\} = 0$$

But this relation holds on the interval $0 < t < A$ if and only if the coefficient of every power of t is zero. Writing this condition for $k = 0, 1, \ldots,$ we find

$$[(z-1) + \alpha_0 z + \beta_0]c_0 = 0$$

$$[(k+z)(k+z-1) + \alpha_0(k+z) + \beta_0]c_k + \sum_{j=0}^{k-1} (j+z)\alpha_{k-j}$$

$$+ \sum_{j=0}^{k-1} c_j\beta_{k-j} = 0 \qquad (k = 1, 2, \ldots)$$

Using the hypothesis $c_0 \neq 0$, and letting $z(z-1) + \alpha_0 z + \beta_0 = f(z)$, **the indicial polynomial,** we may write this set of equations as

$$f(z) = 0, \qquad f(k+z)c_k + \sum_{j=0}^{k-1} [(j+z)\alpha_{k-j}]c_j = 0 \qquad (k = 1, 2, \ldots)$$

$$(4.38)$$

Notice that the sum in (4.38) depends on z, on the functions $\alpha(t)$ and $\beta(t)$, and on the coefficients $c_0, c_1, \ldots, c_{k-1}$, but not on c_k. Now we proceed exactly as in the examples. The indicial equation $f(z) = 0$ determines two roots z_1 and z_2, and we must see whether the recursion formulas (4.38) can be solved for the c_k when z takes the values z_1 or z_2. But the system (4.38) corresponding to the root z_1 can obviously be solved uniquely for c_k in terms of $c_0, c_1, \ldots, c_{k-1}$ $(k = 1, 2, \ldots)$ if $f(z_1 + k) \neq 0$ **for every positive integer k.** Similarly, the system (4.38) corresponding to the root z_2 can be solved uniquely for c_k in terms of $c_0, c_1, \ldots, c_{k-1}$ $(k = 1, 2, \ldots)$ if $f(z_2 + k) \neq 0$ **for every positive integer k.** The resulting functions $\phi_1(t) = t^{z_1}\sum_{k=0}^{\infty}c_k t^k$ and $\phi_2(t) = t^{z_2}\sum_{k=0}^{\infty}c_k t^k$, with coefficients determined by this procedure are candidates for solutions of (4.31) on the interval $0 < t < A$.   We shall call such candidates for solutions **formal solutions** of (4.31).   However, as we have seen in Examples 2 and 3 of Section 4.6, we cannot always find formal solutions for both the indices z_1, z_2.

We now label the roots z_1 and z_2 so that $\Re z_1 \geq \Re z_2$, and we will show that there is always a formal solution of (4.31) of the desired form corresponding to the root z_1 with larger real part.   Indeed, since z_1 and z_2 are the roots of the indicial equation, the indicial polynomial $f(z)$ can be written $f(z) = (z - z_1)(z - z_2)$.   Thus

$$f(z_1 + k) = k(k + z_1 - z_2) \neq 0 \qquad (k = 1, 2, \ldots)$$

since both factors k and $(k + z_1 - z_2)$ have positive real parts.   Therefore the recursive formulas (4.38) give c_k uniquely in terms of $c_0, c_1, \ldots, c_{k-1}$ ($c_0 \neq 0$) for $k = 1, 2, \ldots$ when $z = z_1$, and can be solved recursively for c_k in terms of c_0 ($k = 1, 2, \ldots$).   This procedure gives a formal solution $\phi_1(t)$ corresponding to the root z_1 in some interval with $t > 0$.   Exactly as in the examples of Section 4.6, we verify that the above calculations are valid for $t < 0$ if t^{z_1} is replaced by $|t|^{z_1}$.

We now examine the problem of finding a second, linearly independent, solution corresponding to the index z_2.   (Obviously, if $z_1 = z_2$, there is only one solution of the desired form.)   By the argument used to find the formal solution corresponding to the index z_1, we need only check whether $f(z_2 + k) \neq 0$ for every positive integer k.   But $f(z_2 + k) = k(k - (z_1 - z_2))$, and it is clear that $f(z_2 + k) = 0$ for $k = \hat{k}$ if and only if $z_1 - z_2 = \hat{k}$.   Thus $f(z_2 + k) \neq 0$ for every positive integer k if and only if the difference between the two roots of the indicial equation is not a positive integer.   **If $z_1 - z_2$ is not a positive integer, we may solve the system** (4.38) **corresponding to** $z = z_2$, **and we obtain a second formal solution** $\phi_2(t) = |t|^{z_2} \Sigma_{k=0}^{\infty} c_k t^k$ of (4.31).

If $z_1 - z_2$ is a positive integer m, then the following situation can occur. The recursive formulas (4.38) corresponding to $z = z_2$ can certainly be solved for $c_1, c_2, \ldots, c_{m-1}$ because $f(z_2 + k) = k(k - m) \neq 0$ for $k = 1, 2, \ldots, m - 1$.   Clearly, $f(z_2 + m) = 0$ but if it should happen that $\Sigma_{j=0}^{m-1} [(j + z_2)\alpha_{m-j} + \beta_{m-j}]c_j = 0$, then the equation (4.38) with $z = z_2$, $k = m$ becomes $0 \cdot c_m = 0$, and is satisfied by an arbitrary constant c_m.   We can continue the successive calculation of $c_{m+1}, c_{m+2}, \ldots$ because $f(z_2 + k) = k(k - m) \neq 0$ for $k = m + 1, m + 2, \ldots$.   We will refer to this situation again in Section 4.8.

We may now summarize what our findings up to this point suggest.

Theorem 4.2.   *Consider the differential equation*

$$t^2 y'' + t\alpha(t)y' + \beta(t)y = 0 \tag{4.31}$$

where $\alpha(t)$ and $\beta(t)$ are analytic at $t = 0$ and have expansions $\alpha(t) = \Sigma_{k=0}^{\infty}\alpha_k t^k$, $\beta(t) = \Sigma_{k=0}^{\infty}\beta_k t^k$ which converge for $|t| < r$ for some $r > 0$. Let z_1 and z_2 be the roots of the indicial equation

$$f(z) = z(z - 1) + \alpha_0 z + \beta_0 = 0$$

with $\Re z_1 \geq \Re z_2$. Then there is a solution of the form

$$\phi_1(t) = |t|^{z_1} \sum_{k=0}^{\infty} c_k t^k \qquad (c_0 = 1)$$

in the punctured interval $0 < |t| < r$, whose coefficients c_k can be determined recursively from the equations

$$f(z_1 + k)c_k = -\sum_{j=0}^{k-1} [(j + z)\alpha_{k-j} + \beta_{k-j}]c_j \qquad (k = 1, 2, \ldots) \tag{4.39}$$

If $z_1 - z_2$ is not zero or a positive integer, there is a second, linearly independent, solution of the form

$$\phi_2(t) = |t|^{z_2} \sum_{k=0}^{\infty} \hat{c}_k t^k \qquad (\hat{c}_0 = 1)$$

also in the punctured interval $0 < |t| < r$. The coefficients $\hat{c}_k$ are also determined recursively from the equations (4.39), with z_1 replaced by z_2 and c_k replaced by $\hat{c}_k$.

It should be stressed that it is simpler in practice to substitute the assumed form of the solution into the differential equation than to use the recursive formulas (4.39) to solve for the coefficients.

We have not yet completed the proof of Theorem 4.2. It remains to be shown that the series for $\phi_1(t)$ and $\phi_2(t)$ converge for $0 < |t| < r$. Once this has been done, it follows from the properties of power series that all the calculations which lead from the assumption of the form of the solution to the expressions for $\phi_1(t)$ and $\phi_2(t)$ are justified.

To complete the proof of Theorem 4.2, let us prove the convergence of the series for $\phi_1(t)$ for $|t| < r$. The proof parallels the convergence proof in Theorem 4.1 (p. 135). Since $f(z_1 + k) = k(k + (z_1 - z_2))$, it is easy to see that

$$|f(z_1 + k)| \geq k(k - |z_1 - z_2|) \tag{4.40}$$

Since the series $\Sigma_{j=0}^{\infty}\alpha_j t^j$, $\Sigma_{j=0}^{\infty}\beta_j t^j$ converge for $|t| < r$, by Cauchy's inequality (p. 135) corresponding to every positive number $\rho < r$ there is a constant $M > 0$ such that

$$|\alpha_j|\rho^j \leq M \qquad |\beta_j|\rho^j \leq M \qquad (j = 0, 1, 2, \ldots) \tag{4.41}$$

Using (4.41) and (4.40) in (4.39), we obtain

$$k(k - |z_1 - z_2|)|c_k| \leq M \sum_{j=0}^{k-1} (j + |z_1| + 1)|c_j|\rho^{j-k}$$
$$(k = 1, 2, \ldots) \tag{4.42}$$

Let N be the integer such that $N - 1 \leq |z_1 - z_2| < N$, define $C_0 = |c_0|$, $C_1 = |c_1|, \ldots, C_{N-1} = |c_{N-1}|$, and then define C_k recursively for $k \geq N$ by

$$k(k - |z_1 - z_2|)C_k = M \sum_{j=0}^{k-1} (j + |z_1| + 1)\rho^{j-k}C_j$$
$$(k = N, N + 1, \ldots) \tag{4.43}$$

Comparison of (4.43) with (4.42) shows by induction (see Exercise 1, Section 4.4, p. 136) that $0 \leq |c_k| \leq C_k$ $(k = 0, 1, 2, \ldots)$. Replacing k by $(k - 1)$ in (4.43), we obtain

$$(k - 1)(k - 1 - |z_1 - z_2|)C_{k-1} = M \sum_{j=0}^{k-2} (j + |z_1| + 1)\rho^{j-k+1}C_j \tag{4.44}$$

Combining (4.43) with (4.44), we see that, since

$$\rho M \sum_{j=0}^{k-1} (j + |z_1| + 1)\rho^{j-k}C_j = M \sum_{j=0}^{k-2} (j + |z_1| + 1)\rho^{j-k+1}C_j + M(k + |z_1|)C_{k-1}$$

we have

$$\rho k(k - |z_1 - z_2|)C_k = (k - 1)(k - 1 - |z_1 - z_2|)C_{k-1} + M(k + |z_1|)C_{k-1}$$

Now,

$$\frac{C_k}{C_{k-1}} = \frac{(k-1)(k-1-|z_1-z_2|) + M(k+|z_1|)}{\rho k(k-|z_1-z_2|)}$$

and $\lim_{k\to\infty} C_k/C_{k-1} = 1/\rho$. The ratio test shows that the series $\Sigma_{k=0}^{\infty}C_k t^k$ converges for $|t| < \rho$. This implies, by the comparison test, that $\Sigma_{k=0}^{\infty}c_k t^k$ also converges for $|t| < \rho$. Since this is true for every $\rho < r$, the series $\Sigma_{k=0}^{\infty}c_k t^k$ converges for $|t| < r$. Exactly the same argument can be used to prove the convergence of the series for $\phi_2(t)$, and the proof of Theorem 4.2 is now complete. The reader should observe that the convergence proof is similar to the convergence proof in Theorem 4.1, p. 135, (and in fact contains the earlier convergence proof as a special case). ∎

Example 1.   Consider the equation $t^2y'' + (\frac{3}{2})ty' + ty = 0$. Here $t = 0$ is a regular singular point, with $\alpha(t) = \frac{3}{2}$, $\beta(t) = t$; these functions are obviously analytic at $t = 0$, and their power series expansions, being the functions themselves, converge for $|t| < \infty$. The indicial equation is $z(z-1) + (\frac{3}{2})z = z^2 + z/2 = 0$, and thus $z_1 = 0$, $z_2 = -\frac{1}{2}$. Since $z_1 - z_2$ is not a positive integer, Theorem 4.2 tells us that this differential equation has two linearly independent solutions $\phi_1(t) = 1 + \Sigma_{k=1}^{\infty}c_k t^k$ and $\phi_2(t) = |t|^{-1/2}(1 + \Sigma_{k=1}^{\infty}c_k t^k)$ valid for $0 < |t| < \infty$. Observe also that in spite of the fact that the differential equation is undefined at the singular point $t = 0$ one of the solutions, namely ϕ_1, is analytic at $t = 0$.

•EXERCISES

1.   Write out the statement of Theorem 4.2 for the case of a regular singular point at $t = t_0$. [*Hint:* Recall the discussion at the beginning of Section 4.6, p. 142.]

2.   Prove that if $z_1 - z_2$ is not a positive integer, the solutions ϕ_1 and ϕ_2 are linearly independent.

3.   Use Theorem 4.2 to determine the number of solutions of the form $|t|^z\Sigma_{k=1}^{\infty}c_k t^k$ ($c_0 = 1$) for each of the following, **without solving the differential equation.** Also, use Theorem 4.2 to determine the region of validity of each solution, and whether each solution is analytic at the singular point. Note that in parts (c), (e), (f) the nature of the solution may depend on the values of constants, and discuss the various possibilities.
   (a) $t^2y'' + ty' + (t^2 - \frac{1}{4})y = 0$.
   (b) $3t^2y'' + 5ty' + 3ty = 0$.
   (c) $ty'' + (1 - t)y' + \gamma y = 0$ (γ constant).
   (d) $t^2y'' + ty' + (t^2 - 4)y = 0$.
   (e) $t^2y'' + ty' + (t^2 - \gamma^2)y = 0$ (Bessel equation).

(f) $t(1 - t)y'' + [c - (a + b + 1)t]y' - aby = 0$ (hypergeometric equation).

(g) $t^2y'' + ty' + (1 - t)y = 0$.

(h) $t^2y'' + te^ty' + y = 0$.

4.   For each equation in Exercise 3, find the solutions of the form $|t|^z\sum_{k=0}^{\infty}c_kt^k$ ($c_0 = 1$). For the equation in Exercise 3(c) show that this solution is a polynomial of degree n, a constant multiple of which is called the Laguerre polynomial of degree n, if the constant γ is the nonnegative integer n.

5.   Use the result of Exercise 1 to determine the number of solutions of the form $|t + 1|^z\sum_{k=0}^{\infty}c_k(t + 1)^k$ ($c_0 = 1$), and of the form $|t - 1|^z\sum_{k=0}^{\infty}c_k(t - 1)^k$ ($c_0 = 1$), of the Legendre equation $(1 - t^2)y'' - 2ty' + \alpha(\alpha + 1)y = 0$. Do **not** calculate the coefficients—see Exercise 6 below.

6.   (a) Find a solution of the equation $(1 - t^2)y'' - 2ty' + \alpha(\alpha + 1)y = 0$ of the form $|t - 1|^z\sum_{k=0}^{\infty}c_k(t - 1)^k$ ($c_0 = 1$). [*Hint:* The algebra is easier if you do not multiply by $(1 - t)/(1 + t)$ to put the equation in the form (4.28); since $t = 1 + (t - 1)$ it is easy to expand all the coefficients in powers of $(t - 1)$ and then substitute the assumed form of the solution into the equation.]

(b) Show that for certain values of α there exists a polynomial solution.

4.8   Solutions about a Regular Singular Point— Exceptional Cases

For the differential equation

$$L(y) = t^2y'' + t\alpha(t)y' + \beta(t)y = 0 \tag{4.31}$$

having a regular singular point at $t = 0$, Theorem 4.2 (p. 154) guarantees the existence of at least one solution of the form $\phi_1(t) = |t|^{z_1}\sum_{k=0}^{\infty}c_kt^k$ ($c_0 = 1$), valid in a punctured neighborhood of $t = 0$, where z_1 is that root of the indicial equation which has the larger real part. We have also seen that if the second root z_2 of the indicial equation is either equal to z_1 or differs from z_1 by a positive integer, then equation (4.31) may fail to have a second, linearly independent, solution of the same form as ϕ_1. Our object is to discover the form of a second, linearly independent, solution in these exceptional cases. Our method is based on the device employed in Section 3.4 to find a second solution of a linear differential equation with constant coefficients when its characteristic equation has equal roots. We will discuss both types of exceptional cases, and will summarize our findings in Theorem 4.3. Then we will make a few remarks about the nth-order equation.

Case 1.   ($z_1 = z_2$)   We shall work on the interval $0 < t < r$ in a formal (nonrigorous) way.   In order to proceed, we must first refer to our previous calculations at the beginning of Section 4.7 preceding equation (4.38) (p. 152).   There we found that if $\phi(t) = t^z\Sigma_{k=0}^{\infty}c_kt^k$ for $0 < t < r$ where $c_0 \neq 0$, then

$$L(\phi(t)) = t^z \left\{ (z(z-1) + \alpha_0 z + \beta_0)c_0 + \sum_{k=1}^{\infty} \left[(k+z)(k+z-1)c_k \right.\right.$$
$$\left.\left. + \sum_{j=0}^{k-1} ((j+z)\alpha_{k-j} + \beta_{k-j})c_j \right] t^k \right\}$$
$$= t^z \left\{ c_0 f(z) + \sum_{k=1}^{\infty} [f(z+k)c_k + g_k(z)]t^k \right\} \tag{4.45}$$

where

$$f(z) = z(z-1) + \alpha_0 z + \beta_0 \qquad g_k(z) = \sum_{j=0}^{k-1} [(j+z)\alpha_{k-j} + \beta_{k-j}]c_j$$

We now proceed a little differently than in Section 4.7.   Since $f(z)$ is a quadratic polynomial, numbers z such that $f(z+k) \neq 0$ for $k = 1, 2, \ldots$ certainly exist (there are only two zeros of $f(z)$).   For any such z we may therefore define c_k recursively by the relations

$$c_0(z) = c_0 \neq 0 \qquad f(z+k)c_k = -g_k(z) \qquad (k = 1, 2, \ldots) \tag{4.46}$$

where c_0 is any constant.   In other words, we define $c_k(z)$ as a solution of the recursive system (4.46), but for an unspecified z.   The equation (4.45) then becomes

$$L[\Phi(t, z)] = c_0 t^z f(z) \qquad (c_0 \neq 0) \tag{4.47}$$

Here we have written $\Phi(t, z)$ in place of $\phi(t)$ to emphasize the dependence of the function $\phi(t) = t^z\Sigma_{k=0}c_kt^k$ on both t and z.   It is obvious, incidentally, that the function $\Phi(t, z_1)$ is a solution of (4.31) where z_1 the double root of the indicial equation $f(z) = 0$; this is the solution which we previously called $\phi_1(t)$.   However, (4.47) gives more information than this.

● **EXERCISE**

1. Show by induction that $c_k(z)$, defined by (4.46), is a rational function of z (that is, a quotient of two polynomials in z).

Since $z_1 = z_2$ is a double root of $f(z) = 0$, we have $f(z_1) = f'(z_1) = 0$, see Appendix 2. If we differentiate (4.47) with respect to z we obtain

$$\frac{\partial}{\partial z} L[\Phi(t, z)] = c_0[t^z f'(z) + f(z) \log z] \qquad (c_0 \neq 0)$$

and therefore, inverting the operations $\partial/\partial z$ and L and then setting $z = z_1$ (just as in Section 3.4 (p. 90)), we have

$$\frac{\partial}{\partial z} L[\Phi(t, z)]_{z=z_1} = L\left[\frac{\partial \Phi}{\partial z}(t, z_1)\right] = 0$$

This shows that $(\partial \Phi/\partial z)(t, z_1)$ is also a solution of (4.31); we will denote this solution by $\phi_2(t)$. From the definition of $\Phi(t, z)$ we see that

$$\phi_2(t) = \frac{\partial}{\partial z}\left[t^z \sum_{k=0}^{\infty} c_k(z)t^k\right]_{z=z_1} = t^{z_1} \log t \sum_{k=0}^{\infty} c_k(z_1)t^k + t^{z_1} \sum_{k=0}^{\infty} c_k'(z_1)t^k$$

$$= \phi_1(t) \log t + t^{z_1} \sum_{k=0}^{\infty} c_k'(z_1)t^k$$

where $\phi_1(t)$ is the solution already found in Section 4.7. Since $c_0(z)$ is constant, $c_0'(z_1) = 0$, and the series $\sum_{k=0}^{\infty} c_k'(z_1)t^k$ actually begins with a term in t. Thus we may write

$$\phi_2(t) = \phi_1(t) \log t + t^{z_1} \sum_{k=1}^{\infty} c_k'(z_1)t^k \qquad (4.48)$$

For t negative, we must replace t^{z_1} by $|t|^{z_1}$ and $\log t$ by $\log |t|$.

•EXERCISE

2. Show that $c_k'(z_1)$ exists for $k = 1, 2, \ldots$. [*Hint:* Use the result of Exercise 1 and the fact that $f(z_1 + k) \neq 0$ for $k = 1, 2, \ldots$.]

The result of Exercise 2 shows that the series (4.48) is well defined. Our work suggests that in the case $z_1 = z_2$, (4.31) has a second, linearly independent, solution of the form

$$\phi_2(t) = |t|^{z_1+1} \sum_{k=0}^{\infty} b_k t^k + \phi_1(t) \log |t| \qquad (4.49)$$

with the coefficients b_k determined by substitution of (4.49) into (4.31), p. 157. **In an actual problem** (see Example 1 below) **we first find the solution ϕ_1 as in Theorem 4.2, and then if $z_2 = z_1$ we assume a second solution of the form (4.49), substitute it into the differential equation, and solve for the coefficients b_k.**

To justify (4.49) as a second solution, valid for $0 < |t| < r$ (where the power series expansions of $\alpha(t)$, $\beta(t)$ in (4.31) converge for $|t| < r$), we substitute (4.49) into (4.31) and we find that the coefficients b_k can be determined recursively in terms of the already known coefficients c_k $(k = 0, 1, 2, \ldots)$. The operations required in this substitution are, of course, justified on any interval $0 < |t| < B$ on which both series in (4.49) converge; as before, the point $t = 0$ must be omitted. It can then be shown, as in the proof of Theorem 4.2, that the series in (4.49) converge in $0 < |t| < r$. However, we shall omit the proof.

•EXERCISE

3. Prove that the solutions $\phi_1(t)$ and $\phi_2(t)$ are linearly independent in $0 < |t| < r$.

Example 1. Find two linearly independent solutions of the equation $t^2 y'' + t y' + t y = 0$ valid near $t = 0$. As we saw in Example 2 and Exercise 10, Section 4.6 (p. 148), the indicial equation is $z^2 = 0$, which has $z = 0$ as a double root, and one solution is

$$\phi_1(t) = \sum_{k=0}^{\infty} (-1)^k \frac{t^k}{1^2 \cdot 2^2 \cdot \, \cdots \, \cdot k^2}$$

valid for $0 < |t| < \infty$. We now try to find a second solution of the form

$$\phi_2(t) = |t| \sum_{k=0}^{\infty} b_k t^k + \phi_1(t) \log |t| \tag{4.50}$$

suggested by (4.49). Working on the interval $t > 0$, we find

$$\phi_2'(t) = \sum_{k=0}^{\infty} (k + 1) b_k t^k + \phi_1'(t) \log t + \frac{1}{t} \phi_1(t)$$

$$\phi_2''(t) = \sum_{k=0}^{\infty} (k + 1) k b_k t^{k-1} + \phi_1''(t) \log t + \frac{2}{t} \phi_1'(t) - \frac{1}{t^2} \phi_1(t)$$

Substituting into the differential equation and using the fact that ϕ_1 is a solution, which causes the coefficient of log t to vanish, we find

$$b_0 t + \sum_{k=1}^{\infty} [(k+1)kb_k + (k+1)b_k + b_{k-1}]t^{k+1} + 2t\phi_1'(t) = 0$$

Substituting the series for $\phi_1'(t)$, combining into a single series, and equating the coefficient of each power of t to zero, we find $b_0 = 2$ and

$$(k+1)^2 b_k = -b_{k-1} - \frac{(-1)^{k+1}2(k+1)}{1^2 2^2 \cdots (k+1)^2} \qquad (k = 1, 2, \ldots)$$

This is a recursive relation from which the coefficients b_k can be determined, though not without some difficulty. According to the remarks following the equation (4.49), and also Theorem 4.3 below, the solution ϕ_2 is also valid for $0 < |t| < \infty$.

• EXERCISE

4. Compute at least 4 nonzero terms of the solution ϕ_2 in Example 1.

Case 2. $(z_1 - z_2 = m$ *(positive integer))*   From Theorem 4.2 we already know that there exists a solution ϕ_1 of the form $\phi_1(t) = |t|^{z_1}\sum_{k=0}^{\infty}c_k t^k$ $(c_0 = 1)$, where $\Re z_1 > \Re z_2$. As in Case 1, we proceed without regard for rigor in order to determine the form of a second solution. We refer to the remarks already made about the case $z_1 - z_2 = m$ immediately preceding the statement of Theorem 4.2 in Section 4.7 (p. 153). From these it follows that we can use the previously employed recursion formulas

$$f(k+z)c_k = -g_k(z) \tag{4.46}$$

with $z = z_2$, to determine the numbers $c_1(z_2), \ldots, c_{m-1}(z_2)$ just as before, but since $f(z_2 + m) = f(z_1) = 0$ we cannot define $c_m(z_2)$. As we mentioned in Section 4.7, if in a particular problem it happens that $g_m(z_2)$ is also zero (that is, if $g_m(z)$ has a factor $(z - z_2)$), then we could define $c_m(z_2)$ arbitrarily. We have no difficulty in proceeding to find $c_{m+1}(z_2)$, $c_{m+2}(z_2), \ldots$ from (4.46), and we will obtain a second, linearly independent, solution $\phi_2(t) = |t|^{z_2}\sum_{k=0}^{\infty}c_k(z_2)t^k$. However, if $g_m(z_2) \neq 0$ (and this is the usual case in practice) the above method does not work.

To proceed with the case $g_m(z_2) \neq 0$, we observe that because of its definition (p. 153), $g_k(z)$ is a linear homogeneous function of $c_0, c_1, \ldots,$ c_{k-1}. This remark enables us to introduce $(z - z_2)$ as a factor of $g_k(z)$ by a proper choice of c_0. Namely, we define $c_0(z) = z - z_2$, and $c_1(z)$, $c_2(z), \ldots, c_{m-1}(z)$ by (4.46). Then $c_0(z), c_1(z), \ldots, c_{m-1}(z)$ all have a factor $(z - z_2)$, and $c_0(z_2) = c_1(z_2) = \cdots = c_{m-1}(z_2) = 0$, but (4.46) can be solved for $c_m(z)$ for all z. This means that if we define

$$\psi(t, z) = t^z \sum_{k=0}^{\infty} c_k(z)t^k \qquad (c_0(z) = z - z_2) \tag{4.51}$$

for $t > 0$, and if we substitute (4.51) into the differential equation (4.31), p. 157, then we find, as in Case 1 of this section,

$$L[\psi(t, z)] = c_0(z)f(z)t^z = (z - z_2)f(z)t^z \tag{4.52}$$

This implies that $\psi(t, z_2)$ is a formal solution of (4.31). However, if we examine $\psi(t, z_2)$, we find from (4.51) and $c_0(z_2) = \cdots = c_{m-1}(z_2) = 0$ that $\psi(t, z_2) = t^{z_2}\sum_{k=m}^{\infty} c_k(z_2)t^k = t^{z_2+m}u(t) = t^{z_1}u(t)$, where $u(t)$ is analytic at the origin and $u(0) \neq 0$. In fact, it follows easily that $\psi(t, z_2)$ is a multiple of the solution $\phi_1(t)$ already known, and we have apparently accomplished nothing.

• EXERCISE

5. Show that $\psi(t, z_2) = a\phi_1(t)$ for some constant a.

However, if we differentiate (4.52) with respect to z, we find

$$\frac{\partial}{\partial z} L[\psi(t, z)] = L\left[\frac{\partial \psi}{\partial z}(t, z)\right] = t^z f(z) + (z - z_2)[t^z f'(z) + t^z f(z) \log t]$$

so that $L[(\partial \psi/\partial z)(t, z_2)] = 0$ for each $t > 0$. Thus, at least formally, we have a solution $\phi_2(t) = (\partial \psi/\partial z)(t, z_2)$ of (4.31). From (4.51),

$$\frac{\partial \psi}{\partial z}(t, z_2) = t^{z_2} \sum_{k=0}^{\infty} c_k'(z_2)t^k + t^{z_2} \log t \sum_{k=0}^{\infty} c_k(z_2)t^k \qquad (c_0(z) = z - z_2)$$

and using the information that $c_0(z_2) = c_1(z_2) = \cdots = c_{m-1}(z_2) = 0$, and that $c_k(z_2)$ is a finite constant, we have

$$\phi_2(t) = \frac{\partial \psi}{\partial z}(t, z_2) = t^{z_2} \sum_{k=0}^{\infty} c_k'(z_2)t^k + t^{z_2} \log t \sum_{k=m}^{\infty} c_k(z_2)t^k$$

From Exercise 5 and the calculations preceding it, we see finally that for $t > 0$, our second formal solution has the form $\phi_2(t) = t^{z_2}\sum_{k=0}^{\infty}c_k'(z_2)t^k + a\phi_1(t) \log t$, where a is a constant and ϕ_1 is the solution corresponding to the index z_1.

These findings suggest (see also Theorem 4.3 below) that (4.31), p. 157, has, in the case $z_1 - z_2 = m > 0$ an integer, a second, linearly independent, solution of the form

$$\phi_2(t) = |t|^{z_2} \sum_{k=0}^{\infty} b_k t^k + a\phi_1(t) \log |t| \tag{4.53}$$

valid for $0 < t < r$, where a is a constant (possibly zero), and where ϕ_1 is the solution corresponding to the index z_1 given by Theorem 4.2. It is the form (4.53) which we use for actual calculations in practice and we determine the constants a, b_k by direct substitution into the given differential equation. The procedure justifying (4.53) as a second solution valid for $0 < |t| < r$ would be the same as in Case 1 of this section. If the constant a turns out to be zero, then the solution (4.53) reduces to the special case mentioned earlier in which c_m may be chosen arbitrarily. To illustrate the idea we consider a rather special problem.

Example 2. The equation $t^2y'' + t^2y' - ty = 0$, discussed in Example 3, Section 4.6 (p. 149), has $z_1 = 1$, $z_2 = 0$ as roots of the indicial equation corresponding to the regular singular point $t = 0$, and the solution corresponding to the index $z_1 = 1$ is $\phi_1(t) = |t|$ ($t \neq 0$). Since $z_1 - z_2 = 1$, the expression (4.53) suggests that we should assume a second solution $\phi_2(t)$ of the form

$$\phi_2(t) = \sum_{k=0}^{\infty} b_k t^k + a|t| \log t \tag{4.54}$$

Taking $t > 0$, we find

$$\phi_2'(t) = a + a \log t + \sum_{k=1}^{\infty} kb_k t^{k-1} \qquad \phi_2''(t) = \frac{a}{t} + \sum_{k=1}^{\infty} k(k-1)b_k t^{k-2}$$

Thus the requirement that

$$t^2\phi_2''(t) + t^2\phi_2'(t) - t\phi_2(t) = at + \sum_{k=0}^{\infty} k(k-1)b_k t^k + at^2 + at^2 \log t$$

$$+ \sum_{k=1}^{\infty} kb_k t^{k+1} - at^2 \log t - \sum_{k=0}^{\infty} b_k t^{k+1} = 0$$

implies

$$at + at^2 - b_0 t + \sum_{k=1}^{\infty} [(k+1)kb_{k+1} + (k-1)b_k]t^{k+1} = 0$$
$$a - b_0 = 0$$
$$a + 2 \cdot 1 b_2 = 0$$
$$k(k+1)b_{k+1} = -(k-1)b_k \qquad (k = 2, 3, \ldots)$$

We may choose $b_0 = 1$, and then $a = 1$, $b_2 = -\frac{1}{2}$, $b_3 = \frac{1}{2} \cdot 2 \cdot 3 \cdots$
We note that b_1 is left undetermined; this is because t is a solution of the differential equation and therefore any multiple of t is a solution.   In particular, we may take $b_1 = 0$.   Substitution of these results into (4.54) gives the second solution for $t > 0$.

• EXERCISES

6. Show that formally we obtain the same solution for $t < 0$ from (4.54).

7. For the differential equation in Example 2, obtain a general formula for b_k and show that the solution ϕ_2 is valid for $0 < |t| < \infty$.

8. In Example 2 find the solution ϕ_2 by the method of Section 3.7, p. 99.

We summarize our findings as follows:

Theorem 4.3.   *Consider the differential equation*

$$t^2 y'' + t\alpha(t)y' + \beta(t)y = 0 \tag{4.31}$$

where α and β are analytic at $t = 0$ and have power series expansions valid for $|t| < r$, with some $r > 0$.   Let z_1, z_2 ($\Re z_1 \geq \Re z_2$) be the roots of the indicial equation

$$f(z) = z(z - 1) + \alpha(0)z + \beta(0) = 0$$

Then if $z_1 = z_2$, there are two linearly independent solutions ϕ_1, ϕ_2 of the form

$$\phi_1(t) = |t|^{z_1} \sum_{k=0}^{\infty} c_k t^k \qquad (c_0 = 1)$$

$$\phi_2(t) = |t|^{z_1 + 1} \sum_{k=0}^{\infty} b_k t^k + \phi_1(t) \log |t|$$

valid for $0 < |t| < r$, whose coefficients c_k, b_k may be determined by direct substitution in the equation (4.31).

If $z_1 - z_2$ is a positive integer m, there are two linearly independent solutions ϕ_1, ϕ_2 of the form

$$\phi_1(t) = |t|^{z_1} \sum_{k=0}^{\infty} c_k t^k \qquad (c_0 = 1)$$

$$\phi_2(t) = |t|^{z_2} \sum_{k=0}^{\infty} b_k t^k + a\phi_1(t) \log |t| \qquad (b_0 \neq 0)$$

valid for $0 < |t| < r$, where a is a constant (possibly zero) and the coefficients c_k, b_k may be determined recursively by direct substitution into the equation (4.31).

•EXERCISES

9.   Prove the linear independence of ϕ_1 and ϕ_2 in both cases covered by Theorem 4.3.

10. Write out the statement of Theorem 4.3 for a regular singular point at some point $t = t_0 \neq 0$.

11. Obtain two linearly independent solutions valid near $t = 0$ for each of the following differential equations.

(a) $4ty'' + 2y' + y = 0$.   (c) $t^2y'' + t^2y' - 2y = 0$.

(b) $ty'' + y' - y = 0$.   (d) $t^2y'' + 5ty' + (3 - t^2)y = 0$.

12. Consider the Bessel equation

$$t^2y'' + ty' + (t^2 - \alpha^2)y = 0$$

where $\alpha \geq 0$ is a constant.

(a) Find the roots of the indicial equation.

(b) **Without computing the solutions,** discuss (using Theorems 4.2 and 4.3) the forms of solutions valid near the regular singular point $t = 0$. Be sure to consider all possibilities for different values of α.

13. Find the general solution of the hypergeometric equation $t(1 - t)y'' + [c - (a + b + 1)t]y' - aby = 0$, where a, b, c are positive constants, valid near the regular singular point $t = 0$. [*Hint:* Solve the indicial equation and then consider 5 cases—(i) c not zero or an integer, (ii) $c = 1$, (iii) $c = 0$, (iv) c a positive integer ≥ 2, (v) c a negative integer. The answer to part (i) is

$$\phi_1(t) = 1 + \frac{ab}{1!c} t + \frac{a(a + 1)b(b + 1)}{2!c(c + 1)} t^2 + \cdots$$

$$+ \frac{a(a + 1) \cdots (a + k - 1)b(b + 1) \cdots (b + k - 1)}{k!c(c + 1) \cdots (c + k - 1)} t^k + \cdots$$

$$= F(a, b, c, t) \qquad (|t| < 1)$$

$$\phi_2(t) = |t|^{1-c} F(a - c + 1, b - c + 1, 2 - c, t) \qquad (0 < |t| < 1)$$

(For further details concerning the hypergeometric equation see [12] or [17].)]
14. Repeat Exercise 13 relative to the singular point $t = 1$.

We conclude this section with a few remarks about the case that $t = 0$ is a regular singular point of a general nth-order equation. According to the definition in Section 4.5 (p. 140), we may write such an equation in the form

$$L_n(y) = t^n y^{(n)} + t^{n-1}\alpha_1(t)y^{(n-1)} + \cdots + t\alpha_{n-1}(t)y' + \alpha_n(t)y = 0 \quad (4.55)$$

where $\alpha_1, \alpha_2, \ldots, \alpha_n$ are analytic at $t = 0$. It is apparent that the methods of Section 4.7 and this section are applicable to (4.55). Naturally, the situation can now be considerably more complicated. We again assume a solution of the form $\phi(t) = |t|^z \sum_{k=0}^{\infty} c_k t^k$ $(c_0 = 1)$. Formal substitution into (4.55) leads to

$$L_n(\phi) = t^z \left[f_n(z) + \sum_{k=1}^{\infty} \{f_n(z + k)c_k - g_k(z)\} t^k \right]$$

where $f_n(z)$ is the indicial polynomial.

$$\begin{aligned} f_n(z) = z(z - 1) \cdots (-z - n + 1) \\ + \alpha_1(0)z(z - 1) \cdots (z - n + 2) + \cdots + \alpha_n(0) \end{aligned}$$

of degree n, and $g_k(z)$ is a linear homogeneous expression in $c_0, c_1, \ldots, c_{k-1}$, as in the second order case. Obviously ϕ is a formal solution of (4.55) if the coefficients c_k are determined recursively from the relation $f_n(z + k)c_k = g_k(z)$ (which can certainly be done if $f_n(z + k) \neq 0$ for $k = 1, 2, \ldots$), and if z is a root of the indicial equation $f_n(z) = 0$. There are n roots of the indicial equation; if they are all distinct and no two of them differ by an integer, there will be n linearly independent formal solutions of the assumed form. This leads to an extension of Theorem 4.2 to the case of the equation (4.55). The devices used to obtain Theorem 4.3 for the exceptional cases of equal roots and roots differing by a positive integer in the second-order case can also be adapted to this more general case. The interested reader is referred to more advanced books such as [5], pp. 132–135, or [16]. To examine one very trivial case of (4.55) when $n = 1$, it is suggested that the reader find a series solution valid near $t = 0$ of the equation $ty' + \alpha(t)y = 0$, where α is analytic at $t = 0$ and has a series expansion valid for $|t| < r$, with some $r > 0$.

4.9 The Bessel Equation and Some Properties of Bessel Functions

As an application of Theorems 4.2 and 4.3, we discuss one of the important equations of mathematical physics. The Bessel equation arises in a natural way in many problems having axial (cylindrical) symmetry, and may be written in the form

$$L(y) = t^2 y'' + ty' + (t^2 - p^2)y = 0 \tag{4.56}$$

where p is a constant, possibly complex, with $\Re p \geq 0$. The point $t = 0$ is a regular singular point, and in the notation of Theorems 4.2 and 4.3 $\alpha(t) = 1$ and $\beta(t) = -p^2 + t^2$. Both these functions are analytic at $t = 0$ and their power series expansions converge for $|t| < \infty$. The indicial polynomial is $f(z) = z^2 - p^2$, and its zeros are $z_1 = p$, $z_2 = -p$. According to Theorem 4.2, if $p \neq 0$ and if $z_1 - z_2 = 2p$ is not a positive integer (that is, if p is not zero, an integer, or half an integer), there exist two linearly independent solutions ϕ_1, ϕ_2 of (4.56), valid for $0 < |t| < \infty$, of the form

$$\phi_1(t) = |t|^p \sum_{k=0}^{\infty} c_k t^k \qquad (c_0 \neq 0) \tag{4.57}$$

$$\phi_2(t) = |t|^{-p} \sum_{k=0}^{\infty} \hat{c}_k t^k \qquad (\hat{c}_0 \neq 0) \tag{4.58}$$

where the coefficients c_k and $\hat{c}_k$ are determined recursively by substitution in (4.56).

We first compute the solution ϕ_1 and as usual we assume $t > 0$. Then we find

$$\phi_1'(t) = \sum_{k=0}^{\infty} c_k(p + k)t^{p+k-1} \qquad \phi_1''(t) = \sum_{k=0}^{\infty} c_k(p + k)(p + k - 1)t^{p+k-2}$$

so that

$$L[\phi_1(t)] = t^p \left[f(p)c_0 + f(p + 1)c_1 t + \sum_{k=0}^{\infty} \{f(p + k)c_k + c_{k-2}\}t^k \right] = 0$$

from which we conclude $c_1 = 0$, $f(p + k)c_k + c_{k-2} = 0$ $(k = 2, 3, \ldots)$.

Since $f(p + k) = (p + k)^2 - p^2 = k(2p + k) \neq 0$, we have

$$c_1 = c_3 = c_5 = \cdots = 0$$

$$c_2 = -\frac{c_0}{2^2(p + 1)}, \quad c_4 = \frac{c_0}{2^4 2!(p + 1)(p + 2)}, \quad \cdots$$

$$c_{2m} = \frac{(-1)^m c_0}{2^{2m} m!(p + 1)(p + 2) \cdots (p + m)}, \quad \cdots$$

•EXERCISE

1. Establish the formula for c_{2m} by induction.

We may therefore write the solution as

$$\phi_1(t) = c_0|t|^p \left\{ 1 + \sum_{m=1}^{\infty} \frac{(-1)^m t^{2m}}{2^{2m} m!(p + 1)(p + 2) \cdots (p + m)} \right\} \qquad (4.59)$$

To define the Bessel functions in the usual way, we must make a particular choice of c_0, and for this purpose we need to define the gamma function, which generalizes the notion of the factorial. This function, denoted by Γ, is given by the relation

$$\Gamma(z) = \int_0^\infty e^{-x} x^{z-1} \, dx \qquad (4.60)$$

and elementary tests for improper integrals show that this function is well defined and continuous for $\Re z > 0$. We observe that $\Gamma(1) = \int_0^\infty e^{-x} \, dx = 1$, and $\Gamma(\frac{1}{2}) = \int_0^\infty e^{-x} x^{-1/2} \, dx = 2\int_0^\infty \exp(-y^2) \, dy = \sqrt{\pi}$.* Integration by parts gives the recursion formula $\Gamma(z) = (z - 1)\Gamma(z - 1)$ for $\Re z > 1$, since

$$\Gamma(z) = \lim_{A \to \infty} \int_0^A e^{-x} x^{z-1} \, dx = \lim_{A \to \infty} \left\{ \left[-e^{-x} x^{z-1} \right]_0^A + (z - 1) \int_0^A e^{-x} x^{z-2} \, dx \right\}$$

$$= (z - 1) \int_0^\infty e^{-x} x^{z-2} \, dx = (z - 1)\Gamma(z - 1)$$

---

*To evaluate the integral $I = \int_0^\infty \exp(-y^2) \, dy$ one uses the following trick.

$$I^2 = \left[\int_0^\infty \exp(-y^2) \, dy \right]^2 = \int_0^\infty \exp(-y^2) \, dy \int_0^\infty \exp(-x^2) \, dx$$

$$= \int_0^\infty \int_0^\infty \exp[-(x^2 + y^2)] \, dx \, dy = \int_0^{\pi/2} \int_0^\infty \exp(-r^2) \, r \, dr \, d\theta = \frac{\pi}{4}$$

Thus $I = \sqrt{\pi}/2$, and the steps can be justified by methods of advanced calculus [4, p. 149].

In particular, if z is a positive integer n, we see by repeated application of this formula that $\Gamma(n) = (n - 1)!$ We also remark that it is obvious from the defining relation (4.60) that it does not define $\Gamma(z)$ for $\Re z \le 0$. However, for a positive integer k, $\Gamma(z + k)$ is well defined for $\Re z > -k$. The recursion formula tells us that $\Gamma(z + k) = (z + k - 1)(z + k - 2)$ $\cdots (z + 1)z\Gamma(z)$.   Thus we may define $\Gamma(z)$ for $-k < \Re z < 0$ ($z \ne 0$, $-1, -2, \ldots, -k$) by

$$\Gamma(z) = \frac{\Gamma(z + k)}{z(z + 1) \cdots (z + k - 1)}$$

Doing this for $k = 1, 2, \ldots$ we may define $\Gamma(z)$ for all complex z except $z = 0, -1, -2, \ldots$.   With the aid of (4.60) for $z > 0$ and using this definition for $z < 0$, the reader will easily see that for real z the graph of $\Gamma(z)$ is as given in Figure 4.2.

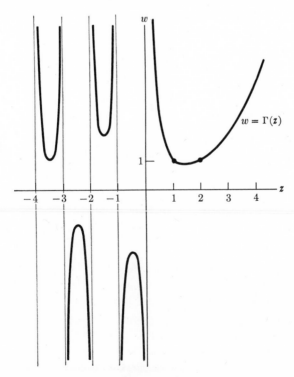

Figure 4.2

We now define c_0 in the solution ϕ_1 given by (4.59) as

$$c_0 = \frac{1}{2^p \Gamma(p + 1)} \tag{4.61}$$

The resulting function, denoted by J_p and called **the Bessel function of the first kind of index** p is given by

$$J_p(t) = \left| \frac{t}{2} \right|^p \sum_{m=0}^{\infty} \frac{(-1)^m}{m! \Gamma(p + m + 1)} \left(\frac{t}{2} \right)^{2m} \tag{4.62}$$

This function is well defined for all t and satisfies the differential equation (4.56), p. 167, for $0 < |t| < \infty$.

● **EXERCISE**

2. Show that all calculations which led to the solution ϕ_1 and then to $J_p(t)$, carry over to $z_2 = -p$ **with no change,** provided $2p$ is not an integer, so that

$$J_{-p}(t) = \left| \frac{t}{2} \right|^{-p} \sum_{m=0}^{\infty} \frac{(-1)^m}{m! \Gamma(m - p + 1)} \left(\frac{t}{2} \right)^{2m} \tag{4.63}$$

is a second, linearly independent, solution of (4.56) for $0 < |t| < \infty$. Observe that this requires the definition of $\Gamma(z)$ for $\Re z < 0$, $z \neq 0, -1, -2, \ldots$.

We have excluded the possibly exceptional cases where p is zero, an integer, or where $2p$ is an integer but p is not an integer. In each of these cases we still obtain the solution $\phi_1(t) = J_p(t)$ just as before. If $2p$ is an integer but p is not an integer, and we attempt to find a second solution $\phi_2(t) = t^{-p} \sum_{k=0}^{\infty} c_k t^k$, we obtain the system of recursion relations (see Exercise 2 above) $c_1 = 0$, $f(-p + k)c_k + c_{k-2} = 0$ $(k = 2, 3, \ldots)$. Since $f(-p + k) = (-p + k)^2 - p^2 = k(k - 2p)$, the method may break down for $k = 2p$, that is, when we try to calculate c_{2p}. However, since $2p$ is an odd integer and since clearly (note that $c_1 = 0$) $c_1 = c_3 = \cdots = c_{2p-2} = 0$, the equation for c_{2p} is $0 \cdot c_{2p} + 0 = 0$; **this may be satisfied with an arbitrary choice of** c_{2p}. Thus we are in the special case mentioned in Section 4.8, Theorem 4.3 (p. 164) where $a = 0$, that is, where no logarithmic term enters in the solution ϕ_2, and we may take as a second, linearly independent, solution the function $J_{-p}(t)$ given by (4.63). This might have been predicted because $\Gamma(m - p + 1)$, which appears in the definition of J_{-p}, is well defined when $2p$ is an integer but p is not an integer.

Up to this point, we have proved the following result:

Theorem 4.4.   *If p is not zero or a positive integer, then the functions $J_p(t)$ and $J_{-p}(t)$ given by (4.62) and (4.63) respectively are two linearly independent solutions of the Bessel equation (4.56) on any interval which does not include $t = 0$.*

• **EXERCISES**

3.   Let ϕ be a solution of the Bessel equation (4.56).   Show that the function ψ defined by $\psi(t) = |t|^{1/2}\phi(t)$ satisfies the equation

$$w'' + \left[1 + \frac{\frac{1}{4} - p^2}{t^2}\right] w = 0 \tag{4.64}$$

4.   Show that

$$J_{1/2}(t) = \left(\frac{2}{\pi t}\right)^{1/2} \sin t, \; J_{-1/2}(t) = \left(\frac{2}{\pi t}\right)^{1/2} \cos t$$

for $0 < t < \infty$.   [*Hint:* Use Exercise 3.]

5.   Use the definition (4.62) to show that

(a) $J_{p-1}(t) + J_{p+1}(t) = \dfrac{2p}{t} J_p(t) \quad (t \neq 0)$.

(b) $J_{p-1}(t) - J_{p+1}(t) = 2J_p'(t)$.

6.   Show that

$$J_{3/2}(t) = \left(\frac{2\pi}{t}\right)^{1/2} \left(\frac{\sin t}{t} - \cos t\right) \qquad J_{-3/2}(t) = \left(\frac{2\pi}{t}\right)^{1/2} \left(-\frac{\cos t}{t} - \sin t\right)$$

for $0 < t < \infty$.   [*Hint:* Use Exercises 4, 5, rather than solving the Bessel equation of index $\frac{3}{2}$ directly.]

With the aid of Exercises 4 and 5 above, one can, as is done in Exercise 6, obtain representations of $J_{n/2}(t)$ and $J_{-n/2}(t)$, where n is a positive integer, in terms of $\sin t$ and $\cos t$.

The cases $p = 0$ and p a positive integer in equation (4.56) (p. 167) still remain to be treated.   In the case $p = 0$, the indicial equation $z^2 = 0$ has zero as a double root, and Theorems 4.2 and 4.3 (pp. 154, 164) give the existence of two linearly independent solutions of the form

$$\phi_1(t) = \sum_{k=0}^{\infty} c_k t^k \qquad (c_0 \neq 0)$$

$$\phi_2(t) = |t| \sum_{k=0}^{\infty} b_k t^k + \phi_1(t) \log |t|$$

As we have already seen, we may take $\phi_1(t) = J_0(t)$, where, from (4.62),

$$J_0(t) = \sum_{m=0}^{\infty} \frac{(-1)^m}{(m!)^2} \left(\frac{t}{2} \right)^{2m} \tag{4.65}$$

Notice that the function $J_0(t)$ is analytic at $t = 0$ even though the differential equation (4.56) (p. 167) makes no sense there. To find a second solution, we take $0 < t < \infty$ and let

$$\phi_2(t) = \sum_{k=0}^{\infty} b_k t^{k+1} + J_0(t) \log t$$

We then compute

$$\phi_2'(t) = \sum_{k=0}^{\infty} (k+1) b_k t^k + J_0'(t) \log t + \frac{1}{t} J_0(t)$$

$$\phi_2''(t) = \sum_{k=1}^{\infty} (k+1) k b_k t^{k-1} + J_0''(t) \log t + \frac{2}{t} J_0'(t) - \frac{1}{t^2} J_0(t)$$

and substitute into (4.56) (with $p = 0$). Thus

$$L[\phi_2(t)] = \sum_{k=0}^{\infty} b_k t^{k+3} + \sum_{k=0}^{\infty} (k+1) b_k t^{k+1} + \sum_{k=1}^{\infty} (k+1) k b_k t^{k+1}$$
$$+ [t^2 J_0''(t) + t J_0'(t) + t^2 J_0(t)] \log t + 2t J_0'(t) = 0$$

and therefore, using the fact that J_0 satisfies (4.56), with $p = 0$,

$$b_0 t + 2^2 b_1 t^2 + \sum_{k=2}^{\infty} [(k+1)^2 b_k + b_{k-2}] t^{k+1} = -2 \sum_{m=1}^{\infty} \frac{(-1)^m 2m t^{2m}}{2^{2m}(m!)^2}$$

Observing that the right side of this equation contains only even powers of t, we obtain

$$b_0 = 0, \quad b_1 = 1, \quad 3^2 b_2 + b_0 = 0, \quad \ldots$$

and finally

$$b_0 = b_2 = \cdots = b_{2m} = 0, \ldots, \quad b_1 = \frac{1}{2^2}, \quad b_3 = -\frac{1}{2^2 4^2}\left(1 + \frac{1}{2}\right), \ldots$$

$$b_{2m+1} = \frac{(-1)^{m-1}}{2^{2m}(m!)^2}\left(1 + \frac{1}{2} + \cdots + \frac{1}{m}\right), \ldots$$

Thus we may define as the second solution of (4.56), with $p = 0$, the function ϕ_2, usually denoted by K_0, given by

$$\phi_2(t) = K_0(t) = -\sum_{m=1}^{\infty} \frac{(-1)^m}{(m!)^2}\left(1 + \frac{1}{2} + \cdots + \frac{1}{m}\right)\left(\frac{t}{2}\right)^{2m}$$
$$+ J_0(t) \log t \quad (4.66)$$

Clearly, (4.66) is also a solution of (4.56) with $p = 0$ for $t < 0$ if we replace $\log t$ by $\log |t|$. The solution K_0 is called the **Bessel function of the second kind of index zero.** Thus we have two linearly independent solutions $J_0(t)$ and $K_0(t)$ of (4.56) with $p = 0$ on any interval not including $t = 0$.

If p is a positive integer n, then it is easily verified from (4.62) and (4.63) (p. 170) that the functions J_n and J_{-n} are linearly dependent.

•EXERCISE

7. Show that $J_{-n}(t) = (-1)^n J_n(t)$ when n is a positive integer.

We also know that in this case the indicial equation has roots n and $-n$, and that the solution $\phi_1(t) = J_n(t)$ of (4.56) with $p = n$ corresponding to the root n exists and is given by (4.62) (p. 170). However, the recursion formulas corresponding to the root $-n$ are $c_1 = 0$, $f(-n + k)c_k + c_{k-2} = 0$ $(k = 2, 3, \ldots)$ [see Exercise 2 (p. 170 and the paragraph which follows it)]. Since $f(-n + k) = (-n + k)^2 - n^2 = k(k - 2n)$, the calculation of the coefficients c_k breaks down for $k = 2n$. We must therefore use Theorem 4.3 to find a second, linearly independent, solution. Accordingly, we substitute the function given by

$$\phi_2(t) = |t|^{-n} \sum_{k=0}^{\infty} b_k t^k + a J_n(t) \log |t|$$

into the differential equation (4.56) with $p = n$. As usual, it suffices to consider the case $t > 0$. Rather than go through the calculations, we formulate a sequence of exercises leading to the desired result.

•EXERCISES

8. Show that the coefficients $b_1, b_2, \ldots, b_{2n-1}$ are given by $b_1 = 0$, $k(k - 2n)b_k + b_{k-2} = 0$ $(k = 2, 3, \ldots, 2n - 1)$; and therefore

$$b_1 = b_3 = \cdots = b_{2n-1} = 0, \qquad b_{2m} = \frac{b_0}{2^{2m}(m!)(n - 1) \cdots (n - m)}$$

$$(m = 1, 2, \ldots, n - 1)$$

9. By examining the coefficient of t^{2n} in $L[\phi_2(t)] = 0$, show that

$$a = -\frac{b_0}{2^{n-1}(n - 1)!}$$

10. By examining the coefficients of t^{2n+1}, t^{2n+3}, $\ldots$ in $L[\phi_2(t)] = 0$, show that $b_{2n+1} = b_{2n+3} = \cdots = 0$, b_{2n} is undetermined, and $2m(2m + 2n)b_{2n+2m} + b_{2n+2m-2} = -2a(n + 2m)d_{2m}$ $(m = 1, 2, \ldots)$, where d_{2m} is the coefficient of t^{2m+n} in the expansion of $J_n(t) = \Sigma_{m=0}^{\infty} d_{2m} t^{n+2m}$.

11. Show that the choice

$$b_{2n} = -\frac{ad_0}{2}\left(1 + \frac{1}{2} + \cdots + \frac{1}{n}\right) \qquad b_0 = -2n^{-1}(n - 1)!$$

(so that $a = 1$), leads to a second solution of the form

$$\phi_2(t) = K_n(t) = -\frac{1}{2}\left|\frac{t}{2}\right|^{-n}\left\{\sum_{k=0}^{n-1}\frac{(n - k - 1)!}{k!}\left(\frac{t}{2}\right)^{2k} + \frac{1}{n!}\left(1 + \frac{1}{2} + \cdots\right.\right.$$

$$\left.+ \frac{1}{n}\right)\left(\frac{t}{2}\right)^{2n}\right\} - \frac{1}{2}\left(\frac{t}{2}\right)^n\sum_{k=0}^{\infty}\frac{(-1)^k}{k!(k + n)!}\left\{\left(1 + \frac{1}{2} + \cdots\right.\right.$$

$$\left.+ \frac{1}{k}\right) + \left(1 + \frac{1}{2} + \cdots + \frac{1}{k + n}\right)\right\}\left(\frac{t}{2}\right)^{2k} + J_n(t)\log|t| \quad (4.67)$$

called the **Bessel function of the second kind of index** n.

We can now summarize our results as follows:

Theorem 4.5. *If $p = 0$, then $J_0(t)$ and $K_0(t)$, given by (4.65) and (4.66) respectively, are two linearly independent solutions of the Bessel equation (4.56) on any interval not containing the origin. If p is a positive integer n, then $J_n(t)$ and $K_n(t)$, given by (4.62) and (4.67) respectively, are two linearly* *independent solutions of the Bessel equation* (4.56) *on any interval not containing the origin.*

•EXERCISES

12. Show that $J_0'(t) = -J_1(t)$.

13. Show that $\int t^n J_{n-1}(t)\, dt = t^n J_n(t)$. [*Hint:* Compute $\{t^n J_n(t)\}'$ and apply Exercise 5 (p. 171).]

14. Prove that between two positive zeros of $J_0(t)$ there is a zero of $J_1(t)$. [*Hint:* Use Exercise 12.]

15. Show that two positive zeros of $J_n(t)$ there is a zero of $J_{n+1}(t)$. [*Hint:* Show that $\{t^{-n} J_n(t)\}' = -t^{-n} J_{n+1}(t)$.]

16. Show that between two positive zeros of $J_{n+1}(t)$ there is a zero of $J_n(t)$.

17. Let ϕ be a solution of $y'' + p(t)y = 0$ which is not identically zero on $a < t < b$, and let ψ be a solution of $y'' + q(t)y = 0$ which is not identically zero on $a < t < b$. Suppose that p and q are both continuous on $a < t < b$, and that $q(t) > p(t)$ for $a < t < b$. Prove that if t_1, t_2 are **successive** points in $a < t < b$ at which $\phi = 0$, then there exists a point ξ, $t_1 < \xi < t_2$, such that $\psi(\xi) = 0$. [*Hint:* Suppose (without loss of generality) that $\phi(t) > 0$ for $t_1 < t < t_2$ and that $\psi(t) > 0$ for $t_1 < T < t_2$. From the differential equations, $(\psi\phi' - \phi\psi')' = \psi\phi'' - \phi\psi'' = [q(t) - p(t)]\phi(t)\psi(t)$. Integrate from t_1 to t_2. Since by hypothesis, $\int_{t_1}^{t_2}[q(t) - p(t)]\phi(t)\psi(t)\, dt > 0$, we obtain $\psi(t_2)\phi'(t_2) - \psi(t_1)\phi'(t_1) > 0$, from which we draw a contradiction.]

18. Show that for every $p > 0$, $J_p(t)$ has an infinite number of zeros on $0 < t < \infty$. [*Hint:* Combine the results of Exercises 3 (p. 171) and 17, where for $t > t_0$ the equation (4.64) satisfied by $t^{1/2} J_p(t)$ may be compared with the equation $w'' + \frac{1}{4}w = 0$ if t_0 is sufficiently large, and every solution of $w'' + \frac{1}{4}w = 0$ has infinitely many zeros on $0 < t < \infty$. Then apply Exercise 17 with $p(t) = \frac{1}{4}$, $q(t) = 1 + (\frac{1}{4} - p^2)/t^2$ for $t > t_0$.]

19. (a) Show that if $p > 0$, $\lambda > 0$, then $\phi_\lambda(t) = \sqrt{t}\, J_p(\lambda t)$ satisfies the equation $y'' + [(\frac{1}{4} - p^2)/t^2]y = -\lambda^2 y$. [*Hint:* Use the equation (4.64) (p. 171).]

(b) Prove that $(\lambda^2 - \mu^2)\int_a^b \phi_\lambda(t)\phi_\mu(t)\, dt = [\phi_\lambda(t)\phi_\mu'(t) - \phi_\mu(t)\phi_\lambda'(t)]_a^b$. *Hint:* Form $(\phi_\lambda\phi_\mu' = \phi_\mu\phi_\lambda')' = \phi_\lambda\phi_\mu'' - \phi_\mu\phi_\lambda''$, and use the differential equation.]

20. Prove that $\int_0^1 t J_p(\lambda t) J_p(\mu t)\, dt = 0$ if $\lambda \neq \mu$ whenever λ and μ are positive zeros of J_p. [*Hint:* Use Exercise 19.]

21. Prove that $\int_0^1 t J_p^2(\lambda t)\, dt = \frac{1}{2}[J_p'(\lambda)]^2$, where $p > 0$, $\lambda > 0$, and $J_p(\lambda) = 0$.

Exercises 20 and 21, with $p = 0$, and Exercise 12 give the useful formula

$$\int_0^1 t J_0(\lambda t) J_0(\mu t)\, dt = \begin{cases} 0 & (\lambda \neq \mu) \\ \frac{1}{2}J_1^2(\lambda) & (\lambda = \mu) \end{cases}$$

where λ, μ are positive zeros of J_0.

The function $K_n(t)$ given by (4.67), and known as the Neumann form of the second solution of the Bessel equation (4.56), is not the most convenient one for all applications.   In particular, as we shall see in Section 4.11, another form is useful in studying the behavior of solutions for large t.   We define the Weber form of the solution

$$Y_n(t) = \frac{2}{\pi}[K_n(t) = (\log 2 - \gamma)J_n(t)] \qquad (n = 0, 1, \ldots) \tag{4.68}$$

where the constant γ, known as Euler's constant, is defined by

$$\gamma = \lim_{k \to \infty} \left(1 + \frac{1}{2} + \cdots + \frac{1}{k} - \log k\right)$$

A proof of the fact that this limit exists may be found in [4, p. 189].

● **EXERCISE**

22. Show that J_n and Y_n are linearly independent solutions of (4.56) on any interval excluding the origin.

In applications, the Bessel equation often arises in a form different from (4.56).   For example, we have already noted that the equation (4.64) can be reduced to (4.56) by a change of dependent variable.   We give some exercises to indicate other equations whose solutions can be expressed in terms of Bessel functions.   In each case, the form of the given solution suggests the appropriate change of independent or dependent variable (or both).

● **EXERCISES**

23. Show that one solution of $t^2y'' + ty' + (k^2t^2 - p^2)y = 0$ is $J_p(kt)$, where k is a constant different from zero.   What is the general solution?

24. Show that one solution of $t^2y'' + ty' - (\beta^2 - \alpha t^{2s})y = 0$ is $J_{\beta/s}(\sqrt{\alpha}\, t^s/s)$, where α, β, s are constants and $\alpha s \neq 0$.   What is the general solution?

25. Show that one solution of $y'' + kt^m y = 0$ is

$$\sqrt{t}\, J_{1/m+2}(2\sqrt{k}\, t^{(m+2)/2}/(m+2))$$

where $mk \neq -2k$; what is the general solution?

26. Show that one solution of $(t^n y')' + kt^m y = 0$ is $t^{(1-n)/2}J_p(\sqrt{k}\, t^s/s)$, where $s = (m - n + 2)/2, p = (1 - n)/2s, n \neq m + 2$.   What is the general solution?

27. Show that one solution of $ty'' + y' + ay = 0$ is $J_0(2(at)^{1/2})$. What is the general solution?

The most general equation whose solution can be expressed in terms of Bessel functions is

$$t^2 y'' + t(a + 2bt^r)y' + [c + dt^{2s} - b(1 - a - r)t^r + b^2 t^{2r}]y = 0$$

one of whose solutions is $t^{(1-a)/2}e^{-bt^r/r}J_p(\sqrt{d}\, t^s/s)$, where $p = [((1 - a)/2)^2]^{1/2}/s - c$ (see [9], pp. 155–156). The equations given in Exercises 23–27 are special cases of this equation; they are more easily applied and perhaps less cumbersome.

If we consider solutions of the Bessel equation for values of t near $t = 0$, we observe that, for example,

$$J_0(t) = 1 - \left(\frac{t}{2}\right)^2 \sum_{m=1}^{\infty} \frac{(-1)^{m+1}}{(m!)^2}\left(\frac{t}{2}\right)^{2m-2} \qquad (|t| < \infty)$$

Since $\sum_{m=1}^{\infty}[(-1)^{m+1}/(m!)^2](t/2)^{2m-2}$ converges uniformly and absolutely for $|t| < \infty$, there exists a constant K such that $|\sum_{m=1}^{\infty}[(-1)^{m+1}/(m!)^2](t/2)^{2m-2}| \leq K$ for $|t| \leq 1$. Then $|J_0(t) - 1| \leq Kt^2/4$ for $|t| \leq 1$, or equivalently, $1 - Kt^2/4 \leq J_0(t) \leq 1 + Kt^2/4$ for $|t| \leq 1$. We may express this by saying that $J_0(t)$ behaves, for small t, like 1 up to terms of order t^2, and we write $J_0(t) = 1 + O(t^2)$ as $t \to 0$. (In general, we write $f(t) = O(g(t))$ as $t \to a$ if $|f(t)/g(t)|$ is bounded as $t \to a$.) A similar argument using the definitions of the Bessel functions and simple properties of power series gives the following estimates.

Theorem 4.6.   *As $t \to 0$*

$$J_0(t) = 1 + O(t^2) \qquad K_2(t) = \log|t| + O(t^2) \qquad Y_0(t) = \frac{2}{\pi}\log|t| + O(t^2)$$

$$J_n(t) = \frac{1}{n!}\left(\frac{t}{2}\right)^n + O(t^{n+2}) \qquad K_n(t) = \frac{(n-1)!}{2}\left|\frac{t}{2}\right|^{-n} + O(t^{-n+2})$$

$$Y_n(t) = \frac{(n-1)!}{\pi}\left|\frac{t}{2}\right|^{-n} + O(t^{-n+2}) \qquad (n \text{ a positive integer})$$

$$J_p(t) = \frac{1}{\Gamma(p+1)}\left|\frac{t}{2}\right|^p + O(t^{p+2}), \; J_{-p}(t) = \frac{1}{\Gamma(1-p)}\left|\frac{t}{2}\right|^{-p} + O(t^{-p+2})$$

$$(p > 0, \, p \text{ not an integer})$$

4.10   Singularities at Infinity

In many problems it is important to study the behavior of solutions of
the equation

$$y'' + p(t)y' + q(t)y = 0 \tag{4.69}$$

as $|t| \to \infty$. The simplest way to treat this problem is to make the change
of variable $t = 1/x$ and to study the behavior of solutions of the resulting
equation as $x \to 0$. Thus, we let ϕ be a solution of (4.69) for $|t| > R$.
Let $\psi(x) = \phi(1/x)$, $\bar{p}(x) = p(1/x)$, $\bar{q}(x) = q(1/x)$; these functions are
well defined for $|x| < 1/R$ and by the chain rule we have

$$\phi'(t) = -\frac{1}{t^2}\psi'(x) = -x^2\psi'(x), \; \phi''(t) = \frac{1}{t^4}\psi''(x) + \frac{2}{t^3}\psi'(x)$$
$$= x^4\psi''(x) + 2x^3\psi'(x)$$

Therefore ψ satisfies the equation

$$x^4z'' + [2x^3 - x^2\bar{p}(x)]z' + \bar{q}(x)z = 0 \tag{4.70}$$

in which x is the independent variable and z is the dependent variable.
Conversely, if ψ satisfies (4.70) and if $\phi(t) = \psi(1/t)$, then ϕ satisfies (4.69).
We may, of course, make a similar transformation for an equation of any
order.

Definition.   *We say that ∞ is an ordinary point, a regular singular
point, or an irregular singular point for the equation (4.69) if and only if
zero is respectively an ordinary point, a regular singular point, or an irregular
singular point for the equation (4.70).*

We remark that a function $f(t)$ is analytic at ∞ if and only if $g(x) =
f(1/x)$ is analytic at $x = 0$, or equivalently, if and only if $f(t) = \Sigma_{k=0}^{\infty}a_k/t^k$,
where the series converges for $|t| > r$, with some $r \geq 0$.

Example 1.   Consider the equation $y'' + ay' + by = 0$, where a and
b are constants. The change of variable $t = 1/x$ transforms this equation
to $x^4z'' + (2x^3 - ax^2)z' + bz = 0$, which obviously has an irregular
singular point at $x = 0$. Thus the given equation has an irregular
singular point at $t = \infty$.

•EXERCISES

1. Show that the Euler equation $t^2y'' + aty' + by = 0$, where a and b are constants, has a regular singular point at ∞.

2. Show that the hypergeometric equation

$$t(1 - t)y'' + [c - (a + b + 1)t]y' - aby = 0$$

has regular singular points at 0, 1, and ∞.

3. Show that the change of variable $t = \tau/\beta$ transforms the hypergeometric equation (Exercise 2) to an equation having regular singular points at $\tau = 0$, $\tau = \beta$, $\tau = \infty$. Let $\beta \to \infty$ in the transformed equation, and show that the resulting equation, called the **confluent hypergeometric equation** has a regular singular point at 0 and an irregular singular point at ∞.

4. Show that the Bessel equation has an irregular singular point at ∞.

5. Prove that ∞ is a regular singular point for the equation (4.69) if and only if (4.69) can be written in the form

$$t^2y'' + t\alpha(t)y' + \beta(t)y = 0$$

where $\alpha(t)$ and $\beta(t)$ are analytic at ∞, that is, $\alpha(t) = \Sigma_{k=0}^{\infty}\alpha_k/t^k$, $\beta(t) = \Sigma_{k=0}^{\infty}\beta_k/t^k$, with these series converging for $|t| > r$ with some $r \geq 0$.

6. Obtain a criterion for ∞ to be an ordinary point for the equation (4.69).

Naturally, Theorems 4.1 (p. 129), 4.2 (p. 154), and 4.3 (p. 164) can be applied to the equation (4.69) at the point $t = \infty$ without change in principle; we must only replace every series in powers of t by a series in powers of $1/t$. For example, if ∞ is an ordinary point, we expand $p(t)$ and $q(t)$ in powers of $1/t$ and we look for two linearly independent solutions, valid near $t = \infty$, of the form $\Sigma_{k=0}^{\infty}c_kt^{-k}$ and $\Sigma_{k=0}^{\infty}d_kt^{-k}$. We substitute into the differential equation to obtain recursion formulas for the coefficients c_k and d_k. For a regular singular point at $t = \infty$, the obvious modifications of Theorems 4.2 and 4.3 hold.

•EXERCISES

7. State the analogues of Theorems 4.1, 4.2, and 4.3 relative to the point at infinity.

8. (a) Compute the roots of the indicial equation relative to the point at infinity of the hypergeometric equation $t(1 - t)y'' + [c - (a + b + 1)t]y' - aby = 0$.

(b) Find two linearly independent solutions valid for large t when $a \neq b$. What is the range of validity of these solutions?

9.   Show that the change of variable $\tau = (1 - t)/t$ transforms the Legendre equation $(1 - t^2)y'' - 2ty' + \alpha(\alpha + 1)y = 0$ into a hypergeometric equation, and calculate a, b, c.   [*Hint:* Put $z(\tau) = y(t(\tau))$, and use the chain rule.]

4.11   Irregular Singular Points, with an Introduction to Asymptotic Expansions

We have encountered equations of importance for applications which have irregular singular points.   For example, the Bessel equation has an irregular singular point at ∞, as does every linear equation with constant coefficients.   To illustrate the type of behavior we may expect at an irregular singular point, we consider the simple first-order equation

$$t^2 y' + y = 0$$

This equation has an irregular singular point at $t = 0$.   However, we can solve it explicitly by separation of variables and we see that every solution has the form $\phi(t) = ce^{1/t} = c\sum_{k=0}^{\infty}(1/k!)t^{-k}$ $(t \neq 0)$ for some constant c. Thus ϕ is **not** of the form $|t|^z \sum_{k=0}^{\infty} c_k t^k$, as it would be if $t = 0$ were a regular singular point (see Theorem 4.2, p. 154, and the discussion at the end of Section 4.8, p. 166).

• EXERCISE

1.   (a) Show that $t = 0$ is an irregular singular point for the equation $t^3 y'' + ty' - y = 0$.
   (b) Find two linearly independent solutions near $t = 0$.   [*Hint:* $\phi_1(t) = t$ is one solution, and another solution can be found by the method of Section 3.7, p. 99.]

The above example shows that the behavior of solutions near an irregular singular point may differ sharply from the behavior of solutions near a regular singular point.   To present further difficulties which can arise, we consider the equation $t^2 y'' + (3t - 1)y' + y = 0$, having an irregular singular point at $t = 0$.   If we try to find a solution of the form $|t|^z \sum_{k=0}^{\infty} c_k t^k$, we obtain $z = 0$, $c_k = k!$ $(k = 0, 1, 2, \ldots)$, giving a formal solution $\sum_{k=0}^{\infty} k! t^k$.   Since this series fails to converge on any t interval, it cannot represent a solution.

It is our purpose to give an introduction to the study of solutions in a neighborhood of an irregular singular point.   A systematic and rigorous treatment would require the tools of complex analysis, and must be deferred to a more advanced course.

In most applications which the reader is likely to encounter, the irregular singular point is at ∞. For this reason, we shall consider the equation

$$y'' + a(t)y' + b(t)y = 0 \tag{4.71}$$

where $a(t)$ and $b(t)$ are analytic at ∞, with expansions

$$a(t) = \sum_{k=0}^{\infty} a_k t^{-k} \qquad b(t) = \sum_{k=0}^{\infty} b_k t^{-k} \tag{4.72}$$

converging in some region $|t| > r$, with $r > 0$, and we shall assume that ∞ is an irregular singular point. If we make the transformation $x = 1/t$ and let $z(x) = y(1/t)$, as in Section 4.10 (p. 178), the equation (4.71) becomes

$$x^4 z'' + \left[2x^3 - x^2 \sum_{k=0}^{\infty} a_k x^k \right] z' + \left[\sum_{k=0}^{\infty} b_k x^k \right] = 0 \tag{4.73}$$

By inspection of equation (4.73) at $x = 0$ we see that **equation (4.71) has an irregular singular point at $t = \infty$ if and only if at least one of the numbers a_0, b_0, b_1 is different from zero.** Since we wish to assume that ∞ is an irregular singular point for (4.71), we shall assume throughout that this is the case.

Motivated by the simple examples at the beginning of this section, where the irregular singular point is at the origin, and by our study of regular singular points, we try to see whether (4.71) can be satisfied **formally** by a series of the form

$$\phi(t) = e^{\lambda t} |t|^z \sum_{k=0}^{\infty} c_k t^{-k} \qquad (c_0 \neq 0)$$

where λ, z, and c_k $(k = 0, 1, 2, \ldots)$ are constants to be determined. We consider first the case $t > 0$, so that $\phi(t) = e^{\lambda t} \sum_{k=0}^{\infty} c_k t^{-k+z}$, and

$$\phi'(t) = \lambda e^{\lambda t} \sum_{k=0}^{\infty} c_k t^{-k+z} + e^{\lambda t} \sum_{k=0}^{\infty} c_k(-k + z)t^{-k-1+z}$$

$$\phi''(t) = \lambda^2 e^{\lambda t} \sum_{k=0}^{\infty} c_k t^{-k+z} + 2\lambda e^{\lambda t} \sum_{k=0}^{\infty} c_k(-k + z)t^{-k-1+z}$$

$$+ e^{\lambda t} \sum_{k=0}^{\infty} c_k(z - k)(z - k - 1)t^{-k-2+z}$$

Using (4.72) and property (vi) (p. 123) for multiplication of power series (here in powers of $1/t$), we also have

$$b(t)\phi(t) = e^{\lambda t}t^z \sum_{k=0}^{\infty} \left(\sum_{j=0}^{k} b_{k-j}c_j \right) t^{-k}$$

$$a(t)\phi'(t) = \lambda e^{\lambda t}t^z \sum_{k=0}^{\infty} \left(\sum_{j=0}^{k} a_{k-j}c_j \right) t^{-k} + e^{\lambda t}t^z \sum_{k=0}^{\infty} \sum_{j=0}^{k} a_{k-j}(z-j)c_j t^{-k-1}$$

Substituting in (4.71), after elementary manipulations with series we obtain (formally)

$$e^{\lambda t}t^z \left[g(\lambda)c_0 + \{g(\lambda)c_1 + (2\lambda + a_0)z + \lambda a_1 + b_1\}t^{-1} + \sum_{k=2}^{\infty} \right.$$

$$\left\{ g(\lambda)c_k + 2\lambda(z-k+1)c_{k-1} + (z-k+1)(z-k+2)c_{k-2} \right.$$

$$\left. + \sum_{j=0}^{k-1} [b_{k-j} + \lambda a_{k-j} + a_{k-1-j}(z-j)]c_j \right\} \left. t^{-k} \right] = 0 \quad (4.74)$$

where

$$g(\lambda) = \lambda^2 + a_0\lambda + b_0 \tag{4.75}$$

To have a solution of the assumed form the coefficients of all powers of $1/t$ in the series (4.74) must vanish. Since we assumed $c_0 \neq 0$, we must choose λ to be a root of the equation $g(\lambda) = 0$. To make the coefficient of t^{-1} vanish, we must have $g(\lambda)c_1 + (2\lambda + a_0)z + \lambda a_1 + b_1 = 0$. Since $g(\lambda) = 0$, this allows us to determine z from the relation

$$(2\lambda + a_0)z = -\lambda a_1 - b_1 \tag{4.76}$$

provided $2\lambda + a_0 \neq 0$. Note that by assumption a_0, a_1, b_1 are not all zero. If the roots λ_1, λ_2 of $g(\lambda) = 0$ are distinct, since $\lambda_1 + \lambda_2 = -a_0$, we see that $2\lambda + a_0 \neq 0$, when λ is either λ_1 or λ_2. If, however, λ is a double root of the equation $g(\lambda) = 0$, the present method breaks down; see Example 3, p. 191 below. More precisely, if $g(\lambda) = 0$ has a double root, then the assumed form of the solution is incorrect. Ignoring this problem for the moment, we consider the case that λ is a simple root of the equation $g(\lambda) = 0$, so that we may determine z uniquely from (4.76). We now proceed as follows. Setting the coefficient of t^{-k} in (4.74) equal to zero and noting that $g(\lambda)c_k = 0$ for $\lambda = \lambda_1$ or λ_2 we find that we can determine

c_{k-1} from the relation

$$[b_1 + \lambda a_1 + (a_0 + 2\lambda)(z - k + 1)]c_{k-1} = -(z - k + 2)(z - k + 1)c_{k-2}$$

$$- \sum_{j=0}^{k-2} [b_{k-j} + \lambda a_{k-j} + a_{k-j-1}(z - j)]c_j \qquad (k = 2, 3, \ldots) \quad (4.77)$$

• **EXERCISE**

2. Verify with the aid of (4.76) that the coefficient of c_{k-1} in (4.77) is different from zero for $k = 2, 3, \ldots$.

These considerations lead to the following result.

Theorem 4.7.   *Consider the equation*

$$y'' + a(t)y' + b(t)y = 0 \tag{4.71}$$

with $a(t)$, $b(t)$ analytic at ∞, and having an irregular singular point at ∞. Then if the equation $g(\lambda) = \lambda^2 + a_0\lambda + b_0 = 0$ has distinct roots λ_1, λ_2 and if z_m is defined by $(2\lambda_m + a_0)z_m = -\lambda_m a_1 - b_1$ $(m = 1, 2)$, then equation (4.71) is formally satisfied by the two series $\phi_m(t) = e^{\lambda_m t}|t|^{z_m}\sum_{k=0}^{\infty}c_k^{(m)}t^{-k}$ with $c_0^{(m)} \neq 0$ $(m = 1, 2)$, whose coefficients $c_k^{(m)}$ are determined recursively from the equations (4.77).

• **EXERCISE**

3. Show that if $\lambda_1 \neq \lambda_2$, then the two series ϕ_1, ϕ_2 determined by Theorem 4.7 are (formally) linearly independent.

To see that Theorem 4.7 by no means finishes the problem even if $\lambda_1 \neq \lambda_2$ (unless it should happen that the series terminate after a finite number of terms), consider the following example.

Example 1.   Consider the equation

$$y'' + \left(1 + \frac{\alpha}{t^2}\right)y = 0 \tag{4.78}$$

where α is a constant, which is of the form (4.71) with $a(t) = 0$, $b(t) = 1 + \alpha/t^2$. Thus $t = \infty$ is an irregular singular point; $g(\lambda) = \lambda^2 + 1$, and the roots of $g(\lambda) = 0$ are $\lambda = \pm i$. By Theorem 4.7, the series $\phi(t) = e^{it}|t|^z\sum_{k=0}^{\infty}c_k t^{-k}$ $(c_0 \neq 0)$, satisfies (4.78) formally. In the notation of (4.72), we have $a_k = 0$ $(k = 0, 1, 2, \ldots)$, and $b_0 = 1$, $b_1 = 0$, $b_2 = \alpha$,

$b_k = 0$ $(k = 3, 4, \ldots)$. Then (4.76) gives $z = 0$, and (4.77) gives the recursion formula

$$2i(-k + 1)c_{k-1} = -(k + 2)(-k + 1)c_{k-2} + \alpha c_{k-2} + \alpha c_{k-2}$$
$$(k = 2, 3, \ldots)$$

or

$$c_{k-1} = -\frac{i}{2} \frac{(k - 2)(k - 1) + \alpha}{k - 1} c_{k-2} \qquad (k = 2, 3, \ldots) \qquad (4.79)$$

We observe that if $\alpha = -(n - 2)(n - 1)$ for some integer $n \geq 2$, then the series terminates after a finite number of terms. However, if α does not have this form, then

$$\left| \frac{c_{k-1}}{c_{k-2}} \right| = \frac{1}{2} \frac{(k - 2)(k - 1) + \alpha}{k - 1} \to \infty \qquad (k \to \infty)$$

Now the ratio test applied to the formal solution $e^{it}\Sigma_{k=0}^{\infty}c_k t^{-k}$ of (4.78) whose coefficients are given by (4.79) shows that **the series diverges for all** t. Therefore it cannot be called a solution of (4.78) in the usual sense. We will still find it convenient to call a series which satisfies a differential equation formally a **formal solution** even if the series fails to converge on any interval.

• EXERCISE

4. Find the formal solution of (4.78) corresponding to the root $\lambda = -i$, and show that it diverges everywhere.

In view of Example 1, it appears that we have reached an impasse. This is particularly serious since the Bessel equation, when written in the form (4.64) (p. 171), is of the form (4.78). However, it turns out that the formal series solution, although divergent everywhere, can still be given a meaning of great practical significance. We can only give an introduction to this subject, and for this purpose we consider another example before returning to the equation (4.78) considered in Example 1.

Example 2. Consider the equation $y' + y = 1/t$. It is easy to verify that the series $\phi(t) = \Sigma_{k=0}^{\infty}k! t^{-k-1}$ diverges for all t but satisfies the differential equation formally. What meaning can we attach to this series? Instead of working with the series, let us begin differently. Since the equation is linear and of first order, it follows from the discussion in Section 2.2 (p. 41) that every solution has the form

$$e^{-t}c + e^{-t} \int_{-\infty}^{t} \frac{e^s}{s} \, ds$$

for some constant c, where the integral converges for $t < 0$. In particular, the function

$$\psi(t) = e^{-t} \int_{-\infty}^{t} \frac{e^s}{s} \, ds$$

is well defined for every $t < 0$ and satisfies the differential equation for $t < 0$. Repeated integration by parts gives

$$\psi(t) = \frac{1}{t} + e^{-t} \int_{-\infty}^{t} \frac{e^s}{s^2} \, ds = \frac{1}{t} + \frac{1}{t^2} + 2!e^{-t} \int_{-\infty}^{t} \frac{e^s}{s^3} \, ds$$

$$= \sum_{k=0}^{n} k! t^{-k-1} + R_n$$

where

$$R_n = (n+1)!e^{-t} \int_{-\infty}^{t} \frac{-e^s}{s^{n+2}} \, ds$$

We observe that the integrated terms in this expression for the solution ψ (well defined for $t < 0$) coincide with the first $(n+1)$-terms of the (divergent) formal series solution. Now, let us examine the remainder term of R_n. We see that for $t < 0$

$$|R_n(t)| \le (n+1)!e^{-t} \frac{1}{|t|^{n+2}} \int_{-\infty}^{t} e^s \, ds = \frac{(n+1)!}{|t|^{n+2}}$$

or

$$\left| \psi(t) - \sum_{k=0}^{n} k! t^{-k-1} \right| \le \frac{(n+1)!}{|t|^{n+2}} \qquad (n = 0, 1, 2, \ldots)$$

or

$$\lim_{t \to \infty} |t|^{n+1} \left| \psi(t) - \sum_{k=0}^{n} k! t^{-k-1} \right| = 0 \qquad (n = 0, 1, \ldots)$$

To put this in another way, we may say that even though the series $\sum_{k=0}^{\infty} k! t^{-k-1}$ diverges for all t, the error made in approximating the solution $\psi(t)$ by the first n terms of the series is less in magnitude than the $(n+1)$st term, for every integer n and for $t < 0$. We note, however, that for a particular value of t, the approximation may not be improved by taking more terms of the series (for example, $t = -1$).

The above considerations suggest the following definition, due to the French mathematician H. Poincaré.

Definition. *The formal series* $\Sigma_{k=0}^{\infty}a_k t^{-k}$ *is said to be an asymptotic expansion of a function* $f(t)$ *defined for* $t \geq r$ *as* $t \to \infty$ *if and only if for each* $n = 0, 1, \ldots ,$

$$t^n \left[f(t) - \sum_{k=0}^{n} a_k t^{-k} \right] \to 0 \qquad (t \to \infty)$$

In this case it is customary to write $f(t) \sim \Sigma_{k=0}^{\infty}a_k t^{-k}$ $(t \to \infty)$.

Slightly more generally, the formal series $e^{bt}\Sigma_{k=0}^{\infty}a_k t^{-k}$ is said to be an asymptotic expansion of a function $f(t)$ as $t \to \infty$, written $f(t) \sim e^{bt}\Sigma_{k=0}^{\infty}a_k t^{-k}$, if and only if for each $n = 0, 1, \ldots ,$

$$t^n \left[e^{-bt}f(t) - \sum_{k=0}^{n} a_k t^{-k} \right] \to 0 \qquad (t \to \infty)$$

A similar definition may be given for $f(t)$ defined for $t < 0$ as $t \to -\infty$. In the above example we have shown that the (divergent) series $\Sigma_{k=0}^{\infty}k\,!t^{-k-1}$ is an asymptotic expansion of the solution $\psi(t)$ as $t \to -\infty$, and its partial sums may be used to evaluate the integral $e^{-t}\int_{-\infty}^{t}(e^s/s)\,ds$. Incidentally, the integral $\int_{-\infty}^{t}(e^s/s)\,ds$ is called the exponential-integral function, denoted by $Ei(t)$, and its values have been tabulated by precisely this method [11, 12].

Of course, every convergent series is also an asymptotic series, but as we have seen, the converse is false. If a formal series $\Phi = \Sigma_{k=0}^{\infty}a_k t^{-k}$ is an asymptotic expansion of a function f as $t \to \infty$, we write $f \sim \Phi$ $(t \to \infty)$. The coefficients a_k in this asymptotic expansion are uniquely determined by the function f, since

$$a_0 = \lim_{t \to \infty} f(t), \quad a_1 = \lim_{t \to \infty} t[f(t) - a_0], \quad \ldots ,$$

$$a_k = \lim_{t \to \infty} t^k \left[f(t) - a_0 - \frac{a_1}{t} - \cdots - \frac{a_{k-1}}{t^{k-1}} \right]$$

However, different functions may have the same asymptotic expansion. For example, e^{-t} and 0 are both represented asymptotically by the zero

series.   Thus if $f \sim \Phi$ $(t \to \infty)$, then $f + e^{-t} \sim \Phi$ $(t \to \infty)$.   More generally, if g is any function asymptotic to zero, then $f + g \sim \Phi$.   Although
we shall not go into these matters, it is possible to operate with asymptotic
series much as with power series.   The interested reader is referred to
other books such as [3], [6], and [16].

To illustrate how some of these ideas may be applied in the case of an
irregular singular point, we return to Example 1, equation (4.78), in the
form

$$y'' + y = -\frac{\alpha}{t^2}y \tag{4.80}$$

We have already seen that (4.80) has a formal solution $e^{it}\Sigma_{k=0}^{\infty}c_k t^{-k}$, where
$c_0 = 1$ and c_k $(k \geq 1)$ is determined recursively from (4.79), and that
this series diverges for every $t > 0$ (p. 184).   We shall now show that the
series represents a solution of the equation **in the sense that** (4.80)
**has a solution ϕ for which the formal series constructed above is an
asymptotic expansion.**   For large t, the equation (4.80) "resembles"
the equation $y'' + y = 0$, and this suggests that (4.80) may have a solution $\phi(t)$ which behaves like e^{it} as $t \to \infty$.   If (4.80) has such a solution,
we can use the method of variation of constants (Section 3.8; see in particular Exercise 3, p. 105) to see that ϕ must satisfy the equation

$$\phi(t) = e^{it}c - \alpha \int_{t_0}^{t} \frac{\sin{(t-s)}}{s^2}\,\phi(s)\,ds \tag{4.81}$$

for some constant c.   The reader may verify that if ϕ satisfies (4.81), then
it also satisfies (4.80).   The form (4.81), however, is not suitable for our
purpose, for even if the integral on the right side exists as $t \to \infty$, this
solution ϕ would not behave like e^{it} **unless** the integral approaches zero.
To obtain a more suitable form, we write

$$\int_{t_0}^{t} \sin{(t-s)}\,\frac{\phi(s)}{s^2}\,ds = \int_{t_0}^{\infty} \sin{(t-s)}\,\frac{\phi(s)}{s^2}\,ds$$
$$- \int_{t}^{\infty} \sin{(t-s)}\,\frac{\phi(s)}{s^2}\,ds$$

If the first integral on the right side exists, it is a solution of the homogeneous equation $y'' + y = 0$ (verify this fact), and may be thrown into the
term $e^{it}c$ in (4.81).   Then, we take $c = 1$ to obtain the new equation

$$\phi(t) = e^{it} + \alpha \int_{t}^{\infty} \sin{(t-s)}\,\frac{\phi(s)}{s^2}\,ds \tag{4.82}$$

It is easy to verify by direct substitution that if ϕ satisfies (4.82), then ϕ satisfies (4.80), and **if it can be shown that a solution ϕ of (4.82) is bounded for $t \geq a > 0$, then the integral in (4.82) approaches zero as $t \to \infty$, and thus $\phi(t) - e^{it} \to 0$ as $t \to \infty$.** It will be shown in Section 7.1, Exercise 4 (p. 317) and Exercise 13 (p. 324) that (4.82) has a solution ϕ on $1 \leq t < \infty$ and that

$$|\phi(t)| \leq e^{|\alpha|} \qquad (1 \leq t < \infty) \tag{4.83}$$

Assuming this result we now obtain

$$
\begin{aligned}
|\phi(t) - e^{it}| &\leq |\alpha| \int_t^\infty |\sin (t - s)| \cdot \frac{|\phi(s)|}{s^2} \, ds \\
&\leq |\alpha| e^{|\alpha|} \int_t^\infty \frac{ds}{s^2} = \frac{|\alpha| e^{|\alpha|}}{t} \qquad (1 \leq t < \infty)
\end{aligned} \tag{4.84}
$$

from (4.82) and thus $\lim\limits_{t \to \infty} (\phi(t) - e^{it}) = 0$, or $\phi(t) \sim e^{it} \ (t \to \infty)$. We also observe that we have obtained the first term of the formal series solution of (4.78). But we can do more; we write (4.82) as

$$\phi(t) = e^{it} + \alpha \int_t^\infty \sin (t - s) \frac{e^{is}}{s^2} \, ds + \alpha \int_t^\infty \sin (t - s) \frac{\phi(s) - e^{is}}{s^2} \, ds \tag{4.85}$$

We now use the estimate (4.84) to obtain

$$
\begin{aligned}
&\left| \phi(t) - e^{it} - \alpha \int_t^\infty \sin (t - s) \frac{e^{is}}{s^2} \, ds \right| \\
&\leq |\alpha| \int_t^\infty |\sin(t - s)| \frac{|\phi(s) - e^{is}|}{s^2} \, ds \leq |\alpha|^2 e^{|\alpha|} \int_t^\infty \frac{ds}{s^3} = \frac{|\alpha|^2 e^{|\alpha|}}{2! t^2}
\end{aligned}
$$

We now evaluate the integral

$$
\begin{aligned}
\int_t^\infty \sin(t - s) \frac{e^{is}}{s^2} \, ds &= \int_t^\infty \frac{e^{i(t-s)} - e^{-i(t-s)}}{2i} \cdot \frac{e^{is}}{s^2} \, ds \\
&= \frac{e^{it}}{2i} \int_t^\infty \frac{ds}{s^2} - \frac{e^{-it}}{2i} \int_t^\infty \frac{e^{2is}}{s^2} \, ds \\
&= \lim_{A \to \infty} \left(\frac{e^{it}}{2it} - \frac{e^{-it}}{2i} \left\{ \left[\frac{e^{2is}}{2is^2} \right]_t^A + \frac{1}{t} \int_t^A \frac{e^{2is}}{s^3} \, ds \right\} \right) \\
&= \frac{e^{it}}{2it} + g(t)
\end{aligned}
$$

where $|g(t)| \leq k/t^2$ for $t \geq 1$ and some constant k. We may now write

$$\left| \phi(t) - e^{it} - \frac{\alpha e^{it}}{2it} - g(t) \right| \leq \frac{|\alpha|^2 e^{|\alpha|}}{2!t^2}$$

or

$$\left| \phi(t) - e^{it} - \frac{\alpha e^{it}}{2it} \right| \leq \frac{|\alpha|^2 e^{|\alpha|}}{2!t^2} + |g(t)| \qquad (t \geq 1)$$

Thus $t[e^{-it}\phi(t) - 1 - \alpha/2it] \to 0$ as $t \to \infty$, or $\phi(t) \sim e^{it}(1 + \alpha/2it)$ as $t \to \infty$. Now we have obtained the first two terms of the formal series solution of (4.78). The above calculations show that **for very large values of t, we obtain a better approximation to the solution by using 2 terms of the formal series than by using 1 term.**

We can repeat the procedure by using $\phi(t) - e^{it}(1 + \alpha/2it) = h(t)$, where $h(t)/t^2$ is bounded as $t \to \infty$, in (4.82) to obtain the first 3 terms of the formal series. We would also see that this gives a still better approximation to the solution for large t. Continuing, we could show that for the solution $\phi(t)$ of (4.78) which behaves like e^{it} as $t \to \infty$,

$$\phi(t) = e^{it} \sum_{k=0}^{n} c_k t^{-k} + h_n(t) \qquad (t \geq 1) \tag{4.86}$$

for every integer $n \geq 0$, where $c_0 = 1$ and c_k is determined from the equation (4.79) (p. 184) for $k \geq 1$, and where $|h_n(t)|/t^{n+1}$ is bounded as $t \to \infty$. Thus $\phi(t) \sim e^{it}\sum_{k=0}^{\infty} c_k t^{-k}$ $(t \to \infty)$. This is the sense in which the divergent series found by formal operations is useful. The expression (4.86) may now be used to approximate the solution $\phi(t)$ for large t.

•EXERCISES

5. Show that the Bessel equation

$$t^2 y'' + t y' + (t^2 - n^2)y = 0$$

has a solution $\phi(t)$ such that

$$\phi(t) \sim \frac{e^{it}}{\sqrt{t}} \left[1 - \frac{\frac{1}{4} - n^2}{2t} - \frac{(\frac{1}{4} - n^2)(\frac{9}{4} - n^2)}{2^2 \cdot 2! t^2} \right.$$
$$\left. + \frac{(\frac{1}{4} - n^2)(\frac{9}{4} - n^2)(\frac{25}{4} - n^2)}{2^3 \cdot 3! t^3} + \cdots \right]$$

as $t \to \infty$. [*Hint:* Use Exercise 3, Section 4.9, p. 171, and the results of this section. You may assume the validity of (4.86).]

6. Using Theorem 4.7 and arguments similar to the above, show that there is also a solution $\psi(t)$ of the Bessel equation such that $\psi(t) \sim e^{-it}/\sqrt{t} \, \Sigma_{k=0}^{\infty} d_k t^{-k}$ as $t \to \infty$ ($d_0 = 1$), and compute the recursion formula for the coefficients d_k and the first four nonzero terms of the asymptotic expansion.

7. By suitably combining the series ϕ and ψ in Exercises 5 and 6, show that there are solutions y_1 and y_2 such that

$$y_1(t) \sim \frac{1}{\sqrt{t}} \left[U_{1n}(t) \cos t + U_{2n}(t) \sin t \right]$$
$$\qquad\qquad (t \to \infty)$$
$$y_2(t) \sim \frac{1}{\sqrt{t}} \left[U_{1n}(t) \sin t - U_{2n}(t) \cos t \right]$$

where

$$U_{1n}(t) = 1 - \frac{(\frac{1}{4} - n^2)(\frac{9}{4} - n^2)}{2^2 \cdot 2! t^2}$$
$$\qquad\qquad + \frac{(\frac{1}{4} - n^2)(\frac{9}{4} - n^2)(\frac{2\,5}{4} - n^2)(\frac{4\,9}{4} - n^2)}{2^1 \cdot 4! t^4} + \cdots$$
$$U_{2n}(t) = \frac{(\frac{1}{4} - n^2)}{2t} - \frac{(\frac{1}{4} - n^2)(\frac{9}{4} - n^2)(\frac{2\,5}{4} - n^2)}{2^3 \cdot 3! t^3} + \cdots$$

It can be proved that the Bessel function $\dot{J}_n(t)$ satisfies

$$J_n(t) \sim \left(\frac{2}{\pi t} \right)^{1/2} \left[U_{1n}(t) \cos \left\{ t - \frac{\pi}{2} \left(n + \frac{1}{2} \right) \right\} \right.$$
$$\left. + U_{2n}(t) \sin \left\{ t - \frac{\pi}{2} \left(n + \frac{1}{2} \right) \right\} \right] \quad (4.87)$$

as $t \to \infty$. To illustrate the use of the asymptotic series in actual calculations, we remark that if we use the series

$$J_0(t) = 1 - \frac{t^2}{2^4} + \frac{t^4}{2^6} - \frac{t^6}{2^8 3^2} + \cdots$$

with $t = 6$, we obtain 0.15067 as an approximation to $J_0(6)$, correct to 4 decimal places, **provided** we use terms of the series up to the one in t^{20}. On the other hand, the asymptotic series (4.87) gives 0.15064, correct to 5 decimal places, with the use of only 4 terms of each of the series $U_{10}(t)$ and $U_{20}(t)$.

From this and similar analysis for $Y_n(t)$, defined by (4.68), p. 176, we can obtain the following result which complements Theorem 4.6 (p. 177).

Theorem 4.8

$$J_n(t) \sim \left(\frac{2}{\pi t}\right)^{1/2} \cos\left[t - \frac{(2n+1)\pi}{4}\right]$$
$$Y_n(t) \sim \left(\frac{2}{\pi t}\right)^{1/2} \sin\left[t - \frac{(2n+1)\pi}{4}\right] \qquad (t \to \infty)$$

One important consequence of Theorem 4.8 is that $J_n(t)$ has infinitely many zeros $0 < t_1 < t_2 < \cdots < t_k < \cdots$, and for large k, $t_{k+1} - t_k$ is close to π. This fact is very useful in the study of boundary value problems involving the Bessel equation.

The above considerations should suggest to the reader that the general theory for the second-order equation (4.71) with an irregular singular point at infinity is quite complicated. By a suitable generalization of the above techniques it may be shown that **if** $g(\lambda) = \lambda^2 + a_0\lambda + b_0$ **has distinct zeros, then corresponding to the formal series obtained in Theorem 4.7, the equation (4.71), p. 181), has solutions** ϕ **and** ψ **having these formal series respectively as asymptotic expansions as** $t \to \infty$.

Finally, we make a few remarks about the case of a double zero of $g(\lambda)$, in which case the above method breaks down completely. We consider an example which indicates the possibilities in the general case.

Example 3.   Consider the equation

$$ty'' - 2ty' + (1 + t)y = 0 \tag{4.88}$$

This has the form of the equation (4.71) with $a(t) = -2$, $b(t) = 1 + 1/t$, and $g(\lambda) = \lambda^2 - 2\lambda + 1$. Thus $\lambda = 1$ is a double root of the equation $g(\lambda) = 0$. Put $y(t) = e^{ct}u(t)$. Then

$$y'(t) = ce^{ct}u(t) + e^{ct}u'(t)$$
$$y''(t) = c^2e^{ct}u(t) + 2ce^{ct}u'(t) + e^{ct}u''(t)$$

Thus

$$ty'' - 2ty' + (1 + t)y = e^{ct}[tu'' + 2(c - 1)tu' + \{tc^2 - 2tc + (1 + t)c\}u]$$

If we choose $c = 1$, we see that u satisfies

$$tu'' + u = 0$$

(This equation actually has $\lambda = 0$ as a double root of the corresponding characteristic equation.) We now make the **stretching transformation** $t = x^2$, and we let $v(x) = u(x^2)$. Then $tu'' + u = (\frac{1}{4})(d^2v/dx^2) - (1/4x)(dv/dx) + v$, and v satisfies the equation

$$v'' - \frac{1}{x} v' + 4v = 0 \tag{4.89}$$

with x as independent variable. For (4.89), the relevant polynomial is $g(\lambda) = \lambda^2 + 4$, and its zeros $\lambda = \pm 2i$ are distinct. Thus the methods of Theorem 4.7 may be applied to (4.89). According to Theorem 4.7, (4.89) has two formal solutions of the form

$$|x|^z \exp{(\pm 2ix)} \sum_{k=0}^{\infty} c_k x^{-k} \qquad (c_0 = 1)$$

where z and c_k $(k = 1, 2, \ldots)$ are determined recursively by substitution. Thus the original equation (4.88) has two formal solutions of the form

$$|t|^{z/2} \exp{(t \pm 2i\sqrt{t})} \sum_{k=0}^{\infty} c_k t^{-k/2} \qquad (c_0 = 1)$$

and it can be shown that there exist solutions ϕ and ψ of (4.88) which have these formal solutions as their respective asymptotic expansions as $t \to \infty$. Thus we see that in the general case, the formal solutions are more complicated than in the case covered by Theorem 4.7 in that the formal series involves fractional powers.

● **EXERCISES**

8. Carry out a similar analysis for the equation $ty'' + y' + y = 0$. Construct two linearly independent formal solutions as $t \to \infty$.

9. Find two linearly independent formal solutions as $t \to \infty$ for the equation $y'' + ty = 0$.

10. Find two linearly independent formal solutions as $t \to \infty$ for the equation $y'' + ((-\frac{1}{4}) + (c/t) + (\frac{1}{4} - m^2)/t^2)y = 0$ (confluent hypergeometric equation), and show that if $c = 0$ one solution is $\sqrt{t}\, J_m(it/2)$.

11. Give a complete discussion of the equation $y'' + (1 + \alpha/t + \beta/t^2)y = 0$ where α, β are **real** constants, both for t near 0 and as $t \to \infty$.

•MISCELLANEOUS EXERCISES

1. Locate and classify the singular points of each of the following differential equations, including $t = \infty$.
   (a) $t^2(t + 1)y'' + ty' + (2t - 1)y = 0.$
   (b) $(t - 1)^2y'' + (t^2 + 1)y = 0.$
   (c) $(\sin t)y' - y = 0.$
   (d) $2t^3y'' + 3ty' - (t + 1)y = 0.$
   (e) $(2t^2 + t^3)y'' - ty' - y = 0.$
   (f) $(\cos t)y'' + (\sin t)y = 0.$

   (g) $\dfrac{1}{1 - t} y'' - y = 0.$

   (h) $t(t + 1)(t + 2)y'' - t^5y = 0.$
   (i) $(t^2 - 1)^2(t - 1)(t + 2)y'' + y' = 0.$
   (j) $t^4y''' + t^3(t + 2)y' - y = 0.$
   (k) $y'' + e^ty = 0.$
   (l) $(1 + t^2)y'' + t^2y' - ty = 0.$
   (m) $t^2(1 - t^2)^2y'' + 2t(1 - t)y' + y = 0.$
   (n) $y''' + (\sec t)y = 0.$

2. For each of the following differential equations, determine the roots of the indicial equation at $t = 0$, the form of the general solution, and the region of validity of the general solution as given by the appropriate theorem.
   (a) $2ty'' + y' - y = 0.$
   (b) $ty'' + 3y' - t^2y = 0.$
   (c) $(3t^2 + t^3)y'' - ty' + y = 0.$
   (d) $t(1 - t)y'' - 2y' + 2y = 0.$
   (e) $ty'' + (1 - t)y' + qy = 0$ (q constant).
   (f) $ty'' + (1 - t)y' + my = 0$ (m a positive integer).
   (g) $t^2y'' + 2ty' + ty = 0.$

   (h) $y'' + \dfrac{4}{t} y' + \left(\dfrac{2}{t^2} + \dfrac{1}{t}\right)y = 0.$

   (i) $(t^2 + t^3)y'' - (t^2 + 1)y' + y = 0.$
   (j) $ty'' - ty' - y = 0.$
   (k) $t^2y'' + ty' + (4 - t)y = 0.$
   (l) $(t^2 - t^3)y'' - 3ty' + 5y = 0.$
   (m) $t^2y'' + ty' + (t^2 - 4)y = 0.$

3. Find the general solution valid in a neighborhood of $t = 0$ of each of the differential equations in Exercise 2.

4. Find the general solution valid in some neighborhood of the indicated singular point of each of the following differential equations, and give the interval on which it is valid.
   (a) $(1 - t^2)y'' - 2ty' + \alpha(\alpha + 1)y = 0$ (Legendre equation); $t = -1.$
   (b) $t(1 - t)y'' + [c - (a + b + 1)t]y' - aby = 0$ (hypergeometric equation); $t = 1.$

(c) $(\log t)y'' + \frac{1}{2}y' + y = 0$; $t = 1$.   (Do not attempt to find the general term.)

5.   Find the general solution valid in some neighborhood of the point $t = \infty$ of each of the following differential equations, and give the interval on which it is valid.

(a) $t^2y'' + aty' + by = 0$ (Euler equation).

(b) $t(1 - t)y'' + [c - (a + b + 1)t]y' - aby = 0$ (hypergeometric equation).

(c) $(1 - t^2)y'' - 2ty' + \alpha(\alpha + 1)y = 0$ (Legendre equation).

(d) $(1 - t^2)y'' - ty' + y = 0$.

(e) $t^4y'' + 2(t^3 - t)y' + y = 0$.

(f) $t^3y'' + (t^2 - t)y' + (2 - t)y = 0$.

(g) $2t^3y'' + t^2y' - (t + 1)y = 0$.

6.   Show that $t = \infty$ is an irregular singular point and determine (formally) the form of the general solution valid for large $|t|$ for each of the following differential equation.   Find whether the series converges on any interval.

(a) $y'' + \dfrac{1}{t}y' - y = 0$.

(b) $y'' - 6y' + 5y = 0$.

(c) $ty'' - (t + 1)y = 0$.

(d) $y'' - ty = 0$.

(e) $ty'' + (c - t)y' - ay = 0$ (confluent hypergeometric equation).

7.   For each of the following differential equations obtain the general solution in terms of Bessel functions.   [*Hint:* See Section 4.9, pp. 176–177]

(a) $ty'' - y' - ty = 0$.

(b) $ty'' - 3y' + ty = 0$.

(c) $t^2y'' + ty' - (t^2 + \frac{1}{4})y = 0$.

(d) $ty'' - y' + 4t^3y = 0$.

8.   (a) Find the general solution of the confluent hypergeometric equation

$$ty'' + (c - t)y' - ay = 0$$

valid near $t = 0$, assuming that c is not an integer.

(b) Define $M(a, c; t)$ to be that solution of the equation in part (a) which is analytic at $t = 0$ and has the value 1 at $t = 0$.   Show that the general solution found in part (a) is

$$\phi(t) = c_1 M(a, c; t) + c_2|t|^{1-c}M(1 + a - c, 2 - c; t)$$

if c is not an integer.

(c) Obtain the general solution of the equation in part (a) when $a = 1$, $c = 1$.

(d) Obtain the general solution of the equation in part (a) when $a = 1$, $c = 0$.

(e) Obtain the form of the general solution of the equation in part (a) valid for large t.

5.1 Introduction

In the problems considered so far, we have singled out a particular solution of a differential equation by specifying some suitable initial conditions. Another important class of problems, called **boundary value problems,** involves the determination of solutions of a differential equation which satisfy prescribed conditions at two given points. Such conditions are called **boundary conditions.**

Example 1. *The rotating string.* To illustrate how boundary value problems arise in the mathematical formulation of physical problems, we consider the possible displacements of a rotating string of length L. We denote by $y(x)$ the displacement of the string at x ($0 \leq x \leq L$), and we suppose that the string is attached to fixed supports on the x axis at $x = 0$ and $x = L$. We wish to determine the possible displacements of the string as a function of x ($0 \leq x \leq L$) when it is allowed to rotate at a uniform (as yet undetermined) angular velocity ω about its equilibrium rest position along the x axis. We assume a tightly stretched flexible string with linear density ρ (that is, a mass of ρ units per unit length), (see Figure 5.1). One possibility is that the string remains in this equilibrium position $y = 0$. We wish to determine whether there are values of the angular velocity (called critical speeds) for which the string can assume some other shape (called a standing wave).

To arrive at a mathematical model for this problem, we shall use Newton's second law of motion together with the following physical assumptions:

(i) The tension is large enough so that the additional stress introduced by curvature of the string is negligible.

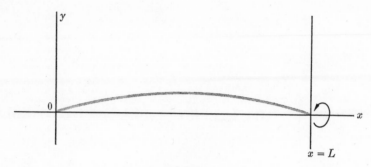

Figure 5.1

(ii) The tensile force at any point acts in a direction tangent to the string and has a constant magnitude T.
(iii) The angle between the direction of the string at any point and the equilibrium position $y = 0$ is small.

We examine the portion of the string between x and $x + \Delta x$, where $0 \leq x \leq L$. The mass of this portion of the string is $\rho \Delta s$, where s is the arc length measured along the string; this mass is approximately $\rho((\Delta x)^2 + (\Delta y)^2)^{1/2}$, if $|\Delta x|$ is small. The rotation of the string about the x axis with angular velocity ω produces an acceleration of magnitude $\omega^2 y$ directed vertically toward the x axis.

● **EXERCISE**

1. Use the argument by which equation (1.5) (p. 9) was derived to show that the rotating string produces an acceleration $-\omega^2 y \mathbf{u}_y$, where $\mathbf{u}_y$ is the unit radial vector. (Here y replaces r and $\theta = \omega t$.)

Since the acceleration vector is vertical, only the vertical component of the tensile forces on this portion of the string is relevant, and this vertical component is

$$T[\sin \alpha(x + \Delta x) - \sin \alpha(x)]$$

where $\alpha(x)$ is the angle between the string at x and the horizontal (see .Figure 5.2). Thus Newton's second law of motion (p. 2) gives

$$T[\sin \alpha(x + \Delta x) - \sin \alpha(x)] = -\rho \omega^2 y \, \Delta x \left(1 + \left(\frac{\Delta y}{\Delta x}\right)^2\right)^{1/2} \qquad (5.1)$$

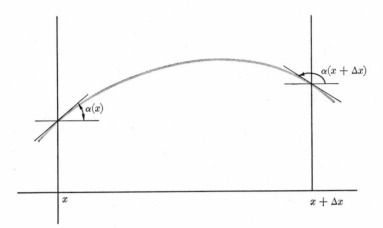

Figure 5.2

If we divide the equation (5.1) by Δx and take the limit as $\Delta x \to 0$, we obtain

$$T\frac{d}{dx}[\sin \alpha(x)] + \rho\omega^2 y\left(1 + \left(\frac{dy}{dx}\right)^2\right)^{1/2} = 0 \tag{5.2}$$

However $\tan \alpha(x) = dy/dx$, and therefore

$$\sin \alpha(x) = \frac{\tan \alpha(x)}{(1 + \tan^2 \alpha(x))^{1/2}} = \frac{dy}{dx}\bigg/\left(1 + \left(\frac{dy}{dx}\right)^2\right)^{1/2} \tag{5.3}$$

Substituting (5.3) into (5.2), we obtain the equation of motion of the string

$$T\frac{d}{dx}\left(\frac{dy}{dx}\bigg/\left(1 + \left(\frac{dy}{dx}\right)^2\right)^{1/2}\right) + \rho\omega^2 y\left(1 + \left(\frac{dy}{dx}\right)^2\right)^{1/2} = 0 \tag{5.4}$$

which we may also write in the form

$$T\frac{d^2y}{dx^2}\left[1 - \frac{dy}{dx} + \left(\frac{dy}{dx}\right)^2\right] + \rho\omega^2 y\left[1 + \left(\frac{dy}{dx}\right)^2\right]^2 = 0 \tag{5.5}$$

• **EXERCISE**

2. Carry out the differentiation in (5.4) and derive the equation (5.5).

We observe that we cannot solve (5.5) by the methods we have studied, and we ask the reader to accept the statement that the equation does not have solutions which can be written in closed form. It is not even obvious that solutions of (5.5) satisfying given initial conditions at $x = 0$ exist on the whole interval $0 \leq x \leq L$, although this can in fact be proved.

To simplify the complicated equation (5.5), we use the assumption (iii) (p. 196), which implies that if $y(x)$ is the displacement of the string, then $|y'(x)| = |\tan \alpha(x)|$ is small for $0 \leq x \leq L$. Then, replacing dy/dx in (5.5) by 0 we obtain the simplified model

$$T \frac{d^2y}{dx^2} + \rho\omega^2 y = 0 \tag{5.6}$$

which we shall use for the differential equation governing the motion of the rotating string.

The differential equation (5.6) alone does not specify the motion of the string completely. We have assumed that both ends of the string are attached to a fixed support. This means that the displacement $y(x)$ of the string must also satisfy the **boundary conditions**

$$y(0) = 0 \qquad y(L) = 0 \tag{5.7}$$

Clearly $y(x) = 0$ is a solution of equation (5.6) satisfying the boundary conditions (5.7); this solution is called **the trivial solution.**

The mathematical problem is to determine the values of ω for which (5.6) has a solution ϕ not identically zero on $0 \leq x \leq L$ which also satisfies the boundary conditions (5.7), and to determine the corresponding solution ϕ. We shall see in the next section how to solve this problem.

We remark that in assuming that dy/dx is small to derive the equation (5.6) we do not rule out the possibility that (5.6) may have solutions for which dy/dx is not small. However, we may expect that only solutions with dy/dx small actually approximate solutions of (5.5), and that the solutions of (5.6) for which dy/dx is not small need not have any physical significance.

•EXERCISES

3. Look up the derivation for the differential equation for the critical speeds of a rotating shaft (see, for example, [9], p. 193).

4. Look up the derivation for the differential equation for the buckling of a column under an axial load (see, for example, [9], p. 198).

We may impose other types of boundary conditions instead of requiring both ends of the string to be attached to a fixed support. For example, we might assume that the end at $x = L$ is attached to a yielding support with a restoring force proportional to the stretching. This gives a boundary condition of the form

$$Ty'(L) = -ky(L)$$

instead of $y(L) = 0$. The "limiting case" of such a condition is called a **free end condition,** $y'(L) = 0$. This corresponds to a string unattached at the end $x = L$.

5.2   Examples of Homogeneous Boundary Value Problems

Before developing a general theory for a class of boundary value problems we consider a number of typical examples in this and the next section.

Example 1.   Let us examine the **boundary value problem** consisting of the differential equation

$$y'' + \lambda y = 0 \tag{5.8}$$

together with the boundary conditions

$$y(0) = 0 \qquad y(\pi) = 0 \tag{5.9}$$

We wish to find all values of λ for which there is a solution ϕ of (5.8) which is not identically zero on $0 \le t \le \pi$ and which satisfies the boundary conditions (5.9).

• **EXERCISE**

1. Transform the problem (5.6), (5.7) (p. 198) for the rotating string into the problem (5.8) (5.9) by making the change of variable $t = \pi x/L$ and letting $\lambda = \rho \omega^2 L^2/T\pi^2$.

The general solution of (5.8) can be written in the form

$$\phi(t) = c_1 \exp\left(i \sqrt{\lambda}\, t\right) + c_2 \exp\left(-i \sqrt{\lambda}\, t\right) \tag{5.10}$$

(see Section 3.4, p. 88) for every λ, **real or complex,** except $\lambda = 0$. We may write $\sqrt{\lambda} = \alpha + i\beta$ with α, β real (see Appendix 3). We shall first show that the boundary conditions (5.9) cannot be satisfied by a **nontrivial** solution of (5.8) unless $\sqrt{\lambda}$ is real, that is, unless $\beta = 0$. With $\sqrt{\lambda} = \alpha + i\beta$, (5.10) becomes

$$\phi(t) = c_1 e^{(-\beta + i\alpha)t} + c_2 e^{(\beta - i\alpha)t}$$

Imposing the boundary conditions (5.9), we obtain

$$\phi(0) = c_1 + c_2 = 0$$
$$\phi(\pi) = c_1 e^{(-\beta + i\alpha)\pi} + c_2 e^{(\beta - i\alpha)\pi} = 0$$

This is a pair of simultaneous algebraic equations for the constants c_1, c_2. By Theorems A1, A2, Appendix 1, there is a nontrivial solution (that is, a solution with c_1, c_2 not both zero) of this algebraic system if and only if the determinant Δ of coefficients is zero.   But

$$\Delta = e^{\beta \pi} e^{-i\alpha \pi} - e^{-\beta \pi} e^{i\alpha \pi}$$

The condition $\Delta = 0$ means that

$$e^{\beta \pi} e^{-i\alpha \pi} - e^{-\beta \pi} e^{i\alpha \pi} = 0$$

or equivalently,

$$e^{2\beta \pi} = e^{2\alpha \pi i} = \cos 2\alpha \pi + i \sin 2\alpha \pi$$

Because β is real, $e^{2\beta \pi}$ is real.   Therefore $\sin 2\alpha \pi = 0$ **and** $\cos 2\alpha \pi = e^{2\beta \pi}$. The first of these equations is satisfied if and only if $\alpha = n = 0, 1, 2, 3, \ldots$, and in this case the second of these equations gives $1 = e^{2\beta \pi}$; from this it follows that $\beta = 0$.

Therefore the boundary value problem (5.8), (5.9) has a nontrivial solution if and only if $\sqrt{\lambda} = n = 1, 2, 3, \ldots$.   (The case $\alpha = 0$, $\beta = 0$ implies $\sqrt{\lambda} = 0$, and is considered separately below.)   The corresponding nontrivial solutions are (from (5.10))

$$\phi(t) = c_1 e^{int} + c_2 e^{-int} \qquad (n = 1, 2, \ldots)$$

However, from the first boundary condition, we know that $c_1 + c_2 = 0$, so that

$$\phi(t) = c_1(e^{int} - e^{-int}) = 2ic_1 \sin nt \qquad (n = 1, 2, \ldots)$$

or finally

$$\phi(t) = A_n \sin nt \qquad (n = 1, 2, \ldots) \tag{5.11}$$

where A_n is an arbitrary (real) constant.   Note that A_n remains completely undetermined by the problem.

It remains to consider the possibility of a nontrivial solution of (5.8), (5.9) for $\lambda = 0$.   In this case the general solution of (5.8) is

$$\phi(t) = c_1 + c_2 t$$

However, this solution satisfies (5.9) if and only if $c_1 = c_2 = 0$, and thus there is no nontrivial solution for $\lambda = 0$.

• EXERCISE

2. Show that $\phi(t) = c_1 + c_2 t$ satisfies (5.9) if and only if $c_1 = c_2 = 0$.

Summarizing, we see that the boundary value problem (5.8), (5.9) has nontrivial solutions if and only if

$$\lambda = n^2 \qquad (n = 1, 2, \ldots)$$

The corresponding nontrivial solutions are

$$\phi_n(t) = A_n \sin nt \qquad (n = 1, 2, \ldots)$$

where A_n is any constant.   The values of λ (in this case $\lambda = n^2$) are called **eigenvalues** (or characteristic values) of the boundary value problem, while corresponding solutions (in this case $A_n \sin nt$) are called **eigenfunctions** (or characteristic functions) of the boundary value problem. The reader will note that the boundary value problem (5.8) and (5.9) has an infinite, but countable, sequence of real positive eigenvalues $\lambda = n^2$; these eigenvalues are not equally spaced and tend to ∞ as $n \to \infty$.

• EXERCISES

3. Assuming that λ is positive, we know that the general solution of (5.8) can be written in the form

$$\phi(t) = c_1 \cos \sqrt{\lambda}\, t + c_2 \frac{\sin \sqrt{\lambda}\, t}{\sqrt{\lambda}}$$

where the factor $\sqrt{\lambda}$ is inserted for convenience. Apply the boundary conditions (5.9) to this form of the solution and determine the eigenvalues and eigenfunctions.

4. Compute the limit as $\lambda \to 0$ of the general solution $\phi(t)$ in Exercise 3.

5. Show that $\int_0^\pi \phi_n(t)\phi_m(t)\, dt = 0$ if $m \neq n$ and $\int_0^\pi [\phi_n(t)]^2\, dt = \pi A_n^2/2$. [*Hint:* $2 \sin nt \sin mt = \cos (m - n)t - \cos (m + n)t$.]

6. Show that for the boundary value problem (5.6), (5.7) (p. 198) for the rotating string there is an infinite sequence of angular velocities $\omega_n = n\pi/L(T/\rho)^{1/2}$ $(n = 1, 2, \ldots)$, for which there is a nontrivial solution, and a corresponding sequence of solutions $\phi_n(x) = A_n \sin (n\pi x/L)$ $(n = 1, 2, \ldots)$, where the A_n are constants which we cannot determine from the problem.

We now observe that the rotating string problem posed in Section 5.1 (p. 195) and solved in Exercise 6 above has solutions which do not satisfy the assumption made in obtaining the linearized equation (5.6) (p. 198), namely, that the angle between the direction of the string and the horizontal is small. For the solution $\phi_n(x) = A_n \sin (n\pi x/L)$, we have $\phi_n'(x) = (n\pi A_n/L) \cos (n\pi x/L)$ $(n = 1, 2, \ldots)$, and this becomes large as n increases. This suggests that in fact only the first few of the eigenfunctions are physically meaningful, and the skillful reader may verify experimentally that this seems to be the case. The mathematical question of whether the solutions of the linear boundary value problem (5.6), (5.7) (p. 198) approximate the solutions of the nonlinear boundary value problem (5.5), (5.7) (p. 197), or even whether there are values of ω for which the nonlinear problem has solutions, is an extremely difficult one to which no satisfactory answer can be given here.

Example 2. Consider the boundary value problem defined on the interval $0 \leq t \leq \pi$ by the differential equation

$$y'' + \lambda y = 0 \tag{5.8}$$

and the boundary conditions

$$y'(0) = 0 \qquad y'(\pi) = 0 \tag{5.12}$$

By an argument similar to that used in Example 1 above, it may be shown that this problem has no complex or negative eigenvalues. (The reader is invited to carry this out as an exercise.) Assuming this fact, we need only consider $\lambda \equiv 0$. For $\lambda > 0$ the general solution of (5.8) is

$$\phi(t) = c_1 \cos \sqrt{\lambda}\, t + c_2 \frac{\sin \sqrt{\lambda}\, t}{\sqrt{\lambda}} \tag{5.13}$$

For $\lambda = 0$ the general solution of (5.8) is

$$\phi(t) = c_1 + c_2 t \tag{5.14}$$

(see also Exercise 4 above).   Using (5.13) for $\lambda > 0$, we have

$$\phi'(t) = -c_1 \sqrt{\lambda} \sin \sqrt{\lambda}\, t + c_2 \cos \sqrt{\lambda}\, t$$

Imposing the boundary conditions (5.12) we obtain

$$\phi'(0) = 0 \cdot c_1 + c_2 = 0$$
$$\phi'(\pi) = -c_1 \sqrt{\lambda} \sin \sqrt{\lambda}\, \pi + c_2 \cos \sqrt{\lambda}\, \pi = 0$$

The determinant of coefficients of this algebraic system is

$$\Delta = \sqrt{\lambda} \sin \sqrt{\lambda}\, \pi$$

and for the case $\lambda > 0$, $\Delta = 0$ if and only if $\lambda = n^2$ $(n = 1, 2, \ldots)$.
The case $\lambda = 0$ is now considered separately.

● **EXERCISE**

7. Show, using (5.14) and (5.12), that $\lambda = 0$ is an eigenvalue of the boundary
value problem (5.8), (5.12).

Thus the boundary value problem (5.8), (5.12) has the sequence of
eigenvalues

$$\lambda = n^2 \qquad (n = 0, 1, 2, \ldots)$$

and

$$\phi_n(t) = A_n \cos nt \qquad (n = 0, 1, \ldots)$$

as corresponding eigenfunctions.   Note that $\phi_0(t)$ is the constant A_0.

● **EXERCISES**

8. Show that $\int_0^\pi \phi_n(t)\phi_m(t)\, dt = 0$ if $m \neq n$, and that $\int_0^\pi [\phi_0(t)]^2\, dt = \pi A_n{}^2/2$
if $n > 0$, while $\int_0^\pi [\phi_0(t)]^2\, dt = \pi A_0{}^2$.

9. Find the eigenvalues and corresponding eigenfunctions of the differential
equation (5.8) subject to the boundary conditions $y(0) = 0$, $y'(\pi) = 0$.

10. Interpret Exercise 9 for the rotating string (see Section 5.1, pp. 195–199).

Example 3. Consider the boundary value problem defined on the interval $0 \leq t \leq \pi$ by the differential equation

$$y'' + \lambda y = 0 \tag{5.8}$$

and the boundary conditions

$$y(0) = 0 \qquad y(\pi) + k y'(\pi) = 0 \tag{5.15}$$

where k is a given, real, nonzero constant. By an argument similar to that used in Example 1 above, it may be shown that this problem has no complex or negative eigenvalues.

•**EXERCISES**

11. Show that the eigenvalues of the boundary value problem (5.8), (5.15) are the solutions (if any) of the transcendental equation

$$\tan \sqrt{\lambda}\, \pi = -k \sqrt{\lambda}$$

12. Show that if λ_n is an eigenvalue of the boundary value problem (5.8), (5.15), then the corresponding eigenfunction is $\phi_n(t) = A_n \sin \sqrt{\lambda_n}\, t$.

The above exercises show that the problem of finding the eigenvalues of the boundary value problem (5.8), (5.15) reduces to the problem of solving the transcendental equation

$$\tan \sqrt{\lambda}\, \pi = -k \sqrt{\lambda} \tag{5.16}$$

Although we cannot solve this equation explicitly, we can show that it has an infinite sequence of solutions. As $\sqrt{\lambda}\, \pi$ increases from $(n - \frac{1}{2})\pi$ to $(n + \frac{1}{2})\pi$, $\tan \sqrt{\lambda}\, \pi$ takes on all real values exactly once, with $\lim_{\sqrt{\lambda} \to n - \frac{1}{2}} \tan \sqrt{\lambda}\, \pi = -\infty$, $\lim_{\sqrt{\lambda} \to n + \frac{1}{2}} \tan \sqrt{\lambda}\, \pi = +\infty$. Thus there is exactly one value $\sqrt{\lambda_n}$ between $(n - \frac{1}{2})$ and $(n + \frac{1}{2})$ such that $\tan \sqrt{\lambda_n}\, \pi = -k \sqrt{\lambda_n}$. This shows that there is an infinite sequence of solutions λ_n of (5.16), and hence an infinite sequence of eigenvalues of the boundary value problem (5.8), (5.15). In fact, if $k > 0$, $-k \sqrt{\lambda}$ decreases as λ increases, and we may conclude that the solution of (5.16) between $(n - \frac{1}{2})$ and $(n + \frac{1}{2})$ tends to $(n - \frac{1}{2})$, so that $\sqrt{\lambda_n}$ is given approximately by $(n - \frac{1}{2})$, for large n. In a similar way, we may see that if $k < 0$, $\sqrt{\lambda_n}$ is given approximately by $(n + \frac{1}{2})$ for large n (see Figure 5.3).

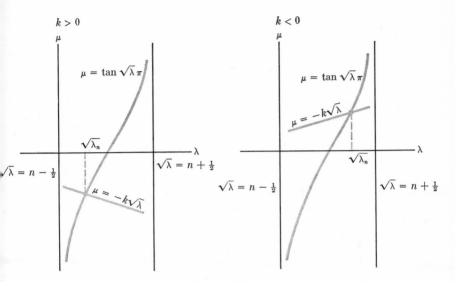

Figure 5.3

In the above discussion, we have ignored the possibility that $\lambda = 0$ may be an eigenvalue. Whether $\lambda = 0$ is an eigenvalue depends on the value of the constant k in the boundary condition at $t = \pi$.

• **EXERCISES**

13. Show that $\lambda = 0$ is not an eigenvalue of the boundary value problem (5.8), (5.15) unless $k = -\pi$.

14. Show that if $k = -\pi$, $\lambda = 0$ is an eigenvalue of the boundary value problem (5.8), (5.15) and $\phi_0(t) = A_0 t$ is a corresponding eigenfunction.

Example 4. Consider the boundary value problem defined on the interval $0 \le t \le \pi$ by the differential equation

$$y'' + \lambda y = 0 \tag{5.8}$$

and the boundary conditions

$$\alpha y(0) + \beta y'(0) = 0 \qquad \gamma y(\pi) + \delta y'(\pi) = 0 \tag{5.17}$$

where α, β, γ, δ are real constants. By an argument similar to that used in Example 1 above, it may be shown that this problem has no complex or negative eigenvalues.

•**EXERCISES**

15. Show that the eigenvalues of the boundary value problem (5.8), (5.17) are the solutions (if any) of the transcendental equation

$$(\alpha\gamma + \beta\delta\lambda) \frac{\sin \sqrt{\lambda}\,\pi}{\sqrt{\lambda}} = -(\alpha\delta - \beta\gamma) \cos \sqrt{\lambda}\,\pi$$

16. Show that the equation in Exercise 15 has an infinite sequence of real positive roots. [*Hint:* If $\beta\delta \neq 0$, the left side of this equation oscillates with amplitude $\beta\delta\sqrt{\lambda}$, which is large for large λ, while the right side is bounded; thus there is a root near each zero of the left side. If $\beta\delta = 0$, the left side oscillates with amplitude $\alpha\gamma/\sqrt{\lambda}$, which is small for large λ (or is identically zero if $\alpha\gamma = 0$); thus there is a root near each zero of the right side.]

17. Show that if $\alpha\gamma = \beta\delta = 0$ but $\alpha\delta - \beta\gamma \neq 0$, the eigenvalues of (5.8), (5.17) are $\lambda = (n + \frac{1}{2})^2$ $(n = 0, 1, 2, \ldots)$.

18. Show that if $\alpha\delta - \beta\gamma = 0$ but either $\alpha\gamma \neq 0$ or $\beta\delta \neq 0$, the eigenvalues of (5.8), (5.17) are $\lambda = n^2$ $(n = 0, 1, 2, \ldots)$.

Example 5. Consider the boundary value problem defined on the interval $0 \leq t \leq 2\pi$ by the differential equation

$$y'' + \lambda y = 0 \tag{5.8}$$

and the **periodic** boundary conditions

$$y(0) - y(2\pi) = 0 \qquad y'(0) - y'(2\pi) = 0 \tag{5.18}$$

By an argument similar to that used in Example 1 above, it may be shown that this problem has no complex or negative eigenvalues. As in the previous examples, we use the general solution

$$\phi(t) = c_1 \cos \sqrt{\lambda}\,t + c_2 \frac{\sin \sqrt{\lambda}\,t}{\sqrt{\lambda}} \tag{5.13}$$

of the differential equation (5.8) for $\lambda > 0$. Examination of the boundary conditions (5.18) show that they are satisfied if $\sqrt{\lambda}$ is a positive integer. Thus there is an infinite sequence of eigenvalues $\lambda = n^2$ $(n = 1, 2, \ldots)$. Corresponding to the eigenvalue n^2 there are **two** linearly independent eigenfunctions, namely, $\phi_n(t) = A_n \sin nt$, and $\psi_n(t) = B_n \cos nt$, for every choice of the constants A_n, B_n ($n = 1, 2, \ldots$). In the examples considered previously there was only one eigenfunction corresponding to each eigenvalue. The reader should note that as there cannot be more than two linearly independent solutions of the differential equation (5.8) for any value of λ (Theorem 3.2, p. 72), there cannot be more than two linearly independent eigenfunctions corresponding to any eigenvalue of any boundary value problem for the differential equation (5.8).

The boundary value problem (5.8), (5.18) has another eigenvalue, namely, $\lambda = 0$. For $\lambda = 0$ the general solution of the differential equation (5.8) is $\phi(t) = c_1 + c_2 t$. The boundary conditions (5.18) give $c_2 = 0$, and we see that $\psi_0(t) = B_0$ is an eigenfunction corresponding to the eigenvalue $\lambda_0 = 0$ for every choice of the constant B_0.

•EXERCISES

19. Show that there are no negative or complex eigenvalues for the boundary value problem (5.8), (5.18).

20. Show that $\int_0^{2\pi} \phi_n(t)\phi_m(t)\, dt = 0$, $\int_0^{2\pi} \psi_n(t)\psi_m(t)\, dt = 0$ for $n \neq m$ and $\int_0^{2\pi} \phi_n(t)\psi_m(t)\, dt = 0$, where ϕ_n, ψ_n are the eigenfunctions of (5.8), (5.18).

21. Show that $\int_0^{2\pi} [\phi_n(t)]^2\, dt = \pi A_n^2$, $\int_0^{2\pi} [\psi_n(t)]^2\, dt = \pi B_n^2$, while $\int_0^{2\pi} [\psi_0(t)]^2\, dt = 2\pi B_0^2$.

22. Show that $A_n \sin nt + B_n \cos nt$ is an eigenfunction of the boundary value problem (5.8), (5.18) corresponding to the eigenvalue $\lambda = n^2$ for every choice of the constants A_n, B_n.

For the reader acquainted with linear algebra, we remark that the eigenfunctions of the boundary value problem (5.8), (5.18) corresponding to the eigenvalue $\lambda = n^2$ form a two-dimensional vector space which has an orthogonal basis consisting of the functions $\sin nt$ and $\cos nt$ ($n = 1, 2, \ldots$). This is the content of Exercises 20–22 above. The eigenfunctions corresponding to the eigenvalue $\lambda = 0$ form a one-dimensional vector space spanned by the constant function 1.

•EXERCISES

23. Find the eigenvalues and eigenfunctions of the boundary value problem defined on the interval $a \leq t \leq b$ by the differential equation $y'' + \lambda y = 0$ and the boundary conditions $y(a) = 0$, $y(b) = 0$.

24. Find the eigenvalues and eigenfunctions of the boundary value problem defined on the interval $0 \leq t \leq 1$ by the differential equation $y'' + \lambda y = 0$ and the boundary conditions $y'(0) = 0$, $y(1) = 0$.

5.3   Examples of Nonhomogeneous Boundary Value Problems—the Green's Function

Example 1.   The physical problem of a rotating string to which a given external force $f(t)$ is applied leads to a **nonhomogeneous boundary value problem** of the form

$$y'' + \lambda y = f(t) \tag{5.19}$$

with boundary conditions such as

$$y(0) = 0 \qquad y(\pi) = 0 \tag{5.20}$$

in the case of fixed end points.   In (5.19), λ is a given constant which we assume to be positive.   We shall see that the problem (5.19), (5.20) is intimately related to the corresponding homogeneous boundary value problem

$$y'' + \lambda y = 0 \tag{5.21}$$

with boundary conditions (5.20) (see Example 1, Section 5.2, p. 199), and it will be essential to distinguish the cases when λ is an eigenvalue and when λ is not an eigenvalue.

By the variation of constants formula (Section 3.8, p. 105; see particularly Exercise 5, p. 106) the general solution of (5.19) is

$$\phi(t) = c_1 \cos \sqrt{\lambda}\, t + c_2 \frac{\sin \sqrt{\lambda}\, t}{\sqrt{\lambda}} + \frac{1}{\sqrt{\lambda}} \int_0^t \sin \sqrt{\lambda}\, (t - s)f(s)\, ds \tag{5.22}$$

where we have used the general solution of the differential equation (5.21) given by (5.13) (p. 202).   We wish to have the solution ϕ defined by (5.22) satisfy the boundary conditions (5.20).   To satisfy the condition $y(0) = 0$ we must clearly have $c_1 = 0$.   The boundary condition $y(\pi) = 0$ gives

$$c_2 \frac{\sin \sqrt{\lambda}\, \pi}{\sqrt{\lambda}} + \frac{1}{\sqrt{\lambda}} \int_0^\pi \sin \sqrt{\lambda}\, (\pi - s)f(s)\, ds = 0 \tag{5.23}$$

If, for the given λ, $\sin \sqrt{\lambda}\, \pi \neq 0$, equation (5.23) can be solved uniquely and we obtain

$$c_2 = - \frac{1}{\sin \sqrt{\lambda}\, \pi} \int_0^\pi \sin \sqrt{\lambda}\, (\pi - s)f(s)\, ds$$

Therefore, from (5.22) we have

$$\phi(t) = -\frac{\sin \sqrt{\lambda}\, t}{\sqrt{\lambda} \sin \sqrt{\lambda}\, \pi} \int_0^\pi \sin \sqrt{\lambda}\, (\pi - s) f(s)\, ds$$

$$+ \frac{1}{\sqrt{\lambda}} \int_0^t \sin \sqrt{\lambda}\, (t - s) f(s)\, ds \qquad (5.24)$$

We emphasize that the condition $\sin \sqrt{\lambda}\, \pi \neq 0$ **is precisely the condition that λ is not an eigenvalue of the homogeneous problem** (5.21), (5.20) (see Example 1, Section 5.2, p. 200).

If $\lambda = \lambda^*$ is an eigenvalue of the homogeneous problem (5.21), (5.20), that is, if $\sin \sqrt{\lambda^*}\, \pi = 0$ and $\lambda^* = n^2$ for some positive integer n (see Example 1, Section 5.2, p. 200), then the equation (5.23) is satisfied with an **arbitrary** choice of c_2 if and only if

$$\int_0^\pi f(s) \sin \sqrt{\lambda^*}\, (\pi - s)\, ds = 0$$

or equivalently if and only if

$$\int_0^\pi f(s) \sin \sqrt{\lambda^*}\, s\, ds = 0 \qquad (5.25)$$

• **EXERCISE**

1. Derive (5.25). [Hir.t: $\sin \sqrt{\lambda^*}\, (\pi - s) = \sin \sqrt{\lambda^*}\, \pi \cos \sqrt{\lambda^*}\, s - \cos \sqrt{\lambda^*}\, \pi \sin \sqrt{\lambda^*}\, s$, and $\sin \sqrt{\lambda^*}\, \pi = 0$.]

If λ^* is an eigenvalue and the condition (5.25) is satisfied, the solution is

$$\phi(t) = c_2 \frac{\sin \sqrt{\lambda^*}\, t}{\sqrt{\lambda^*}} + \frac{1}{\sqrt{\lambda^*}} \int_0^t f(s) \sin \sqrt{\lambda^*}\, (t - s)\, ds$$

where c_2 is arbitrary and cannot be determined from the boundary conditions because $\sin \sqrt{\lambda^*}\, t/\sqrt{\lambda^*}$ is an eigenfunction of the homogeneous problem (5.21), (5.20). Thus if $\lambda = \lambda^*$ is an eigenvalue, the nonhomogeneous problem (5.19), (5.20) cannot have a **unique** solution. Either it has a family of solutions if the condition (5.25) is satisfied, or it has **no** solution if the condition (5.25) is not satisfied.

If λ is not an eigenvalue of the homogeneous problem (5.21), (5.20), then the solution ϕ, given by (5.24), of the nonhomogeneous problem

(5.19), (5.20) is unique. To show this, we suppose that ψ is another solution of (5.19) satisfying (5.20). Then $\phi - \psi$ is a solution of the homogeneous equation (5.21) [Section 3.2, p. 68] satisfying the boundary conditions (5.20). Therefore if $\phi - \psi$ is not identically zero on $0 \le t \le \pi$, λ is an eigenvalue of the homogeneous problem (5.21), (5.20), contradicting the assumption.

Suppose λ is not an eigenvalue of the homogeneous problem (5.21), (5.20); $\lambda \ne n^2$ $(n = 1, 2, \ldots)$ (see Example 1, Section 5.2, p. 200). Then we may rewrite the expression (5.24) for the (unique) solution ϕ of (5.19), (5.20) as

$$\phi(t) = \left[\int_0^t \frac{\sin \sqrt{\lambda}\,(t - s)}{\sqrt{\lambda}} f(s)\, ds - \int_0^t \frac{\sin \sqrt{\lambda}\, t \sin \sqrt{\lambda}\,(\pi - s)}{\sqrt{\lambda} \sin \sqrt{\lambda}\, \pi} f(s)\, ds \right.$$

$$\left. - \int_t^\pi \frac{\sin \sqrt{\lambda}\, t \sin \sqrt{\lambda}\,(\pi - s)}{\sqrt{\lambda} \sin \sqrt{\lambda}\, \pi} f(s)\, ds \right]$$

The first two terms in this expression may be combined.

•EXERCISE

2. Show that

$$\frac{\sin \sqrt{\lambda}\,(t - s)}{\sqrt{\lambda}} - \frac{\sin \sqrt{\lambda}\, t \sin \sqrt{\lambda}\,(\pi - s)}{\sqrt{\lambda} \sin \sqrt{\lambda}\, \pi} = - \frac{\sin \sqrt{\lambda}\, s \sin \sqrt{\lambda}\,(\pi - t)}{\sqrt{\lambda} \sin \sqrt{\lambda}\, \pi}$$

Therefore

$$\phi(t) = - \int_0^t \frac{\sin \sqrt{\lambda}\, s \sin \sqrt{\lambda}\,(\pi - t)}{\sqrt{\lambda} \sin \sqrt{\lambda}\, \pi} f(s)\, ds$$

$$- \int_t^\pi \frac{\sin \sqrt{\lambda}\, t \sin \sqrt{\lambda}\,(\pi - s)}{\sqrt{\lambda} \sin \sqrt{\lambda}\, \pi} f(s)\, ds \quad (5.26)$$

It is convenient to define the function

$$G(t, s, \lambda) = \begin{cases} - \dfrac{\sin \sqrt{\lambda}\, s \sin \sqrt{\lambda}\,(\pi - t)}{\sqrt{\lambda} \sin \sqrt{\lambda}\, \pi} & \text{if } 0 \le s \le t \\[4mm] - \dfrac{\sin \sqrt{\lambda}\, t \sin \sqrt{\lambda}\,(\pi - s)}{\sqrt{\lambda} \sin \sqrt{\lambda}\, \pi} & \text{if } t \le s \le \pi \end{cases} \quad (5.27)$$

and to write the solution (5.26) as

$$\phi(t) = \int_a^b G(t, s, \lambda) f(s) \, ds \qquad (0 \le t \le \pi) \tag{5.28}$$

The function $G(t, s, \lambda)$, defined for $0 \le t, s \le \pi$, and $\lambda \ne n^2$ ($n = 1$, $2, \ldots$) is called the **Green's function** for the nonhomogeneous boundary value problem (5.19), (5.20). When this Green's function, which does not depend on the forcing function f, is known, the solution of (5.19), (5.20) is given by (5.28) for every forcing function f.

• **EXERCISES**

3. Show that $G(s, t, \lambda) = G(t, s, \lambda)$ provided $\lambda \ne n^2$ ($n = 1, 2, \ldots$).

4. Show that $G(t, s, \lambda)$ is continuous for $0 \le t, s \le \pi$ and $(\partial G/\partial t)(t, s, \lambda)$ is continuous for $t \ne s$ but

$$\lim_{h \to 0+} \left[\frac{\partial G}{\partial t}(s + h, s, \lambda) - \frac{\partial G}{\partial t}(s - h, s, \lambda) \right] = -1$$

5. Show that $G(t, s, \lambda)$, considered as a function of t for each fixed s, satisfies the differential equation (5.21) except for $t = s$.

6. Show that $G(t, s, \lambda)$, considered as a function of t for each fixed s, satisfies the boundary conditions $y(0) = 0$, $y(\pi) = 0$.

It is possible to show that the Green's function is unique, and that it is completely determined by the properties given in Exercises 3–6, that is, there is no other function having these properties (see [1], pp. 41–47; [5], pp. 190–192).

• **EXERCISES**

7. Discuss the case $\lambda = 0$ of the nonhomogeneous boundary value problem (5.19), (5.20), that is, find the solution of the problem $y'' = f(t)$, $y(0) = 0$, $y(\pi) = 0$ and determine the Green's function $H(t, s)$ for this problem. Show, that $H(t, s) = \lim_{\lambda \to 0} G(t, s, \lambda)$, where $G(t, s, \lambda)$ is given by (5.27). [*Hint:* Recall that $\lim_{x \to 0} (\sin ax / x) = a$.]

8. Find the solution of the nonhomogeneous boundary value problem $y'' + \lambda y = \cos kt$, $y(0) = 0$, $y(\pi) = 0$, where k is a given positive constant. [*Hint:* Treat the cases $\lambda \ne k^2$ and $\lambda = k^2$ separately.]

9. Show that the Green's function $G(t, s, \lambda)$ for the boundary value problem $y'' + \lambda y = f(t)$, $y'(0) = 0$, $y'(\pi) = 0$ (see Example 2, Section 5.2, p. 202) is

given by

$$G(t, s, \lambda) = \begin{cases} \dfrac{\cos \sqrt{\lambda}\, t \cos \sqrt{\lambda}\,(\pi - s)}{\sqrt{\lambda} \sin \sqrt{\lambda}\,\pi} & \text{if } 0 \leq t \leq s \\[3mm] \dfrac{\cos \sqrt{\lambda}\, s \cos \sqrt{\lambda}\,(\pi - t)}{\sqrt{\lambda} \sin \sqrt{\lambda}\,\pi} & \text{if } s \leq t \leq \pi \end{cases}$$

10. Show that the solution ϕ of the differential equation $y'' = f(t)$ satisfying the boundary conditions $y(0) + y(1) = 0$, $y'(0) + y'(1) = 0$ may be written $\phi(t) = \int_0^1 G(t, s) f(s)\, ds$, where

$$G(t, s) = \begin{cases} -\dfrac{1}{4} + \dfrac{1}{2}\,(s - t) & \text{if } s \geq t \\[3mm] -\dfrac{1}{4} + \dfrac{1}{2}\,(t - s) & \text{if } s \leq t \end{cases}$$

that is, $G(t, s) = -\frac{1}{4} - \frac{1}{2}|t - s|$.

So far we have only studied problems with homogeneous boundary conditions. To illustrate the treatment of inhomogeneous boundary conditions consider the following problem.

Example 2.   Given the boundary value problem defined by the differential equation

$$y'' + \lambda y = 0 \tag{5.21}$$

with the boundary conditions

$$y(0) = A \qquad y(\pi) = B \tag{5.29}$$

where A and B are given constants. We shall show that this problem may be reduced to one in which the differential equation becomes inhomogeneous and the boundary conditions become homogeneous, thereby reducing the problem to one which we have already handled, in Example 1 above.

Let $g(t)$ be any function with two continuous derivatives on $0 \leq t \leq \pi$ such that

$$g(0) = A \qquad g(\pi) = B$$

for example, $g(t) = A + (B - A)(t/\pi)$ is such a function.   Let $y(t) = z(t) + g(t)$; then $y'(t) = z'(t) + g'(t)$, $y''(t) = z''(t) + g''(t)$, and

$$y''(t) + \lambda y(t) = z''(t) + g''(t) + \lambda[z(t) + g(t)]$$

Thus the original boundary value problem is replaced by the problem

$$z'' + \lambda z = -[g''(t) + \lambda g(t)]$$
$$z(0) = 0 \qquad z(\pi) = 0$$

which is of the form (5.19), (5.20) with $f(t) = -[g''(t) + \lambda g(t)]$, and has a solution given in Example 1.   With the particular choice of g suggested above, the problem becomes

$$z'' + \lambda z = -\lambda \left[A + (B - A)\frac{t}{\pi} \right]$$
$$z(0) = 0 \qquad z(\pi) = 0$$

so that $f(t) = -\lambda[A + (B - A)(t/\pi)]$

Example 3.   For the problem

$$y'' + \lambda y = h(t) \tag{5.30}$$

with the boundary conditions

$$y(0) = A \qquad y(\pi) = B$$

where h is a given function and A and B are given constants, we consider two simpler problems.   First, we consider the problem with the homogeneous differential equation solved in Example 2.   We let $\phi_1(t)$ be the solution of the boundary value problem (5.21), (5.29).   Next, let $\phi_2(t)$ be the solution of the boundary value problem (5.30) with homogeneous boundary conditions

$$y(0) = 0 \qquad y(\pi) = 0 \tag{5.20}$$

which was obtained in Example 1.   Then if λ is not an eigenvalue of the homogeneous boundary value problem (5.21), (5.20), the unique solution of the given problem is $\phi(t) = \phi_1(t) + \phi_2(t)$.

●**EXERCISES**

11. Show that $\phi(t) = \phi_1(t) + \phi_2(t)$ is a solution of (5.30), (5.29).
12. Show that the solution ϕ is unique if $\lambda \neq n^2$ ($n = 1, 2, \ldots$).
13. Solve the boundary value problem

$$y'' + 2y = 1$$
$$y(0) = 0 \qquad y(\pi) = 1$$

14. Solve the boundary value problem

$$y'' + 2y = 1$$
$$y'(0) = 0 \qquad y(\pi) = 1$$

5.4 Self-Adjoint Boundary Value Problems for the Operator $L(y) = -y''$

In Section 5.2 we have studied several different homogeneous boundary value problems associated with the linear differential equation

$$L(y) = -y'' = \lambda y \tag{5.31}$$

We observed that these problems had some features in common, namely, (i) all the eigenvalues of each problem were real, and (ii) each problem had an infinite sequence of eigenvalues tending to $+\infty$. In this section we shall examine the question of how general these properties are, that is, for what boundary conditions they hold.

Let $u(t)$ and $v(t)$ be given functions (possibly complex-valued) which are continuous and have continuous first and second derivatives on an interval $a \leq t \leq b$. We shall use $\bar{u}(t)$ to denote the complex conjugate of $u(t)$. We use integration by parts twice to attempt to evaluate $\int_a^b Lu(t)\bar{v}(t) \, dt$, obtaining

$$\begin{aligned}
\int_a^b L(u(t))\bar{v}(t) \, dt &= -\int_a^b u''(t)\bar{v}(t) \, dt \\
&= -[u'(t)\bar{v}(t)]_a^b + \int_a^b u'(t)\bar{v}(t) \, dt \\
&= [u(t)\bar{v}'(t) - u'(t)\bar{v}(t)]_a^b = \int_a^b u(t)\bar{v}''(t) \, dt \\
&= W(u, \bar{v})(t)]_a^b + \int_a^b u(t)(\overline{Lv(t)}) \, dt
\end{aligned} \tag{5.32}$$

where $W(u, \bar{v})(t)$ denotes the Wronskian of the functions u and $\bar{v}$ (see Section 3.3, p. 75).

Now, suppose that u and v both satisfy a pair of given boundary conditions at a and b which make the expression $W(u, \bar{v})(t)]_a^b = 0$. For example, we may require both u and v to satisfy **separated** boundary conditions of the form

$$\alpha y(a) + \beta y'(a) = 0 \qquad \gamma y(b) + \delta y'(b) = 0 \tag{5.33}$$

where $\alpha, \beta, \gamma, \delta$ are given real constants with at least one of α, β and at least one of γ, δ different from zero. If $\beta \neq 0$, then the first condition in (5.33) becomes $y'(a) = -(\alpha/\beta)y(a)$, and if u and v both satisfy this condition,

$$
\begin{aligned}
W(u, \bar{v})(a) &= u(a)\bar{v}'(a) - u'(a)\bar{v}(a) \\
&= -\frac{\alpha}{\beta}[u(a)\bar{u}(a) - u(a)\bar{u}(a)] = 0
\end{aligned}
\tag{5.34}
$$

●**EXERCISE**

1. If $\beta = 0$ but $\alpha \neq 0$, show that (5.34) remains valid for functions u, v satisfying $\alpha y(a) = 0$.

A similar argument using the second condition in (5.33) shows that $W(u, \bar{v})(b) = 0$. Thus we see that if u and v both satisfy the separated boundary conditions (5.33), then $W(u, \bar{v})(t)]_a^b = 0$.

Another type of boundary conditions which may be imposed is **periodic** boundary conditions,

$$y(a) - y(b) = 0 \qquad y'(a) - y'(b) = 0 \tag{5.35}$$

●**EXERCISE**

2. Show that if u and v both satisfy the periodic boundary conditions (5.35), then $W(u, \bar{v})(t)]_a^b = 0$.

The vanishing of $W(u, \bar{v})(t)]_a^b$ in (5.32) has important implications for the boundary value problem on the interval $a \leq t \leq b$ defined by the differential equation (5.31) and the boundary conditions which imply $W(u, \bar{v})(t)]_a^b = 0$:

Definition.   *A boundary value problem consisting of the differential equation (5.31) together with a pair of boundary conditions at a and b having* *the property that* $W(u, \bar{v})(t)]_a^b = 0$ *for any functions u and v both satisfying these boundary conditions is said to be self-adjoint.*

For a self-adjoint boundary value problem the relation (5.32) becomes

$$\int_a^b [Lu(t)\bar{v}(t) - u(t)\overline{Lv}(t)]\, dt = 0 \tag{5.36}$$

provided u and v satisfy the boundary conditions.   In particular, we have already shown that (5.31), (5.33) and (5.31), (5.35) are self-adjoint boundary value problems.   As the following exercises show, there are other self-adjoint boundary value problems associated with the differential equation (5.31).

• EXERCISES

3. Show that the boundary value problem $y'' + \lambda y = 0$, $y(0) + y(\pi) = 0$, $y'(0) + y'(\pi) = 0$ is self-adjoint.

4. Determine a condition on the real constants α, β, γ, δ for which the boundary value problem $y'' + \lambda y = 0$, $y(\pi) - \alpha y(0) - \beta y'(0) = 0$, $y'(\pi) - \gamma y(0) - \delta y'(0) = 0$ is self-adjoint.

If u is an eigenfunction of a self-adjoint boundary value problem associated with the differential equation (5.31) corresponding to an eigenvalue λ, then by taking $v = u$ in (5.36) and using $Lu = \lambda u$, we obtain

$$(\lambda - \bar{\lambda}) \int_a^b u(t)\bar{u}(t)\, dt = 0 \tag{5.37}$$

By the definition of an eigenfunction, $u(t)\bar{u}(t) = |u(t)|^2$ is not identically zero.   Therefore $\int_a^b u(t)\bar{u}(t)\, dt > 0$,   and   we   may   divide   (5.37)   by $\int_a^b u(t)\bar{u}(t)\, dt$ to obtain $\lambda = \bar{\lambda}$.   Therefore the eigenvalue λ must be real. Of course, this argument does not prove that the self-adjoint boundary value problem associated with the differential equation (5.31) has any eigenvalues.   We have, however, shown by a separate argument that there is an infinite sequence of real eigenvalues for separated boundary conditions (see Exercises 15, 16, Section 5.2, p. 206) and for periodic boundary conditions (see Example 5, Section 5.2, p. 206).

For real λ, the differential equation (5.31) has real coefficients, and in view of the discussion in Section 3.4 (p. 85), we may restrict our attention in the future to real solutions of (5.31).   Thus we shall assume that all functions are real, and dispense with the complex conjugates in equations (5.32) and (5.36).

In Exercise 5, Section 5.2 (p. 202) (and similarly in subsequent exercises 8, 20, 21 for other boundary value problems) we showed that the eigenfunctions $\phi_n(t) = A_n \sin nt$ $(n = 1, 2, \ldots)$ of the boundary value problem (5.8), (5.9) (p. 199) satisfy the relation

$$\int_0^\pi \phi_n(t)\phi_m(t)\, dt = 0 \qquad (n \neq m)$$

This was done by a direct evaluation of the integral. This property of eigenfunctions is true for general self-adjoint boundary value problems, and in order to establish this, we must define the concept of orthogonality of functions.

Definition.   *Two continuous real functions $f(t)$, $g(t)$ defined on $a \leq t \leq b$ are said to be orthogonal on $a \leq t \leq b$ if and only if*

$$\int_a^b f(t)g(t)\, dt = 0$$

Thus Exercise 5, Section 5.2 (p. 202) shows that the eigenfunctions $\phi_n(t) = A_n \sin nt$ $(n = 1, 2, \ldots)$ are orthogonal on $0 \leq t \leq \pi$.

Let u be a (real) eigenfunction corresponding to an eigenvalue λ and let v be a (real) eigenfunction corresponding to an eigenvalue $\mu \neq \lambda$ of a self-adjoint boundary value problem for the differential equation (5.31). Then, using $Lu = \lambda u$, $Lv = \mu v$ in (5.36), we obtain

$$(\lambda - \mu) \int_a^b u(t)v(t)\, dt = 0$$

Since $\lambda \neq \mu$, we must have

$$\int_a^b u(t)v(t)\, dt = 0 \tag{5.38}$$

which says that the eigenfunctions u and v corresponding to different eigenvalues of the boundary problem are orthogonal on the interval $a \leq t \leq b$.

We summarize what we have shown up to this point in the following theorem.

Theorem 5.1.   *For a self-adjoint boundary value problem consisting of the differential equation*

$$Ly = -y'' = \lambda y \tag{5.31}$$

and self-adjoint boundary conditions such as

$$\alpha y(a) + \beta y'(a) = 0 \qquad \gamma y(b) + \delta y'(b) = 0 \qquad (5.33)$$

or

$$y(a) - y(b) = 0 \qquad y'(a) - y'(b) = 0 \qquad (5.35)$$

(but not restricted to these), *all eigenvalues are real and eigenfunctions corresponding to different eigenvalues are orthogonal on $a \le t \le b$.*

We have already shown in equation (5.34) (p. 215) that if u and v are eigenfunctions of the boundary value problem (5.31), (5.33), with separated boundary conditions corresponding to the same eigenvalue, then $W(u, v)(a) = 0$ (and also $W(u, v)(b) = 0$). Since u and v also satisfy the differential equation (5.31), it follows that u and v are linearly dependent on $a \le t \le b$ (by Theorems 3.3 and 3.4, pp. 76, 78). Therefore, a self-adjoint boundary value problem for the differential equation (5.31) with separated boundary conditions cannot have two linearly independent eigenfunctions corresponding to any eigenvalue. This is not true in the case of periodic boundary conditions (5.35). For, as we have seen in Example 5, Section 5.2 (p. 206), there may be two linearly independent eigenfunctions corresponding to the same eigenvalue. The reader should note that while the problem (5.31), (5.35) with periodic boundary conditions is self-adjoint (Exercise 2, p. 215), $W(u, \bar{v})(a) \ne 0$, $W(u, \bar{v})(b) \ne 0$ for functions u and v which satisfy the boundary conditions (5.35).

Theorem 5.1 says nothing about whether a self-adjoint boundary value problem for the differential equation (5.31) actually has any eigenvalues. The examples considered in Section 5.2 suggest that there is an infinite sequence of eigenvalues, but this has not been proved in the completely general case.

Theorem 5.2. *A self-adjoint boundary value problem consisting of the differential equation (5.31) and any self-adjoint boundary conditions such as (5.33) or (5.35) has an infinite sequence of eigenvalues tending to $+\infty$.*

Theorem 5.2 has been established in Exercises 15, 16, Section 5.2 (p. 206) for separated boundary conditions (5.33) and in Example 5, Section 5.2 (p. 206) for periodic boundary conditions (5.35). The reader interested in the proof in the general case should consult [1], Chapter 10; [5], Chapter 7; or [19], Chapter 2.

5.5 Sturm–Liouville Problems

We now consider the more general second-order equation

$$a_0(t)y'' + a_1(t)y' + a_2(t)y = \lambda y \tag{5.39}$$

where a_0, a_1, and a_2 are continuous and $a_0 \neq 0$ on an interval $a \leq t \leq b$, with homogeneous boundary conditions at a and b. However, we make a preliminary simplification. If we multiply the equation (5.39) by

$$\frac{1}{a_0(t)} \exp\left(\int_a^t \frac{a_1(s)}{a_0(s)}\, ds\right)$$

and use the identity

$$\exp\left(\int_a^t \frac{a_1(s)}{a_0(s)}\, ds\right) y'' + \frac{a_1(t)}{a_0(t)} \exp\left(\int_a^t \frac{a_1(s)}{a_0(s)}\, ds\right) y'$$
$$= \left[\exp\left(\int_a^t \frac{a_1(s)}{a_0(s)}\right) y'(t)\right]'$$

we obtain

$$\left(\exp\left(\int_a^t \frac{a_1(s)}{a_0(s)}\, ds\right) y'\right)' + \frac{a_2(t)}{a_0(t)} \exp\left(\int_a^t \frac{a_1(s)}{a_0(s)}\, ds\right) y$$
$$= \lambda \frac{1}{a_0(t)} \exp\left(\int_a^t \frac{a_1(s)}{a_0(s)}\, ds\right) y$$

This equation may be written in the form

$$Ly = -(p(t)y')' + q(t)y = \lambda r(t)y \tag{5.40}$$

where

$$p(t) = \exp\left(\int_a^t \frac{a_1(s)}{a_0(s)}\, ds\right) \qquad q(t) = -\frac{a_2(t)}{a_0(t)} \exp\left(\int_a^b \frac{a_1(s)}{a_0(s)}\, ds\right) \qquad \text{and}$$
$$r(t) = -\frac{1}{a_0(t)} \exp\left(\int_a^t \frac{a_1(s)}{a_0(s)}\, ds\right)$$

are continuous on $a \leq t \leq b$, $p(t) > 0$ on $a \leq t \leq b$, and $r(t) \neq 0$ on $a \leq t \leq b$. Either $r(t) > 0$ on $a \leq t \leq b$ or $r(t) < 0$ on $a \leq t \leq b$. If $r(t) < 0$ on $a \leq t \leq b$, we may replace λ by $-\lambda$ to obtain an equation of the form (5.40) with $r(t) > 0$ on $a \leq t \leq b$.

We shall now study boundary value problems consisting of the differential equation (5.40) with $p(t) > 0$, $r(t) > 0$ on $a \leq t \leq b$, and either **separated boundary conditions**

$$\alpha y(a) + \beta y'(a) = 0 \qquad \gamma y(b) + \delta y'(b) = 0 \tag{5.41}$$

where $\alpha, \beta, \gamma, \delta$ are given real constants, or **periodic boundary conditions**

$$y(a) - y(b) = 0 \qquad y'(a) - y'(b) = 0 \tag{5.42}$$

In the case of periodic boundary conditions we shall also require $p(a) = p(b)$. Such a boundary value problem is called a **Sturm–Liouville problem.***

•EXERCISES

1. Show that, with L as defined in (5.40),

$$\int_a^b [Lu(t)\bar{v}(t) - u(t)\overline{Lv}(t)] \, dt = p(t) W(u, \bar{v})(t)]_a^b$$

for functions u and v which are continuous and have continuous second derivatives on $a \leq t \leq b$. [*Hint:* Imitate the proof leading up to equation (5.32) (p. 214).]

2. Show that if u and v satisfy either the separated boundary conditions (5.41) or the periodic boundary conditions (5.42) (with the additional assumption $p(a) = p(b)$ for periodic boundary conditions), then $p(t) W(u, \bar{v})(t)]_a^b = 0$.

From Exercises 1 and 2 we deduce immediately that a Sturm–Liouville problem is **self-adjoint,** in the sense that

$$\int_a^b [Lu(t)\bar{v}(t) - u(t)\overline{Lv}(t)] \, dt = 0 \tag{5.43}$$

for every pair of functions u and v which satisfy the boundary conditions (5.41) or (5.42). The boundary conditions are used only to establish the self-adjointness condition (5.43). Obviously, as in the special case of the operator $L(y) = -y''$ considered in the preceding section, any boundary conditions which lead to (5.43), even if they are not of the form (5.41) or (5.42), define boundary value problems for which our results are valid.

From (5.43) we deduce, exactly as in Theorem 5.1 (p. 217) that all eigenvalues of a Sturm–Liouville problem are real. The orthogonality

---

* After the German mathematician Sturm (1803–1855) and French mathematician Liouville (1809–1887), who independently were the first to formulate these problems.

of eigenfunctions of (5.40), (5.41) or (5.40), (5.42) corresponding to different eigenvalues now takes a slightly different form from that of Theorem 5.1.   Namely, let u be a (real) eigenfunction corresponding to an eigenvalue λ and let v be a (real) eigenfunction corresponding to an eigenvalue $\mu \neq \lambda$.   Then, since $Lu = \lambda r(t)u$ and $Lv = \mu r(t)v$, (5.43) gives

$$(\lambda - \mu) \int_a^b r(t)u(t)v(t) \, dt = 0$$

Since $\lambda \neq \mu$, we have

$$\int_a^b r(t)u(t)v(t) \, dt = 0 \tag{5.44}$$

This motivates the following definition:

Definition.   *Functions u and v satisfying (5.44) are said to be othogonal on $a \leq t \leq b$ with respect to the weight function $r(t)$.*

If $r(t) \equiv 1$, as it is in the differential equation $y'' + \lambda y = 0$ considered in Section 5.2, orthogonality with respect to the weight function $r(t)$ reduces to the ordinary orthogonality defined earlier (p. 217).

We have now developed the following analogue of Theorem 5.1 for the general Sturm–Liouville problem.

Theorem 5.3.   *For a Sturm–Liouville problem, consisting of the differential equation*

$$L(y) = -(p(t)y')' + q(t)y = \lambda r(t)y \tag{5.40}$$

where p, q, r are continuous on $a \leq t \leq b$, and $p(t) > 0$, $r(t) > 0$ on $a \leq t \leq b$, and the boundary conditions

$$\alpha y(a) + \beta y'(a) = 0 \qquad \gamma y(b) + \delta y'(b) = 0 \tag{5.41}$$

where α, β, γ, δ are real constants, or

$$y(a) - y(b) = 0 \qquad y'(a) - y'(b) = 0 \tag{5.42}$$

(with $p(a) = p(b)$ for the boundary conditions (5.42)), all eigenvalues are real and eigenfunctions corresponding to different eigenvalues are orthogonal on $a \leq t \leq b$ with respect to the weight function $r(t)$.

Actually, we have proved Theorem 5.3 for any self-adjoint boundary value problem, not merely for the particular boundary conditions (5.41) or (5.42).

• EXERCISES

3. Show that there cannot be two linearly independent eigenfunctions corresponding to the same eigenvalue for the differential equation (5.40) with separated boundary conditions (5.41).

4. Determine a condition on the real constants α, β, γ, δ for which the boundary value problem defined by the differential equation (5.40) and the boundary conditions $y(\pi) - \alpha y(0) - \beta y'(0) = 0$, $y'(\pi) - \gamma y(0) - \delta y'(0) = 0$ is self-adjoint.   (Compare Exercise 4, Section 5.4, p. 216.)

The question of existence of eigenvalues for the general Sturm–Liouville problem is more difficult than for the particular equation $y'' + \lambda y = 0$. We shall state an analogue of Theorem 5.2 (p. 218), but we refer the reader to a more advanced source, such as [1], Chapter 10; [5], Chapter 7; or [19], Chapter 2 for the proof.

Theorem 5.4.   *The Sturm–Liouville problem consisting of the differential equation* (5.40) *and the boundary conditions* (5.41) *or* (5.42) *(with $p(a) = p(b)$ in the case of* (5.42)*) has an infinite sequence of eigenvalues tending to $+\infty$.*

5.6   Remarks on a Singular Boundary Value Problem

In many applications we are faced with boundary value problems of Sturm–Liouville type for which the hypotheses that p, q, r are continuous and that $p(t) > 0$ and $r(t) > 0$ for $a \leq t \leq b$ made earlier are not satisfied. For example, some problems involving cylindrical symmetry lead to a boundary value problem consisting of the differential equation

$$L(y) = -(ty')' + \frac{m^2}{t} y = \lambda t y \tag{5.45}$$

where m is a known integer, together with boundary conditions at $t = 0$ and $t = 1$.   Comparing this with equation (5.40) (p. 219), we see that $p(t) = t$, $q(t) = m^2/t$, $r(t) = t$, and the hypotheses of Theorems 5.3 and 5.4 are certainly not satisfied at $t = 0$.   Thus Theorems 5.3 and 5.4 cannot be applied directly.   Such problems are called **singular** boundary value problems.

Even though the hypotheses of Theorems 5.3 and 5.4 are not satisfied, we may consider the integral

$$\int_0^1 [Lu(t)\bar{v}(t) - u(t)\overline{Lv}(t)]\, dt$$

which played an essential role in the theory, where the integral may be improper. For the particular case of

$$L(y) = -(ty')' + \frac{m^2}{t} y$$

we obtain, after integrating by parts,

$$\int_0^1 [Lu(t)\bar{v}(t) - u(t)\overline{Lv}(t)]\, dt = \lim_{\epsilon \to 0+} \int_\epsilon^1 [Lu(t)\bar{v}(t) - u(t)\overline{Lv}(t)]\, dt$$

$$= \lim_{\epsilon \to 0+} \int_\epsilon^1 \left\{ \left[-(tu'(t))' + \frac{m^2}{t} u(t) \right] \bar{v}(t) - u(t) \left[(t\bar{v}'(t))' + \frac{m^2}{t} \bar{v}(t) \right] \right\} dt$$

$$= \lim_{\epsilon \to 0+} \int_\epsilon^1 [-(tu'(t))'\bar{v}(t) + u(t)(t\bar{v}'(t))']\, dt$$

$$= \lim_{\epsilon \to 0+} \left\{ [-tu'(t)\bar{v}(t)]_\epsilon^1 + \int_\epsilon^1 tu'(t)\bar{v}'(t)\, dt + [tu(t)\bar{v}'(t)]_\epsilon^1 \right.$$
$$\left. - \int_\epsilon^1 u'(t)t\bar{v}'(t)\, dt \right\}$$

$$= \lim_{\epsilon \to 0+} [t\{u(t)\bar{v}'(t) - u'(t)\bar{v}(t)\}]_\epsilon^1$$

$$= u(1)\bar{v}'(1) - u'(1)\bar{v}(1) - \lim_{\epsilon \to 0+} \epsilon[u(\epsilon)\bar{v}'(\epsilon) - u'(\epsilon)\bar{v}(\epsilon)]$$

$$= W(u, \bar{v})(1) - \lim_{\epsilon \to 0+} \epsilon W(u, \bar{v})(\epsilon)$$

We therefore see that we may impose a homogeneous boundary condition on u and v at $t = 1$, such as $u(1) = 0$, $v(1) = 0$, or $\gamma u(1) + \delta u'(1) = 0$, $\gamma v(1) + \delta v'(1) = 0$ to ensure that $W(u, \bar{v})(1) = 0$. If, in addition, we require $u(t)$, $u'(t)$, $v(t)$, $v'(t)$ to be bounded* on any interval containing $t = 0$, we will have

$$\lim_{\epsilon \to 0+} \epsilon W(u, \bar{v})(\epsilon) = 0$$

and therefore

$$\int_0^1 [Lu(t)\bar{v}(t) - u(t)\overline{Lv}(t)]\, dt = 0 \tag{5.46}$$

---

* This requirement explains why in Chapter 4 we were interested in solutions analytic at a singular point; for example, $J_0(0) = 1$, $J_n(0) = 0$ ($n = 1, 2, \ldots$).

Since this relation was all that was used in proving Theorem 5.3, the result of Theorem 5.3 remains valid for the equation (5.45) and boundary conditions of the form

$$y(1) = 0, \quad y(t), \quad y'(t) \text{ bounded at } t = 0 \tag{5.47}$$

or

$$\gamma y(1) + \delta y'(1) = 0; \quad y(t), \quad y'(t) \text{ bounded at } t = 0 \tag{5.48}$$

Observe that the condition that $y(t)$ and $y'(t)$ be bounded at $t = 0$ is of a different type from the boundary conditions imposed previously. Moreover, this condition is inherent in the differential equation and arbitrary values cannot be assigned at $t = 0$. It is possible to prove an analogue of Theorem 5.4 for such problems, but we consider only the special case (5.45), (5.47).

Carrying out the differentiation in (5.45) and multiplying by t, we obtain the equation

$$t^2 y'' + t y' + (\lambda t^2 - m^2)y = 0 \tag{5.49}$$

which is a form of the Bessel equation that has been studied in Section 4.9. We recall from Exercise 23 (p. 176) that the general solution of (5.49), with m an integer or zero, is

$$\phi(t) = c_1 J_m (\sqrt{\lambda}\, t) + c_2 K_m(\sqrt{\lambda}\, t)$$

We recall also, see Theorem 4.6 (p. 177), that the solution $K_m(\sqrt{\lambda}\, t)$ is unbounded on any interval containing the origin. Thus if $\phi(t)$ is to be a bounded solution of (5.45) on $0 \leq t \leq 1$,

$$\phi(t) = c_1 J_m(\sqrt{\lambda}\, t) \tag{5.50}$$

Notice that $\phi'(t) = c_1 \sqrt{\lambda}\, J'_m(\sqrt{\lambda}\, t)$, and from the power series representation (4.62) (p. 170), $\phi'(t)$ is also bounded on $0 \leq t \leq 1$. Therefore (5.50) satisfies the differential equation (5.45) and the second condition in (5.47). It remains to determine λ so that the first condition in (5.47) is satisfied, that is, we wish to determine λ so that

$$J_m(\sqrt{\lambda}) = 0 \tag{5.51}$$

By the analogue of Theorem 5.3 for this problem, we know that λ must be real.

Instead of invoking an analogue of Theorem 5.4, we can give an independent proof of the fact that the equation (5.51) has an infinite sequence of real positive solutions. This proof has already been outlined in Exercises 17, 18, Section 4.9 (p. 175). Let this sequence of solutions of (5.51) be $\mu_n{}^2$ $(n = 1, 2, \ldots)$. (These solutions are tabulated in [11] or [12].) The corresponding eigenfunctions of the boundary value problem (5.45), (5.47) are

$$\phi_n(t) = A_n J_m(\mu_n t) \qquad (n = 1, 2, \ldots)$$

By the analogue of Theorem 5.3, these eigenfunctions are orthogonal on $0 \leq t \leq 1$ with respect to the weight function $r(t) = t$. This fact was also established independently in Exercises 19, 20, Section 4.9 (p. 175).

The above considerations suggest how one may attack a singular boundary value problem. Whether this approach is successful depends on how the coefficients in the differential equation behave near the singular point. The interested reader is referred to [1], Chapter 10; [5], Chapters 9, 10; or [19], Chapter 5 for other problems of this type.

•EXERCISES

1. Show that the Legendre equation

$$(1 - t^2)y'' - 2ty' + \lambda y = 0$$

can be written in the form $Ly = -((1 - t^2)y')' = \lambda y$.

2. Recall that $t = \pm 1$ are regular singular points while $t = 0$ is an ordinary point for the Legendre equation. Consider the singular boundary value problem consisting of the Legendre equation together with the condition that the solution be bounded on $-1 \leq t \leq 1$. Show that this problem has an infinite sequence of eigenvalues $\lambda = n(n + 1)$ $(n = 1, 2, \ldots)$, and compute the corresponding eigenfunctions. [*Hint:* See Example 2 and Exercises 9–17, Section 4.3, pp. 129–131.]

3. Prove that the analogue of Theorem 5.3 for the boundary value problem in Exercise 2 is valid. [*Hint:* Consider

$$\int_{-1}^{1} [Lu(t)\bar{v}(t) - u(t)\overline{Lv}(t)]\, dt$$

and imitate the analysis given above for the Bessel equation.]

5.7   Nonhomogeneous Boundary Value Problems and Green's Function

In Section 5.3 (p. 208) we discussed nonhomogeneous boundary value problems for the operator $L(y) = -y''$. We showed that there was a unique solution provided the corresponding homogeneous problem had no solution, and that this solution could be written as an integral involving the Green's function. In this section, we shall consider the analogous problem of solving a nonhomogeneous boundary value problem corresponding to a more general Sturm–Liouville operator.

Let us begin by studying the boundary value problem defined by the nonhomogeneous differential equation

$$L(y) = -(p(t)y')' + q(t)y = \lambda r(t)y + f(t) \tag{5.52}$$

and the boundary conditions

$$y(a) = 0 \qquad y(b) = 0 \tag{5.53}$$

We shall assume throughout that p, q, r, and f are continuous on $a \leq t \leq b$ and that $p(t) > 0$, $r(t) > 0$ for $a \leq t \leq b$. We shall establish the following result.

Theorem 5.5.   *The nonhomogeneous boundary problem* (5.52), (5.53) *has a unique solution ϕ for a given value of λ, provided the corresponding homogeneous boundary value problem*

$$L(y) = -(p(t)y') + q(t)y = \lambda r(t)y \tag{5.54}$$

with the same boundary conditions (5.53) *has no nontrivial solution* (that is, provided λ is not an eigenvalue of (5.54), (5.53)). *This solution ϕ may be written in the form*

$$\phi(t) = \int_a^b G(t, s, \lambda)f(s) \, ds \qquad (a \leq t \leq b) \tag{5.55}$$

where the function $G(t, s, \lambda)$, called the Green's function for the problem (5.52), (5.53), *has the following properties.*

(i) $G(t, s, \lambda)$ *is a continuous function of* (t, s, λ) *for* $a \leq t, s \leq b$ *and for λ not an eigenvalue of* (5.54), (5.53).

(ii) $(\partial G/\partial t)(t, s, \lambda)$ *is a continuous function of* (t, s, λ) *for* $t \neq s$ *and for* λ *not an eigenvalue of* (5.54), (5.53); *moreover*

$$\lim_{h \to 0+} \left[\frac{\partial G}{\partial t} (s + h, s, \lambda) - \frac{\partial G}{\partial t} (s - h, s, \lambda) \right] = - \frac{1}{p(s)}$$

(iii) $G(t, s, \lambda)$, *considered as a function of* t, *satisfies the homogeneous differential equation* (5.54) *for each* t *except* $t = s$.

(iv) $G(t, s, \lambda)$, *considered as a function of* t, *satisfies the boundary conditions* (5.53) *for each* s, $a \leq s \leq b$.

(v) $G(t, s, \lambda) = G(s, t, \lambda)$ *if* $a \leq t, s \leq b$ *and if* λ *is real but not an eigenvalue of* (5.54), (5.53).

Proof.   Let $\phi_1(t, \lambda)$, $\phi_2(t, \lambda)$ be the solutions of the differential equation (5.54) such that

$$\phi_1(a, \lambda) = 1, \quad \phi_1'(a, \lambda) = 0, \quad \phi_2(a, \lambda) = 0, \quad \phi_2'(a, \lambda) = 1 \qquad (5.56)$$

Then ϕ_1 and ϕ_2 exist on the whole interval $a \leq t \leq b$ by Theorem 3.1 (p. 65) and are linearly independent on $a \leq t \leq b$ by Theorem 3.2 (p. 72). Using Theorem 3.4 (p. 78), we calculate their Wronskian

$$W(\phi_1, \phi_2)(t) = \exp \left(- \int_a^t \frac{p'(s)}{p(s)} \, ds \right) = \frac{p(a)}{p(t)}$$

The general solution of the nonhomogeneous differential equation (5.52) may be obtained from the variation of constants formula (3.34) (p. 105). It has the form

$$\phi(t) = c_1\phi_1(t, \lambda) + c_2\phi_2(t, \lambda) - \frac{1}{p(a)} \int_a^t [\phi_2(t, \lambda)\phi_1(s, \lambda) \\ - \phi_1(t, \lambda)\phi_2(s, \lambda)]f(s) \, ds \qquad (5\ 57)$$

In view of (5.56), the boundary condition $\phi(a) = 0$ gives $c_1 = 0$. The boundary condition $\phi(b) = 0$ gives

$$c_2\phi_2(b, \lambda) - \frac{1}{p(a)} \int_a^b [\phi_2(b, \lambda)\phi_1(s, \lambda) - \phi_1(b, \lambda)\phi_2(s, \lambda)]f(s) \, ds = 0 \qquad (5.58)$$

The equation (5.58) may be solved for c_2 if $\phi_2(b, \lambda) \neq 0$. This condition $\phi_2(b, \lambda) \neq 0$ merely says that λ is not an eigenvalue of the homogeneous boundary value problem (5.54), (5.53), for if $\phi_2(b, \lambda) = 0$, then $\phi_2(t, \lambda)$ is an eigenfunction, while if $\phi_2(b, \lambda) \neq 0$ there is no solution ψ of (5.54) with $\psi(a) = \psi(b) = 0$. Thus the hypotheses of the theorem assure $\phi_2(b, \lambda) \neq 0$, and we may solve (5.58) for c_2. Substituting the value for c_2 obtained from (5.58) into (5.57), we obtain the solution of the nonhomogeneous boundary value problem (5.52), (5.53).

$$
\begin{aligned}
\phi(t) &= \frac{\phi_2(t, \lambda)}{p(a)\phi_2(b, \lambda)} \int_a^b [\phi_1(s, \lambda)\phi_2(b, \lambda) - \phi_1(b, \lambda)\phi_2(s, \lambda)]f(s)\, ds \\
&\quad - \frac{1}{p(a)} \int_a^t [\phi_2(t, \lambda)\phi_1(s, \lambda) - \phi_1(t, \lambda)\phi_2(s, \lambda)]f(s)\, ds \\
&= \frac{\phi_2(t, \lambda)}{p(a)\phi_2(b, \lambda)} \int_a^t [\phi_1(s, \lambda)\phi_2(b, \lambda) - \phi_1(b, \lambda)\phi_2(s, \lambda)]f(s)\, ds \\
&\quad + \frac{\phi_2(t, \lambda)}{p(a)\phi_2(b, \lambda)} \int_t^b [\phi_1(s, \lambda)\phi_2(b, \lambda) - \phi_1(b, \lambda)\phi_2(s, \lambda)]f(s)\, ds \\
&\quad - \frac{1}{p(a)} \int_a^t [\phi_2(t, \lambda)\phi_1(s, \lambda) - \phi_1(t, \lambda)\phi_2(s, \lambda)]f(s)\, ds
\end{aligned}
$$

We may write this in the form (5.55) as desired, with

$$
G(t, s, \lambda) = \begin{cases}
\dfrac{1}{p(a)\phi_2(b, \lambda)} [\phi_1(t, \lambda)\phi_2(s, \lambda)\phi_2(b, \lambda) - \phi_2(t, \lambda)\phi_2(s, \lambda)\phi_1(b, \lambda)] \\
\qquad\qquad\qquad\qquad\qquad\qquad\qquad\qquad\qquad \text{if } s \leq t \\
\dfrac{1}{p(a)\phi_2(b, \lambda)} [\phi_2(t, \lambda)\phi_1(s, \lambda)\phi_2(b, \lambda) - \phi_2(t, \lambda)\phi_2(s, \lambda)\phi_1(b, \lambda)] \\
\qquad\qquad\qquad\qquad\qquad\qquad\qquad\qquad\qquad \text{if } s \geq t
\end{cases} \tag{5.59}
$$

From this explicit representation (5.59) it is easy to verify that $G(t, s, \lambda)$ has the properties (i)–(v) given in the statement of the theorem. The only part of the theorem not yet proved is the uniqueness of the solution (5.55) of the nonhomogeneous problem (5.52), (5.53). Since the difference between two solutions of this nonhomogeneous problem is a solution of the homogeneous problem (5.54), (5.53), the assumption that λ is not an eigenvalue implies that the difference between two solutions of the nonhomogeneous problem (5.52), (5.53) is identically zero, that is, the solution (5.55) of the problem (5.52), (5.53) is unique. ∎

•EXERCISES

1. Verify that the function $G(t, s, \lambda)$ given by (5.59) has the properties (i)–(v) listed in the statement of Theorem 5.5 (p. 226).

2. Show that if λ is an eigenvalue, the equation (5.58) becomes

$$\frac{\phi_1(b, \lambda)}{p(a)} \int_a^b \phi_2(s, \lambda) f(s) \, ds = 0$$

3. Show that when λ is an eigenvalue, the boundary value problem (5.52), (5.53) has a solution if and only if f is orthogonal to the eigenfunction $\phi_2(t, \lambda)$ on $a \leq t \leq b$.

4. Solve the boundary value problem (5.52), (5.53) when λ is an eigenvalue and f is orthogonal to the eigenfunction $\phi_2(t, \lambda)$ on $a \leq t \leq b$. Show also that the solution is not unique in this case.

When one attempts to construct a Green's function for a boundary value problem with more general boundary conditions than (5.53), the above method is not the easiest approach. We therefore look at the question of solving a nonhomogeneous boundary value problem from a slightly different point of view. We begin by constructing a function with the properties (i)–(v) of Theorem 5.5 (p. 226) and then we shall use this function to form the solution of the nonhomogeneous boundary value problem.

We consider the boundary value problem defined by the nonhomogeneous differential equation

$$-(p(t)y')' + q(t)y = \lambda r(t)y + f(t) \tag{5.52}$$

and the general separated boundary conditions

$$\alpha y(0) + \beta y'(0) = 0 \qquad \gamma y(b) + \delta y'(b) = 0 \tag{5.60}$$

We assume, as before, that p, q, r, and f are continuous and $p(t) > 0$, $r(t) > 0$ for $a \leq t \leq b$. Let $\psi_1(t, \lambda)$ be a solution, not identically zero, of (5.52) which satisfies the boundary condition $\alpha y(a) + \beta y'(a) = 0$, and let $\psi_2(t, \lambda)$ be a solution, not identically zero, of (5.52) which satisfies the other boundary condition $\gamma y(b) + \delta y'(b) = 0$. If λ is not an eigenvalue of the corresponding homogeneous boundary value problem (5.54), (5.60), then the solutions $\psi_1(t, \lambda)$, $\psi_2(t, \lambda)$ are linearly independent on $a \leq t \leq b$.

•EXERCISE

5. Show that if $\psi_1(t, \lambda)$ and $\psi_2(t, \lambda)$ are linearly dependent on $a \leq t \leq b$, then λ is an eigenvalue and $\psi_1(t, \lambda)$ (or $\psi_2(t, \lambda)$) is a corresponding eigenfunction of the homogeneous boundary value problem.

The most general function of (t, s, λ) which satisfies the differential equation (5.54) for $a \leq t \leq s$ and the boundary condition at a has the form

$$G(t, s, \lambda) = c_1(s, \lambda)\psi_1(t, \lambda) \qquad (0 \leq t \leq s)$$

Similarly the most general function of (t, s, λ) which satisfies the differential equation (5.54) for $s \leq t \leq b$ and the boundary condition at b has the form

$$G(t, s, \lambda) = c_2(s, \lambda)\psi_2(t, \lambda) \qquad (s \leq t \leq b)$$

Thus the function $G(t, s, \lambda)$ defined by

$$G(t, s, \lambda) = \begin{cases} c_1(s, \lambda)\psi_1(t, \lambda) & (a \leq t \leq s) \\ c_2(s, \lambda)\psi_2(t, \lambda) & (s \leq t \leq b) \end{cases}$$

is the most general function having the properties (iii), (iv) of Theorem 5.5 (p. 227).   The symmetry property (v) implies

$$c_1(s, \lambda)\psi_1(t, \lambda) = G(t, s, \lambda) = G(s, t, \lambda) = c_2(t, \lambda)\psi_2(s, \lambda)$$

if $t \leq s$.   This gives

$$\frac{c_1(s, \lambda)}{\psi_2(s, \lambda)} = \frac{c_2(t, \lambda)}{\psi_1(t, \lambda)}$$

and since the left side of this equation is independent of t while the right side is independent of s, both sides must be independent of both s and t. Now, we may write $c_1(s, \lambda) = k\psi_2(s, \lambda)$, $c_2(t, \lambda) = k\psi_1(t, \lambda)$, and

$$G(t, s, \lambda) = \begin{cases} k\psi_2(s, \lambda)\psi_1(t, \lambda) & (a \leq t \leq s) \\ k\psi_1(s, \lambda)\psi_2(t, \lambda) & (s \leq t \leq b) \end{cases}$$

It is easy to verify that this function G has the property (i) of continuity in (t, s, λ) for $a \leq t, s \leq b$ if λ is not an eigenvalue.   The partial derivative $(\partial G/\partial t)(t, s, \lambda)$ is continuous except for $t \neq s$, and

$$\lim_{h \to 0+} \left[\frac{\partial G}{\partial t}(s + h, s, \lambda) - \frac{\partial G}{\partial t}(s - h, s, \lambda) \right]$$
$$= \lim_{h \to 0+} [k\psi_1(s, \lambda)\psi_2'(s + h, \lambda) - k\psi_2(s, \lambda)\psi_1'(s + h, \lambda)]$$
$$= k[\psi_1(s, \lambda)\psi_2'(s, \lambda) - \psi_2(s, \lambda)\psi_1'(s, \lambda)]$$
$$= kW(\psi_1, \psi_2)(s)$$

where $W(\psi_1, \psi_2)(s)$ is the Wronskian of ψ_1, ψ_2, as defined in Section 3.3 (p. 75). By Abel's formula (see Theorem 3.4, p. 78),

$$W(\psi_1, \psi_2)(s) = W(\psi_1, \psi_2)(a) \cdot \frac{p(a)}{p(s)}$$

Thus we may satisfy condition (ii) of Theorem 5.5 (p. 227) by choosing $k = 1/p(a)W(\psi_1, \psi_2)(a)$. We now have the function

$$G(t, s, \lambda) = \begin{cases} \dfrac{\psi_2(s, \lambda)\psi_1(t, \lambda)}{p(a)W(\psi_1, \psi_2)(a)} & (a \leq t \leq s) \\[3mm] \dfrac{\psi_1(s, \lambda)\psi_2(t, \lambda)}{p(a)W(\psi_1, \psi_2)(a)} & (s \leq t \leq b) \end{cases} \qquad (5.61)$$

defined for $a \leq t$, $s \leq b$, λ not an eigenvalue, which has the properties (i)–(v) of Theorem 5.5. If we form the function

$$\begin{aligned} \phi(t) &= \int_a^b G(t, s, \lambda)f(s)\,ds \\ &= \frac{\psi_2(t, \lambda)}{p(a)W(\psi_1, \psi_2)(a)} \int_a^b \psi_1(s, \lambda)f(s)\,ds \\ &\quad + \frac{\psi_1(t, \lambda)}{p(a)W(\psi_1, \psi_2)(a)} \int_t^b \psi_2(s, \lambda)f(s)\,ds \end{aligned} \qquad (5.62)$$

we may easily verify by direct substitution that ϕ is the unique solution of the nonhomogeneous boundary value problem (5.52), (5.60) if λ is not an eigenvalue of the homogeneous problem (5.54), (5.60).

• EXERCISES

6. Show that $\phi(t)$ given by (5.62) satisfies the differential equation (5.52) and the boundary conditions (5.60) if λ is not an eigenvalue.

7. Show that the problem (5.52), (5.60) has a unique solution if λ is not an eigenvalue.

The Green's function which we have constructed here reduces to the one constructed by a different approach in Theorem 5.5 when we take $\beta = \delta = 0$ in the boundary conditions (5.60). In fact, the following is true.

Theorem 5.6. *There is only one Green's function for the boundary value problem* (5.52), (5.60) *which is continuous for $a \leq t$, $s \leq b$, λ not an* *eigenvalue, and such that the unique solution of the problem* (5.52), (5.60) *is given by* (5.62) *for every continuous function* $f(t)$.

Proof. We assume that $G_1(t, s, \lambda)$ and $G_2(t, s, \lambda)$ are two such Green's functions. Since λ is not an eigenvalue of the homogeneous problem, the problem (5.52), (5.60) has a unique solution $\phi(t)$ and by uniqueness we must have

$$\int_a^b G_1(t, s, \lambda) f(s) \, ds = \int_a^b G_2(t, s, \lambda) f(s) \, ds$$

or equivalently

$$\int_a^b [G_1(t, s, \lambda) - G_2(t, s, \lambda)] f(s) \, ds = 0 \tag{5.63}$$

for $a \le t \le b$, and for every continuous function f. We choose the particular function

$$f(s) = G_1(t, s, \lambda) - G_2(t, s, \lambda)$$

for any fixed t ($a \le t \le b$) and for λ not an eigenvalue. Then (5.63) becomes

$$\int_a^b [G_1(t, s, \lambda) - G_2(t, s, \lambda)]^2 \, ds = 0$$

and since $G_1(t, s, \lambda) - G_2(t, s, \lambda)$ is continuous, this implies

$$G_1(t, s, \lambda) = G_2(t, s, \lambda) \qquad (a \le s \le b)$$

for every t ($a \le t \le b$) and λ not an eigenvalue. This proves the uniqueness of the Green's function. ∎

• EXERCISES

8. Verify, by using (5.61), the previously constructed Green's functions in Section 5.3, namely, equation (5.27) (p. 210) for Example 1, and Exercises 9 and 10 (pp. 211, 212).

9. Show that the Green's function for the problem

$$- (ty')' + \frac{m^2}{t} y - \lambda t y + f(t)$$

$y(1) = 0$, $y(t)$, and $y'(t)$ bounded at $t = 0$ (see Section 5.6, p. 222) is

$$
G(t, s, \lambda) = \begin{cases}
\dfrac{1}{J_m(\sqrt{\lambda})} [J_m(\sqrt{\lambda}\, t) J_m(\sqrt{\lambda}\, s) K_m(\sqrt{\lambda}) \\
\qquad\qquad - K_m(\sqrt{\lambda}\, t) J_m(\sqrt{\lambda}\, s) J_m(\sqrt{\lambda})] & (s \leq t) \\[2ex]
\dfrac{1}{J_m(\sqrt{\lambda})} [J_m(\sqrt{\lambda}\, t) J_m(\sqrt{\lambda}\, s) K_m(\sqrt{\lambda}) \\
\qquad\qquad - J_m(\sqrt{\lambda}\, t) K_m(\sqrt{\lambda}\, s) J_m(\sqrt{\lambda})] & (t \leq s)
\end{cases}
$$

•MISCELLANEOUS EXERCISES

1. Determine all real eigenvalues and corresponding eigenfunctions of each of the following boundary value problems. If the eigenvalues are roots of a transcendental equation which cannot be solved explicitly, give the equation for the eigenvalues and the form of the eigenfunctions.

(a) $y'' + \lambda y = 0$, $y(0) = 0$, $y'(\pi) = 0$.

(b) $y'' + \lambda y = 0$, $y'(0) + 2y'(1) = 0$, $y(1) = 0$.

(c) $y'' + \lambda y = 0$, $y(0) = 0$, $y(\pi) + y'(\pi) = 0$.

(d) $y'' + y' + (\lambda + 1)y = 0$, $y(0) = 0$, $y(\pi) = 0$.

(e) $y'' + (1 + \lambda)y' + \lambda y = 0$, $y'(0) = 0$, $y(1) = 0$.

(f) $t^2 y'' - \lambda t y' + \lambda y = 0$, $y(1) = 0$, $y(2) - y'(2) = 0$.

(g) $y^{(4)} - \lambda y = 0$, $y'(0) = y'(1) = y'''(0) = y'''(1) = 0$.

2. Construct the Green's function for each of the following boundary value problems and use it to find the solution for the boundary value problem.

(a) $y'' - y = t^2$, $y(0) = 0$, $y(1) = 0$.

(b) $y'' + 4y = t^2$, $y(0) = 0$, $y(1) = 0$.

(c) $y'' + \lambda y = f(t)$, $y'(0) = 0$, $y(1) = 0$.

(d) $y'' + \lambda y = \sin 2\pi t$, $y(0) = 0$, $y(1) = 0$.

3. Test whether each of the following boundary value problems is self-adjoint.

(a) $y'' + \lambda y = 0$, $y(0) + 2y'(0) + 2y(\pi) = 0$, $y(0) + y(\pi) - y'(\pi) = 0$.

(b) $y'' + y' + y + \lambda y = 0$, $y(0) = 0$, $y(1) = 0$.

(c) $(ty')' + 2y + \lambda t^2 y = 0$, $y(1) - y'(1) - y'(2) = 0$,

$$y(1) + y(2) + y'(2) = 0.$$

(d) $y'' + \lambda y = 0$, $y(0) - y(\pi) = 0$, $y'(0) + y'(\pi) = 0$.

(e) $y' + \lambda y = 0$, $y(0) - y(1) = 0$.

(f) $iy' - \lambda y = 0$, $y(0) - y(1) = 0$.

4. Consider the boundary value problem

$$y'' + \lambda y = 0$$

with the boundary conditions

$$m_{11}y(0) + m_{12}y'(0) + n_{11}y(\pi) + n_{12}y'(\pi) = 0$$
$$m_{21}y(0) + m_{22}y'(0) + n_{21}y(\pi) + n_{22}y'(\pi) = 0$$

where the m_{ij}, n_{ij} are real constants.   Show that this boundary value problem is self-adjoint if (and only if) $m_{11}m_{22} - m_{21}m_{12} = n_{11}n_{22} - n_{21}n_{12}$.

5.   Consider the differential equation

$$L(y) = -(p(t)y')' + q(t)y = \lambda r(t)y$$

where p, q, r are real continuous functions on $a \leq t \leq b$ with $p > 0$, $r > 0$, and where $[p(t)r(t)]^{1/2}$ and $p'(t)$ are continuous on $a \leq t \leq b$.   Show that the changes of variables (known as the Liouville transformation).

$$z = \frac{1}{K} \int_a^t \left[\frac{r(s)}{p(s)} \right]^{1/2} ds$$

$$K = \frac{1}{\pi} \int_a^b \left[\frac{r(s)}{p(s)} \right]^{1/2} ds$$

$$u = [p(s)r(s)]^{1/4}y$$

$$\rho = K^2\lambda$$

changes this differential equation to

$$(*) \quad -\frac{d^2u}{dz^2} + g(z)u = \rho u \quad (0 \leq z \leq \pi)$$

where

$$g(z) = \frac{f''(z)}{f(z)} - K^2k(z)$$

$$k(z) = \frac{q(t)}{r(t)}$$

$$f(z) = [p(t)r(t)]^{1/4}$$

The form of the equation (*) is useful in studying the asymptotic expression for the eigenvalues as $n \to \infty$, for the Sturm–Liouville boundary value problem; see [19], p. 113.

6.   Transform each of the following differential equations to the Liouville normal form
(a) $t^2y'' + ty' + (\lambda t^2 - p^2)y = 0$.
(b) $(1 - t^2)y'' - 2ty' + \lambda y = 0$.
(c) $y'' - 2ty' + (\lambda - 1)y = 0$.

7.   Find the eigenvalues and eigenfunctions of the boundary value problem

$$y'' + \lambda r(t)y = 0 \quad y(0) = 0 \quad y(\pi) = 0$$

where

$$r(t) = \begin{cases} 4 & \left(0 \le t \le \dfrac{\pi}{2}\right) \\ 1 & \left(\dfrac{\pi}{2} < t \le \pi\right) \end{cases}$$

Are the eigenfunctions and their derivatives continuous at $t = \pi/2$? (*Hint:* Find the solutions of the differential equation satisfying respectively $y(0) = 0$ and $y(\pi) = 0$, and choose λ to make the solutions match at $t = \pi/2$.)

8. Find the eigenvalues and eigenfunctions of the boundary value problem

$$y'' + \lambda y = 0 \qquad y(0) = 0 \qquad y\left(\frac{\pi}{2}\right) = 0 \qquad y(\pi) = 0$$

9. Show that the boundary value problem

$$y'' + \lambda y = 0 \qquad y'(0) + 2y'(\pi) = 0 \qquad y(\pi) = 0$$

is not self-adjoint and has no real eigenvalues. Show that there is an infinite sequence of complex eigenvalues.

10. Show that every complex number λ is an eigenvalue of the nonself-adjoint boundary value problem

$$y'' + \lambda y = 0 \qquad y(0) - y(\pi) = 0 \qquad y'(0) + y'(\pi) = 0$$

11. Show that the nonself-adjoint boundary value problem

$$y'' + \lambda y = 0 \qquad 2y(0) - y(\pi) = 0 \qquad 2y'(0) + y(\pi) = 0$$

has no eigenvalues, real or complex.

12. For each of the following boundary value problems, determine, at least approximately, the eigenvalues (if any exist) and the corresponding eigenfunctions. Also, determine the Green's function.
  (a) $-y'' + 2y' - y = \lambda y$ \qquad $y(0) = 0$ \qquad $y(1) = 0$.
  (b) $-y'' - 4y' - 4y = \lambda y$ \qquad $y(0) = 0$ \qquad $y'(L) = 0$.

13. Determine the eigenvalues and eigenfunctions of the boundary value problem defined by the differential equation

$$y^{(4)} - \lambda y = 0$$

and each of the following sets of boundary conditions
  (a) $y(0) = 0$ \qquad $y''(0) = 0$ \qquad $y(L) = 0$ \qquad $y''(L) = 0$.
  (b) $y(0) = 0$ \qquad $y''(0) = 0$ \qquad $y(L) = 0$ \qquad $y'(L) = 0$.
  (c) $y(0) = 0$ \qquad $y'(0) = 0$ \qquad $y''(L) = 0$ \qquad $y'''(L) = 0$.

14. Solve, if possible, each of the following boundary value problems
(a) $y'' + \lambda y = 0$ $\qquad$ $y(-1) = 0$ $\qquad$ $y(1) = 1.$
(b) $y'' + \lambda y = 0$ $\qquad$ $y(1) - y'(0) = 0$ $\qquad$ $y(1) = 1.$
(c) $-y'' - 4y' - 4y = \lambda y$ $\qquad$ $y(0) = 1$ $\qquad$ $y'(L) = 0.$
(d) $y'' + \lambda y = t$ $\qquad$ $y(-1) = 0$ $\qquad$ $y(1) = 1.$
(e) $y'' + \lambda y = \sin t$ $\qquad$ $y(1) - y'(0) = 0$ $\qquad$ $y(1) = 1.$
(f) $y'' + 4y = \cos t$ $\qquad$ $y(0) = 0$ $\qquad$ $y(\pi) = 0.$
(g) $y'' + 4y = \cos t$ $\qquad$ $y'(0) = 0$ $\qquad$ $y'(\pi) = 0.$
(h) $y'' + y = 1$ $\qquad$ $y(-L) = 0$ $\qquad$ $y'(L) = 0.$
(i) $y'' + y = 1$ $\qquad$ $y(0) = 0$ $\qquad$ $y(1) = 0.$

Chapter 6 || SYSTEMS OF DIFFERENTIAL EQUATIONS

6.1 Introduction

Mathematical models of physical problems can often be expressed conveniently as systems of differential equations, rather than as single differential equations. This is true of all problems of motion of several interacting particles, electrical networks (more complicated than a single R-L-C circuit), biological problems involving more than one species, etc. We shall illustrate by considering a simple problem.

Example 1. (The reader is urged to reread the discussion of a single mass–spring system in Section 1.1, p. 2.) Consider a mass m_1 suspended vertically from a rigid support by a weightless spring of natural length L_1, with a second mass m_2 suspended from the first by means of a second weightless spring of natural length L_2 as shown in Figure 6.1. We shall make the same assumptions here as we did for the single mass–spring system in Section 1.1. In particular, we assume that the masses m_1 and m_2 can be treated as point masses, that both springs obey Hooke's law and have respectively the spring constants k_1, k_2. We let $y(t)$, $z(t)$ be the respective displacements at time t of the masses m_1, m_2 from equilibrium (that is, the point at which the system remains at rest, before being set into motion). As in the simple case, the quantities y and z are vector functions of time. However, the motion being along a straight line, no confusion will arise if vector notation is not employed. We also assume that air resistance is negligible and that no external forces other than gravity act on the system.

The description of the model is completed by specification of $y(0)$, $y'(0)$, $z(0)$, $z'(0)$, the initial displacement and initial velocity of each mass.

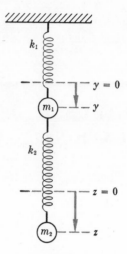

Figure 6.1

To derive the equations for the motion under the present hypotheses, we apply the same technique as in the simple case in Chapter 1. It is easy to see that at any time t the net force acting on the mass m_2 is $-k_2[z(t) - y(t)]$, while that acting on the mass m_1 is $-k_1 y(t) + k_2[z(t) - y(t)]$.

• **EXERCISE**

1. Show that at any time t the net force acting on m_1 is $-k_1 y(t) + k_2[z(t) - y(t)]$. [*Hint:* Let $L_1 + a_1$ be the equilibrium position of the mass m_1 measured downward from the vertical support; let $L_1 + L_2 + a_2$ be the equilibrium position of m_2 measured downward from the support assuming $m_1 = 0$. Now add the mass m_1 to obtain the equilibrium position of the system. Write down the sum of the forces acting on m_1 and m_2 and then evaluate the constants a_1, a_2—see Section 1.1. Note that the final expression for the net force is independent of m_1, m_2, L_1, L_2, a_1, a_2.]

Thus by Newton's second law we have immediately

$$m_1 y'' = -k_1 y + k_2(z - y)$$
$$m_2 y'' = -k_2(z - y) \tag{6.1}$$

as the differential equations describing the motion. As pointed out above, we also prescribe the initial values $y(0)$, $y'(0)$, $z(0)$, $z'(0)$. Thus our problem has led us to an initial value problem for **a system** of two differential equations, each of second order.

By a solution of this problem we mean **a pair** of functions y, z defined for $t \geq 0$, twice differentiable, satisfying for each t the equation (6.1) and for $t = 0$ the given initial conditions. Naturally, the same questions about the accuracy of the present model and about the reasonableness of the various hypotheses can be asked just as in the simpler problems considered in Chapter 1.

• **EXERCISES**

2. Derive the equations of motion of the system shown in Figure 6.1 if it is assumed that air resistance is proportional to velocity.

3. Consider three masses m_1, m_2, m_3 connected by means of three springs (obeying Hooke's law) with constants k_1, k_2, k_3 and moving on a frictionless horizontal table as shown in Figure 6.2, with the mass m_3 subjected to a given

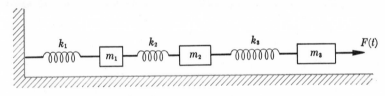

Figure 6.2

external force $F(t)$. Let $x_1(t)$, $x_2(t)$, $x_3(t)$ be the displacements respectively of m_1, m_2, m_3 at any time t measured from equilibrium at time $t = 0$. (At equilibrium the springs are in their natural, unstretched position.) Derive the equations of motion for this system and write down the initial conditions assuming that the system starts from rest.

It is clear that if n springs and n masses are used in the above problems, then the equations of motion would consist of n equations for the displacements of the masses, each equation being of second order.

• **EXERCISE**

4. Use Kirchoff's law (sum of voltage drops around a closed circuit equals zero) to write the differential equations satisfied by the currents i_1 and i_2 in the idealized circuit shown in Figure 6.3, where L_1, L_2 are given constant inductances, R_1, R_2 are given constant resistances, and E is a given impressed voltage. (Recall that $Li'(t)$ is the voltage drop across an inductor of inductance L due to a current $i(t)$ and $Ri(t)$ is the voltage drop across a resistance R due to a current $i(t)$.)

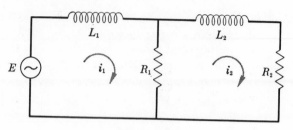

Figure 6.3

6.2 Systems of First-Order Equations

The examples in Section 6.1 cannot be conveniently expressed in terms of single differential equations. In this chapter we shall study systems of first-order differential equations of the form

$$
\begin{aligned}
y_1' &= f_1(t, y_1, y_2, \ldots, y_n) \\
y_2' &= f_2(t, y_1, y_2, \ldots, y_n) \\
&\ \ \vdots \\
y_n' &= f_n(t, y_1, y_2, \ldots, y_n)
\end{aligned}
\tag{6.2}
$$

where $f_1, f_2, \ldots, f_n$ are n given functions defined in some region D of $(n + 1)$-dimensional Euclidean space and $y_1, y_2, \ldots, y_n$ are the n unknown functions. We shall see below that the systems considered in Section 6.1 are special cases of the system (6.2). **To solve** (6.2) (compare Section 1.4, p. 15) means to find an interval I on the t axis and n functions $\phi_1, \ldots, \phi_n$ defined on I such that

(i) $\phi_1'(t), \phi_2'(t), \ldots, \phi_n'(t)$ exist for each t in I.
(ii) the point $(t, \phi_1(t), \ldots, \phi_n(t))$ remains in D for each t in I.
(iii) $\phi_j'(t) = f_j(t, \phi_1(t), \phi_2(t), \ldots, \phi_n(t))$ for each t in I $(j = 1, \ldots, n)$.

Thus (6.2) is the analogue of the single equation $y' = f(t, y)$ studied in Chapters 1 and 2. Naturally, the functions f_j may be real or complex valued. We shall assume the real case unless otherwise stated. While the geometric interpretation is no longer so immediate as in the case

$n = 1$, a solution of (6.2) (that is, a set of n functions $\phi_1, \ldots, \phi_n$ on an interval I) can be visualized as a curve in the $(n + 1)$-dimensional region D, with each point p on the curve given by the coordinates $(t, \phi_1(t), \ldots, \phi_n(t))$ and with $\phi_i'(t)$ being the component of the tangent vector to the curve in the direction y_i. This interpretation reduces to the one already given when $n = 1$ and the curve in D defined by any solution of (6.2) can therefore again be called a **solution curve**. **The initial value problem** associated with a system such as (6.2) is the problem of finding a solution (in the sense defined above) passing through a given point P_0: $(t_0, \eta_1, \eta_2, \ldots, \eta_n)$ (we do not write $(t_0, y_{10}, \ldots, y_{n0})$ to avoid double subscripts) of D. In general, we cannot expect to be able to solve (6.2) except in very special cases. Nevertheless, it is desired to obtain as much information as possible about the behavior of solutions of systems. For this reason we shall develop a considerable amount of theory for systems of differential equations.

We first note that (6.1) and the systems derived from physical consider-ations in the exercises in Section 6.1 are systems of second-order equations while (6.2) is a system of first-order equations. We shall first show that the system (6.2) of first-order equations is sufficiently general to include all such problems, and in particular all single nth-order equations are included as a special case in (6.2). We shall also see that the theory of nth-order equations, including all of Chapter 3, is a special case of the corresponding theory for systems of first-order equations.

Example 1. Consider the second-order equation

$$y'' = g(t, y, y') \tag{6.3}$$

where g is a given function. Put $y = y_1$, $y' = y_2$; then one has $y_1' = y_2$ and from (6.3) $y'' = y_2' = g(t, y_1, y_2)$. Thus (6.3) is apparently equiva-lent to the system of two first-order equations

$$\begin{aligned} y_1' &= y_2 \\ y_2' &= g(t, y_1, y_2) \end{aligned} \tag{6.4}$$

which is a special case of (6.2) with $n = 2$, $f_1(t, y_1, y_2) = y_2$, $f_2(t, y_1, y_2) = g(t, y_1, y_2)$. To see this equivalence let ϕ be a solution of (6.3) on some interval I; then $y_1 = \phi(t)$, $y_2 = \phi'(t)$ is a solution of (6.4) on I. Con-versely, let ϕ_1, ϕ_2 be a solution of (6.4) on I, then $y = \phi_1(t)$ (that is, the first component) is a solution of (6.3) on I.

•EXERCISES

1. Write a system of two first-order differential equations equivalent to the second-order equation

$$\theta'' + \frac{g}{L} \sin \theta = 0$$

with initial conditions $\theta(0) = \theta_0$, $\theta'(0) = 0$, which describes the motion of a simple pendulum (Section 1.2, p. 10).

2. Show that the equation $y''' + 3y'' - 4y' + 2y = 0$ is equivalent to the system of three first-order equations

$$y_1' = y_2$$
$$y_2' = y_3$$
$$y_3' = -2y_1 + 4y_2 - 3y_3$$

Example 2.   The scalar equation of nth order

$$y^{(n)} = g(t, y, y', \ldots, y^{(n-1)}) \tag{6.5}$$

can be reduced to a system of n first-order equations by the change of variable $y_1 = y$, $y_2 = y'$, $\ldots$, $y_n = y^{(n-1)}$. Then (6.5) is seen to be equivalent to the system

$$y_1' = y_2$$
$$y_2' = y_3$$
$$\cdot$$
$$\cdot \tag{6.6}$$
$$\cdot$$
$$y_{n-1}' = y_n$$
$$y_n' = g(t, y_1, y_2, \ldots, y_n)$$

another special case of (6.2).

•EXERCISE

3. Establish the equivalence of (6.5) and (6.6).

Example 3.   Returning to the system (6.1) of two second-order equations governing the motion of the system of two masses in Figure 6.1, we let $y_1 = y$, $y_2 = y'$, $y_3 = z$, $y_4 = z'$, and we find that (6.1) is equivalent to the system of four first-order equations

$$
\begin{aligned}
y_1' &= y_2 \\
y_2' &= -\left(\frac{k_1}{m_1} + \frac{k_2}{m_1}\right) y_1 + \frac{k_2}{m_1} y_3 \\
y_3' &= y_4 \\
y_4' &= -\frac{k_2}{m_2}(y_3 - y_1)
\end{aligned}
\tag{6.7}
$$

which is another special case of (6.2).

• EXERCISES

4. Establish the equivalence of the systems (6.1) and (6.7).

5. Write the systems of second-order equations derived in Exercises 2 and 3 (Section 6.1, p. 239) as equivalent systems of first-order equations.

6. Reduce the system

$$
\begin{aligned}
y_1' + y_2' &= y_1{}^2 + y_2{}^2 \\
2y_1' + 3y_2' &= 2y_1 y_2
\end{aligned}
$$

to the form (6.2).   [*Hint:* Solve for y_1' and y_2'.]

To study systems of first-order equations such as (6.2) systematically it is convenient to introduce vectors. We define $\mathbf{y}$ to be a point in n-dimensional Euclidean space, E_n, with coordinates $(y_1, \ldots, y_n)$. Unless otherwise indicated, E_n will represent **real** n-dimensional Euclidean space, that is, the coordinates $(y_1, \ldots, y_n)$ of the vector $\mathbf{y}$ are real numbers. However, the entire theory developed here carries over to the complex case with only minor changes, which will be indicated where necessary. We next define functions

$$
\hat{f}_j(t, \mathbf{y}) = f_j(t, y_1, \ldots, y_n) \qquad (j = 1, \ldots, n)
$$

and thus the system (6.2) can be written in the form

$$
\begin{aligned}
y_1' &= \hat{f}_1(t, \mathbf{y}) \\
y_2' &= \hat{f}_2(t, \mathbf{y}) \\
&\ \vdots \\
y_n' &= \hat{f}_n(t, \mathbf{y})
\end{aligned}
\tag{6.8}
$$

Proceeding heuristically (we will be more precise below), we next observe that $\hat{f}_1, \ldots, \hat{f}_n$ can be regarded as n components of the vector valued function **f** defined by

$$\mathbf{f}(t, \mathbf{y}) = (\hat{f}_1(t, \mathbf{y}), \ldots, \hat{f}_n(t, \mathbf{y}))$$

We also define

$$\mathbf{y}' = (y_1', \ldots, y_n')$$

Thus the system of n first-order equations (6.2) (and all the systems which arose earlier in this section (see also (6.8))) can be written in the very compact form

$$\mathbf{y}' = \mathbf{f}(t, \mathbf{y}) \tag{6.9}$$

(6.9) resembles the familiar single first-order equation $y' = f(t, y)$, with y, f replaced by the vectors **y**, **f**, respectively.

Example 4.   We may write the system (6.4) above

$$y_1' = y_2$$
$$y_2' = g(t, y_1, y_2)$$

as $\mathbf{y}' = \mathbf{f}(t, \mathbf{y})$ with $\mathbf{y} = (y_1, y_2)$ and

$$\hat{f}_1(t, \mathbf{y}) = f_1(t, y_1, y_2) = y_2$$
$$\hat{f}_2(t, \mathbf{y}) = f_2(t, y_1, y_2) = g(t, y_1, y_2)$$

so that

$$\mathbf{f}(t, \mathbf{y}) = (y_2, g(t, y_1, y_2))$$

• EXERCISE

7. Write the systems (6.6), (6.7) and the systems in Exercises 2, 5, 6 each in the form $\mathbf{y}' = \mathbf{f}(t, \mathbf{y})$ and in each case determine the vector **f**.

We shall assume that the reader is familiar with the elements of vector algebra.   However, we recall certain basic well-known facts, as well as some which may not be so familiar, in order to proceed with a systematic study of (6.9).   We define the zero vector **0** (the origin of E_n) by $\mathbf{0} = (0, \ldots, 0)$ and for any point $\mathbf{y} \in E_n$ we define $c\mathbf{y}$, where c is any real or complex number, by the relation

$$c\mathbf{y} = (cy_1, cy_2, \ldots, cy_n)$$

If **y** and **z** are two vectors in E_n we define their sum **y** + **z** to be the vector

$$\mathbf{y} + \mathbf{z} = (y_1 + z_1, y_2 + z_2, \ldots, y_n + z_n)$$

and, of course, **y** − **z** = **y** + (−**z**). Two vectors **y** and **z** are equal if and only if $y_i = z_i$ $(i = 1, \ldots, n)$. The Euclidean length of the vector **y** is defined by the relation

$$\|\mathbf{y}\| = [|y_1|^2 + \cdots + |y_n|^2]^{1/2} = \left[\sum_{i=1}^{n} |y_i|^2 \right]^{1/2}$$

Notice that $|y_i|$ is well defined for y_i complex and thus $\|\mathbf{y}\|$ is also defined for a complex vector **y**. We need the notion of length in order to measure distances between solutions of systems. However, for the purpose of dealing with systems such as (6.9) it turns out to be more convenient to define a different quantity for the length (or norm) of a vector **y** than the familiar Euclidean length, namely,

$$|\mathbf{y}| = |y_1| + |y_2| + \cdots + |y_n| = \sum_{i=1}^{n} |y_i|$$

Again, $|\mathbf{y}|$ is well defined for either real or complex vectors **y**. No confusion need arise from using the absolute value sign for different purposes; on the left-hand side $|\mathbf{y}|$ is the notation for length of the vector **y**; on the right-hand side we sum the absolute values of the components of **y**. Observe, for example, if **y** = $(3 + i, \ 3 - i)$, then $\|\mathbf{y}\| = [|3 + i|^2 + |3 - i|^2]^{1/2} = (10 + 10)^{1/2} = (20)^{1/2}$ and $|\mathbf{y}| = |3 + i| + |3 - i| = (10)^{1/2} + (10)^{1/2} = 2(10)^{1/2}$; clearly $|\mathbf{y}| > \|\mathbf{y}\|$ in this case and in fact, $|\mathbf{y}| = \sqrt{2} \ \|\mathbf{y}\|$. In general, the quantities $\|\mathbf{y}\|$ and $|\mathbf{y}|$ are related, as follows.

• EXERCISE

8. If $\mathbf{y} \in E_n$, show that

$$\|\mathbf{y}\| \le |\mathbf{y}| \le \sqrt{n} \ \|\mathbf{y}\|$$

[*Hint:* Use the inequality $2|uv| \le |u|^2 + |v|^2$ and show $\|\mathbf{y}\|^2 \le |\mathbf{y}|^2 \le n\|\mathbf{y}\|^2$.]

The important point about this inequality is that $|\mathbf{y}|$ is small if and only if $\|\mathbf{y}\|$ is small.

The length function $|\mathbf{y}|$ has the following important properties:

(i) $|\mathbf{y}| \ge 0$ and $|\mathbf{y}| = 0$ if and only if **y** = **0**.

(ii) if c is any complex number, $|c\mathbf{y}| = |c| \ |\mathbf{y}|$.

(iii) for all **y** and **z**, $|\mathbf{y} + \mathbf{z}| \le |\mathbf{y}| + |\mathbf{z}|$.

The proofs are immediate from well-known properties of complex numbers. For example, to prove (ii) we have

$$|c\mathbf{y}| = \sum_{j=1}^{n} |cy_j| = \sum_{j=1}^{n} |c|\,|y_j| = |c| \sum_{j=1}^{n} |y_j| = |c|\,|\mathbf{y}|$$

Similarly for (iii) we use the inequality $|u + v| \leq |u| + |v|$ valid for any complex numbers u and v.

•EXERCISE

9. Show that the Euclidean length $\|\mathbf{y}\|$ of a vector $\mathbf{y}$ also satisfies the properties (i), (ii), (iii) above. [*Hint:* To prove (iii) you will need to apply the Schwarz inequality for sums, that is,

$$\left| \sum_{i=1}^{n} a_i b_i \right|^2 \leq \sum_{i=1}^{n} |a_i|^2 \sum_{i=1}^{n} |b_i|^2$$

to the term $2\Re \left(\sum_{i=1}^{n} y_i \bar{z}_i \right)$ which arises in the expansion of

$$\|\mathbf{y} + \mathbf{z}\|^2 = \sum_{i=1}^{n} |y_i + z_i|^2 = \sum_{i=1}^{n} (y_i + \bar{z}_i)\overline{(y_i + z_i)}$$

$$= \sum_{i=1}^{n} |y_i|^2 + 2\Re \left(\sum_{i=1}^{n} y_i \bar{z}_i \right) + \sum_{i=1}^{n} |z_i|^2 \Big]$$

Using the length function we define **the distance between two vectors y and z**, $d(\mathbf{y}, \mathbf{z})$, by the relation

$$d(\mathbf{y}, \mathbf{z}) = |\mathbf{y} - \mathbf{z}|$$

The distance function $d(\mathbf{y}, \mathbf{z})$ has the following important properties:

(i) $d(\mathbf{y}, \mathbf{z}) \geq 0$ and $d(\mathbf{y}, \mathbf{z}) = 0$ if and only if $\mathbf{y} = \mathbf{z}$.
(ii) $d(\mathbf{y}, \mathbf{z}) = d(\mathbf{z}, \mathbf{y})$.
(iii) $d(\mathbf{y}, \mathbf{z}) \leq d(\mathbf{y}, \mathbf{v}) + d(\mathbf{v}, \mathbf{z})$ (triangle inequality).

The proofs of these properties follow immediately from the corresponding properties (i), (ii), (iii) of the length function. For example, to prove (iii) we have $d(\mathbf{y}, \mathbf{z}) = |\mathbf{y} - \mathbf{z}| = |(\mathbf{y} - \mathbf{v}) + (\mathbf{v} - \mathbf{z})| \leq |\mathbf{y} - \mathbf{v}| + |\mathbf{v} - \mathbf{z}| = d(\mathbf{y}, \mathbf{v}) + d(\mathbf{v}, \mathbf{z})$.

Any function satisfying the properties (i), (ii), (iii) is called a **distance function.** For example, $\rho(y, z) = \|y - z\|$ for any vectors y, z is such a function, and represents the Euclidean distance between the points y and z in E_n.

•EXERCISE

10. Show that $\rho(\mathbf{y}, \mathbf{z}) = \|\mathbf{y} - \mathbf{z}\|$ also satisfies the properties of a distance function. [*Note:* The proof of (iii) is harder than for the distance function d. You will need to use the Schwarz inequality as in Exercise 9 above.]

To define continuity, differentiability, and integrability of vector functions, we need the notion of limit for vectors. We use the distance function d to define convergence. **A sequence $\{\mathbf{y}^{(k)}\}$ of vectors in E_n is said to converge to the vector y if and only if $d(\mathbf{y}^{(k)}, \mathbf{y}) = |\mathbf{y}^{(k)} - \mathbf{y}| \to 0$ as $k \to \infty$** and in this case we write $\lim\limits_{k \to \infty} \mathbf{y}^{(k)} = \mathbf{y}$ or $\{\mathbf{y}^{(k)}\} \to \mathbf{y}$. Since

$$|\mathbf{y}^{(k)} - \mathbf{y}| = |y_1{}^{(k)} - y_1| + |y_2{}^{(k)} - y_2| + \cdots + |y_n{}^{(k)} - y_n|$$

where $\mathbf{y}^{(k)} = (y_1{}^{(k)}, \ldots, y_n{}^{(k)})$, $\mathbf{y} = (y_1, \ldots, y_n)$, the above definition says that the sequence of vectors $\{\mathbf{y}^{(k)}\} \to \mathbf{y}$ as $k \to \infty$, if and only if each component of $\mathbf{y}^{(k)}$ (these form a sequence of real or complex numbers) tends to the corresponding component of the vector **y**. It is clear that all properties of limits of sequences of complex numbers may now be assumed to hold for sequences of vectors without further explanation.

If we use the Euclidean distance function $\rho(\mathbf{y}, \mathbf{z}) = \|\mathbf{y} - \mathbf{z}\|$, we say that the sequence $\{\mathbf{y}^{(k)}\}$ converges to the vector y if and only if $\rho(\mathbf{y}^{(k)}, \mathbf{y}) = \|y^{(k)} - y\| \to 0$ as $k \to \infty$. It seems clear that the concept of convergence should not depend on the particular distance function used. We establish this for the distance functions $d(\mathbf{y}, \mathbf{z})$ and $\rho(\mathbf{y}, \mathbf{z})$ in Exercise 11 below.

•EXERCISE

11. Let $\{\mathbf{y}^{(k)}\}$ be a sequence of vectors. Show that $|\mathbf{y}^{(k)} - \mathbf{y}| \to 0$ as $k \to \infty$ if and only if $\|\mathbf{y}^{(k)} - \mathbf{y}\| \to 0$ as $k \to \infty$. [*Hint:* Use Exercise 8.]

A vector valued function g $= \mathbf{g}(t)$ is a correspondence which assigns to each number t in an interval I one and only one vector $\mathbf{g}(t)$; we write $\mathbf{g}(t) = (g_1(t), \ldots, g_n(t))$ and we call g_k the kth component (real or complex-valued scalar function) **of the vector function g.** Because of our definition of convergence we should now define **g** to be continuous, differentiable, or integrable on I if and only if each component of $\mathbf{g}$ has this property.

If $\mathbf{g}$ is differentiable on I we denote its derivative by $\mathbf{g}'$ and we define

$$\mathbf{g}' = (g_1', g_2', \ldots, g_n')$$

Similarly, if $\mathbf{g}$ is continuous on I we denote its integral from a to b (a and b on I) by $\int_a^b \mathbf{g}(s)\, ds$ and we define

$$\int_a^b \mathbf{g}(s)\, ds = \left(\int_a^b g_1(s)\, ds, \int_a^b g_2(s)\, ds, \ldots, \int_a^b g_n(s)\, ds \right)$$

We take note of the very important inequality

$$\left| \int_a^b \mathbf{g}(s)\, ds \right| \le \int_a^b |\mathbf{g}(s)|\, ds \qquad (a < b) \tag{6.10}$$

To prove (6.10) we have

$$\left| \int_a^b \mathbf{g}(s)\, ds \right| = \left| \int_a^b g_1(s)\, ds \right| + \cdots + \left| \int_a^b g_n(s)\, ds \right|$$
$$\le \int_a^b |g_1(s)|\, ds + \cdots + \int_a^b |g_n(s)|\, ds = \int_a^b |\mathbf{g}(s)|\, ds$$

● **EXERCISE**

12. Justify each step in the proof of inequality (6.10). Note that in the middle steps you have ordinary absolute values.

It is also true that

$$\left\| \int_a^b \mathbf{g}(s)\, ds \right\| \le \int_a^b \|\mathbf{g}(s)\|\, ds$$

for any continuous vector $\mathbf{g}$, but the proof is more difficult than the one for (6.10).

We can now return to the system

$$\mathbf{y}' = \mathbf{f}(t, \mathbf{y}) \tag{6.9}$$

where the vector valued function $\mathbf{f}$ is defined in some $(n + 1)$-dimensional region D in $(t, y_1, y_2, \ldots, y_n)$ space. To find a solution of (6.9) (compare Section 1.4, p. 15) means to find a real interval I and a vector function $\boldsymbol{\phi}$ defined on I such that

(i) $\boldsymbol{\phi}'(t)$ exists for each t on I.
(ii) The point $(t, \boldsymbol{\phi}(t))$ lies in D for each t on I.
(iii) $\boldsymbol{\phi}'(t) = \mathbf{f}(t, \boldsymbol{\phi}(t))$ for every t on I.

Thus the analogy between (6.9) and a single scalar equation of first order is complete. Just as for the scalar equation, to solve an initial value problem for the system (6.9) with the initial condition $\phi(t_0) = \eta$, (t_0, η) a point of D, means to find a solution ϕ of (6.9) in the above sense passing through the point (t_0, η) of D, that is, satisfying $\phi(t_0) = \eta$. While it is not in general possible to solve (6.9) explicitly, we can illustrate the concepts with some simple problems.

Example 5.   The system

$$y_1' = y_2$$
$$y_2' = y_1$$

is of the form (6.9) with $\mathbf{y} = (y_1, y_2)$, $\mathbf{f}(t, \mathbf{y}) = (y_2, y_1)$. Clearly, D is all of (t, y_1, y_2) space and $\phi(t) = (e^t, e^t)$ is a solution valid for $-\infty < t < \infty$, since (i), (ii), (iii) of the definition are satisfied. Note that $c\phi$, c a constant, is also a solution.

•EXERCISES

13. Can you find (guess) another solution $\psi(t)$ of the system in Example 5 on $-\infty < t < \infty$ which is not of the form $c\phi(t)$?

14. Find a solution ϕ of the system

$$y_1' = -y_1$$
$$y_2' = y_1 + y_2$$

which satisfies the initial condition $\phi(0) = (2, 1)$. [*Hint:* Solve the first equation and substitute in the second equation.] What is the interval I of validity?

15. Find a solution ϕ of the system

$$y_1' = -y_1$$
$$y_2' = y_1 + ty_2$$

satisfying the initial condition $\phi(0) = (2, 1)$.

16. Describe a method for solving the "triangular system"

$$y_1' = a_ny_1 + a_{12}y_2 + \cdots + a_{1n}y_n$$
$$y_2' = \qquad\quad a_{22}y_2 + \cdots + a_{2n}y_n$$
$$\cdot$$
$$\cdot$$
$$\cdot$$
$$y_{n-1}' = \qquad\qquad\qquad\quad a_{n-1,n-1}y_{n-1} + a_{n-1,n}y_n$$
$$y_n' = \qquad\qquad\qquad\qquad\qquad\qquad a_{nn}y_n$$

where a_{ij} ($j \geq i$), are constants; note that a_{ij} with $j < i$ are zero.

17. Find a solution ϕ of the system

$$y_1' = y_1 + y_2 + f(t)$$
$$y_2' = y_1 + y_2$$

where $f(t)$ is a continuous function, satisfying the initial condition $\phi(0) = (0, 0)$. [*Hint:* Define $v(t) = y_1(t) + y_2(t)$.]

18. In Exercise 14 compute another solution ψ satisfying the initial condition $\psi(0) = (2, 2)$. Then compute $|\phi(t) - \psi(t)|$, where ϕ is the solution in Exercise 14.

The reader will notice that all the examples in the exercises above are of the form (6.9), but at the same time they are: (i) linear in the components of y and (ii) of a very special "triangular" form, which makes it possible for us to solve them explicitly. We shall have much more to say about general linear systems in the remainder of the chapter. As already remarked, there are few systems of the form (6.9) of any real interest, other than those which are linear in the components of y with constant coefficients, which can actually be solved explicitly. We therefore refrain from making up special "textbook" problems for this purpose. On the other hand, one wishes to analyze the behavior of solutions of systems of the form (6.9) that cannot be solved explicitly. The first question that comes to mind in this analysis is: Does the given system have a unique solution satisfying the given initial condition? The following result provides an answer in the affirmative in most problems which arise in practice. We note that because of the equivalence between nth-order equations and systems of first-order equations already established, this result includes all results of this type discussed in Chapter 1 as very special cases. For the proof of this result we refer to Chapter 7, Theorems 7.6–7.8.

In what follows we let D represent a region in $(n + 1)$-dimensional space with the property that (compare Section 1.8) given any point (t_0, η) in D, the interior of the $(n + 1)$-dimensional "box"

$$B = \{(t, y) \mid |t - t_0| < a, \ |y - \eta| < b\}$$

will, for $a, b > 0$ and sufficiently small, lie entirely in D. (We note that if we use the Euclidean norm $\|y - \eta\| < b$ then the set

$$C = \{(t, y) \mid |t - t_0| < a, \ \|y - \eta\| < b\}$$

would specify a "cylinder" whose cross section by a hyperplane $t = $ constant would be an n-dimensional sphere.) The most important special cases: the whole space, a half space $\{(t, \mathbf{y}) \mid 0 < t < \infty, |y| \geq 0\}$, and "infinite strips" (for example, $\{(t, \mathbf{y}) \mid |t - t_0| < \infty, |y| < 2\}$) have the above property.

For systems of first-order differential equations one has the following existence and uniqueness theorem (compare Theorem 1.1, p. 24).

Theorem 6.1. *Let* **f** *be a vector function* (with n components) *defined in a domain D of* $(n + 1)$-*dimensional Euclidean space. Let the vectors* **f**, $\partial \mathbf{f}/\partial y_k$ $(k = 1, \ldots, n)$ *be continuous in D. Then given any point* $(t_0, \boldsymbol{\eta})$ *in D there exists a unique solution* $\boldsymbol{\phi}$ *of the system*

$$\mathbf{y}' = \mathbf{f}(t, \mathbf{y}) \tag{6.9}$$

satisfying the initial condition $\boldsymbol{\phi}(t_0) = \boldsymbol{\eta}$. *The solution* $\boldsymbol{\phi}$ *exists on any interval I containing* t_0 *for which the points* $(t, \boldsymbol{\phi}(t))$, *with t in I, lie in D. Furthermore, the solution* $\boldsymbol{\phi}$ *is a continuous function of the "triple"* $(t, t_0, \boldsymbol{\eta})$.

The reader is advised to refer to the discussion and examples following Theorem 1.1 (p. 24). All remarks and examples about the scalar equation, of course, apply to systems of differential equations.

Example 6. Discuss the problem of existence and uniqueness of solutions of the initial value problem for the system

$$y_1' = ty_2 + y_3$$
$$y_2' = (\cos t)y_1 + t^2y_3$$
$$y_3' = y_1 - y_2$$

This system is of the form $\mathbf{y}' = \mathbf{f}(t, \mathbf{y})$ with $\mathbf{y} = (y_1, y_2, y_3)$, $\mathbf{f}(t, \mathbf{y}) = (ty_2 + y_3, (\cos t)y_1 + t^2y_3, y_1 - y_2)$; hence $\mathbf{f}(t, \mathbf{y})$ is continuous for $|t| < \infty$, $|y| < \infty$. Moreover, $\partial \mathbf{f}/\partial y_1 = (0, \cos t, 1)$, $\partial \mathbf{f}/\partial y_2 = (t, 0, -1)$, $\partial \mathbf{f}/\partial y_3 = (1, t^2, 0)$, which are also continuous for $|t| < \infty$, $|y| < \infty$. Thus D is all of four-dimensional (t, y_1, y_2, y_3) space and by Theorem 6.1, through any point $(t_0, \boldsymbol{\eta})$ there passes a unique solution $\boldsymbol{\phi}$ existing on some interval containing t_0. It can be shown, see Theorem 6.3 below, that the solution $\boldsymbol{\phi}$ actually exists on the interval $-\infty < t < \infty$.

• EXERCISES

19. Verify that the systems in Exercises 14, 15, 16, 17 satisfy the hypothesis of Theorem 6.1 in the domain D: $-\infty < t < \infty$, $|y| < \infty$.

20. Discuss the existence and uniqueness of solutions of the system

$$y_1' = y_1{}^2$$
$$y_2' = y_1{}^2 + y_2$$

21. Find a solution $\phi = (\phi_1, \phi_2)$ of the system in Exercise 20 which satisfies the initial condition $\phi_1(-1) = 1$, $\phi_2(-1) = 0$. Discuss the interval I on which the solution ϕ exists.

6.3   The Gronwall Inequality

In the systematic study of systems of differential equations we shall often need to make use of an important inequality, which we now digress to state and prove.   This inequality, known as the Gronwall inequality, will be applied in Section 6.4 below, and also in several places in Chapter 7.

Theorem 6.2.   (Gronwall inequality.)   *Let K be a nonnegative constant and let f and g be continuous nonnegative functions on some interval $\alpha \leq t \leq \beta$ satisfying the inequality*

$$f(t) \leq K + \int_\alpha^t f(s)g(s)\, ds$$

for $\alpha \leq t \leq \beta$.   Then

$$f(t) \leq K \exp\left(\int_\alpha^t g(s)\, ds\right)$$

for $\alpha \leq t \leq \beta$.

Proof.   Let $U(t) = K + \int_\alpha^t f(s)g(s)\, ds$, and observe that $U(\alpha) = K$. Then $f(t) \leq U(t)$ by hypothesis, and, by the fundamental theorem of integral calculus and because $g(t) \geq 0$,

$$U'(t) = f(t)g(t) \leq U(t)g(t) \qquad (\alpha \leq t \leq \beta)$$

We multiply this inequality by $\exp\left(-\int_\alpha^t g(s)\, ds\right)$ and apply the identity

$$U'(t) \exp\left(-\int_\alpha^t g(s)\, ds\right) - U(t)g(t) \exp\left(-\int_\alpha^t g(s)\, ds\right)$$
$$= \left[U(t) \exp\left(-\int_\alpha^t g(s)\, ds\right)\right]'$$

to obtain

$$\frac{d}{dt}\left[U(t) \exp\left(- \int_\alpha^t g(s)\,ds \right) \right] \le 0$$

Integration from α to t gives

$$U(t) \exp\left(- \int_\alpha^t g(s)\,ds \right) - U(\alpha) \le 0$$

or, since $f(t) \le U(t)$ and $U(\alpha) = K$,

$$f(t) \le U(t) \le K \exp\left(\int_\alpha^t g(s)\,ds \right) \qquad (\alpha \le t \le \beta)$$

which is the desired inequality. ∎

•EXERCISES

1. Let K_1 and K_2 be positive constants and let f be a continuous non-negative function on an interval $\alpha \le t \le \beta$ satisfying the inequality

$$f(t) \le K_1 + K_2 \int_\alpha^t f(s)\,ds$$

Show that

$$f(t) \le K_1 e^{K_2(t-\alpha)}$$

2. Find all continuous nonnegative functions f on $0 \le t \le 1$ such that

$$f(t) \le \int_0^t f(s)\,ds \qquad 0 \le t \le 1$$

6.4   Linear Systems

We shall now look at linear systems of differential equations (that is, the system (6.9), p. 251, in which $\mathbf{f}(t, \mathbf{y})$ is linear in the components of $\mathbf{y}$) in considerable detail.

Example 1.   We begin with the following special case:

$$\begin{aligned}
y_1' &= y_1 - ty_2 + e^t \\
y_2' &= t^2 y_1 - y_3 \\
y_3' &= y_1 + y_2 - y_3 + 2e^{-t}
\end{aligned} \qquad (6.11)$$

which is, of course, of the form (6.9) with $\mathbf{y} = (y_1, y_2, y_3)$, $\mathbf{f}(t, \mathbf{y}) = (y_1 - ty_2, t^2y_1 - y_3, y_1 + y_2 - y_3) + (e^t, 0, 2e^{-t})$. We observe that the vector $(y_1 - ty_2, t^2y_1 - y_3, y_1 + y_2 - y_3)$ can be represented as the matrix-vector product $A(t)\mathbf{y}$, where

$$A(t) = \begin{pmatrix} 1 & -t & 0 \\ t^2 & 0 & -1 \\ 1 & 1 & -1 \end{pmatrix}$$

and where we now interpret the vector $\mathbf{y}$ as a **column vector**. Thus the system (6.11) can be written as $\mathbf{y}' = A(t)\mathbf{y} + \mathbf{g}(t)$, where $\mathbf{g}(t)$ is the given vector $(e^t, 0, 2e^{-t})$ interpreted now also as a column vector for consistency.

•EXERCISE

1. Represent each of the systems in Example 5 and in Exercises 14, 15, 16, 17, Section 6.2 (p. 249) in the form $\mathbf{y}' = A(t)\mathbf{y} + \mathbf{g}(t)$. Identify the matrix $A(t)$ and the vector $\mathbf{g}(t)$.

More generally we see that the system (6.9), p. 251, with $\mathbf{f}(t, \mathbf{y})$ linear in the components of $\mathbf{y}$ has the form

$$\begin{cases} y_1' = a_{11}(t)y_1 + a_{12}(t)y_2 + \cdots + a_{1n}(t)y_n + g_1(t) \\ y_2' = a_{21}(t)y_1 + a_{22}(t)y_2 + \cdots + a_{2n}(t)y_n + g_2(t) \\ \quad\vdots \qquad\qquad \vdots \qquad\qquad\qquad \vdots \qquad\quad \vdots \\ y_n' = a_{n1}(t)y_1 + a_{n1}(t)y_2 + \cdots + a_{nn}(t)y_n + g_n(t) \end{cases} \tag{6.12}$$

and can be represented in the form

$$\mathbf{y}' = A(t)\mathbf{y} + \mathbf{g}(t) \tag{6.13}$$

where

$$A(t) = \begin{pmatrix} a_{11}(t) & a_{12}(t) & \cdots & a_{1n}(t) \\ a_{21}(t) & a_{22}(t) & \cdots & a_{2n}(t) \\ \vdots & \vdots & & \vdots \\ a_{n1}(t) & a_{n2}(t) & \cdots & a_{nn}(t) \end{pmatrix} \text{ and } \mathbf{g}(t) = \begin{pmatrix} g_1(t) \\ g_2(t) \\ \vdots \\ g_n(t) \end{pmatrix}$$

and where $\mathbf{y}$ is the column vector with components $y_1, \ldots, y_n$.

•**EXERCISE**

2. Write the scalar equation $y^{(n)} + a_1(t)y^{(n-1)} + \cdots + a_{n-1}(t)y' + a_n(t)y = b(t)$ as a system $\mathbf{y}' = A(t)\mathbf{y} + \mathbf{g}(t)$. Determine the matrix $A(t)$ and the vector $\mathbf{g}(t)$.

We assume that the reader is familiar with the elementary matrix operations of addition and multiplication, and with the properties of determinants. We will deal for the most part with $n \times n$ matrices and with vectors, either column vectors (n-by-1 matrices) or occasionally also row vectors (1-by-n matrices). We shall denote square matrices by capital letters and vectors by small letters. We denote by 0 the n-by-n matrix with all elements zero and by E the n-by-n identity matrix, that is, the matrix with each diagonal element 1 and all other elements zero. We have $AE = EA = A$ for every n-by-n matrix A; also $E\mathbf{b} = \mathbf{b}$ for any column vector $\mathbf{b}$. We recall that the n-by-n matrices A and B are said to commute if and only if $AB = BA$. Unless otherwise stated, all matrices will be n-by-n.

If A is a matrix we let det A denote the determinant of A. We have the following basic properties, which are assumed to be familiar:

(i) For matrices A and B, det $(AB) = $ det A det B.

(ii) If det $A \neq 0$, A is called nonsingular and has an inverse A^{-1} such that

$$AA^{-1} = A^{-1}A = E$$

Moreover,

$$A^{-1} = \frac{\tilde{A}}{\det A}$$

where $\tilde{A}$ is the n-by-n matrix whose elements $\tilde{a}_{ij}$ are the cofactors of a_{ji} in A $(i, j = 1, \ldots, n)$.

•**EXERCISE**

3. Use the result of (i) and (ii) to show that det $(A^{-1}) = 1/$det A.

(iii) Consider the system of linear algebraic equations

$$A\mathbf{x} = \mathbf{b} \tag{6.14}$$

where A is a given matrix, $\mathbf{b}$ is a given (column) vector, and $\mathbf{x}$ is the unknown vector. The system (6.14) has a unique solution if and only if det $A \neq 0$. This solution is given by $\mathbf{x} = A^{-1}\mathbf{b}$; in particular if $\mathbf{b} = \mathbf{0}$, then $\mathbf{x} = \mathbf{0}$. If $\mathbf{b} = \mathbf{0}$, the system has a **nontrivial** solution (that is, a solution $\mathbf{x} \neq \mathbf{0}$), if and only if det $A = 0$.

(iv) If det $A \neq 0$, the n columns of A considered as vectors are linearly independent, and conversely, if the n columns of A are linearly independent then det $A \neq 0$.

• EXERCISES

4. Prove property (iv).

5. State (look up) the theorem concerning the system (6.14) in the case det $A = 0$ but $\mathbf{b} \neq \mathbf{0}$.

We define the **norm** (length) **of a matrix** A, denoted by $|A|$, by

$$|A| = \sum_{i,j=1}^{n} |a_{ij}| \tag{6.15}$$

that is, as the sum of the absolute values of all the elements.   Notice that if A is n-by-1 or 1-by-n, that is, a vector, then (6.15) reduces to our previous definition of the length (norm) of a vector.   We readily verify that the matrix norm satisfies the following properties:

(i) $|A + B| \leq |A| + |B|$

(ii) $|AB| \leq |A| \cdot |B|$

(iii) $|A\mathbf{b}| \leq |A| \cdot |\mathbf{b}|$

for matrices A, B of complex numbers and column vectors $\mathbf{b}$ with n components.   The above norm is convenient for our purposes; other matrix norms satisfying the properties (i), (ii), (iii) are possible.

• EXERCISE

6. Prove the properties (i), (ii), (iii) of the norm $|A|$.

In Section 6.2 (p. 247) we defined the concept of convergence of a sequence of vectors in terms of a vector norm and used it to discuss continuity, differentiability, and integrability of vector functions.   We now use the matrix norm (6.15) to do the same for matrices.

Definition.   *The sequence $\{A^{(k)}\}$ converges to the matrix A if and only if the sequence of real numbers $\{|A - A^{(k)}|\}$ has limit zero, and in this case* *we write*

$$\{A^{(k)}\} \to A \quad or \quad \lim_{k \to \infty} A^{(k)} = A$$

Clearly, because of the definition of the norm, this means that $\{A^{(k)}\} \to A$ if and only if the sequence $\{a_{ij}^{(k)}\}$ of complex numbers, representing the element in the ith row and jth column in the matrices $\{A^{(k)}\}$, converges to the element a_{ij} of the matrix A as $k \to \infty$ for each of the n^2 elements $(i, j = 1, \ldots, n)$. **A matrix function $A(t)$ is a correspondence which assigns to each point t of an interval I one and only one n by n matrix $A(t)$.** Using the remark following the definition of convergence of a sequence of matrices, we see that it is consistent to say that a matrix $A(t)$ is continuous, differentiable, or integrable on an interval I if and only if each of its n^2 elements $a_{ij}(t)$ is continuous, differentiable, or integrable respectively on I.

We shall often need to use the important inequality

$$\left| \int_c^d A(t)\mathbf{b}(t) \, dt \right| \le \int_c^d |A(t)| \, |\mathbf{b}(t)| \, dt \tag{6.16}$$

for $c < d$, assuming, for example, that $A(t)$ and $\mathbf{b}(t)$ are continuous on $c \le t \le d$.

•EXERCISES

7. Prove the inequality (6.16). [*Hint:* Use (6.10) and property (iii), p. 256.]

8. Let $\Phi(t)$ be a nonsingular matrix, differentiable on a real t interval I. Prove that $\Phi^{-1}(t)$ is differentiable and find a formula for $(\Phi^{-1})'(t)$. [*Hint:* For the second part use $\Phi(t)\Phi^{-1}(t) = E$ and differentiate.]

We now return to the linear system

$$\mathbf{y}' = A(t)\mathbf{y} + \mathbf{g}(t) \tag{6.13}$$

where we assume that the matrix $A(t)$ and the vector $\mathbf{g}(t)$ are continuous on an interval I. Then the vector function $\mathbf{f}(t, \mathbf{y}) = A(t)\mathbf{y} + \mathbf{g}(t)$ of Theorem 6.1 is continuous for $(t, \mathbf{y})$ in D, where D is the strip $\{(t, y) \mid t \in I, |\mathbf{y}| < \infty \}$, and $\partial \mathbf{f}/\partial y_k = \text{col} \, (a_{1k}(t), a_{2k}(t), \ldots, a_{nk}(t)) \, (k = 1, \ldots, n)$ where col stands for column. Thus $\partial \mathbf{f}/\partial y_k$ are also continuous in D for $k = 1, \ldots, n$. Thus by Theorem 6.1, (6.13) has a unique solution $\phi(t)$, passing through any given point $(t_0, \boldsymbol{\eta})$ with t_0 in I; and this solution exists on some interval containing the point t_0 in its interior. Theorem 6.1 also says that the solution ϕ exists on any interval in J containing the point t_0 and contained in the interval I for which the points $(t, \phi(t))$ with t in J lie in D. For the present case of D this means that the solution exists on the whole interval I (finite or infinite) provided it can be proved that $|\phi(t)|$, the norm of the solution ϕ, is bounded by a constant independent of t (**such a bound is called an *a priori* bound**). This is indeed always possible if I is a closed bounded interval.

Theorem 6.3.   *If $A(t)$, $\mathbf{g}(t)$ are continuous on some interval $a \leq t \leq b$, if $a \leq t_0 \leq b$ and if $|\mathbf{\eta}| < \infty$, equation (6.13) has a unique solution $\phi(t)$ satisfying the initial condition $\phi(t_0) = \mathbf{\eta}$ and existing on the interval $a \leq t \leq b$.*

Proof.   Let $\phi(t)$ be the unique solution satisfying $\phi(t_0) = \mathbf{\eta}$, existing for t on an interval J. To show that this solution exists on the whole interval $a \leq t \leq b$, it suffices, by the above remarks, to show that $|\phi(t)|$ is bounded by a constant independent of t. For t in J substitution of ϕ into (6.13) gives

$$\phi'(t) = A(t)\phi(t) + \mathbf{g}(t)$$

Integration gives

$$\phi(t) - \phi(t_0) = \int_{t_0}^{t} A(s)\phi(s)\, ds + \int_{t_0}^{t} \mathbf{g}(s)\, ds \qquad (t \text{ in } J)$$

from which, using the initial condition and taking norms, we obtain

$$|\phi(t)| \leq |\mathbf{\eta}| + \left| \int_{t_0}^{t} A(s)\phi(s)\, ds \right| + \left| \int_{t_0}^{t} \mathbf{g}(s)\, ds \right|$$

We continue with the argument for $t \geq t_0$; using properties of the norm and the inequality (6.16) we have

$$|\phi(t)| \leq |\mathbf{\eta}| + \int_{t_0}^{t} |A(s)|\, |\phi(s)| + \int_{t_0}^{t} |\mathbf{g}(s)|\, ds \qquad (t \text{ in } J)$$

Since

$$|\mathbf{\eta}| + \int_{t_0}^{t} |g(s)|\, ds \leq |\mathbf{\eta}| + \max_{a \leq t \leq b} |\mathbf{g}(t)|(t - t_0)$$
$$\leq |\mathbf{\eta}| + \max_{a \leq t \leq b} |\mathbf{g}(t)|(b - a) = K_1$$

and

$$\int_{t_0}^{t} |A(s)|\, |\phi(s)|\, ds \leq \max_{a \leq t \leq b} |A(t)| \left(\int_{t_0}^{t} |\phi(s)|\, ds \right) = K_2 \int_{t_0}^{t} |\phi(s)|\, ds$$

this inequality can be written as

$$|\phi(t)| \leq K_1 + K_2 \int_{t_0}^{t} |\phi(s)|\, ds \qquad (t \text{ in } J)$$

where K_1 and K_2 are constants.   Note that the constants K_1 and K_2 are nonnegative and independent of t.

• **EXERCISE**

9. Show that for $t \leq t_0$ we have $|\phi(t)| \leq K_1 + K_2 \int_{t}^{t_0} |\phi(s)|\, ds$.

Then by the Gronwall inequality (Section 6.3, p. 252), we obtain, both for $t \leq t_0$ and for $t \geq t_0$,

$$|\phi(t)| \leq K_1 e^{K_2|t-t_0|} \leq K_1 e^{(b-a)K_2} \qquad (t \text{ in } J)$$

This shows that $|\phi(t)|$ is bounded by a constant.   By Theorem 6.1, therefore, $\phi(t)$ exists on the entire interval $a \leq t \leq b$, and this completes the proof. ∎

We remark that, interpreted geometrically, this proof shows that the solution remains inside an $(n+1)$-dimensional "box" of "base" $a \leq t \leq b$ and "height" $2|\mathbf{y}|$, where $|\mathbf{y}| \leq K_1 e^{K_2(b-a)}$.

We note also that if $A(t)$ and $\mathbf{g}(t)$ in (6.14) are continuous on $-\infty < t < \infty$ the above arguments apply to every **finite** subinterval; of course, in this case the solution $\phi(t)$ may not remain bounded as $t \to \pm \infty$.   The same remark applies if $A(t)$ and $\mathbf{g}(t)$ are continuous on $a < t < b$, but not necessarily on $a \leq t \leq b$.   This leads to the following consequence of Theorem 6.3.

Corollary to Theorem 6.3.   *If $A(t)$, $\mathbf{g}(t)$ are continuous on an interval I, closed or open, finite or infinite, and if $t_0 \in I$, $|\mathbf{y}| < \infty$, then the equation (6.13) has a unique solution $\phi(t)$ satisfying the initial condition $\phi(t_0) = \mathbf{v}$ and existing on I.*

• **EXERCISES**

10. Prove the above corollary.

11. Suppose $A(t)$ and $\mathbf{g}(t)$ are continuous for $-\infty < t < \infty$ and that $\int_{-\infty}^{\infty} |A(t)|\, dt < \infty$ and $\int_{-\infty}^{\infty} |\mathbf{g}(t)|\, dt < \infty$.   Show that the solution $\phi(t)$ of $\mathbf{y}' = A(t)\mathbf{y} + \mathbf{g}(t)$ exists for $-\infty < t < \infty$ and compute a bound for $|\phi(t)|$ valid for $-\infty < t < \infty$.

12. State the analogue of Theorem 6.3 and its corollary for the scalar equation

$$a_0(t)y^{(n)} + a_1(t)y^{(n-1)} + \cdots + a_{n-1}(t)y' + a_n(t)y = b(t)$$

where $a_0, a_1, a_2, \ldots, a_n, g$ are continuous functions and $a_0 \neq 0$ on a bounded interval $a \leq t \leq b$ (compare Theorem 3.1, p. 65, which is this result for $n = 2$).

6.5   Linear Homogeneous Systems

We are now ready to discuss the structure of solutions of the linear system (6.13) and we begin with the linear homogeneous system

$$\mathbf{y}' = A(t)\mathbf{y} \qquad (6.17)$$

We assume that the n-by-n matrix $A(t)$ is continuous on an interval I and then by Theorem 6.3 and its corollary, Section 6.4, we see immediately that given any point $(t_0, \boldsymbol{\eta})$, t_0 in I, there exists one and only one solution $\boldsymbol{\phi}$ of (6.17) such that $\boldsymbol{\phi}(t_0) = \boldsymbol{\eta}$.   In particular, and this is most important for what follows, given the point $(t_0, \mathbf{0})$, t_0 any point of I, (6.17) has **the unique solution** $\boldsymbol{\phi} \equiv \mathbf{0}$ on I, satisfying the initial condition $\boldsymbol{\phi}(t_0) = \mathbf{0}$, because by inspection $\mathbf{0}$ is always a solution of (6.17), and by Theorem 6.3 this is the only solution through $(t_0, \mathbf{0})$.

To obtain a result about the structure of solutions of the linear homogeneous system (6.17) we first observe that if $\boldsymbol{\phi}_1$ and $\boldsymbol{\phi}_2$ are any solutions of (6.17) on an interval I, and c_1 and c_2 are any (real or complex) constants, then the linearity of (6.17) tells us that

$$(c_1\boldsymbol{\phi}_1 + c_2\boldsymbol{\phi}_2)' = c_1\boldsymbol{\phi}_1' + c_2\boldsymbol{\phi}_2' = c_1A\boldsymbol{\phi}_1 + c_2A\boldsymbol{\phi}_2 = A(c_1\boldsymbol{\phi}_1 + c_2\boldsymbol{\phi}_2)$$

that is, $c_1\boldsymbol{\phi}_1 + c_2\boldsymbol{\phi}_2$ is again a solution of (6.17) on I.   In the language of linear algebra this shows that the solutions of (6.17) form a vector space over the complex numbers.   We denote this vector space by V.

We remind the reader that an abstract vector space over the real (or complex) numbers is a set of elements for which operations of addition and multiplication by scalars satisfying certain well-known properties are defined.

•EXERCISES

1. Look up the axioms for an abstract vector space.

2. Verify that the set of real (or complex) functions continuous on an interval I forms a vector space over the real (or complex) numbers, with addition and multiplication by scalars defined in the usual way.

3. Verify that the set of real (or complex) vector functions $\mathbf{f}(t) = (f_1(t),$ . . . , $f_n(t))$ continuous on an interval I forms a vector space over the real (or complex) numbers, with addition and multiplication by scalars defined in the usual way.

A subset S of a vector space is called a **subspace** if it is closed under the formation of sums and products by scalars. It is easy to prove directly from the definition of a vector space that any subspace of a vector space is itself a vector space with the same operations.

•**EXERCISE**

4. Prove that a subspace of a vector space is a vector space.

Combining the results of Exercises 3 and 4 we see that the set of solutions V of (6.17) is a subspace of the vector space of continuous vector functions over the real (or complex) numbers, and is therefore a vector space. It is now natural to ask what is the dimension of the vector space V. In order to discuss this problem, and indeed to define the dimension of a vector space, we must recall the definitions of linear dependence and independence of sets of vectors.

Definition. *A set of vectors* $\mathbf{v}_1,$ $\mathbf{v}_2,$ . . . , $\mathbf{v}_k$ *is linearly dependent if there exist scalars* $c_1, c_2,$ . . . , $c_k,$ *not all zero, such that the linear combination*

$$c_1\mathbf{v}_1 + c_2\mathbf{v}_2 + \cdots + c_k\mathbf{v}_k = \mathbf{0}$$

Definition. *A set of vectors* $\mathbf{v}_1,$ $\mathbf{v}_2,$ . . . , $\mathbf{v}_k$ *is linearly independent if it is not linearly dependent.*

These definitions contain the ones of linear dependence and independence of functions given in Section 3.3 (p. 69), as the reader should verify. There the underlying vector space is the vector space of continuous functions on an interval I; see Exercise 2 above.

•**EXERCISES**

5. Formulate the definitions of linear dependence and independence of a set of vector functions $\mathbf{f}_{(1)}(t),$ . . . , $\mathbf{f}_{(k)}(t)$ continuous on an interval I. (See Exercise 3 above for the underlying vector space.)

6. Show that the vectors

$$\mathbf{v}_1 = \begin{pmatrix} 1 \\ 0 \\ 0 \end{pmatrix}, \quad \mathbf{v}_2 = \begin{pmatrix} 0 \\ 1 \\ 0 \end{pmatrix}, \quad \mathbf{v}_3 = \begin{pmatrix} 0 \\ 0 \\ 1 \end{pmatrix}$$

are linearly independent in E_3.   [*Hint:* Suppose they are linearly dependent and obtain a contradiction.]

7. Show that the vectors

$$\mathbf{v}_1 = \begin{pmatrix} 1 \\ 2 \\ 3 \end{pmatrix}, \quad \mathbf{v}_2 = \begin{pmatrix} 1 \\ 3 \\ 5 \end{pmatrix}, \quad \mathbf{v}_3 = \begin{pmatrix} 1 \\ 10 \\ -5 \end{pmatrix}, \quad \mathbf{v}_4 = \begin{pmatrix} 0 \\ -1 \\ 17 \end{pmatrix}$$

are linearly dependent in E_3.

8. Show that the vectors (functions)

$$\mathbf{v}_1 = \exp(r_1 t), \qquad \mathbf{v}_2 = \exp(r_2 t)$$

are linearly independent if $r_1 \neq r_2$ in the space of continuous functions on $-\infty < t < \infty$.   [*Hint:* See Example 2, Section 3.3, p. 70.]

9. Show that the vectors

$$\mathbf{v}_1 = \begin{pmatrix} \exp(r_1 t) \\ r_1 \exp(r_2 t) \end{pmatrix} \qquad \mathbf{v}_2 = \begin{pmatrix} \exp(r_2 t) \\ r_2 \exp(r_2 t) \end{pmatrix}$$

are linearly independent if $r_1 \neq r_2$ in the space of continuous vector functions with two components on $-\infty < t < \infty$.

10. Repeat Exercise 9 for the vectors

$$\mathbf{v}_1 = \begin{pmatrix} \cos t \\ -\sin t \end{pmatrix} \qquad \mathbf{v}_2 = \begin{pmatrix} \sin t \\ \cos t \end{pmatrix}$$

A set S of vectors is said to form a **basis** of a vector space V if it is linearly independent and if every vector in V can be expressed as a linear combination of vectors in S.

•EXERCISES

11. Show that if S is a basis of a vector space V, then the expression of every vector in V as a linear combination of vectors in S is unique. [*Hint:* Suppose a vector $\mathbf{v}$ may be expressed as $\mathbf{v} = c_1\mathbf{v}_1 + c_2\mathbf{v}_2 + \cdots + c_k\mathbf{v}_k = d_1\mathbf{v}_1 + d_2\mathbf{v}_2 + \cdots + d_k\mathbf{v}_k$, where S consists of the vectors $\mathbf{v}_1, \mathbf{v}_2, \ldots, \mathbf{v}_k$. Show that $c_1 = d_1, c_2 = d_2, \ldots, c_k = d_k$.]

12. Show that the vectors $\mathbf{v}_1, \mathbf{v}_2, \mathbf{v}_3$ in Exercise 6 above form a basis of E_3.

13. Show that the vectors

$$\mathbf{w}_1 = \begin{pmatrix} 1 \\ 2 \\ 3 \end{pmatrix} \quad \mathbf{w}_2 = \begin{pmatrix} 0 \\ 1 \\ 5 \end{pmatrix} \quad \mathbf{w}_3 = \begin{pmatrix} 0 \\ 0 \\ 4 \end{pmatrix}$$

also form a basis of E_3.

14. Show that any linearly independent set of 3 vectors in E_3 is a basis of E_3.

We can now define the dimension of a vector space V to be the number of elements in any basis of V. A vector space is called **finite-dimensional** if it has a finite basis. Thus, for example, E_n has dimension n. It can be shown that every basis of a finite-dimensional vector space has the same number of elements. We note that the space C of continuous functions on a finite interval is not finite-dimensional because the infinite set $1, t, t^2, \ldots, t^n, \ldots$, which is certainly contained in C, is linearly independent on any interval.

We now return to the problem of finding the dimension of the vector space V of solutions of (6.17). We have the answer in the following basic result.

Theorem 6.4.   *If the complex n-by-n matrix $A(t)$ is continuous on an interval I, then the solutions of the system (6.17), p. 260, on I form a vector space of dimension n over the complex numbers.*

Proof.   We have already established that the solutions form a vector space V over the complex numbers. To establish that the dimension of V is n, we need to construct a basis for V consisting of n linearly independent vectors in V, that is, of n linearly independent solutions of (6.17) on I, which span V. We proceed as follows. Let t_0 be any point of I and let $\delta_1, \delta_2, \ldots, \delta_n$ be any n linearly independent points (vectors) in Euclidean n-space E_n. For example,

$$\delta_j = \begin{pmatrix} 0 \\ \cdot \\ \cdot \\ \cdot \\ 0 \\ 1 \\ 0 \\ \cdot \\ \cdot \\ \cdot \\ 0 \end{pmatrix} \quad \leftarrow j\text{th row} \qquad (j = 1, 2, \ldots, n)$$

are obviously n such vectors.   By Theorem 6.3 and its corollary (p. 259), the system (6.17) possesses n solutions $\phi_1, \phi_2, \ldots, \phi_n$, each of which exists on the entire interval I, and each solution ϕ_j satisfies the initial condition

$$\phi_j(t_0) = \delta_j \qquad (j = 1, 2, \ldots, n) \tag{6.18}$$

We first show that the solutions $\phi_1, \phi_2, \ldots, \phi_n$ are linearly independent on I. Suppose they are not. Then there exist complex constants $a_1, a_2, \ldots, a_n$, **not all zero,** such that

$$a_1\phi_1(t) + a_2\phi_2(t) + \cdots + a_n\phi_n(t) = 0 \qquad \text{for every } t \text{ on } I$$

In particular, putting $t = t_0$, and using the initial conditions (6.18), we have

$$a_1\delta_1 + a_2\delta_2 + \cdots + a_n\delta_n = 0$$

But this is impossible (**unless** $a_1, a_2, \ldots, a_n$ are all zero) because it contradicts the assumed linear independence of $\delta_1, \delta_2, \ldots, \delta_n$.

To complete the proof we must show that these n linearly independent solutions of (6.17) span V, that is, that they have the property that every solution $\psi(t)$ of (6.17) can be expressed as a linear combination of the solutions $\phi_1, \phi_2, \ldots, \phi_n$. We proceed as follows. Compute the value of the solution ψ at t_0 and let $\psi(t_0) = \delta$. Since the constant vectors $\delta_1, \delta_2, \ldots, \delta_n$ are linearly independent in Euclidean n-space E_n, they form a basis for E_n and there exist unique constants $c_1, c_2, \ldots, c_n$ such that the constant vector δ can be represented as

$$\delta = c_1\delta_1 + c_2\delta_2 + \cdots + c_n\delta_n$$

(see Exercise 12, p. 262, for the case $n = 3$).   Now, consider the vector

$$\phi(t) = c_1\phi_1(t) + c_2\phi_2(t) + \cdots + c_n\phi_n(t)$$

Clearly, $\phi(t)$ is a solution of (6.17) on I. (Why? Prove this.) Moreover, the initial value of ϕ is (using (6.18))

$$\phi(t_0) = c_1\delta_1 + c_2\delta_2 + \cdots + c_n\delta_n = \delta$$

Therefore $\phi(t)$ and $\psi(t)$ are both solutions of (6.17) on I with $\phi(t_0) = \psi(t_0) = \delta$. Therefore, by the uniqueness part of Theorem 6.3 (p. 258),

$\phi(t) = \psi(t)$ for every t on I and the solution $\psi(t)$ is expressed as the unique linear combination

$$\psi(t) = c_1\phi_1(t) + c_2\phi_2(t) + \cdots + c_n\phi_n(t) \qquad \text{for every } t \text{ on } I \quad (6.19)$$

• **EXERCISE**

15. Show that this expression of $\psi(t)$ as a linear combination of $\phi_1(t)$, . . . , $\phi_n(t)$ is unique. [*Hint:* See Exercise 11, p. 262.]

Thus we have shown that the solutions ϕ_1, ϕ_2, . . . , ϕ_n of (6.17) span the vector space V.   Since they are also linearly independent, they form a basis for the solution space V, and the dimension of V is n.   This completes the proof of Theorem 6.4.   We often say that the linearly independent solutions ϕ_1, . . . , ϕ_n form a **fundamental set of solutions**. There are clearly infinitely many different fundamental sets of solutions of (6.17).   (Why?) ▌

• **EXERCISES**

16. Prove the following analogue of Theorem 6.4 for systems with real coefficients: If the real n-by-n matrix $A(t)$ is continuous on an interval I, then the solutions of (6.17) on I form a vector space of dimension n over the real numbers.

17. Write the linear homogeneous scalar equation

$$a_0(t)y^{(n)} + a_1(t)y^{(n-1)} + \cdots + a_{n-1}(t)y' + a_n(t)y = 0$$

where $a_0, a_1, \ldots, a_n$ are continuous on I and $a_0(t) \neq 0$, as a system and interpret Theorem 6.4 for this equation.   Compare Theorem 3.2 (p. 72) for the case $n = 2$, and Exercise 6, Section 3.3 (p. 75), for the general case.

We can interpret Theorem 6.4 in a different and useful way.   A matrix of n rows whose columns are solutions of (6.17) is called a **solution matrix**.   Now if we form an n-by-n matrix using the above n linearly independent solutions as columns we will have a solution matrix on I, but also its columns will be linearly independent solutions of (6.17) on I.   A solution matrix whose columns are linearly independent on I is called a **fundamental matrix** for (6.17) on I.   Let us denote the fundamental matrix formed from the solutions ϕ_1, ϕ_2, . . . , ϕ_n as columns by Φ. Then the statement that every solution ψ is the linear combination (6.19) for some unique choice of the constants c_1, . . . , c_n is simply that

$$\psi(t) = \Phi(t)\mathbf{c} \qquad (6.20)$$

where Φ is the fundamental matrix constructed above and $\mathbf{c}$ is the column vector with components $c_1, \ldots, c_n$. It is clear that if $\tilde{\Phi}(t)$ is any other fundamental matrix of (6.17) in I then the above solution ψ can be expressed as

$$\psi(t) = \tilde{\Phi}(t)\tilde{\mathbf{c}} \qquad \text{for every } t \text{ on } I$$

for a suitably chosen constant vector $\tilde{\mathbf{c}}$. Clearly, every solution of (6.17) on I can be expressed in this form by using any fundamental matrix.

•EXERCISE

18. Given that $\psi(t_0) = \mathbf{o}$, determine the vector $\tilde{\mathbf{c}}$.

We see from the above discussion that to find any solution of (6.17) on I we need to find n linearly independent solutions on I, or equivalently, we need to find a fundamental matrix. A natural question, then, is the following: Suppose we have found a solution matrix of (6.17) on some interval I. Can we test in some simple way whether this solution matrix is a fundamental matrix? We shall see (Theorem 6.6 below) that any solution matrix $\Phi(t)$, not necessarily the special solution matrix used in (6.20), is a fundamental matrix of (6.17) if and only if $\det \Phi(t) \neq 0$ on I. However, it is convenient to establish an important auxiliary result first.

Theorem 6.5.   (Abel's formula.)   *If Φ is a solution matrix of (6.17) on I and if t_0 is any point of I, then*

$$\det \Phi(t) = \det \Phi(t_0) \exp\left[\int_{t_0}^{t} \sum_{j=1}^{n} a_{jj}(s)\, ds \right] \qquad \text{for every } t \text{ in } I \qquad (6.21)$$

It follows immediately from Theorem 6.5 (since t_0 is arbitrary) that either $\det \Phi(t) \neq 0$ for each t in I or $\det \Phi(t) = 0$ for every t in I.

Proof of Theorem 6.5.   Let us denote the columns of Φ by $\phi_1, \phi_2, \ldots, \phi_n$; let ϕ_j have components $(\phi_{1j}, \phi_{2j}, \ldots, \phi_{nj})$. Then the statement that ϕ_j is a solution of (6.17) on I can be written in terms of components as

$$\phi_{ij}' = \sum_{k=1}^{n} a_{ik}\phi_{kj} \qquad (i, j = 1, \ldots, n) \qquad (6.22)$$

It is now necessary to recall that the derivative of $\det \Phi$ is a sum of n determinants:

$$
(\det \Phi)' =
\begin{vmatrix}
\phi'_{11} & \phi'_{12} & \cdots & \phi'_{1j} & \cdots & \phi'_{1n} \\
\phi_{21} & \phi_{22} & \cdots & \phi_{2j} & \cdots & \phi_{2n} \\
\cdot & \cdot & & \cdot & & \cdot \\
\cdot & \cdot & & \cdot & & \cdot \\
\cdot & \cdot & & \cdot & & \cdot \\
\phi_{n1} & \phi_{n2} & \cdots & \phi_{nj} & \cdots & \phi_{nn}
\end{vmatrix}
$$

$$
+
\begin{vmatrix}
\phi_{11} & \phi_{12} & \cdots & \phi_{1j} & \cdots & \phi_{1n} \\
\phi'_{21} & \phi'_{22} & \cdots & \phi'_{2j} & \cdots & \phi'_{2n} \\
\phi_{31} & \phi_{32} & \cdots & \phi_{3j} & \cdots & \phi_{3n} \\
\cdot & \cdot & & \cdot & & \cdot \\
\cdot & \cdot & & \cdot & & \cdot \\
\cdot & \cdot & & \cdot & & \cdot \\
\phi_{n1} & \phi_{n2} & \cdots & \phi_{nj} & \cdots & \phi_{nn}
\end{vmatrix}
+ \cdots
$$

$$
+
\begin{vmatrix}
\phi_{11} & \phi_{12} & \cdots & \phi_{1j} & \cdots & \phi_{1n} \\
\cdot & \cdot & & \cdot & & \cdot \\
\cdot & \cdot & & \cdot & & \cdot \\
\cdot & \cdot & & \cdot & & \cdot \\
\phi_{n-1,1} & \phi_{n-1,2} & \cdots & \phi_{n-1,j} & \cdots & \phi_{n-1,n} \\
\phi'_{n1} & \phi'_{n2} & \cdots & \phi'_{nj} & \cdots & \phi'_{nn}
\end{vmatrix}
$$

Using (6.22), we obtain

$$
(\det \Phi)' =
\begin{vmatrix}
\sum\limits_{k=1}^{n} a_{1k}\phi_{k1} & \sum\limits_{k=1}^{n} a_{1k}\phi_{k2} & \cdots & \sum\limits_{k=1}^{n} a_{1k}\phi_{kn} \\
\phi_{21} & \phi_{22} & \cdots & \phi_{2n} \\
\cdot & \cdot & & \cdot \\
\cdot & \cdot & & \cdot \\
\cdot & \cdot & & \cdot \\
\phi_{n1} & \phi_{n2} & \cdots & \phi_{nn}
\end{vmatrix}
$$

$$
+
\begin{vmatrix}
\phi_{11} & \phi_{12} & \cdots & \phi_{1n} \\
\sum\limits_{k=1}^{n} a_{2k}\phi_{k1} & \sum\limits_{k=1}^{n} a_{2k}\phi_{k2} & \cdots & \sum\limits_{k=1}^{n} a_{2k}\phi_{kn} \\
\phi_{31} & \phi_{32} & \cdots & \phi_{3n} \\
\cdot & \cdot & & \cdot \\
\cdot & \cdot & & \cdot \\
\cdot & \cdot & & \cdot \\
\phi_{n1} & \phi_{n2} & \cdots & \phi_{nn}
\end{vmatrix}
+ \cdots
$$

$$
+
\begin{vmatrix}
\phi_{11} & \phi_{12} & \cdots & \phi_{1n} \\
\cdot & \cdot & & \cdot \\
\cdot & \cdot & & \cdot \\
\cdot & \cdot & & \cdot \\
\phi_{n-1,1} & \phi_{n-1,2} & \cdots & \phi_{n-1,n} \\
\sum\limits_{k=1}^{n} a_{nk}\phi_{k1} & \sum\limits_{k=1}^{n} a_{nk}\phi_{k2} & \cdots & \sum\limits_{k=1}^{n} a_{nk}\phi_{kn}
\end{vmatrix}
$$

267

Using elementary row operations we can evaluate each determinant. For example, in the first determinant we multiply the second row by a_{12}, the third by $a_{13}, \ldots$, the nth by a_{1n}, add these $n-1$ rows and then subtract the result from the first row. The resulting first row will be $a_{11}\phi_{11}a_{12}\phi_{12} \cdots a_{1n}\phi_{1n}$, so that the value of the first determinant is $a_{11} \det \Phi$. Proceeding similarly with the other determinants we obtain

$$(\det \Phi)' = a_{11} \det \Phi + a_{22} \det \Phi + \cdots + a_{nn} \det \Phi$$

for every t on I, or equivalently,

$$(\det \Phi)' = \left(\sum_{k=1}^{n} a_{kk}(t) \right) \det \Phi \tag{6.23}$$

which is a first-order **scalar equation** for $\det \Phi$. Its solution is seen without difficulty to be (6.21). ∎

•EXERCISES

19. Show that (6.21) is the unique solution of the scalar equation

$$y' = \left(\sum_{k=1}^{n} a_{kk}(t) \right) y$$

satisfying the initial condition $y(t_0) = \det \Phi(t_0)$.

20. Show that the jth determinant in the expression for $(\det \Phi)'$ in the proof of Theorem 6.5 is $a_{jj} \det \Phi$.

21. Write the scalar equation $a_0(t)y^{(n)} + \cdots + a_{n-1}(t)y' + a_n(t)y = 0$ where $a_0, a_1, \ldots, a_n$ are continuous on I and $a_0(t) \neq 0$ on 'I as a system. Then show that for this specific system $\det \Phi$ is precisely the Wronskian (see Section 3.3, p. 75). A special case of the above Theorem 6.5 is Exercise 12, Section 3.3 (p. 78), and also Theorem 3.4 (p. 78).

We now use Theorem 6.5 to establish the main result.

Theorem 6.6. (Compare Theorem 3.3, p. 76, for the special second-order scalar equation.) *A solution matrix Φ of (6.17) on an interval I is a fundamental matrix of (6.17) on I if and only if $\det \Phi(t) \neq 0$ for every t on I.*

Proof of Theorem 6.6. If $\det \Phi(t) \neq 0$ for every t on I the columns of the solution matrix are obviously linearly independent on I, and therefore Φ is a fundamental matrix of (6.17) on I.

Conversely, if Φ is a fundamental matrix, then every solution ϕ of (6.17) on I has the form $\phi(t) = \Phi(t)\mathbf{c}$ for some constant vector $\mathbf{c}$.   For each fixed t_0 in I and any vector $\phi(t_0)$, because $\Phi(t)$ is a fundamental matrix, the system of algebraic equations $\phi(t_0) = \Phi(t_0)\mathbf{c}$ has a unique solution for $\mathbf{c}$.   Therefore (see property (iii) of determinants given in Section 6.4, p. 255), $\det \Phi(t_0) \neq 0$.   Now, Abel's formula (Theorem 6.5, p. 266) gives $\det \Phi(t) \neq 0$ for every t on I.   This completes the proof of Theorem 6.6. ∎

The reader is warned that a matrix may have its determinant identically zero on some interval, although its columns are linearly independent. Indeed, let

$$\Phi(t) = \begin{pmatrix} 1 & t & t^2 \\ 0 & 2 & t \\ 0 & 0 & 0 \end{pmatrix}$$

Then clearly $\det \Phi(t) = 0$, $-\infty < t < \infty$, and yet the columns are linearly independent.   This, according to Theorem 6.6, cannot happen for solutions of (6.17).

• EXERCISE

22. State Theorem 6.6 for the scalar equation in Exercise 21 in terms of the Wronskian determinant (compare Theorem 3.3, p. 76, for the special case $n = 2$).

It is important from the practical point of view to remark that Theorems 6.5 and 6.6 together imply that to test whether a solution matrix of (6.17) is a fundamental matrix, it suffices to evaluate its determinant at one point!   This point can frequently be chosen to make the calculation a simple one.

• EXERCISES

23. Show, with the aid of Theorem 6.5, that

$$\begin{pmatrix} \cos t & \sin t \\ -\sin t & \cos t \end{pmatrix}$$

is a fundamental matrix for the system $\mathbf{y}' = A\mathbf{y}$ where

$$A = \begin{pmatrix} 0 & 1 \\ -1 & 0 \end{pmatrix}$$

24. Show, with the aid of Theorems 6.5, 6.6, that

$$\begin{pmatrix} e^{r_1 t} & e^{r_2 t} \\ r_1 e^{r_1 t} & r_2 e^{r_2 t} \end{pmatrix}$$

is a fundamental matrix for the system $\mathbf{y}' = A\mathbf{y}$, where

$$A = \begin{pmatrix} 0 & 1 \\ -a_2 & -a_1 \end{pmatrix}$$

and r_1, r_2 are the distinct roots of the quadratic equation $z^2 + a_1 z + a_2 = 0$. (We shall learn in Section 6.7 how to construct this fundamental matrix.)

If Φ is a fundamental matrix of (6.17) on I and C is a nonsingular constant (complex) matrix, then ΦC is clearly a solution matrix (prove this), and since $\det \Phi C = \det \Phi \cdot \det C$ it follows from Theorem 6.6 that ΦC is also a fundamental matrix on I.

•**EXERCISE**

25. Show that $C\Phi$, where C is a constant matrix and Φ is a fundamental matrix, need not be a solution matrix of (6.17).

Now suppose Φ and Ψ are two fundamental matrices of (6.17) on I. Letting ψ_j be the jth column of Ψ, it follows from (6.20) that $\psi_j = \Phi \mathbf{c}_j$, $j = 1, \ldots, n$, where $\mathbf{c}_j$ are suitable constant vectors. Therefore, if we define C as the constant matrix whose columns are the vectors $\mathbf{c}_j$, $j = 1, \ldots, n$, we have at once that $\Psi(t) = \Phi(t)C$ for every t on I. Since $\det \Phi$ and $\det \Psi$ are both different from zero on I (why?), we also have $\det C \neq 0$ so that C is a nonsingular constant matrix. These remarks put together give the following relation between different fundamental matrices.

Theorem 6.7. *If Φ is a fundamental matrix for (6.17) on I and C is a nonsingular constant matrix, then ΦC is also a fundamental matrix for (6.17) on I. Every fundamental matrix of (6.17) is of this form for some nonsingular matrix C.*

•**EXERCISE**

26. Consider the system $\mathbf{y}' = A(t)\mathbf{y}$, where $A(t)$ is continuous for $-\infty < t < \infty$ and $A(t)$ is periodic with period 2π, that is, $A(t + 2\pi) = A(t)$. Show that if $\Phi(t)$ is a fundamental matrix on $-\infty < t < \infty$ then so is $\Phi(t + 2\pi)$.

[*Hint:* Substitute and apply the theory of this section.] Thus prove that

$$\Phi(t + 2\pi) = \Phi(t)C$$

for some nonsingular matrix C.

The result established in Exercise 26 is fundamental to the theory of linear systems with periodic coefficients. To proceed with this theory would require the result that the nonsingular constant matrix C has a logarithm. The interested reader may return to this topic after he has completed Section 6.7 below, by consulting, for example, [5], Chapter 3, Section 5.

•EXERCISES

27. (a) Show that

$$\Phi(t) = \begin{pmatrix} t^2 & t \\ 2t & 1 \end{pmatrix}$$

is a fundamental matrix for the system $\mathbf{y}' = A(t)\mathbf{y}$ where

$$A(t) = \begin{pmatrix} 0 & 1 \\ -2/t^2 & 2/t \end{pmatrix}$$

on any interval I not including the origin.
(b) Does the fact that $\det \Phi(0) = 0$ contradict Theorem 6.6?

28. Show that if a real homogeneous system of two first-order equations has a fundamental matrix

$$\begin{pmatrix} e^{it} & e^{-it} \\ ie^{it} & -ie^{-it} \end{pmatrix}$$

then $\begin{pmatrix} \cos t & \sin t \\ -\sin t & \cos t \end{pmatrix}$ is also a fundamental matrix. Can you find another

real fundamental matrix?

The reader who has followed the development of linear equations of order n in Chapter 3 should have noticed that we have now obtained here as a very special case essentially all of the basic theory of Section 3.3 (pp. 69–81) and with considerably more ease. In fact, the development of first-order systems in some ways is easier than what was done for the very special second-order equations. The use of matrix and vector space theory greatly simplifies the development.

6.6   Linear Nonhomogeneous Systems

We now use the theory developed in Sections 6.4 and 6.5 to discuss the form of solution of the nonhomogeneous system

$$\mathbf{y}' = A(t)\mathbf{y} + \mathbf{g}(t) \tag{6.24}$$

where $A(t)$ is a given continuous matrix and $\mathbf{g}(t)$ is a given continuous vector on an interval I.   The vector $\mathbf{g}(t)$ is usually referred to as a forcing term because if (6.24) describes a physical system, $\mathbf{g}(t)$ represents an external force.   By Theorem 6.3 and its corollary (p. 259), we know that given any point $(t_0,\ \boldsymbol{\eta})$, t_0 in I, there is a unique solution $\boldsymbol{\phi}$ of (6.24) existing in all of I, such that $\boldsymbol{\phi}(t_0) = \boldsymbol{\eta}$.

To construct solutions of (6.24) we let $\Phi(t)$ be a fundamental matrix of the homogeneous system $\mathbf{y}' = A(t)\mathbf{y}$ on I; Φ exists as a consequence of Theorem 6.4 (see also remarks immediately following its proof, p. 265). Suppose $\boldsymbol{\phi}_1$ and $\boldsymbol{\phi}_2$ are any two solutions of (6.24) on I.   Then $\boldsymbol{\phi}_1 - \boldsymbol{\phi}_2$ is a solution of the homogeneous system on I.

●**EXERCISE**

1. Verify this fact.

By Theorem 6.4, and the remarks immediately following its proof, there exists a constant vector $\mathbf{c}$ such that

$$\boldsymbol{\phi}_1 - \boldsymbol{\phi}_2 = \Phi\mathbf{c} \tag{6.25}$$

●**EXERCISE**

2. Assuming uniqueness for the solution of the initial value problem for the homogeneous system, use the above argument to establish uniqueness of solution of the initial value problem for (6.24).

Formula (6.25) tells us that to find any solution of (6.24) we need only know one solution of (6.24).   (Every other solution differs from the known one by some solution of the homogeneous system.)   There is a simple method, known as variation of constants, to determine a solution of (6.24) **provided we know a fundamental matrix for the homogeneous system** $\mathbf{y}' = A(t)\mathbf{y}$.   Let Φ be such a fundamental matrix on I. We attempt to find a solution $\boldsymbol{\psi}$ of (6.24) of the form

$$\boldsymbol{\psi}(t) = \Phi(t)\mathbf{v}(t) \tag{6.26}$$

where $\mathbf{v}$ is a vector to be determined.   (Note that if $\mathbf{v}$ is a constant vector then ψ satisfies the homogeneous system and thus for the present purpose $\mathbf{v}(t) = \mathbf{c}$ is ruled out.)   Suppose such a solution exists.   Then substituting (6.26) into (6.24), we find for all t on I

$$\psi'(t) = \Phi'(t)\mathbf{v}(t) + \Phi(t)\mathbf{v}'(t) = A(t)\Phi(t)\mathbf{v}(t) + \mathbf{g}(t)$$

Since Φ is a fundamental matrix of the homogeneous system, $\Phi'(t) = A(t)\Phi(t)$, and the terms involving $A(t)\Phi(t)\mathbf{v}(t)$ cancel.   Therefore if $\psi(t) = \Phi(t)\mathbf{v}(t)$ is a solution of (6.24) we must determine $\mathbf{v}(t)$ from the relation

$$\Phi(t)\mathbf{v}'(t) = \mathbf{g}(t)$$

Since $\Phi(t)$ is nonsingular on I we can premultiply by $\Phi^{-1}(t)$ and we have, on integrating,

$$\mathbf{v}(t) = \int_{t_0}^{t} \Phi^{-1}(s)\mathbf{g}(s)\, ds \qquad (t_0, t \text{ on } I)$$

and therefore (6.26) becomes

$$\psi(t) = \Phi(t) \int_{t_0}^{t} \Phi^{-1}(s)\mathbf{g}(s)\, ds \qquad (t_0, t \text{ on } I) \tag{6.27}$$

Thus if (6.24) has a solution ψ of the form (6.26) then ψ is given by (6.27).   Conversely, define ψ by (6.27), where Φ is a fundamental matrix of the homogeneous system on I.   Then, differentiating (6.27) and using the fundamental theorem of calculus, we have

$$\psi'(t) = \Phi'(t) \int_{t_0}^{t} \Phi^{-1}(s)\mathbf{g}(s)\, ds + \Phi(t)\Phi^{-1}(t)\mathbf{g}(t)$$
$$= A(t)\Phi(t) \int_{t_0}^{t} \Phi^{-1}(s)\mathbf{g}(s)\, ds + \mathbf{g}(t)$$

and using (6.27) again,

$$\psi'(t) = A(t)\psi(t) + \mathbf{g}(t)$$

for every t on I.   Obviously, $\psi(t_0) = \mathbf{0}$.   Thus we have proved the **variation of constants formula:**

Theorem 6.8.   *If Φ is a fundamental matrix of $\mathbf{y}' = A(t)\mathbf{y}$ on I, then the function*

$$\psi(t) = \Phi(t) \int_{t_0}^{t} \Phi^{-1}(s)\mathbf{g}(s)\, ds$$

is the (unique) *solution of* (6.24) *satisfying the initial condition*

$$\psi(t_0) = 0 \qquad \text{and valid on } I$$

Combining Theorem 6.8 with the remarks made at the beginning of this section we see that every solution ϕ of (6.24) on I has the form

$$\phi(t) = \phi_h(t) + \psi(t) \tag{6.28}$$

where ψ is the solution of equation (6.24) satisfying the initial condition $\psi(t_0) = 0$, and ϕ_h is that solution of the homogeneous system satisfying the same initial condition at t_0 as ϕ, for example, $\phi_h(t_0) = \eta$.

• EXERCISES

3. Consider the system $\mathbf{y}' = A\mathbf{y} + \mathbf{g}(t)$, where

$$A = \begin{pmatrix} 2 & 1 \\ 0 & 2 \end{pmatrix} \qquad \mathbf{y} = \begin{pmatrix} y_1 \\ y_2 \end{pmatrix} \qquad \mathbf{g}(t) = \begin{pmatrix} \sin t \\ \cos t \end{pmatrix}$$

Verify that

$$\Phi(t) = \begin{pmatrix} e^{2t} & te^{2t} \\ 0 & e^{2t} \end{pmatrix}$$

is a fundamental matrix of $\mathbf{y}' = A\mathbf{y}$. Find that solution ϕ of the nonhomogeneous system for which $\phi(0) = \begin{pmatrix} 1 \\ -1 \end{pmatrix}$.

4. Find the solution ϕ of the system $\mathbf{y}' = A\mathbf{y} + \mathbf{g}(t)$, where A is the same as in Exercise 3 above with $\mathbf{g}(t) = \begin{pmatrix} 0 \\ e^{2t} \end{pmatrix}$, satisfying the initial condition $\phi(0) = \begin{pmatrix} 1 \\ -1 \end{pmatrix}$.

5. Consider the system $\mathbf{y}' = A(t)\mathbf{y} + \mathbf{g}(t)$, where

$$A(t) = \begin{pmatrix} 0 & 1 \\ -2/t^2 & 2/t \end{pmatrix} \qquad \mathbf{g}(t) = \begin{pmatrix} t^4 \\ t^3 \end{pmatrix}$$

Find the solution ϕ satisfying the initial condition $\phi(2) = \begin{pmatrix} 1 \\ 4 \end{pmatrix}$ and determine the interval of validity of this solution. [*Hint:* Use the fundamental matrix given in Exercise 27, Section 6.5, p. 271.]

6.   Consider the second-order scalar equation

$$y'' + p(t)y' + q(t)y = f(t) \tag{6.29}$$

with p, q, f continuous on an interval I. Let ϕ_1, ϕ_2 be linearly independent (scalar) solutions of the homogeneous equation associated with (6.29).

(a) Write (6.29) as an equivalent system of two first-order equations and show that

$$\Phi(t) = \begin{pmatrix} \phi_1 & \phi_2 \\ \phi_1' & \phi_2' \end{pmatrix}$$

is a fundamental matrix of the associated homogeneous system on I.

(b) Use Theorem 6.8 to find the solution ψ of the inhomogeneous system in part (a) for which $\psi(t_0) = 0$, t_0 on I.   (Or obtain this solution directly.)

(c) Writing $\psi = \begin{pmatrix} \psi_1 \\ \psi_2 \end{pmatrix}$ show that

$$\psi_1(t) = \int_{t_0}^{t} \frac{\phi_2(t)\phi_1(s) - \phi_1(t)\phi_2(s)}{W(s)} f(s)\ ds$$

where $W(t) = \det \Phi(t)$, is that solution of (6.29) for which $\psi_1(0) = 0$, $\psi_1'(0) = 0$. Compare this result with Theorem 3.11 (p. 102) and the formula (3.34), p. 105, for the second-order equation.

7.   Consider the scalar equation of order n,

$$L_n(y) = a_0(t)y^{(n)} + a_1(t)y^{(n-1)} + \cdots + a_n(t)y = f(t)$$

where $a_0, a_1, \ldots, a_n$, and f are continuous on an interval I and $a_0(t) \neq 0$ on I. Let $\phi_1, \ldots, \phi_n$ be n linearly independent solutions of the homogeneous equation $L_n(y) = 0$.

(a) Write the equation $L_n(y) = f(t)$ as an equivalent system of n first-order equations and find a fundamental matrix of the corresponding homogeneous system in terms of $\phi_1, \ldots, \phi_n$.

(b) Use the method of this section to prove Theorem 3.12 (p. 102).

(c) Use Theorem 6.8 to find a particular solution of the nonhomogeneous system and thus deduce a solution of $L_n(y) = f(t)$. Compare this with the development involving equation (3.35), p. 107.

Exercises 6 and 7 above show that the entire theory of the linear nonhomogeneous scalar equation studied in Chapter 3 is contained in the development of this section.

6.7   Linear Systems with Constant Coefficients

The results of Section 6.6 show that in order to solve any linear system we need to find a fundamental matrix of the corresponding homogeneous system. If the homogeneous system has constant coefficients, that is, $A(t) \equiv A$, a constant matrix, we can obtain explicitly a fundamental matrix of the linear homogeneous system

$$\mathbf{y}' = A\mathbf{y} \tag{6.30}$$

and use this fundamental matrix to solve the inhomogeneous system by Theorem 6.8. We must first define the exponential of a matrix, e^M or exp M, where M is an n-by-n matrix. We say (see also the discussion of convergence of a sequence of matrices using the matrix norm (6.15) (p. 256)) that a series $\Sigma_{k=0}^{\infty} U_k$ of matrices converges if and only if the sequence $\Sigma_{k=0}^{m} U_k$ of partial sums converges, where convergence of a sequence of matrices is defined in Section 6.4 (p. 256). The limit of this sequence of partial sums is called the **sum** of the series.

Combining the definition of convergence of a sequence of matrices with the Cauchy criterion for sequences of real or complex numbers, we can establish the following result:

Lemma 6.1.   *A sequence $\{A_k\}$ of matrices converges if and only if given a number $\epsilon > 0$, there exists an integer $N = N(\epsilon) > 0$, such that $|A_m - A_p| < \epsilon$ whenever $m, p > N$.*

• **EXERCISE**

1. Interpret Lemma 6.1 to obtain a similar criterion for the convergence of a series of matrices $\Sigma_{k=0}^{\infty} U_k$.

We now define exp M to be the sum of the series

$$\exp M = E + M + \frac{M^2}{2!} + \frac{M^3}{3!} + \cdots + \frac{M^k}{k!} + \cdots \tag{6.31}$$

(E is the n-by-n identity matrix). We have a right to do this only if we can first show that this series converges for every complex n-by-n matrix M. To see whether it does, we define the partial sums

$$S_k = E + M + \frac{M^2}{2!} + \cdots + \frac{M^k}{k!} \tag{6.32}$$

and we use the Cauchy criterion for sequences of matrices (Lemma 6.1 above). Thus using the matrix norm we have for $m > p$

$$|S_m - S_p| = \left| \sum_{k=p+1}^{m} \frac{M^k}{k!} \right| \leq \sum_{k=p+1}^{m} \frac{|M|^k}{k!}$$

•EXERCISE

2. Use properties of the matrix norm to justify the above calculation; note this calculation is possible because the sums in (6.32) are finite.

From elementary calculus we know that for any matrix M, $e^{|M|} = \sum_{k=0}^{\infty} \frac{|M|^k}{k!}$ (**note that $|M|$ is a real number**). Hence, the right-hand side of (6.32) is the partial sum of a series of positive numbers which is known to converge. Therefore, by the Cauchy criterion for convergence of series of real numbers, we see that given $\epsilon > 0$, there exists an integer $N > 0$, such that

$$|S_m - S_p| < \epsilon \qquad \text{for } m, p > N$$

this proves the convergence of the series on the right side of (6.31) and thus establishes the validity of (6.31) for every matrix M.

Noting that $|E| = n$ we have immediately

$$|\exp M| \leq (n-1) + |M| + \frac{|M|^2}{2!} + \cdots + \frac{|M|^k}{k!} + \cdots$$
$$= (n-1) + e^{|M|}$$

It can be shown that if P is another n-by-n matrix we have

$$\exp M \cdot \exp P = \exp (M + P) \tag{6.33}$$

if M and P commute ($MP = PM$).

•EXERCISE

3. Prove (6.33) if M and P commute.

A useful property is that if T is a nonsingular n-by-n matrix

$$T^{-1}(\exp M)T = \exp (T^{-1}MT) \tag{6.34}$$

•**EXERCISE**

4. Verify (6.34). [*Hint:* Use (6.31).]

We are now ready to establish the basic result for linear systems with constant coefficients

$$\mathbf{y}' = A\mathbf{y} \tag{6.30}$$

Theorem 6.9. *The matrix*

$$\Phi(t) = \exp(At) \tag{6.35}$$

is the fundamental matrix of (6.30) *with* $\Phi(0) = E$ *on* $-\infty < t < \infty$.

Proof of Theorem 6.9. That $\Phi(0) = E$ is obvious from (6.31). Using (6.31) with $M = At$ (well defined for $-\infty < t < \infty$ and every n-by-n matrix A) we have by differentiation

$$(\exp At)' = A + \frac{A^2 t}{1!} + \frac{A^3 t^2}{2!} + \cdots + \frac{A^k t^{k-1}}{(k-1)!} + \cdots = A \exp At$$

$-\infty < t < \infty$. Therefore $\exp At$ is a solution matrix of (6.30) (its columns are solutions of (6.30)). Since $\det \Phi(0) = \det E = 1$, Theorem 6.5 (Abel's formula), p. 266, with $t_0 = 0$ gives

$$\det(\exp At) = \exp\left(\sum_{k=0}^{n} a_{kk} \right) t \neq 0 \qquad (-\infty < t < \infty)$$

Therefore, by Theorem 6.6 (p. 268), $\Phi(t)$ is a fundamental matrix of (6.30). This completes the proof of Theorem 6.9. ∎

•**EXERCISE**

5. Prove

$$(\exp At)' = A + \frac{A^2 t}{1!} + \frac{A^3 t^2}{2!} + \cdots + \frac{A^k t^{k-1}}{(k-1)!} + \cdots \qquad (-\infty < t < \infty)$$

It follows from Theorem 6.9 and equation (6.20), p. 265, above that every solution ϕ of the system (6.30) has the form

$$\phi(t) = (\exp At)\mathbf{c} \qquad (-\infty < t < \infty) \tag{6.36}$$

for a suitably chosen constant vector $\mathbf{c}$.

• EXERCISES

6. Show that if ϕ is that solution of (6.30) satisfying $\phi(t_0) = \eta$ then

$$\phi(t) = [\exp A(t - t_0)]\eta \qquad (-\infty < t < \infty) \tag{6.37}$$

7. Show that if $\Phi(t) = e^{tA}$, then $\Phi^{-1}(t) = e^{-tA}$

Example 1.   Find a fundamental matrix of the system $\mathbf{y}' = A\mathbf{y}$ if A is a diagonal matrix,

$$A = \begin{bmatrix} d_1 & & & 0 \\ & d_2 & & \\ & & \cdot & \\ & & & \cdot \\ 0 & & & d_n \end{bmatrix}$$

From (6.31)

$$\exp(At) = E + \begin{bmatrix} d_1 & & 0 \\ & \cdot & \\ & & \cdot \\ 0 & & d_n \end{bmatrix}\frac{t}{1!} + \begin{bmatrix} d_1{}^2 & & 0 \\ & \cdot & \\ & & \cdot \\ 0 & & d_n{}^2 \end{bmatrix}\frac{t^2}{2!} + \cdots$$

$$+ \begin{bmatrix} d_1{}^k & & 0 \\ & \cdot & \\ & & \cdot \\ 0 & & d_n{}^k \end{bmatrix}\frac{t^k}{k!} + \cdots = \begin{bmatrix} e^{d_1 t} & & & 0 \\ & e^{d_2 t} & & \\ & & \cdot & \\ 0 & & & e^{d_n t} \end{bmatrix}$$

and by Theorem 6.9 this is a fundamental matrix.   This result is, of course, obvious since in the present case each equation of the system is $y'_k = d_k y_k$ $(k = 1, \ldots, n)$ and can be integrated.

Example 2.   Find a fundamental matrix of $\mathbf{y}' = A\mathbf{y}$ if

$$A = \begin{bmatrix} 3 & 1 \\ 0 & 3 \end{bmatrix}$$

Solution.   Since $A = \begin{bmatrix} 3 & 0 \\ 0 & 3 \end{bmatrix} + \begin{bmatrix} 0 & 1 \\ 0 & 0 \end{bmatrix}$ and since these two matrices commute, we have

$$\exp At = \exp \begin{bmatrix} 3 & 0 \\ 0 & 3 \end{bmatrix} t \cdot \exp \begin{bmatrix} 0 & 1 \\ 0 & 0 \end{bmatrix} t$$

$$= \begin{bmatrix} e^{3t} & 0 \\ 0 & e^{3t} \end{bmatrix} \left[E + \begin{bmatrix} 0 & 1 \\ 0 & 0 \end{bmatrix} t + \begin{bmatrix} 0 & 1 \\ 0 & 0 \end{bmatrix}^2 \frac{t^2}{2!} + \cdots \right]$$

But $\begin{bmatrix} 0 & 1 \\ 0 & 0 \end{bmatrix}^2 = \begin{bmatrix} 0 & 0 \\ 0 & 0 \end{bmatrix}$ and the infinite series terminates after two terms. Therefore,

$$\exp At = e^{3t} \begin{bmatrix} 1 & t \\ 0 & 1 \end{bmatrix}$$

and by Theorem 6.9 this is a fundamental matrix. This can also be obtained easily by integrating the system, starting with the second equation.

•EXERCISES

8. Find a fundamental matrix of the system $\mathbf{y}' = A\mathbf{y}$ if

$$A = \begin{bmatrix} -2 & 1 & 0 \\ 0 & -2 & 1 \\ 0 & 0 & -2 \end{bmatrix}$$

and check your answer by direct integration of the given system.

9. Find a fundamental matrix of the system $\mathbf{y}' = A\mathbf{y}$ if

$$A = \begin{bmatrix} 0 & 1 & & & 0 \\ & & \cdot & \cdot & \\ & & & \cdot & \cdot \\ & & & & 1 \\ & & & & 0 \end{bmatrix} \quad \text{where } A \text{ is an } n\text{-by-}n \text{ matrix}$$

10. Find a fundamental matrix of the system $\mathbf{y}' = A\mathbf{y}$, where A is the n-by-n matrix

$$A = \begin{bmatrix} 2 & 1 & & & 0 \\ & 2 & 1 & & \\ & & \cdot & \cdot & \\ & & & \cdot & \cdot \\ & & & & 1 \\ & & & & 2 \end{bmatrix}$$

The reader will have noticed that the examples and exercises presented so far, all of which involve the calculation of e^{tA}, are of a rather special form.   In order to be able to handle more complicated problems and in order to obtain a general representation of solutions of (6.30) in a more explicit form than merely exp (tA), we need to introduce the notion of **eigenvalue** of a matrix.

Consider the system $\mathbf{y}' = A\mathbf{y}$, and look for a solution of the form

$$\phi(t) = e^{\lambda t}\mathbf{c}$$

where the constant λ and the vector $\mathbf{c}$ are to be determined.   Such a form is suggested by the above examples.   Substitution shows that $e^{\lambda t}\mathbf{c}$ is a solution if and only if

$$\lambda e^{\lambda t}\mathbf{c} = Ae^{\lambda t}\mathbf{c}$$

Since $e^{\lambda t} \neq 0$, this condition becomes

$$(\lambda E - A)\mathbf{c} = \mathbf{0}$$

which can be regarded as a linear homogeneous algebraic system for the vector $\mathbf{c}$.   This system has a nontrivial solution if and only if λ is chosen in such a way that

$$\det(\lambda E - A) = 0$$

This suggests the following definition.

If A is any n-by-n matrix, the polynomial in λ of degree n, $p(\lambda) = \det(\lambda E - A)$, is called **the characteristic polynomial** of A; its n roots (not necessarily distinct) are called the **eigenvalues** (also characteristic values) of A.   We remark that if $\lambda = 0$ is not an eigenvalue of A, $p(0) = \det A \neq 0$, and thus A is nonsingular.   For a given eigenvalue λ_0, we say that a nonzero vector $\mathbf{c}_0$ is an **eigenvector** corresponding to the eigenvalue λ_0 if and only if $(\lambda_0 E - A)\mathbf{c}_0 = \mathbf{0}$.

Example 3.   Find the eigenvalues of the matrix

$$A = \begin{bmatrix} 2 & 1 \\ -1 & 4 \end{bmatrix}$$

Consider the equation $\det(\lambda E - A) = 0$.

$$\begin{vmatrix} \lambda - 2 & -1 \\ 1 & \lambda - 4 \end{vmatrix} = (\lambda - 2)(\lambda - 4) + 1 = \lambda^2 - 6\lambda + 9 = 0$$

Thus $\lambda = 3$ is an eigenvalue of A of multiplicity two.   To find a corresponding eigenvector we consider the system

$$(3E - A)c = 0$$

or

$$\begin{pmatrix} 1 & -1 \\ 1 & -1 \end{pmatrix} \begin{pmatrix} c_1 \\ c_2 \end{pmatrix} = \begin{pmatrix} 0 \\ 0 \end{pmatrix}$$

Thus any vector $c = \alpha \begin{pmatrix} 1 \\ 1 \end{pmatrix}$, where α is any scalar, is an eigenvector corresponding to the eigenvalue $\lambda = 3$.   The reader will note that even though the eigenvalue has multiplicity 2, the corresponding eigenvectors form a subspace of E_2 whose dimension is only one.

•EXERCISES

11. Compute the eigenvalues and eigenvectors of each of the following matrices.   Also find the dimension of the subspace spanned by the eigenvectors.

(a) $\begin{bmatrix} 3 & 5 \\ -5 & 3 \end{bmatrix}$ (b) $\begin{bmatrix} -3 & 1 & 7 \\ 0 & 4 & -1 \\ 0 & 0 & 2 \end{bmatrix}$

(c) $\begin{bmatrix} 1 & 0 & 3 \\ 8 & 1 & -1 \\ 5 & 1 & -1 \end{bmatrix}$ (d) $\begin{bmatrix} 3 & -1 & -4 & 2 \\ 2 & 3 & -2 & -4 \\ 2 & -1 & -3 & 2 \\ 1 & 2 & -1 & -3 \end{bmatrix}$

12. Show that if A is a triangular matrix, of the form

$$A = \begin{bmatrix} a_{11} & a_{12} & \cdots & a_{1n} \\ 0 & a_{22} & & \cdot \\ & 0 & & \\ \cdot & & \cdot & \cdot & \cdot \\ \cdot & & & \cdot & \cdot \\ \cdot & & & & \cdot & \cdot \\ 0 & \cdots & & 0 & a_{nn} \end{bmatrix}$$

the eigenvalues of A are $\lambda_i = a_{ii}$ $(i = 1, \ldots, n)$.

Suppose the constant $n \times n$ matrix A has n linearly independent eigenvectors $v_1, \ldots, v_n$ corresponding to the eigenvalues $\lambda_1, \ldots, \lambda_n$. These vectors form a basis of E_n.   In particular, if $\lambda_1, \ldots, \lambda_n$ are distinct, this will be the case.   It follows from our earlier discussion that $\exp(\lambda_j t) v_j$ $(j = 1, \ldots, n)$ are solutions of $y' = Ay$ (the reader may easily verify this directly).   Since these solutions are obviously linearly independent on $-\infty < t < \infty$, it follows that the matrix $\Phi(t)$ whose columns are $\exp(\lambda_1 t)\mathbf{v}_1, \ldots, \exp(\lambda_n t)\mathbf{v}_n$ is a fundamental matrix on $-\infty < t < \infty$. We shall denote this by

$$\Phi(t) = (\exp(\lambda_1 t)\mathbf{v}_1, \ldots, \exp(\lambda_n t)\mathbf{v}_n)$$

Incidentally, since e^{tA} is also a fundamental matrix (even though we have not calculated it explicitly), it follows from Theorem 6.7 (p. 270) that

$$e^{tA} = \Phi(t)C$$

for some nonsingular constant matrix C. This technique can always be used to construct a fundamental matrix if the eigenvalues of A are distinct.

If the eigenvalues are not all distinct, it may still be possible to find n linearly independent eigenvectors; for example, if A is a diagonal constant matrix whose diagonal entries are not all distinct. In this case we may again apply the above technique to find a fundamental matrix of $\mathbf{y}' = A\mathbf{y}$. However, the technique will fail if the eigenvectors do not form a basis for E_n. As shown in Example 2 above (p. 279), there may then be solutions which cannot be expressed using only exponential functions and **constant** vectors.

To determine the form of e^{tA} when A is an arbitrary matrix, we require the following result from linear algebra, which we ask the reader to accept. We note that the following method, which leads to the formula (6.40) below, is always applicable, and includes the above technique as a special case.

Let A be a (complex) n-by-n matrix. Compute $\lambda_1, \lambda_2, \ldots, \lambda_k$, the distinct eigenvalues of A with respective multiplicities $n_1, n_2, \ldots, n_k$, where $n_1 + n_2 + \cdots + n_k = n$. Corresponding to each eigenvalue λ_j of multiplicity n_j consider the system of linear equations

$$(A - \lambda_j E)^{n_j}\mathbf{x} = 0 \qquad (j = 1, 2, \ldots, k) \tag{6.38}$$

The solutions of each such linear system obviously span a subspace of E_n which we call X_j $(j = 1, 2, \ldots, k)$. The result from linear algebra needed (see [7], pp. 109–115) tells us that **for every** $x \in E_n$, **there exist unique vectors** $\mathbf{x}_1, \mathbf{x}_2, \ldots, \mathbf{x}_k$, where $\mathbf{x}_j \in X_j$, **such that**

$$\mathbf{x} = \mathbf{x}_1 + \mathbf{x}_2 + \cdots + \mathbf{x}_k \tag{6.39}$$

and $A\mathbf{x}_j \in X_j$ $(j = 1, \ldots, k)$. It is important to know that the linear algebraic system (6.38) has n_j linearly independent solutions so that the dimension of X_j is n_j. In the language of linear algebra, E_n is the **direct sum** of subspaces $X_1, X_2, \ldots, X_k$,

$$E_n = X_1 \oplus X_2 \oplus \cdots \oplus X_k$$

such that the dimension of X_j is n_j, X_j is invariant under A, and the transformation defined by the matrix $A - \lambda_j E$ is **nilpotent** on X_j of index at most n_j (this is just another way of stating (6.38)).

It may, in fact, happen that $(A - \lambda_j E)^q \mathbf{x} = 0$ for all $\mathbf{x}$ in X_j and some $q < n_j$.

Example 4. If

$$A = \begin{bmatrix} 4 & 1 & 0 & 0 & 0 \\ 0 & 4 & 1 & 0 & 0 \\ 0 & 0 & 4 & 0 & 0 \\ 0 & 0 & 0 & 4 & 0 \\ 0 & 0 & 0 & 0 & 4 \end{bmatrix}$$

then E_n is E_5, and $\lambda = 4$ is the only eigenvalue, with multiplicity 5; that is, $k = 1$. Since there is only one eigenvalue, no decomposition into subspaces is necessary, and $E_5 = X_1$. According to the theorem, $n_1 = 5$, so that certainly $(A - 4E)^5 = 0$. However, as the reader can easily verify, $(A - 4E)^3 = 0$ but $(A - 4E)^2 \neq 0$. Therefore $q = 3 < n_1 = 5$.

To apply this theory to the linear system (6.30), we look for that solution $\phi(t)$ satisfying the initial condition $\phi(0) = \eta$. By Theorem 6.9, we know that $\phi(t) = e^{tA}\eta$ and our object is to evaluate $e^{tA}\eta$ explicitly, that is, to see exactly what the components of ϕ are. We compute $\lambda_1, \lambda_2, \ldots, \lambda_k$, the distinct eigenvalues of A of multiplicities $n_1, n_2, \ldots, n_k$, respectively. We apply the theorem to the initial vector η and in accordance with (6.39) we have

$$\eta = \mathbf{v}_1 + \mathbf{v}_2 + \cdots + \mathbf{v}_k$$

where $\mathbf{v}_j$ is some suitable vector in the subspace X_j $(j = 1, \ldots, k)$. Since the subspace X_j is generated by the system (6.38), $\mathbf{v}_j$ must be some solution of (6.38). Now

$$e^{tA}\mathbf{v}_j = e^{\lambda_j t} e^{(A - \lambda_j E)t} \mathbf{v}_j = e^{\lambda_j t}\left(E + t(A - \lambda_j E) + \frac{t^2}{2!}(A - \lambda_j E)^2 + \cdots \right.$$

$$\left. + \frac{t^{n_j - 1}}{(n_j - 1)!}(A - \lambda_j E)^{n_j - 1} \right)\mathbf{v}_j$$

for $-\infty < t < \infty$, where the series in parentheses terminates because v_j is a solution of (6.38); thus the term involving $(A - \lambda_j E)^{n_j}$ and all subsequent terms are zero. Observe that the vectors $w_j = (A - \lambda_j E)^p v_j$, for $p = 0, 1, \ldots, n_j - 1$, belong to the subspace X_j because

$$(A - \lambda_j E)^{n_j} w_j = (A - \lambda_j E)^{n_j}[(A - \lambda_j E)^p v_j] = (A - \lambda_j E)^{n_j+p} v_j = 0$$

Thus the vector $e^{tA} v_j$ remains in X_j for $-\infty < t < \infty$.

Applying the above calculations to the solution $\phi(t) = e^{tA}\eta$ of (6.30), we have

$$\phi(t) = e^{tA}\eta = e^{tA} \sum_{j=1}^{k} v_j = \sum_{j=1}^{k} e^{tA} v_j$$

$$= \sum_{j=1}^{k} e^{\lambda_j t}\left[E + t(A - \lambda_j E) + \cdots + \frac{t^{n_j-1}}{(n_j - 1)!}(A - \lambda_j E)^{n_j-1} \right] v_j$$

or finally,

$$\phi(t) = \sum_{j=1}^{k} e^{\lambda_j t}\left[\sum_{i=0}^{n_j-1} \frac{t^i}{i!}(A - \lambda_j E)^i \right] v_j \qquad (-\infty < t < \infty) \qquad (6.40)$$

We point out again that if $(A - \lambda_j E)^{q_j} = 0$, where $q_j < n_j$, then the sum on i in equation (6.40) will contain only q_j, rather than n_j, terms. This formula also tells us precisely how the components of the solution behave as functions of t for any given coefficient matrix A.

Example 5. Solve the linear system (6.30) (p. 278) if A is the matrix in Example 3 above. Also obtain a fundamental matrix.

From Example 3 we know that $\lambda_1 = 3$ is an eigenvalue of multiplicity 2. In the above notation $n_1 = 2$. Therefore only the subspace X_1 (in this case $X_1 = E_2$) is relevant. We readily calculate

$$A - 3E = \begin{bmatrix} -1 & 1 \\ -1 & 1 \end{bmatrix}$$

and we also see

$$(A - 3E)^2 = \begin{bmatrix} 0 & 0 \\ 0 & 0 \end{bmatrix}$$

so that (6.38) (p. 283) is satisfied for every vector in E_2. Substituting in (6.40) with $n_1 = 2$, $\eta = \begin{pmatrix} \eta_1 \\ \eta_2 \end{pmatrix}$, we find

$$\phi(t) = e^{3t}[E + t(A - E)]\eta$$

and therefore

$$\phi(t) = e^{3t}\left[E + t\begin{pmatrix} -1 & 1 \\ -1 & 1 \end{pmatrix}\right]\begin{pmatrix} \eta_1 \\ \eta_2 \end{pmatrix}$$

$$= e^{3t}\begin{bmatrix} \eta_1 + t(-\eta_1 + \eta_2) \\ \eta_2 + t(-\eta_1 + \eta_2) \end{bmatrix} \tag{6.41}$$

is the solution with $\phi(0) = \eta$. To construct a fundamental matrix we may appeal to Theorem 6.9 (p. 278), which says that exp (tA) is a fundamental matrix. So far, we have computed, in equation (6.41), exp $(tA)\eta$ for an arbitrary constant vector η. But exp $(tA) = $ exp $(tA)\begin{pmatrix} 1 & 0 \\ 0 & 1 \end{pmatrix} = \left(\text{exp }(tA)\begin{pmatrix} 1 \\ 0 \end{pmatrix},\text{ exp }(tA)\begin{pmatrix} 0 \\ 1 \end{pmatrix}\right)$, where the solution vectors exp $(tA)\begin{pmatrix} 1 \\ 0 \end{pmatrix}$ and exp $(tA)\begin{pmatrix} 0 \\ 1 \end{pmatrix}$ are found from (6.41) by substituting $\eta = \begin{pmatrix} 1 \\ 0 \end{pmatrix}$ and $\eta = \begin{pmatrix} 0 \\ 1 \end{pmatrix}$ respectively. Therefore, a fundamental matrix is

$$\Phi(t) = \text{exp }(tA) = e^{3t}\begin{pmatrix} 1-t & t \\ -t & 1+t \end{pmatrix}$$

Example 6. Consider the system

$$\begin{aligned} x_1' &= 3x_1 - x_2 + x_3 \\ x_2' &= 2x_1 + x_3 \\ x_3' &= x_1 - x_2 + 2x_3 \end{aligned}$$

which has coefficient matrix

$$A = \begin{pmatrix} 3 & -1 & 1 \\ 2 & 0 & 1 \\ 1 & -1 & 2 \end{pmatrix}$$

Find that solution ϕ satisfying the initial condition $\phi(0) = \begin{pmatrix} \eta_1 \\ \eta_2 \\ \eta_3 \end{pmatrix} = \eta$, and find also a fundamental matrix.

The characteristic polynomial of A is det $(\lambda E - A) = (\lambda - 1)(\lambda - 2)^2$, and therefore the eigenvalues are $\lambda_1 = 1$, $\lambda_2 = 2$ with multiplicities $n_1 = 1$, $n_2 = 2$, respectively.

In the notation of (6.38) we consider the systems of algebraic equations

$$(A - E)\mathbf{x} = 0 \quad \text{and} \quad (A - 2E)^2\mathbf{x} = 0$$

in order to determine the subspaces X_1 and X_2 of E_3.   Taking these in succession we have first

$$(A - E)\mathbf{x} = \begin{pmatrix} 2 & -1 & 1 \\ 2 & -1 & 1 \\ 1 & -1 & 1 \end{pmatrix} \mathbf{x} = 0 \quad \text{or} \quad \begin{cases} 2x_1 - x_2 + x_3 = 0 \\ 2x_1 - x_2 + x_3 = 0 \\ x_1 - x_2 + x_3 = 0 \end{cases}$$

Thus X_1 is the subspace spanned by the vectors $\begin{pmatrix} x_1 \\ x_2 \\ x_3 \end{pmatrix}$ with $x_1 = 0$, $x_2 = x_3$ and clearly dim $X_1 = 1$.   Next,

$$(A - 2E)^2\mathbf{x} = \begin{pmatrix} 0 & 0 & 0 \\ -1 & 1 & 0 \\ -1 & 1 & 0 \end{pmatrix} \mathbf{x} = 0 \quad \text{or} \quad \begin{cases} -x_1 + x_2 = 0 \\ -x_1 + x_2 = 0 \end{cases}$$

Thus X_2 is the subspace spanned by vectors $\begin{pmatrix} x_1 \\ x_2 \\ x_3 \end{pmatrix}$ with $x_1 = x_2$ and x_3 arbitrary; clearly dim $X_2 = 2$.   The reader is advised to picture these subspaces in E_3.

We now wish to write the initial vector $\boldsymbol{\eta}$ as

$$\boldsymbol{\eta} = \mathbf{v}_1 + \mathbf{v}_2 \quad \text{where } \mathbf{v}_1 \in X_1, \mathbf{v}_2 \in X_2$$

and we find, after an elementary calculation,

$$\mathbf{v}_1 = \begin{pmatrix} 0 \\ \eta_2 - \eta_1 \\ \eta_2 - \eta_1 \end{pmatrix} \qquad \mathbf{v}_2 = \begin{pmatrix} \eta_1 \\ \eta_1 \\ \eta_3 - \eta_2 + \eta_1 \end{pmatrix}$$

Thus by the formula (6.40), we find that the solution $\boldsymbol{\phi}$ such that $\boldsymbol{\phi}(0) = \boldsymbol{\eta}$ is given by

$$\boldsymbol{\phi}(t) = e^t\mathbf{v}_1 + e^{2t}(E + t(A - 2E))\mathbf{v}_2$$

$$= e^t \begin{pmatrix} 0 \\ \eta_2 - \eta_1 \\ \eta_2 - \eta_1 \end{pmatrix} + e^{2t} \left(E + t \begin{pmatrix} 1 & -1 & 1 \\ 2 & -2 & 1 \\ 1 & -1 & 0 \end{pmatrix} \right) \begin{pmatrix} \eta_1 \\ \eta_1 \\ \eta_3 - \eta_2 + \eta_1 \end{pmatrix}$$

$$= e^t \begin{pmatrix} 0 \\ \eta_2 - \eta_1 \\ \eta_2 - \eta_1 \end{pmatrix} + e^{2t} \begin{pmatrix} 1+t & -t & t \\ 2t & 1 - 2t & t \\ t & -t & 1 \end{pmatrix} \begin{pmatrix} \eta_1 \\ \eta_1 \\ \eta_3 - \eta_2 + \eta_1 \end{pmatrix}$$

Putting $\boldsymbol{\eta}$ successively equal to $\begin{pmatrix} 1 \\ 0 \\ 0 \end{pmatrix}, \begin{pmatrix} 0 \\ 1 \\ 0 \end{pmatrix}, \begin{pmatrix} 0 \\ 0 \\ 1 \end{pmatrix}$ in analogy with Example 5, p. 286, we obtain the three linearly independent solutions such that the matrix

$$\Phi(t) = e^{tA} = \begin{pmatrix} (1+t)e^{2t} & -te^{2t} & te^{2t} \\ -e^t + (1+t)e^{2t} & e^t - te^{2t} & te^{2t} \\ -e^t + e^{2t} & e^t - te^{2t} & e^{2t} \end{pmatrix}$$

having these solutions as columns is the fundamental matrix which reduces to the identity matrix when $t = 0$.

Example 7.   Find a fundamental matrix for the system $\mathbf{y}' = A\mathbf{y}$ with

$$A = \begin{pmatrix} 4 & 1 & 0 & 0 & 0 \\ 0 & 4 & 1 & 0 & 0 \\ 0 & 0 & 4 & 0 & 0 \\ 0 & 0 & 0 & 4 & 0 \\ 0 & 0 & 0 & 0 & 4 \end{pmatrix}$$

Using the results of Example 4, p. 284, we have $(A - 4E)^3 = 0$ so that $(A - 4E)^3\mathbf{x} = 0$ for any vector $\mathbf{x}$ in E_5 and the initial vector $\boldsymbol{\eta}$ remains arbitrary. Since there is only one eigenvalue (4) only the subspace $X_1 = E_5$ is relevant and we have from (6.40) $\boldsymbol{\phi}(t) = e^{4t}\left[E + t(A - 4E) + \dfrac{t^2}{2!}(A - 4E)^2 \right]\boldsymbol{\eta}$. Therefore,

$$\boldsymbol{\phi}(t) = e^{4t}\left[E + t\begin{pmatrix} 0 & 1 & 0 & 0 & 0 \\ 0 & 0 & 1 & 0 & 0 \\ 0 & 0 & 0 & 0 & 0 \\ 0 & 0 & 0 & 0 & 0 \\ 0 & 0 & 0 & 0 & 0 \end{pmatrix} + \frac{t^2}{2!}\begin{pmatrix} 0 & 0 & 1 & 0 & 0 \\ 0 & 0 & 0 & 0 & 0 \\ 0 & 0 & 0 & 0 & 0 \\ 0 & 0 & 0 & 0 & 0 \\ 0 & 0 & 0 & 0 & 0 \end{pmatrix} \right]\boldsymbol{\eta}$$

Again letting $\boldsymbol{\eta}$ successively assume the values

$$\boldsymbol{\eta}_1 = \begin{pmatrix} 1 \\ 0 \\ 0 \\ 0 \\ 0 \end{pmatrix} \quad \boldsymbol{\eta}_2 = \begin{pmatrix} 0 \\ 1 \\ 0 \\ 0 \\ 0 \end{pmatrix} \quad \boldsymbol{\eta}_3 = \begin{pmatrix} 0 \\ 0 \\ 1 \\ 0 \\ 0 \end{pmatrix} \quad \boldsymbol{\eta}_4 = \begin{pmatrix} 0 \\ 0 \\ 0 \\ 1 \\ 0 \end{pmatrix} \quad \boldsymbol{\eta}_5 = \begin{pmatrix} 0 \\ 0 \\ 0 \\ 0 \\ 1 \end{pmatrix}$$

in the above formula, the resulting solutions will be linearly independent and can be used as columns of a fundamental matrix.   Thus

$$\Phi(t) = e^{4t} \begin{pmatrix} 1 & t & \dfrac{t^2}{2!} & 0 & 0 \\ 0 & 1 & t & 0 & 0 \\ 0 & 0 & 1 & 0 & 0 \\ 0 & 0 & 0 & 1 & 0 \\ 0 & 0 & 0 & 0 & 1 \end{pmatrix}$$

is a fundamental matrix.

•EXERCISES

Find a fundamental matrix for each of the following systems $y' = Ay$ having the coefficient matrix given.   Also find a particular solution satisfying the given initial condition.

13. $A = \begin{pmatrix} 1 & 2 \\ 4 & 3 \end{pmatrix}$; $\eta = \begin{pmatrix} 3 \\ 3 \end{pmatrix}$.

14. $A = \begin{pmatrix} 2 & -3 \\ 3 & -4 \end{pmatrix}$; $\eta = \begin{pmatrix} 1 \\ 2 \end{pmatrix}$.

15. $A = \begin{pmatrix} 1 & 0 & 3 \\ 8 & 1 & -1 \\ 5 & 1 & -1 \end{pmatrix}$; $\eta = \begin{pmatrix} 0 \\ -2 \\ -7 \end{pmatrix}$.

16. $A = \begin{pmatrix} 3 & -1 & -4 & 2 \\ 2 & 3 & -2 & -4 \\ 2 & -1 & -3 & 2 \\ 1 & 2 & -1 & -3 \end{pmatrix}$; $\eta = \begin{pmatrix} 1 \\ 0 \\ -1 \\ 0 \end{pmatrix}$.

[*Note:* the characteristic polynomial is $(\lambda - 1)^2 \cdot (\lambda + 1)^2$.]

17. Find that solution of the system

$$\begin{aligned} y_1' &= y_1 + y_2 + \sin t \\ y_2' &= 2y_1 + \cos t \end{aligned}$$

such that $y_1(0) = 1$, $y_2(0) = 1$.   [*Hint:* Find a fundamental matrix of the homogeneous system; then use the variation of constants formula in Section 6.6 (p. 274).]

Consider the scalar linear differential equation of second order

$$y'' + py' + qy = 0 \tag{6.42}$$

where p and q are constants.   We learned in Section 3.4 (pp. 88, 90) how to construct the general solution for (6.42).   We can also do this as a special case of the theory developed here.

•EXERCISES

18. Show that equation (6.42) is equivalent to the system $\mathbf{y}' = A\mathbf{y}$ with

$$A = \begin{pmatrix} 0 & 1 \\ -q & -p \end{pmatrix} \cdot$$

and compute the eigenvalues λ_1, λ_2 of A.

19. Compute a fundamental matrix for the system in Exercise 18 if $\lambda_1 \neq \lambda_2$, that is, if $p^2 \neq 4q$, and construct the general solution of equation (6.42) in this case.

20. Compute a fundamental matrix for the system in Exercise 18 in the case $\lambda_1 = \lambda_2 = \lambda$, that is, $p^2 = 4q$ and construct the general solution of (6.42) in the case $p^2 = 4q$. Note that $A - \lambda E$ is never zero in this case so that the fundamental matrix, as well as the general solution of (6.42), must necessarily contain a term in $te^{\lambda t}$.

21. Generalize the results of Exercises 18, 19, 20 to the scalar equation

$$y''' + p_1 y'' + p_2 y' + p_3 y = 0$$

where p_1, p_2, p_3 are constants.   (Needless to say, you are not expected actually to solve a cubic equation.)

The reader who has not studied Chapter 3 should at this point compare the results of the above exercises with those of Section 3.4 and he should work the exercises in that section.

Using the variation of constants formula (Theorem 6.8, p. 274) we may find a particular solution of the nonhomogeneous system

$$\mathbf{y}' = A\mathbf{y} + \mathbf{g}(t) \tag{6.43}$$

where A is a constant matrix and $\mathbf{g}$ is a given continuous function. The variation of constants formula with $\Phi(t) = \exp(tA)$ as a fundamental matrix of the homogeneous system, now becomes particularly simple in appearance. We have $\Phi^{-1}(s) = \exp(-sA), \Phi(t)\Phi^{-1}(s) = \exp[(t-s)A]$; if the initial condition is $\boldsymbol{\phi}(t_0) = \boldsymbol{\eta}, \boldsymbol{\phi}_h(t) = \exp[(t-t_0)A]\boldsymbol{\eta}$ and the solution of (6.43) is

$$\boldsymbol{\phi}(t) = \exp[(t-t_0)A]\boldsymbol{\eta} + \int_{t_0}^{t} \exp[(t-s)A]\mathbf{g}(s)\,ds \qquad (-\infty < t < \infty) \tag{6.44}$$

where e^{tA} is the fundamental matrix of the homogeneous system, which we can construct by the method of this section.

Example 8. Solve the initial value problem

$$\mathbf{y}' = A\mathbf{y} + \mathbf{g}(t)$$

where A is the constant matrix in Example 5, p. 285, and where $\mathbf{g}(t) = \begin{pmatrix} e^{3t} \\ 1 \end{pmatrix}$, with the initial condition $\boldsymbol{\phi}(0) = \boldsymbol{\eta}$. From Example 5 we have

$$\Phi(t) = e^{tA} = e^{3t} \begin{pmatrix} 1-t & t \\ -t & 1+t \end{pmatrix}$$

$$\Phi(t)\Phi^{-1}(s) = e^{(t-s)A} = e^{3(t-s)} \begin{pmatrix} 1-(t-s) & t-s \\ -(t-s) & 1+(t-s) \end{pmatrix}$$

$$e^{(t-s)A}\mathbf{g}(s) = e^{3t} \begin{pmatrix} 1-(t-s)+e^{-3s}(t-s) \\ -(t-s)+e^{-3s}(1+t-s) \end{pmatrix}$$

Therefore,

$$\boldsymbol{\phi}(t) = e^{3t} \begin{pmatrix} 1-t & t \\ -t & 1+t \end{pmatrix} \boldsymbol{\eta} + e^{3t} \int_0^t \begin{pmatrix} 1-(t-s)+e^{-3s}(t-s) \\ -(t-s)+e^{-3s}(1+t-s) \end{pmatrix} ds$$

and the integral is easily evaluated.

•EXERCISES

22. Write the solution $\boldsymbol{\phi}(t)$ of the system (6.43) if A is the matrix in Example 6 (p. 286) and $\mathbf{g}$ is any vector with 3 continuous components, subject to the initial condition $\boldsymbol{\phi}(0) = \boldsymbol{\eta}$.

23. By converting to an equivalent system find the general solution of the scalar equation

$$y'' - y = f(t)$$

where f is continuous, by using the theory of this section.

24. Given the matrix

$$A = \begin{pmatrix} 0 & 1 \\ -1 & 0 \end{pmatrix}$$

Show that $A^2 = -E$, $A^3 = -A$, $A^4 = E$, and compute A^m, where m is an arbitrary positive integer.

25. Use the result of Exercise 24 and the definition (6.31), p. 276, to show that

$$e^{tA} = \begin{pmatrix} \cos t & \sin t \\ -\sin t & \cos t \end{pmatrix}$$

[*Note:* This approach is easier in this case than by using equation (6.40).]

26. Use the results of this section and of Exercise 25 to find the general solution of the scalar equation

$$y'' + y = f(t)$$

where f is continuous (compare Exercise 3, Section 3.8, p. 105).

The reader who has not studied Chapter 3 should at this point compare the results of the above exercises with those of Section 3.8 and he should work the exercises in that section, both by the method given here and the method of judicious guessing given in Section 3.8 **where applicable.**

6.8 Asymptotic Behavior of Solutions of Linear Systems with Constant Coefficients

In many problems, in order to apply formula (6.44), and others derivable from it, we need to obtain a useful estimate for the norm of $\exp(tA)$ for $t \geq 0$. For example, in order to measure the growth of solutions of (6.43) as $t \to \infty$ we need to estimate $|\phi(t)|$ as $t \to \infty$ where $\phi(t)$ is given by (6.44). This, however, cannot be done without a useful estimate for $|\exp(tA)|$.

Theorem 6.10. *If $\lambda_1, \lambda_2, \ldots, \lambda_k$ are the distinct eigenvalues of A, where λ_j has multiplicity n_j and $n_1 + n_2 + \cdots + n_k = n$, and if ρ is any number larger than the real part of $\lambda_1, \ldots, \lambda_k$, that is,*

$$\rho > \max_{j=1,\ldots,k} (\Re\lambda_j) \tag{6.45}$$

then there exists a constant $K > 0$ such that

$$|\exp(tA)| \leq K \exp(\rho t) \qquad (0 \leq t < \infty) \tag{6.46}$$

Proof. We have seen that e^{tA} is a fundamental matrix of the linear system $\mathbf{y}' = A\mathbf{y}$. Combining this fact with the formula (6.40) (p. 285) for any solution $\phi(t)$ of this system, we see that every element of the matrix e^{tA} is of the form $\sum_{j=1}^{k} p_j(t)e^{\lambda_j t}$, where $p_j(t)$ is a polynomial of degree not more than $(n_j - 1)$. If ρ is chosen to satisfy the inequality (6.45), then $|e^{\lambda_j t}| = e^{(\Re\lambda_j)t} < e^{\rho t}$ and every term in the sum $\sum_{j=1}^{k} p_j(t)e^{\lambda_j t}$ is at most $Me^{\rho t}$ $(0 \leq t < \infty)$. As there are at most n^2 such terms in the matrix e^{tA}, (6.46) holds with $K = Mn^2$. ∎

We also remark that the constant ρ in (6.46) may be chosen as any number greater than or equal to the largest of $\Re\lambda_1$, $\Re\lambda_2$, . . . , $\Re\lambda_n$, whenever every eigenvalue whose real part is equal to this maximum, is itself simple. In particular, this is always true if A has no multiple eigenvalues.

As far as applications are concerned, the following consequence of Theorem 6.10 is of great importance.

Corollary to Theorem 6.10. *If all eigenvalues of A have real parts negative, then every solution $\phi(t)$ of the system*

$$\mathbf{y}' = A\mathbf{y}$$

approaches zero as $t \to +\infty$. More precisely, there exist constants $\tilde{K} > 0$, $\sigma > 0$ such that

$$|\phi(t)| < \tilde{K}e^{-\sigma t} \qquad (0 \le t < \infty) \tag{6.47}$$

It is, of course, also true that under the hypothesis of the corollary, there exist constants $K > 0$, $\sigma > 0$ such that

$$|\exp tA| \le Ke^{-\sigma t} \qquad (0 \le t < \infty) \tag{6.48}$$

To prove the corollary we choose $-\sigma$ ($\sigma > 0$) as any number larger than the real part of every eigenvalue ($-\sigma$ plays the role of ρ in Theorem 6.10). By Theorem 6.9 every solution has the form $\exp (tA)\mathbf{c}$ for some constant vector $\mathbf{c}$. By Theorem 6.10

$$|\phi(t)| \le |\exp (tA)|\,|\mathbf{c}| \le K|\mathbf{c}|e^{-\sigma t} = \tilde{K}e^{-\sigma t} \qquad (0 \le t < \infty)$$

•EXERCISE

1. Show that if all eigenvalues have real part negative or zero and if those eigenvalues with zero part are simple, there exists a constant $K > 0$ such that $|\exp tA| \le K$ ($0 \le t < \infty$), and hence every solution of $\mathbf{y}' = A\mathbf{y}$ is bounded on $0 \le t < \infty$.

We also remark that using Theorem 6.10 in (6.44) (p. 290), for example, we obtain the following estimate for solution of (6.43)

$$|\phi(t)| \le K|\eta|e^{\rho(t-t_0)} + K \int_{t_0}^{t} \exp [\rho(t - s)]|\mathbf{g}(s)|\,ds \qquad (0 \le t_0 \le t < \infty)$$

where K, ρ are defined by the theorem. If we have more information on $\mathbf{g}(t)$ and on the eigenvalues of A, we can deduce more from this estimate. An example is given by the following exercise.

• **EXERCISE**

2. Show that if the hypothesis of Exercise 1 is satisfied and if $\int_{t_0}^{\infty} |\mathbf{g}(s)| \, ds < \infty$, then every solution $\phi(t)$ of (6.43) on $0 \leq t_0 \leq t < \infty$ is bounded.

Another consequence of Theorem (6.10) is the fact that every solution of a linear system of differential equations grows no faster than an exponential function. This fact is needed in the study of the Laplace transform (Chapter 9).

Theorem 6.11. *Suppose that in the linear nonhomogeneous system (6.43) the function $\mathbf{g}(t)$ grows no faster than an exponential function, that is, there exist real constants $M > 0$, $T \geq 0$, a such that*

$$|\mathbf{g}(t)| \leq Me^{at} \qquad (t \geq T)$$

Then every solution ϕ of (6.43) grows no faster than an exponential function, that is, there exists real constants $K > 0$, b such that

$$|\phi(t)| \leq Ke^{bt} \qquad (t \geq T)$$

The derivative $\phi'(t)$ also grows no faster than an exponential function.

Proof. It follows from Theorem (6.3) (p. 258) that every solution ϕ of (6.43) exists on $0 \leq t < \infty$. By the variation of constants formula (6.44), every solution of (6.43) has the form

$$\phi(t) = e^{tA}\mathbf{c} + \int_0^t e^{(t-s)A}\mathbf{g}(s) \, ds$$

for a suitably chosen constant vector **c**. By Theorem 6.10, there exists a real number ρ and a constant $K_1 \geq 0$ such that

$$|e^{tA}| \leq K_1 e^{\rho t} \qquad (0 \leq t < \infty)$$

Here ρ may be any number larger than the real part of every eigenvalue of A as defined in the inequality (6.45). We now write the variation of constants formula in the form

$$\phi(t) = e^{tA}\mathbf{c} + \int_0^T e^{(t-s)A}\mathbf{g}(s) \, ds + \int_T^t e^{(t-s)A}\mathbf{g}(s) \, ds$$

Letting $K_2 = \sup_{0 \le t \le T} |\mathbf{g}(s)|$ and using the known bounds on $|\mathbf{g}(s)|$ for $t \ge T$ and on $|e^{tA}|$, we obtain the estimate

$$|\boldsymbol{\phi}(t)| \le K_1|\mathbf{c}|e^{\rho t} + K_1 \int_0^T e^{\rho(t-s)} K_2 \, ds + K_1 \int_T^t e^{\rho(t-s)} Me^{as} \, ds$$

From this, we obtain

$$|\boldsymbol{\phi}(t)| \le Ke^{bt} \qquad (t \ge T)$$

where b is the larger of a and ρ.   Using this estimate in the system (6.43), we see that $\boldsymbol{\phi}'(t)$ also satisfies an equality of the same type.   Of course, the constant K does not have the same value as in (6.46). ∎

•EXERCISES

3. Evaluate the constant K in Theorem 6.11.

4. Obtain an explicit estimate for $|\boldsymbol{\phi}'(t)|$ in Theorem 6.11.

5. Let ϕ be a solution of the nth-order linear equation

$$u^{(n)} + a_1{}^{(n-1)} + \cdots + a_n u = f(t)$$

where $a_1, a_2, \ldots, a_n$ are constants, and where f is continuous on $0 \le t < \infty$ and grows no faster than an exponential function.   Show that $\phi(t)$, $\phi'(t)$, $\ldots$, $\phi^{(n)}(t)$ all grow no faster than an exponential function.

6.9   Autonomous Systems—Phase Space— Two-Dimensional Systems

In the system $\mathbf{y}' = \mathbf{f}(t, \mathbf{y})$ a case of considerable importance in applications occurs if $\mathbf{f}$ does not depend on t explicitly.   Such systems are called **autonomous.**   We will therefore study the system

$$\mathbf{y}' = \mathbf{g}(\mathbf{y}) \tag{6.49}$$

where $\mathbf{g}$ is a real function defined in some real n-dimensional domain D in $\mathbf{y}$ space.   The reader will note that D is now n-dimensional, not $(n + 1)$-dimensional.   The implication of this will be clear in a moment. We shall assume throughout that $\mathbf{g}$ and $\partial \mathbf{g}/\partial y_j$, $j = 1, \ldots, n$ are continuous in D, so that by Theorem 6.1 (p. 251), given any $(t_0, \boldsymbol{\eta})$, $\boldsymbol{\eta}$ in D, there exists a unique real solution $\boldsymbol{\phi}$ of (6.49) satisfying the initial condition $\boldsymbol{\phi}(t_0) = \boldsymbol{\eta}$.   This solution exists on some interval I and is a continuous function of $(t, t_0, \boldsymbol{\eta})$ with t, t_0 on I, $\boldsymbol{\eta}$ in D.   We observe that a linear system with constant coefficients $\mathbf{y}' = A\mathbf{y}$ is autonomous, as is any scalar differential equation in which the independent variable does not enter explicitly, for example $\theta'' + (g/L) \sin \theta = 0$, the pendulum equation derived in Section 1.2 (p. 10).

Autonomous systems have several important properties.   If $\boldsymbol{\phi}(t)$ is a solution of (6.49) existing for $-\infty < t < \infty$, then it is easily verified by direct substitution that for any constant a, $\boldsymbol{\phi}(t + a)$ is also a solution of (6.49).   We therefore say that **an autonomous system is invariant under translations of the independent variable.**   In particular, if $\boldsymbol{\phi}(t)$ is that solution for which $\boldsymbol{\phi}(\cap) = \boldsymbol{\eta}$, then $\boldsymbol{\phi}(t - t_0)$ is that solution of (6.49) satisfying the initial condition $\boldsymbol{\phi}(t_0) = \boldsymbol{\eta}$.   (For linear systems with constant coefficients this was established in equation (6.37), p. 279.)

Solutions of autonomous systems are conveniently represented by curves in n-space rather than $(n + 1)$-dimensional space.   The reason for this is that to every autonomous system such as (6.49) there corresponds a unique vector field $\mathbf{g}(\mathbf{y})$ at points of the domain D in Euclidean n-space and this vector field is independent of t.   Thus if we think of (6.49) as representing the equations of motion of a moving particle, then to each point $\mathbf{y}$ in D there corresponds the vector $\mathbf{g}(\mathbf{y})$ which is the velocity vector of the particle at $\mathbf{y}$, and this velocity vector does not depend on t. Let $\boldsymbol{\phi}(t, \boldsymbol{\eta})$ be that solution of (6.49) satisfying the initial condition $\boldsymbol{\phi}(t_0, \boldsymbol{\eta}) = \boldsymbol{\eta}$, where $\boldsymbol{\eta}$ is any point of D.   Then $\boldsymbol{\phi}$ represents the motion of the particle obeying the law (6.49) passing through the point $\boldsymbol{\eta}$ in D at time $t = t_0$, and we can completely characterize this motion by the curve C (see Figure 6.4) in the n-dimensional region D prescribed by the parametric equation $\mathbf{y} = \boldsymbol{\phi}(t, \boldsymbol{\eta})$, where the time t plays the role of a parameter.   We can assign a direction to the curve C corresponding to the direction of increasing t, indicated by an arrow in Figure 6.4.

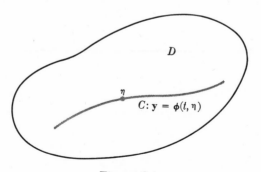

Figure 6.4

Example 1. In the special case of a dynamical system with one degree of freedom (mass–spring, pendulum, etc.) in which x is the displacement and the acceleration x'' is determined by a scalar equation of the form

$$x'' = F(x, x')$$

we write $y_1 = x$, $y_2 = x'$ and obtain the autonomous system

$$y_1' = y_2$$
$$y_2' = F(y_1, y_2)$$

Now, the solutions (motions) can be represented by curves in the (y_1, y_2) plane. This displacement-velocity plane is often referred to as the **Poincaré* phase plane.** More generally, if (6.49) represents the motion of a dynamical system with n degrees of freedom, its motion can be represented by curves in the **phase space** of $2n$ dimensions.

With reference to the above discussion and because (6.49) is invariant under translation of time, $\phi(t + t_0, \eta)$ is, for any constant t_0, also a solution (6.49). It may be interpreted as that solution (motion) which passes through the point η at time $t = 0$ (not at time t_0). This is not the same motion as that represented by the solution $\phi(t, \eta)$. The two solutions differ by the **phase** t_0. But the motions $\phi(t, \eta)$ and $\phi(t + t_0, \eta)$ are represented by the same curve C. In fact, for any constant a, the motion $\phi(t + a, \eta)$ is also represented by the curve C. The curve C is called an **orbit, trajectory,** or **path** of (6.49). From the above remarks we see that for a given orbit C there are infinitely many motions—in fact, a one parameter family of solutions—differing from one another by a phase.

Example 2. Consider the system $\mathbf{y}' = A\mathbf{y}$, where $A = \begin{pmatrix} -2 & 0 \\ 0 & -3 \end{pmatrix}$, $\mathbf{y} = \begin{pmatrix} y_1 \\ y_2 \end{pmatrix}$. Then in the above notation $\mathbf{g}(y) = A\mathbf{y}$; D is the whole (y_1, y_2) (phase) plane. A fundamental matrix is $\begin{pmatrix} e^{-2t} & 0 \\ 0 & e^{-3t} \end{pmatrix}$ and thus every solution is of the form $\phi(t, \eta) = \begin{pmatrix} e^{-2t}\eta_1 \\ e^{-3t}\eta_2 \end{pmatrix}$ for some constant vector $\eta = \begin{pmatrix} \eta_1 \\ \eta_2 \end{pmatrix}$. Here we have arbitrarily chosen $t_0 = 0$. Notice that

---

* The eminent French mathematician Henri Poincaré pioneered much of the research in the qualitative theory of differential equations.

$\phi(t - t_0, \eta)$ is that solution passing through the point η at $t = t_0$. Let $P = (\eta_1, \eta_2)$ be any point in the (y_1, y_2) plane. Then the solution $\phi(t, \eta)$ for $t > 0$ is represented by the parametric equations $y_1 = e^{-2t}\eta_1$, $y_2 = e^{-3t}\eta_2$ for $t > 0$ and this represents the portion of the curve shown in

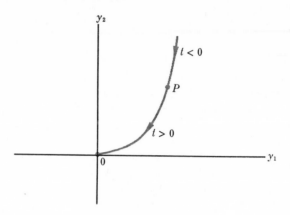

Figure 6.5

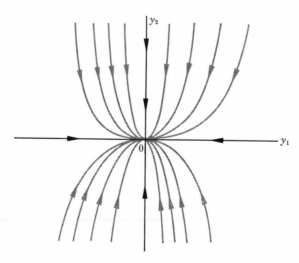

Figure 6.6

Figure 6.5 between P and the origin, as is verified by elementary calculus; the arrow indicates the direction of increasing t. Notice that the slope of the tangent to this curve, dy_2/dy_1, also tends to zero as $t \to +\infty$. Similarly, $t < 0$ represents the portion of the curve in Figure 6.5 above

the point P.   It should be noted that $\lim\limits_{t \to +\infty} \phi(t, \eta) = 0$, that is, both the
solution and also the orbit approach the origin as $t \to +\infty$.   Proceeding
in this way by choosing various points of the phase plane as initial points,
we obtain the so-called **phase portrait** of the system, shown in Figure 6.6.
Again, every orbit approaches the origin (as $t \to +\infty$).

• EXERCISES

1. Obtain the phase portrait of the system $\mathbf{y}' = A\mathbf{y}$, where $A = \begin{pmatrix} 2 & 0 \\ 0 & 3 \end{pmatrix}$.

2. Obtain the phase portrait of the system $\mathbf{y}' = A\mathbf{y}$, where $A = \begin{pmatrix} -2 & 1 \\ 0 & -2 \end{pmatrix}$.

3. Obtain the phase portrait of the system $\mathbf{y}' = A\mathbf{y}$, where $A = \begin{pmatrix} 2 & 0 \\ 0 & -3 \end{pmatrix}$.

4. Obtain the phase portrait for the scalar equation $x'' + 4x = 0$.   [*Hint:*
Use the system $y_1' = y_2$, $y_2' = -4y_1$.]

5. Write the simple pendulum equation $\theta'' + (g/L) \sin \theta = 0$ as the system

$$
\begin{aligned}
y_1' &= y_2 \\
y_2' &= -(g/L) \sin y_1
\end{aligned}
$$

where $y_1 = \theta$, $y_2 = \theta'$.   Assuming that $|y_1|$ is small, replace $\sin y_1$ by y_1 and
draw the resulting phase portrait.

We conclude this section with a complete discussion of the phase por-
traits of linear two-dimensional systems in general.   The motivation for
these considerations is the following: Suppose that in the case $n = 2$,
$\mathbf{g}(\mathbf{y})$ in (6.49) has the form

$$
\mathbf{g}(\mathbf{y}) = \begin{pmatrix} g_1(y_1, y_2) \\ g_2(y_1, y_2) \end{pmatrix}
$$

where

$$
\begin{aligned}
g_1(y_1, y_2) &= a_{11}y_1 + a_{12}y_2 + h_1(y_1, y_2) \\
g_2(y_1, y_2) &= a_{21}y_1 + a_{22}y_2 + h_2(y_1, y_2)
\end{aligned}
$$

where a_{11}, a_{12}, a_{21}, a_{22} are real constants with $a_{11}a_{22} - a_{12}a_{21} \neq 0$ and where
h_1, h_2 are real, continuously differentiable functions defined in some
domain D in the plane having the origin $y_1 = y_2 \neq 0$ in its interior and
h_1, h_2 are "small" when $|y_1|$, $|y_2|$ are small, for example, in the sense that
$\lim\limits_{y_1{}^2+y_2{}^2 \to 0} h_j(y_1, y_2)/(y_1{}^2 + y_2{}^2)^{1/2} = 0$ $(j = 1, 2)$.   This condition certainly
holds if, for example, h_1, h_2 are **analytic** at $y_1 = y_2 = 0$ and have their

Taylor expansions begin with quadratic terms.   Then (6.49) becomes

$$\mathbf{y}' = A\mathbf{y} + \mathbf{h}(\mathbf{y})$$ (6.50)

where

$$A = \begin{pmatrix} a_{11} & a_{12} \\ a_{21} & a_{22} \end{pmatrix} \quad \mathbf{y} = \begin{pmatrix} y_1 \\ y_2 \end{pmatrix} \quad \mathbf{h}(\mathbf{y}) = \begin{pmatrix} h_1(y_1, y_2) \\ h_2(y_1, y_2) \end{pmatrix}$$

and with det $A \neq 0$ and with $|\mathbf{h}(\mathbf{y})|$ small when $|\mathbf{y}|$ is small in some appropriate sense.   We shall call $\mathbf{h}(\mathbf{y})$ the perturbation term and (6.50) the perturbed system.   Many problems arising in applications have the form (6.50).

Example 3.   Consider the simple pendulum equation $\theta'' + (g/L) \sin \theta = 0$.   Then if $y_1 = \theta$, $y_2 = \theta'$,

$$y_1' = y_2$$

$$y_2' = -(g/L) \sin y_1 = -(g/L)y_1 + \frac{g}{L}\left(\frac{y_1{}^3}{3!} - \frac{y_1{}^5}{5!} + \cdots\right)$$

Thus here in the notation (6.50)

$$A = \begin{pmatrix} 0 & 1 \\ -g/L & 0 \end{pmatrix}, \; h_1(y_1, y_2) \equiv 0, \; h_2(y_1, y_2) = \frac{g}{L}\left(\frac{y_1{}^3}{3!} - \frac{y_1{}^5}{5!} + \cdots\right)$$

and the above hypotheses are satisfied.

Intuitively, we expect that if $|\mathbf{h}(\mathbf{y})|$ is small for small $|\mathbf{y}|$, then the behavior of solutions of (6.50) **near enough to the origin** would be similar to the behavior of the system in which the perturbations are zero. This latter system is linear with constant coefficients:

$$\mathbf{y}' = A\mathbf{y}$$ (6.51)

and thus easy to analyze.   It can be shown that this intuition is essentially, but not completely, correct.

Here we shall be content to analyze the general two-dimensional linear system with constant coefficients.   This, of course, includes the linearized form in Example 3 as a special case.

In order to carry out such a study it is convenient to introduce a concept which will help us to simplify the general problem.

Definition. *Two n-by-n matrices A and B are said to be similar, written A ∼ B, if and only if there exists a nonsingular n-by-n matrix T such that*

$$T^{-1}AT = B$$

Similar matrices have many important properties, of which we pick out only the following: If $A \sim B$, then A and B have the same characteristic polynomial, and therefore the same eigenvalues. (The converse is not necessarily true; matrices with the same eigenvalues may not be similar.) To prove the above statement, we observe that if $T^{-1}AT = B$, then

$$
\begin{aligned}
\det(\lambda E - B) &= \det(\lambda E - T^{-1}AT) \\
&= \det[T^{-1}(\lambda E - A)T] \\
&= \det T^{-1} \det(\lambda E - A) \det T \\
&= \det(\lambda E - A)
\end{aligned}
$$

• **EXERCISES**

6. Justify each step of the calculation in the above proof.

7. Show that the matrices

$$A = \begin{pmatrix} 0 & 0 \\ 0 & 0 \end{pmatrix} \qquad B = \begin{pmatrix} 0 & 1 \\ 0 & 0 \end{pmatrix}$$

have the same eigenvalues but are not similar. [*Hint:* Suppose they are similar, so that $T^{-1}AT = B$ for some nonsingular matrix T, and obtain a contradiction.]

8. Show that the matrices

$$A = \begin{pmatrix} 1 & 1 \\ 2 & 0 \end{pmatrix} \qquad B = \begin{pmatrix} 2 & 0 \\ 0 & -1 \end{pmatrix}$$

are similar. [*Hint:* Letting

$$T = \begin{pmatrix} t_{11} & t_{12} \\ t_{21} & t_{22} \end{pmatrix}$$

we have from the definition $T^{-1}AT = B$ that

$$\begin{pmatrix} 1 & 1 \\ 2 & 0 \end{pmatrix} T = T \begin{pmatrix} 2 & 0 \\ 0 & -1 \end{pmatrix}$$

Substitute for T, carry out the multiplication, and solve for the elements t_{11}, t_{12}, t_{21}, t_{22} of T. We get

$$T = \begin{pmatrix} 1 & 1 \\ 1 & -2 \end{pmatrix}$$

as our answer.]

[*Note:* Since A and B are similar, the eigenvalues of A are those of B, and since B is diagonal these are 2, -1. For an alternative way of computing T, see Appendix 4.]

For any linear system

$$\mathbf{y}' = A\mathbf{y} \tag{6.51}$$

with constant coefficients, we can attempt to simplify the coefficient matrix A by a transformation of coordinates. Let us make the change of variable $\mathbf{y} = T\mathbf{z}$, where T is a nonsingular constant matrix (to be determined), and substitute. We have

$$\mathbf{y}' = T\mathbf{z}' = AT\mathbf{z}$$

and therefore $\mathbf{z}$ satisfies the system

$$\mathbf{z}' = (T^{-1}AT)\mathbf{z} \tag{6.52}$$

We therefore see that **the original and transformed systems have coefficient matrices which are similar.** Our objective is to see whether the matrix T can be chosen in such a way that the transformed system takes a simpler form than the original system. One can in fact always do this, as shown in Appendix 4 for 2-by-2 matrices. In fact, if A is any n-by-n matrix with n linearly independent eigenvectors $\mathbf{v}_1, \ldots, \mathbf{v}_n$ (A need not have distinct eigenvalues), then A is similar to a diagonal matrix. This can be seen by choosing

$$T = (\mathbf{v}_1, \ldots, \mathbf{v}_n)$$

then, as can easily be verified, $T^{-1}AT = D$ where D is a diagonal matrix whose entries are the eigenvalues of A. Once the solution $\mathbf{z}$ of (6.52) is found, the corresponding solution of (6.51) is given by $T\mathbf{z}$.

Consider now the case of a general real two-dimensional system of the form (6.51) with $A = \begin{pmatrix} a_{11} & a_{12} \\ a_{21} & a_{22} \end{pmatrix}$. For simplicity, and because this is the case that arises in applications most frequently, we consider only the case $\det A = a_{11}a_{22} - a_{12}a_{21} \neq 0$. This means that zero is not an eigenvalue of A. As shown in Appendix 4, there is a **real** nonsingular matrix T such that $T^{-1}AT$ is equal to one of the following six matrices.

(i) $\begin{pmatrix} \lambda & 0 \\ 0 & \mu \end{pmatrix}$ where $\mu < \lambda < 0$
      or $0 < \mu < \lambda$

(ii) $\begin{pmatrix} \lambda & 0 \\ 0 & \lambda \end{pmatrix}$ where $\lambda > 0$
      or $\lambda < 0$

(iii) $\begin{pmatrix} \lambda & 0 \\ 0 & \mu \end{pmatrix}$ $\mu < 0 < \lambda$

(iv) $\begin{pmatrix} \lambda & 1 \\ 0 & \lambda \end{pmatrix}$ where $\lambda > 0$
      or $\lambda < 0$

(v) $\begin{pmatrix} \sigma & \nu \\ -\nu & \sigma \end{pmatrix}$ $\sigma, \nu \neq 0$
      $\sigma > 0$ or $\sigma < 0$

(vi) $\begin{pmatrix} 0 & \nu \\ -\nu & 0 \end{pmatrix}$ $\nu \neq 0$

The cases (v), (vi) correspond to complex conjugate eigenvalues of A, $\sigma \pm i\nu$ and $\pm i\nu$, respectively. In the remaining four cases the eigenvalues λ, μ are real. We obtain the possible phase portraits of (6.52) by assuming that $T^{-1}AT$ is one of the forms (i)–(vi). We emphasize that at this stage we in no way imply that these phase portraits of (6.52) also represent the phase portraits of the perturbed system (6.50), although such would be the hope, at least for $|\mathbf{y}|$ small. We also remark that the actual phase portraits of the linear system (6.51) differ from those constructed below for the system (6.52) by the fact that the nonsingular transformation matrix T distorts but does not change the character of these portraits.

Case (i). (This is essentially Example 2 and Exercise 1 above.) The solution of (6.52) through the point $(\eta_1, \eta_2) \neq (0, 0)$ at $t = 0$ is $\phi(t) = \begin{pmatrix} e^{\lambda t}\eta_1 \\ e^{\mu t}\eta_2 \end{pmatrix}$. If $\mu < \lambda < 0$ we have $\phi(t) \to 0$ as $t \to +\infty$ and we obtain the phase portrait in Figure 6.7 with every orbit tending to the origin as $t \to +\infty$. If $0 < \mu < \lambda$ we obtain the phase portrait in Figure 6.8 with every orbit tending away from the origin as $t \to \infty$.   Arrows indicate the direction of increasing t.   The origin in Figures 6.7 and 6.8 corresponding to Case (i) is called an **improper node**.

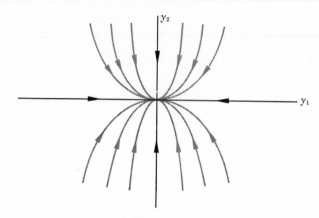

Figure 6.7

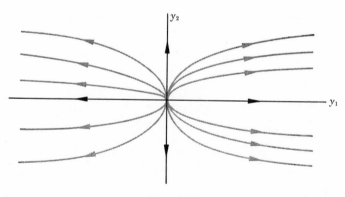

Figure 6.8

• **EXERCISE**

9. Justify the phase portrait for Case (i) $0 < \mu < \lambda$.

Case (ii).   Here the solution of (6.5) through $(\eta_1, \eta_2) \neq (0, 0)$ at $t = 0$ is $\phi(t) = \begin{pmatrix} e^{\lambda t}\eta_1 \\ e^{\mu t}\eta_2 \end{pmatrix}$ and if $\lambda > 0$ we obtain the phase portrait in Figure 6.9 whereas the case $\lambda < 0$ corresponds to Figure 6.10.   Note that all orbits are straight lines tending away from the origin if $\lambda > 0$ and toward the origin if $\lambda < 0$.

The ratio $\phi_2(t)/\phi_1(t)$ if $\eta_1 \neq 0$ is constant, as is $\phi_1(t)/\phi_2(t)$ if $\eta_1 = 0$.   The origin in Case (ii) is called a **proper node**.

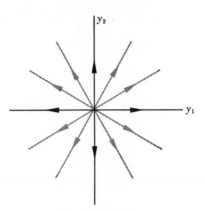

Figure 6.9

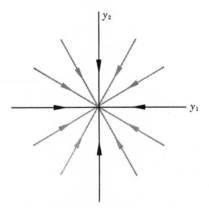

Figure 6.10

Case (iii).   Here $\phi(t) = \begin{pmatrix} e^{\lambda t}\eta_1 \\ e^{\mu t}\eta_2 \end{pmatrix}$, with $\mu < 0$ and $\lambda > 0$, is the solution through (η_1, η_2) at $t = 0$.   Now, as $t \to \infty$, $\phi_1(t) \to \pm \infty$ according as $\eta_1 > 0$ or $\eta_1 < 0$ and $\phi_2(t) \to 0$ as $t \to +\infty$.   It is easy to see that if $|\lambda| = |\mu|$ the orbits would be rectangular hyperbolas; for arbitrary $\lambda > 0$, $\mu < 0$ they resemble these curves as shown in Figure 6.11.   Quite naturally, the origin in Case (iii) is called a **saddle point**.

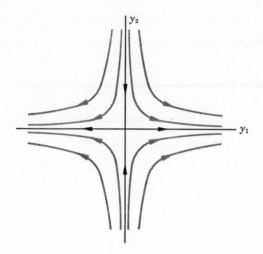

Figure 6.11

• **EXERCISE**

10. Construct the phase portrait in Case (iii) if $\lambda < 0$ and $\mu > 0$.

Case (iv). Here $\phi(t) = \begin{pmatrix} \eta_1 + \eta_2 t \\ \eta_2 \end{pmatrix} e^{\lambda t}$ is that solution passing through (η_1, η_2) at $t = 0$ and if $\lambda < 0$ the phase portrait is easily characterized by the fact that every orbit tends to the origin as $t \to +\infty$ and has the same limiting direction at $(0, 0)$. For, $dy_2/dy_1 = \phi_2'/\phi_1' = (\lambda\phi_2/\lambda\phi_1 + \phi_2) \to 0$ as $t \to +\infty$ (see Figure 6.12). The origin in Case (iv) is called (as in Case (i)) an **improper node.**

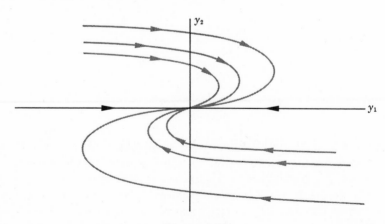

Figure 6.12

• **EXERCISE**

11. Construct the phase portrait in Case (iv) with $\lambda > 0$.

Case (v).   Here the solution, for the case $\sigma > 0$, passing through the point (η_1, η_2) at $t = 0$ is

$$\phi(t) = e^{\sigma t} \left(\begin{array}{c} \eta_1 \cos \nu t + \eta_2 \sin \nu t \\ -\eta_1 \sin \nu t + \eta_2 \cos \nu t \end{array} \right)$$

Let $\rho = (\eta_1{}^2 + \eta_2{}^2)^{1/2}$, $\cos \alpha = \eta_1/\rho$, $\sin \alpha = \eta_2/\rho$.   Then

$$\phi(t) = e^{\sigma t} \left(\begin{array}{c} \rho \cos (\nu t - \alpha) \\ -\rho \sin (\nu t - \alpha) \end{array} \right)$$

Letting r, θ be the polar coordinates, $y_1 = r \cos \theta$, $y_2 = r \sin \theta$, we may write the solution in polar form $r(t) = \rho e^{\sigma t}$, $\theta(t) = -(\nu t - \alpha)$.   Eliminating the parameter t we have $r = Ae^{(-\rho/\nu)\theta}$, where $A = \rho e^{(\sigma/\nu)\alpha}$.   Thus the phase portrait is a family of spirals as shown in Figure 6.13 for the

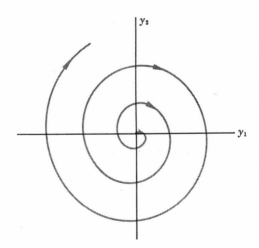

Figure 6.13

case $\sigma > 0$, $\nu > 0$ and the origin is called a **spiral point.**   In this case the orbits tend away from zero as $t \to +\infty$ (or, equivalently, approach zero as $t \to -\infty$).

• **EXERCISE**

12. Sketch the phase portrait for the Case (v) in case $\sigma < 0$, $\nu < 0$.

Case (vi). This is a special case of Case (v) with $\sigma = 0$. From the above formulas we see that the orbits are concentric circles of radius ρ oriented as shown for $\nu > 0$ in Figure 6.14. The origin is called a **center.**

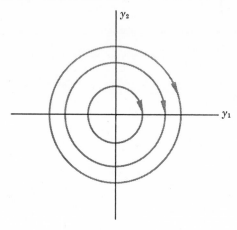

Figure 6.14

• **EXERCISE**

13. Sketch the phase portrait in Case (vi) when $\nu < 0$.

We observe from the possible cases considered above that all solutions of (6.52) and also their orbits tend to the origin as $t \to +\infty$ if and only if both eigenvalues of A have negative real parts; in this case we say that the origin is an **attractor** of the linear system (6.52). One of the results which can be established is that the origin remains an attractor when we add the perturbation terms. Notice that in case of a saddle point or center, the origin is not an attractor, and, as might be expected, these are the most difficult cases to treat when perturbation terms are added.

• **EXERCISES**

Sketch the phase portrait of each of the following scalar equations by converting to an equivalent system. Identify the origin and decide whether it is an attractor.

14. $x'' + x = 0$.

15. $x'' - 3x' + x = 0$.

16. $x'' + 3x' + x = 0$.

17. $x'' + 3x' - x = 0$.

18. $x'' - 3x' + 2x = 0$.

19. $x'' + 3x' + 2x = 0$.

20. $x'' - 2x' + x = 0$.

21. $x'' - x' - 6x = 0$.

•MISCELLANEOUS EXERCISES

1. Find a fundamental matrix for the system $\mathbf{y}' = A\mathbf{y}$, where A is the matrix.

(a) $A = \begin{pmatrix} 2 & 1 \\ 3 & 4 \end{pmatrix}$.

(b) $A = \begin{pmatrix} -1 & 8 \\ 1 & 1 \end{pmatrix}$.

(c) $A = \begin{pmatrix} 1 & 1 \\ 3 & -2 \end{pmatrix}$.

(d) $A = \begin{pmatrix} 2 & -3 \\ 1 & -2 \end{pmatrix}$.

(e) $A = \begin{pmatrix} 5 & 3 \\ -3 & -1 \end{pmatrix}$.

(f) $A = \begin{pmatrix} 1 & -1 & 1 \\ 1 & 1 & -1 \\ 2 & -1 & 0 \end{pmatrix}$.

(g) $A = \begin{pmatrix} -3 & 4 & -2 \\ 1 & 0 & 1 \\ 6 & -6 & 5 \end{pmatrix}$.

(h) $A = \begin{pmatrix} 2 & 1 & 0 \\ 1 & 3 & -1 \\ -1 & 2 & 3 \end{pmatrix}$.

(i) $A = \begin{pmatrix} 4 & -1 & -1 \\ 1 & 2 & -1 \\ 1 & -1 & 2 \end{pmatrix}$.

(j) $A = \begin{pmatrix} -1 & 1 & -2 \\ 4 & 1 & 0 \\ 2 & 1 & -1 \end{pmatrix}$.

(k) $A = \begin{pmatrix} 2 & 1 & 0 \\ 0 & 2 & 4 \\ 1 & 0 & -1 \end{pmatrix}$.

(l) $A = \begin{pmatrix} 2 & -1 & -1 \\ 2 & -1 & -2 \\ -1 & 1 & 2 \end{pmatrix}$.

(m) $A = \begin{pmatrix} 4 & -1 & 0 \\ 3 & 1 & -1 \\ 1 & 0 & 1 \end{pmatrix}$.

2. Sketch the phase portrait for each of the systems in Exercises 1(a), 1(b), 1(c), 1(d), 1(e), and determine in each case whether the origin is a node, saddle point, spiral point, or center. For which of these is the origin an attractor?

3. Find the general solution of the system $\mathbf{y}' = A\mathbf{y} + \mathbf{b}(t)$ in each of the following cases

(a) $A = \begin{pmatrix} 0 & 1 \\ 1 & 0 \end{pmatrix}$ $\quad \mathbf{b}(t) = \begin{pmatrix} 2e^t \\ t^2 \end{pmatrix}$.

(b) $A = \begin{pmatrix} -1 & 2 \\ -2 & 3 \end{pmatrix}$ $\quad \mathbf{b}(t) = \begin{pmatrix} 1 \\ 0 \end{pmatrix}$.

(c) $A = \begin{pmatrix} 4 & -3 \\ 2 & -1 \end{pmatrix}$ $\quad \mathbf{b}(t) = \begin{pmatrix} \sin t \\ -2\cos t \end{pmatrix}$.

(d) $A = \begin{pmatrix} 2 & 1 \\ 1 & 2 \end{pmatrix}$ $\quad \mathbf{b}(t) = \begin{pmatrix} 2e^t \\ -3e^{4t} \end{pmatrix}$.

(e) $A = \begin{pmatrix} 1 & -1 \\ 2 & -1 \end{pmatrix}$ $\quad \mathbf{b}(t) = \begin{pmatrix} 1/\cos t \\ 0 \end{pmatrix}$.

4. Suppose m is not an eigenvalue of the matrix A. Show that the non-homogeneous system

$$\mathbf{y}' = A\mathbf{y} + \mathbf{c}e^{mt}$$

has a solution of the form

$$\phi(t) = \mathbf{p}e^{mt}$$

and calculate the vector $\mathbf{p}$ in terms of A and $\mathbf{c}$.

5. Suppose m is not an eigenvalue of the matrix A. Show that the non-homogeneous system

$$\mathbf{y}' = A\mathbf{y} + \sum_{j=0}^{k} \mathbf{c}_j t^j e^{mt}$$

has a solution of the form

$$\phi(t) = \sum_{j=0}^{k} \mathbf{p}_j t^j e^{mt}$$

[*Hint:* Show that $\mathbf{p}_j$ satisfies the algebraic system

$$(A - mE)\mathbf{p}_k = -\mathbf{c}_k$$
$$(A - mE)\mathbf{p}_j = (j+1)\mathbf{p}_{j+1} - \mathbf{c}_j \qquad (j = 0, 1, \ldots, k-1)$$

and that these systems can be solved recursively.]

6. Consider the system

$$t\mathbf{y}' = A\mathbf{y}$$

where A is a constant matrix. Show that $|t|^A = e^{A \log |t|}$ is a fundamental matrix for $t \neq 0$ in two ways: (a) by direct substitution, (b) by making the change of variable $|t| = e^s$. (This system is the natural generalization of the Euler equation (3.21), p. 96.)

7. Find the general solution of the system

$$t\mathbf{y}' = A\mathbf{y} + \mathbf{b}(t)$$

8. Consider the system of differential equations

$$y_1'' - 3y_1' + 2y_1 + y_2' - y_2 = 0$$
$$y_1' - 2y_1 + y_2' + y_2 = 0$$

(a) Show that this system is equivalent to the system of first-order equations $\mathbf{u}' = A\mathbf{u}$, where

$$\mathbf{u} = \begin{pmatrix} u_1 \\ u_2 \\ u_3 \end{pmatrix} = \begin{pmatrix} y_1 \\ y_1' \\ y_2 \end{pmatrix} \qquad A = \begin{pmatrix} 0 & 1 & 0 \\ -4 & 4 & 2 \\ 2 & -1 & -1 \end{pmatrix}$$

(b) Find a fundamental matrix for the system in part (a).

(c) Find the general solution of the original system.

(d) Find the solution of the original system satisfying the initial conditions
$y_1(0) = 0$, $y_1'(0) = 1$, $y_2(0) = 0$.

9. Repeat the procedure of Exercise 8 for the system

$$y_1'' + y_2'' - y_2' + y_2 = 0$$
$$y_1' + y_1 + y_2'' + y_2' = 0$$

In part (d) find that solution satisfying the initial conditions $y_1(0) = 0$, $y_1'(0) = 1$, $y_2(0) = 0$, $y_2'(0) = 2$.

10. Consider the matrix differential equation

$$Y' = AY + YB$$

where A, B, and Y are $n \times n$ matrices.

(a) Show that the solution satisfying the initial condition $Y(0) = C$, where C is a given $n \times n$ matrix, is given by

$$Y(t) = e^{At}Ce^{Bt}$$

(b) Show that

$$Z = -\int_0^\infty e^{At}Ce^{Bt}\, dt$$

is the unique solution of the matrix equation

$$AX + XB = C$$

whenever the integral exists.

(c) Show that the integral for Z in part (b) exists if all eigenvalues of both A and B have negative real parts.

11. Let $Y(t)$ be the solution of the matrix differential equation

$$Y' = A(t)Y \qquad Y(0) = E$$

and let $Z(t)$ be the solution of the matrix differential equation

$$Z' = ZB(t) \qquad Z(0) = E$$

where $A(t)$ and $B(t)$ are continuous on an interval I containing the origin. Show that the solution of the matrix differential equation

$$X' = A(t)X + XB(t) \qquad X(0) = C$$

for any given constant matrix C, is $Y(t)CZ(t)$.

12. (a) Consider the electrical circuit shown in Figure 6.15, with currents and voltages (with polarities) as shown. Use Kirchoff's laws successively at the nodes A, B, C, and show that the circuit is governed by the system

$$\frac{5}{3} v_1'' = -i_1 + i_s$$

$$\frac{1}{6} v_2' = i_1 - v_2$$

$$\frac{3}{5} i_1' = v_1 - v_2$$

for the unknowns v_1, v_2, i_1; i_s is known.

(b) Find the general solution of the system derived in part (a).

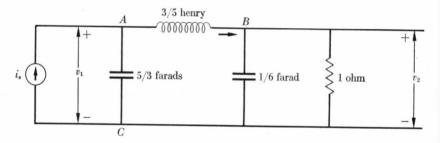

Figure 6.15

Remark: Consider the mechanical system shown in Figure 6.16, consisting of two masses m_1 and m_2 connected by a spring with spring constant k, sliding on frictionless supports. A force $F(t)$ is applied to m_2, and m_1 is connected to a rigid wall by a dashpot (resistance) with damping constant p. Let y_1 and y_2 denote the positions of m_1 and m_2 respectively, and define $v_1 = y_1'$, $v_2 = y_2'$, $z = y_2 - y_1$. Then the motion of the system is governed by the

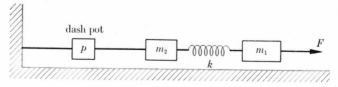

Figure 6.16

system of differential equations

$$m_1v_1' = kz + F(t)$$
$$z' = v_2 - v_1$$
$$m_2v_2' + pv_2 + kz = 0$$

which is equivalent to the circuit equations of part (a) if we make the identifications $F = i_s$, $-zk = i_1$, $m_1 = \frac{5}{3}$, $m_2 = \frac{1}{6}$, $p = 1$, $k = \frac{5}{3}$.

13. A weight of mass m is connected to a rigid wall by a spring with spring constant k. A second weight of mass m is connected to this weight by a second spring with spring constant k. A force F is applied to this second weight. The whole system slides on a frictionless table (see Figure 6.17).

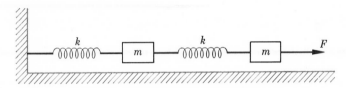

Figure 6.17

Let y denote the displacement of the first weight from equilibrium and let z denote the displacement of the second weight from equilibrium.

(a) Show that the motion of the system is governed by

$$my'' = -ky + k(z - y) = -2ky + kz$$
$$mz'' = -k(z - y) + F(t)$$

(b) Show that the solution of the homogeneous system, with $F(t) \equiv 0$, is a superposition of two simple harmonic motions with natural frequencies

$$\frac{1}{2\pi}\left(\frac{3 + \sqrt{5}}{2}\right)^{1/2}\left(\frac{k}{m}\right)^{1/2} \text{ and } \frac{1}{2\pi}\left(\frac{3 - \sqrt{5}}{2}\right)^{1/2}\left(\frac{k}{m}\right)^{1/2}$$

(c) Obtain an expression for the general solution of the nonhomogeneous system.

Chapter 7 ‖ EXISTENCE THEORY

7.1 Existence of Solutions

We have seen in Section 1.3 (p. 13) that if the mathematical model for some physical problem is an ordinary differential equation with initial conditions, the model should have the following properties in order to serve as a plausible representation of the physical problem:

(i) A solution satisfying the given initial conditions should exist.

(ii) Each set of initial conditions should lead to a unique solution.

(iii) The solution should depend continuously on the initial conditions.

In Section 1.8 (p. 22) we stated some theorems giving conditions under which these properties hold. We did this initially for first-order equations, then for second-order equations, and finally for equations of higher order. This chapter will be devoted to the proofs of these results. We will concentrate on the proof of Theorem 1.1 (p. 24), which deals with first-order equations. In Section 7.4, we will show how these results generalize to systems of first-order equations, and in particular to scalar equations of higher order.

We begin with the problem of proving the existence of a solution ϕ of the differential equation

$$y' = f(t, y) \tag{7.1}$$

satisfying the initial condition

$$\phi(t_0) = y_0 \tag{7.2}$$

on some interval containing t_0. This is called a **local problem,** since it is concerned only with existence of solutions near the initial point

(t_0, y_0).   To treat this problem we make certain hypotheses on f in some rectangle centered at (t_0, y_0).   This will mean that we can apply the local result of this section at every point in a region D in which f satisfies these hypotheses.

Suppose f is continuous in D and that (t_0, y_0) is an arbitrary point of D. The first step in our development is the observation that the initial value problem (7.1), (7.2) is **equivalent** to the problem of finding a **continuous** function $y(t)$, defined in some interval I containing t_0, such that $y(t)$ satisfies **the integral equation***

$$y(t) = y_0 + \int_{t_0}^{t} f(s, y(s)) \, ds \qquad (t \in I) \tag{7.3}$$

This equivalence is made precise as follows.

Lemma 7.1.   *If ϕ is a solution of the initial value problem (7.1), (7.2) on an interval I, then ϕ satisfies (7.3) on I.   Conversely, if $y(t)$ is a solution of (7.3) on some interval J containing t_0, then $y(t)$ satisfies (7.1) on J and also the initial condition (7.2).*

Proof.   If ϕ is a solution of (7.1) on I satisfying (7.2), we have

$$\phi'(t) = f(t, \phi(t)) \quad (t \in I)$$

and integrating from t_0 to any t on I we obtain

$$\phi(t) - \phi(t_0) = \int_{t_0}^{t} f(s, \phi(s)) \, ds$$

Imposing the initial condition (7.2) we see that ϕ satisfies (7.3).

Conversely, if $y(t)$ is a continuous solution of (7.3), then by the continuity of f, $y(t)$ is differentiable.   Thus by the fundamental theorem of calculus applied to (7.3) we have that $y(t)$ satisfies

$$y'(t) = f(t, y(t)) \qquad (t \in J)$$

and putting $t = t_0$ in (7.3) we have $y(t_0) = y_0$.   This completes the proof. ∎

Lemma 7.1 permits us to establish existence of a solution of (7.1), (7.2) by proving existence of a solution of (7.3).   This is important because integrals are in general easier to estimate than derivatives.

---

* Equation (7.3) is called an **integral equation** (of Volterra type) because the unknown function appears both under and outside the integral sign.

•EXERCISES

1. Determine the integral equation equivalent to the initial value problem

$$y' = t^2 + y^4 \qquad y(0) = 1$$

2. Prove that the initial value problem

$$y'' + g(t, y) = 0 \qquad y(0) = y_0 \qquad y'(0) = z_0 \tag{7.4}$$

where g is continuous in some region D containing $(0, y_0)$, is equivalent to the integral equation

$$y(t) = y_0 + z_0 t - \int_0^t (t - s) g(s, y(s))\, ds \tag{7.5}$$

[*Hint:* To show that if ϕ is a solution of (7.4) on I then ϕ satisfies (7.5) on I, integrate (7.4) twice and use the fact that

$$\int_0^t \left\{ \int_0^s g(\tau, \phi(\tau))\, d\tau \right\} ds = \int_0^t \left\{ \int_\tau^t ds \right\} g(\tau, \phi(\tau))\, d\tau$$
$$= \int_0^t (t - \tau) g(\tau, \phi(\tau))\, d\tau$$

To prove that a solution of (7.5) is a solution of (7.4) proceed as in the proof of Lemma 7.1.   But now you will need to use the formula

$$\frac{d}{dt} \int_0^t H(t, s)\, ds = H(t, t) + \int_0^t \frac{\partial H}{\partial t}(t, s)\, ds$$

easily proved by the chain rule, assuming only that H, $\partial H / \partial t$ are continuous on some rectangle containing $s = t = 0$.]

3. Construct an equivalent integral equation to the initial value problem

$$y'' + \mu^2 y = g(t, y) \qquad y(0) = y_0 \qquad y'(0) = z_0$$

assuming that g is continuous in a region D containing $(0, y_0)$ and where $\mu > 0$ is a constant.   [*Hint:* Assuming a solution ϕ of the differential equation on an interval I which satisfies the initial conditions, apply the variation of constants formula (Section 3.8, p. 105).   To prove the converse, proceed as in Exercise 2.   *Answer:*

$$y(t) = y_0 \cos \mu t + \frac{z_0}{\mu} \sin \mu t + \int_0^t \frac{\sin \mu (t - s)}{\mu} g(s, y(s))\, ds$$

4. Prove that if ϕ is a solution of the integral equation

$$y(t) = e^{it} + \alpha \int_t^\infty \sin (t - s) \frac{y(s)}{s^2} \, ds$$

(assuming the existence of the integral), then ϕ satisfies the differential equation $y'' + (1 + \alpha/t^2)y = 0$ (see equation (4.82), p. 187).

Returning to the main question of proving the existence of solutions of (7.3) (and thereby of (7.1), (7.2)), we outline a plausible method of attacking this problem. We start by using the constant function $\phi_0(t) = y_0$ as an approximation to a solution. We substitute this approximation into the right side of (7.3) and use the result

$$\phi_1(t) = y_0 + \int_{t_0}^t f(s, \phi_0(s)) \, ds$$

as a next approximation to a solution. Then we substitute this approximation $\phi_1(t)$ into the right side of (7.3) to obtain what we hope is a still better approximation $\phi_2(t)$, given by

$$\phi_2(t) = y_0 + \int_{t_0}^t f(s, \phi_1(s)) \, ds$$

and we continue the process. Our goal is to find a function ϕ with the property that when it is substituted in the right side of (7.3) the result is the same function ϕ. If we continue our approximation procedure, we may hope that the sequence of functions $\{\phi_k(t)\}$, called **successive approximations,** converges to a limit function which has this property. Under suitable hypotheses this is the case, and precisely this approach is used to prove the existence of a solution of the integral equation (7.3).

●**EXERCISE**

5. Construct the successive approximations to the solution ϕ of the differential equation $y' = -y$ which satisfies $\phi(0) = 2$. Do these successive approximations converge to a familiar function, and if so is this function a solution of the problem?

We will consider the problem (7.1), (7.2) first with f and $\partial f/\partial y$ continuous on a rectangle $R = \{(t, y) \mid |t - t_0| < a, |y - y_0| < b\}$ centered at (t_0, y_0). We assume that f and $\partial f/\partial y$ are bounded on R (if, as often happens in practice, the functions f and $\partial f/\partial y$ are continuous on $\bar{R}$, the closure of R defined by $\bar{R} = \{(t, y) \mid |t - t_0| \le a, \ |y - y_0| \le b\}$, then they are necessarily bounded on $\bar{R}$), that is, that there exist constants $M > 0$, $K > 0$ such that

$$|f(t, y)| \le M \qquad \left| \frac{\partial f}{\partial y}(t, y) \right| \le K \tag{7.6}$$

for all points (t, y) in R. If (t, y_1) and (t, y_2) are two points in R, then by the mean value theorem, there exists a number η between y_1 and y_2 such that

$$f(t, y_2) - f(t, y_1) = \frac{\partial f}{\partial y}(t, \eta)(y_2 - y_1)$$

Since the point (t, η) is also in R, $\left| \dfrac{\partial f}{\partial y}(t, \eta) \right| \le K$, and we obtain

$$|f(t, y_2) - f(t, y_1)| \le K|y_2 - y_1| \tag{7.7}$$

valid whenever (t, y_1) and (t, y_2) are in R.

Definition. *A function f which satisfies an inequality of the form* (7.7) *for all* (t, y_1), (t, y_2) *in a region D is said to satisfy a Lipschitz condition in D.*

The above argument shows that if f and $\partial f/\partial y$ are continuous on $\bar{R}$, then f satisfies a Lipschitz condition in R. It is possible for f to satisfy a Lipschitz condition in a region without having a continuous partial derivative with respect to y there, for example, $f(t, y) = t|y|$ defined in any region containing $(0, 0)$. In this chapter, we assume the continuity of $\partial f/\partial y$ for simplicity, but we could instead assume that f satisfies a Lipschitz condition without substantial changes in the proofs.

Example 1. If $f(t, y) = y^{1/3}$ in the rectangle $\bar{R} = \{(t, y) \mid |t| \le 1, \ |y| \le 2\}$, then f does not satisfy a Lipschitz condition in $\bar{R}$.

To establish this, we only need to produce a suitable pair of points for which (7.7) fails to hold with any constant K. Consider the points

$$(t, y_1), (t, 0), \text{ with } -1 \le t \le 1, y_1 > 0$$

Then

$$\frac{f(t, y_1) - f(t, 0)}{y_1 - 0} = \frac{y_1^{1/3}}{y_1} = y_1^{-2/3}$$

Now choosing $y_1 > 0$ sufficiently small, it is clear that $K = y_1^{-2/3}$ can be made larger than any preassigned constant. Therefore, (7.7) fails to hold for any K.

• **EXERCISES**

6. Compute a Lipschitz constant K as in (7.7) and then show that each of the following functions f satisfy the Lipschitz condition in the regions indicated.

(a) $f(t, y) = t^2 + y^4$, $\{(t, y) \mid |t| \leq 1, |y| \leq 3\}$.

(b) $f(t, y) = p(t) \cos y + q(t) \sin y$, $\{(t, y) \mid |t| \leq 100, |y| < \infty\}$, where p, q are continuous functions on $-100 \leq t \leq 100$.

(c) $f(t, y) = t \exp(-y^2)$, $\{(t, y) \mid |t| \leq 1, |y| < \infty\}$.

7. Show that $f(t, y) = t|y|$ satisfies a Lipschitz condition in the region $\{(t, y) \mid |t| \leq 1, |y| < \infty\}$.

We have already indicated that we will use an approximation procedure to establish the existence of solutions. Now, let us define the **successive approximations** in the general case by the equations

$$
\begin{aligned}
\phi_0(t) &= y_0 \\
\phi_{j+1}(t) &= y_0 + \int_{t_0}^t f(s, \phi_j(s)) \, ds \qquad (j = 0, 1, 2, \ldots)
\end{aligned}
\tag{7.8}
$$

Before we can do anything with these successive approximations, we must show that they are defined properly. This means that in order to define ϕ_{j+1} on some interval I, we must first know that the point $(s, \phi_j(s))$ remains in the rectangle R for every s in I.

Lemma 7.2. *Define α to be the smaller of the positive numbers a and b/M. Then the successive approximations ϕ_j given by (7.8) are defined on the interval I given by $|t - t_0| < \alpha$, and on this interval,*

$$
|\phi_j(t) - y_0| \leq M|t - t_0| < b \qquad (j = 0, 1, 2, \ldots)
\tag{7.9}
$$

Proof. The proof is by induction. It is obvious that $\phi_0(t)$ is defined on I and satisfies (7.9) with $j = 0$ on I. Now assume that for any $j = n \geq 1$, ϕ_n is defined and satisfies (7.9) on I (then, of course, the point $(t, \phi_n(t))$ remains in R for $t \in I$). Then by (7.8), ϕ_{n+1} is defined on I. To complete the proof we need to show that for $t \in I$, $\phi_{n+1}(t)$ remains in R, or analytically that ϕ_{n+1} satisfies (7.9) with $j = n + 1$. But from (7.8), the induction hypothesis, and (7.6) we have

$$|\phi_{n+1}(t) - y_0| = \left| \int_{t_0}^{t} f(s, \phi_n(s)) \, ds \right| \leq \left| \int_{t_0}^{t} |f(s, \phi_n(s))| \, ds \right|$$
$$\leq M|t - t_0| < M\alpha \leq b$$

This establishes the lemma. ∎

In order to explain the choice of α in Lemma 7.2, we observe that the condition $|f(t, y)| \leq M$ implies that a solution ϕ of (7.1), (7.2) cannot cross the lines of slope M and $-M$ through the initial point (t_0, y_0). The relation (7.9) established in the above lemma says that the successive approximations ϕ_j do not cross these lines either. The length of the interval I depends on where these lines meet the rectangle R. If they meet the vertical sides of the rectangle (Figure 7.1), then we define $\alpha = a$, while if they meet the top and bottom of the rectangle (Figure 7.2), then

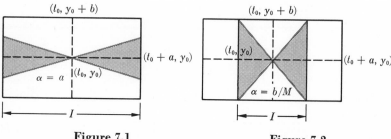

Figure 7.1   Figure 7.2

we define $\alpha = b/M$. In either case, all the successive approximations remain in the triangles indicated in the figures.

We can now state and prove the fundamental local existence theorem.

Theorem 7.1. *Suppose f and $\partial f/\partial y$ are continuous and bounded on the rectangle R and satisfy the bounds (7.6). Then the successive approximations ϕ_j, given by (7.8), converge (uniformly) on the interval $I: |t - t_0| < \alpha$, to a solution ϕ of the differential equation (7.1) which satisfies the initial conditions (7.2).*

Proof. Lemma 7.2 shows that the successive approximations ϕ_j are defined on the interval I. The next step is to estimate the difference between ϕ_j and ϕ_{j+1}. We work on the interval $t_0 \le t < t_0 + \alpha$ to the right of t_0, but the argument can easily be modified to give the result on the interval $t_0 - \alpha < t \le t_0$. We define

$$r_j(t) = |\phi_{j+1}(t) - \phi_j(t)| \qquad (j = 0, 1, 2, \ldots)$$

Then, using the definition (7.8) and the Lipschitz condition (7.7), we have

$$
\begin{aligned}
r_j(t) = |\phi_{j+1}(t) - \phi_j(t)| &= \left| \int_{t_0}^{t} [f(s, \phi_j(s)) - f(s, \phi_{j-1}(s))] \, ds \right| \\
&\le \int_{t_0}^{t} |f(s, \phi_j(s)) - f(s, \phi_{j-1}(s))| \, ds \\
&\le K \int_{t_0}^{t} |\phi_j(s) - \phi_{j-1}(s)| \, ds \\
&= K \int_{t_0}^{t} r_{j-1}(s) \, ds \qquad (j = 1, 2, \ldots) \qquad (7.10)
\end{aligned}
$$

The case $j = 0$ is slightly different. We have, from (7.6)

$$
\begin{aligned}
r_0(t) = |\phi_1(t) - \phi_0(t)| &= \left| \int_{t_0}^{t} f(s, \phi_0(s)) \, ds \right| \\
&\le \int_{t_0}^{t} |f(s, \phi_0(s))| \, ds \le M(t - t_0) \qquad (7.11)
\end{aligned}
$$

From (7.10) and (7.11) we will prove by induction that

$$r_j(t) \le \frac{MK^j(t - t_0)^{j+1}}{(j+1)!} \qquad (j = 0, 1, 2, \ldots; t_0 \le t < t_0 + \alpha) \qquad (7.12)$$

The case $j = 0$ of (7.12) is already established. Assume that (7.12) is true for $j = p - 1$ for some integer $p > 1$; then (7.10) gives, on using the induction hypothesis,

$$
\begin{aligned}
r_p(t) &\le K \int_{t_0}^{t} r_{p-1}(s) \, ds \le K \int_{t_0}^{t} r_{p-1}(s) \, ds \le K \int_{t_0}^{t} \frac{MK^{p-1}(s - t_0)^p}{p!} \, ds \\
&= \frac{MK^p(t - t_0)^{p+1}}{(p+1)!} \qquad (t_0 \le t < t_0 + \alpha)
\end{aligned}
$$

which is (7.12) for $j = p$. This proves (7.12).

•**EXERCISE**

8. Prove the analogue of the inequality (7.12) for the interval $t_0 - \alpha < t \le t_0$.

Combining (7.12) with the result of Exercise 8, we have

$$r_j(t) \le \frac{MK^j|t - t_0|^{j+1}}{(j+1)!} = \frac{M[K|t - t_0|]^{j+1}}{K(j+1)!} < \frac{M(K\alpha)^{j+1}}{K(j+1)!}$$

$$(j = 0, 1, 2, \ldots ; |t - t_0| < \alpha) \quad (7.13)$$

It follows from (7.13) that the series $\Sigma_{j=0}^{\infty} r_j(t)$ is dominated on the interval $|t - t_0| < \alpha$ by the series of positive constants $(M/K)\Sigma_{j=0}^{\infty}(K\alpha)^{j+1}/(j+1)!$, which converges to $(M/K)e^{K\alpha}$. By the comparison test (Section 4.2, p. 124), the series $\Sigma_{j=0}^{\infty} r_j(t)$ converges (in fact, uniformly) on $|t - t_0| < \alpha$. In view of the definition of the r_j, this implies the absolute (and uniform) convergence on $|t - t_0| < \alpha$ of the series $\Sigma_{j=0}^{\infty}[\phi_{j+1}(t) - \phi_j(t)]$.

Since $\phi_j(t) = \phi_0(t) + \Sigma_{m=0}^{j-1}[\phi_{m+1}(t) - \phi_m(t)]$, this also proves the convergence of the sequence $\{\phi_j(t)\}$ for every t in the interval I to some function of t, which we call $\phi(t)$. We will show that this function $\phi(t)$ is continuous and satisfies the integral equation (7.3) on I.

From the definition of $\phi(t)$,

$$\phi(t) = \phi_0(t) + \sum_{n=0}^{\infty} (\phi_{n+1}(t) - \phi_n(t))$$

therefore,

$$\phi(t) - \phi_j(t) = \sum_{n=j}^{\infty} (\phi_{n+1}(t) - \phi_n(t))$$

Now, from (7.13)

$$|\phi(t) - \phi_j(t)| \le \sum_{n=j}^{\infty} |\phi_{n+1}(t) - \phi_n(t)| \le \sum_{n=j}^{\infty} r_n(t)$$

$$\le \frac{M}{K} \sum_{n=j}^{\infty} \frac{(K\alpha)^{n+1}}{(n+1)!} \le \frac{M}{K} \frac{(K\alpha)^{j+1}}{(j+1)!} \sum_{n=0}^{\infty} \frac{(K\alpha)^n}{n!} \quad (7.14)$$

$$= \frac{M}{K} \frac{(K\alpha)^{j+1}}{(j+1)!} e^{K\alpha} \quad (t \in I)$$

It is an elementary exercise to see that

$$\epsilon_j = \frac{(K\alpha)^{j+1}}{(j+1)!} \to 0 \qquad \text{as } j \to \infty$$

To prove the continuity of $\phi(t)$ on I, let $\epsilon > 0$ be given. We have
$\phi(t+h) - \phi(t) = \phi(t+h) - \phi_j(t+h) + \phi_j(t+h) - \phi_j(t) + \phi_j(t) - \phi(t)$,
and thus

$$\begin{aligned} |\phi(t+h) - \phi(t)| &\leq |\phi(t+h) - \phi_j(t+h)| + |\phi_j(t+h) - \phi_j(t)| \\ &+ |\phi_j(t) - \phi(t)| \leq 2\epsilon_j + |\phi_j(t+h) - \phi_j(t)| \end{aligned}$$

by the above estimate. Choosing j sufficiently large and $|h|$ sufficiently small, and using $\lim_{j \to \infty} \epsilon_j = 0$ and the continuity of the $\phi_j(t)$, we can make

$$|\phi(t+h) - \phi(t)| < \epsilon$$

We now wish to show that the limit function $\phi(t)$ satisfies the integral equation (7.3). We will do this by letting $j \to \infty$ in the definition (7.8) of the successive approximations and by showing that

$$\lim_{j \to \infty} \int_{t_0}^{t} f(s, \phi_j(s)) \, ds = \int_{t_0}^{t} f(s, \phi(s)) \, ds \tag{7.15}$$

Once this is done the proof of the theorem is completed by applying Lemma 7.1 (p. 315). To prove (7.15), we have, using the Lipschitz condition (7.7) and the estimate (7.14),

$$\left| \int_{t_0}^{t} [f(s, \phi(s)) - f(s, \phi_j(s))] \, ds \right| \leq K \left| \int_{t_0}^{t} |\phi(s) - \phi_j(s)] \, ds \right|$$

$$\leq \epsilon_j \frac{M}{K} e^{K\alpha} \cdot K\alpha$$

and this approaches zero as $j \to \infty$ for every t on I. This establishes (7.15) and completes the proof. ∎

Incidentally, we have also established the following useful consequence in the course of the proof of (7.14).

Corollary.   *The error committed by stopping with the* jth *approximation* $\phi_j(t)$ *satisfies the estimate*

$$|\phi(t) - \phi_j(t)| \leq \frac{M}{K} \frac{(K\alpha)^{j+1}}{(j+1)!} e^{K\alpha}$$

for every t *on* I.

• EXERCISES

9.   Construct the successive approximations to the solution ϕ of the differential equation $y' = y$ which satisfies $\phi(0) = 1$.

10.   Construct the successive approximations to the solution ϕ of the problem in Exercise 9, but using $\phi_0(t) = \cos t$ instead of $\phi_0(t) = 1$.   Do these successive approximations converge, and, if so, what is their limit?

11.   Construct the successive approximations ϕ_0, ϕ_1, ϕ_2, ϕ_3 to the solution ϕ of the differential equation $y' = \cos y$ which satisfies $\phi(0) = 0$.

12.   Consider the integral equation

$$y(t) = y_0 + z_0 t + \int_0^t (t - s)g(s, y(s))\, ds \tag{7.4}$$

of Exercise 2 (p. 316), where $g(t, y)$, $(\partial g/\partial y)(t, y)$ are continuous on the rectangle $R\colon |t| \leq a, |y - y_0| \leq b$.   (Thus, they are automatically bounded on R.) Let $|g(t, y)| \leq M$, $|(\partial g/\partial y)(t, y)| \leq K$ for all $(t, y) \in R$.   Define

$$\phi_0(t) = y_0$$
$$\phi_n(t) = y_0 + y_0 t + \int_0^t (t - s)g(s, \phi_{n-1}(s))\, ds \qquad (n = 1, 2, \ldots)$$

Show that
(a) the ϕ_n are well defined for $|t| \leq \alpha$, where

$$\alpha = \min\left(a, \frac{b}{\tilde{M}}\right) \qquad \tilde{M} = |z_0| + M\frac{a}{2}$$

(b) Show that $\{\phi_n\}$ converges to a solution of the integral equation (7.4) on $|t| \leq \alpha$.

This together with Exercise 2 establishes the existence of solutions of the initial value problem $y'' + g(t, y) = 0$, $y(0) = y_0$, $y'(0) = z_0$.

13.   Consider the integral equation

$$y(t) = e^{it} + \alpha \int_t^\infty \sin(t - s)\frac{y(s)}{s^2}\, ds$$

of Exercise 4.   Define the successive approximations

$$\phi_0(t) = 0$$
$$\phi_n(t) = e^{it} + \alpha \int_t^\infty \sin{(t-s)}\frac{\phi_{n-1}(s)}{s^2}\,ds \qquad (1 \leq t < \infty)$$

(a) Show by induction that

$$|\phi_n(t) - \phi_{n-1}(t)| \leq \frac{|\alpha|^{n-1}}{(n-1)!t^{n-1}} \qquad (1 \leq t < \infty; n = 1, 2, \ldots)$$

Since $\phi_n(t) = \phi_0(t) + (\phi_1 - \phi_0) + \cdots + (\phi_n(t) - \phi_{n-1}(t))$ this shows that the ϕ_n are well defined for $1 \leq t < \infty$, and $\{\phi_n\}$ converge uniformly for $1 \leq t < \infty$ to a continuous limit function ϕ.

(b) Show that the limit function satisfies the integral equation.

(c) Using

$$|\phi_n(t)| \leq |\phi_1(t) - \phi_0(t)| + \cdots + |\phi_n(t) - \phi_{n-1}(t)|$$

and the above estimate for $|\phi_n(t) - \phi_{n-1}(t)|$, show that the limit function satisfies the estimate

$$|\phi(t)| \leq e^{|\alpha|} \qquad (1 \leq t < \infty)$$

This together with Exercise 4 (p. 317) supplies the missing steps which were assumed in the justification of the asymptotic series solution of the equation

$$y'' + \left(1 + \frac{\alpha}{t^2}\right)y = 0$$

in Section 4.11 (p. 187).

We have suggested in Section 1.8 (p. 26) that Theorem 7.1 is not the best possible result of its type.   Under the hypotheses of Theorem 7.1, we also have uniqueness of solutions of (7.1), (7.2), as we shall prove in the following section.   However, we may have existence of solutions without uniqueness.   In fact, the following result is true.

Theorem 7.2.   *Suppose f is continuous on the rectangle R, and suppose $|f(t, y)| \leq M$ for all points (t, y) in R.   Let α be the smaller of the positive numbers a and b/M.   Then there is a solution ϕ of the differential equation (7.1) which satisfies the initial condition (7.2) existing on the interval $|t - t_0| < \alpha$.*

We shall make no attempt to prove Theorem 7.2, as its proof is considerably more difficult than the proof of Theorem 7.1. It cannot be proved by the method of successive approximations, as the successive approximations may not converge under the hypotheses of Theorem 7.2. A proof may be found in [5], Chapter 1, Theorem 1.2. The hypotheses of Theorem 7.2 do not guarantee uniqueness, as is shown by the following example.

Example 2. We have previously (Section 1.8, p. 25) discussed the equation $y' = 3y^{2/3}$, with $f(t, y) = 3y^{2/3}$, $(\partial f/\partial y)(t, y) = 2y^{-1/3}$. Since $\partial f/\partial y$ is not continuous for $y = 0$, we cannot apply Theorem 7.1 to deduce the existence of a solution of $y' = f(t, y)$ through the point $(0, 0)$. By the method of Example 1 we see that f does not satisfy a Lipschitz condition either. Since f is continuous in the whole (t, y) plane, we can apply Theorem 7.2 to this problem. In fact, there is an infinite number of solutions through $(0, 0)$. For each constant $c \geq 0$, the function ϕ_c defined by

$$\phi_c(t) = \begin{cases} 0 & (-\infty < t \leq c) \\ (t - c)^3 & (c \leq t < \infty) \end{cases}$$

is a solution of $y' = 3y^{2/3}$ through $(0, 0)$. In addition, the identically zero function is a solution of this initial value problem.

•EXERCISES

14. Do the successive approximations for solutions ϕ of $y' = 3y^{2/3}$ with $\phi(0) = 0$ converge to a solution?

15. Do the successive approximations for solutions of the problem considered in Exercise 14, but using

$$\phi_0(t) = \begin{cases} 0 & (0 \leq t \leq 1) \\ t - 1 & (1 \leq t < \infty) \end{cases}$$

instead of $\phi_0(t) = 0$, converge to a solution?

If f and $\partial f/\partial y$ are continuous on a region D, not necessarily a rectangle, then given any point (t_0, y_0) in D we can construct a rectangle R lying entirely in D with center at (t_0, y_0). The hypotheses of Theorem 7.1 are then satisfied in R and Theorem 7.1 gives us the existence of a solution $\phi(t)$ of $y' = f(t, y)$ through the point (t_0, y_0) on some interval about t_0. In fact, this solution may exist on a larger interval than the one constructed in the proof of Theorem 7.1. It can be shown that the solution exists for all values of t for which the points $(t, \phi(t))$ lie in D. A proof of this result may be found in [5], Chapter 1, Theorem 4.1.

7.2 Uniqueness of Solutions

The second property which we wish a mathematical model for a physical problem to exhibit is uniqueness. Thus our next goal is to prove that under suitable hypotheses there is only one solution of the differential equation (7.1) which satisfies the initial condition (7.2). We have seen by examples that the assumption of continuity of f is not enough to guarantee uniqueness. On the other hand, we have stated that the hypotheses of Theorem 7.1 are enough to guarantee uniqueness. The main purpose of this section is to prove that assertion. The principal tool in the proof is the Gronwall inequality (Section 6.3, p. 252).*

Theorem 7.3. *Suppose f and $\partial f/\partial y$ are continuous and bounded on the rectangle R defined by the inequalities $|t - t_0| < a$, $|y - y_0| < b$. Then there exists at most one solution of (7.1) satisfying the initial condition (7.2).*

We recall that under the hypotheses of Theorem 7.3 we have already established the existence of at least one solution ϕ of (7.1), (7.2) existing on the interval $|t - t_0| < \alpha$, where α is defined in Theorem 7.1. We also recall that the hypotheses of Theorem 7.3 imply the inequality (7.7) (the Lipschitz condition).

Proof of Theorem 7.3. Suppose that ϕ_1 and ϕ_2 are two solutions of (7.1),(7.2) which both exist on some common interval J containing t_0. Since, by Lemma 7.1, every solution of (7.1), (7.2) also satisfies the integral equation (7.3), we have

$$\phi_1(t) = y_0 + \int_{t_0}^{t} f(s, \phi_1(s)) \, ds$$
$$\phi_2(t) = y_0 + \int_{t_0}^{t} f(s, \phi_2(s)) \, ds$$

for every t in J. Subtracting these two equations, we obtain

$$\phi_2(t) - \phi_1(t) = \int_{t_0}^{t} [f(s, \phi_2(s)) - f(s, \phi_1(s))] \, ds$$

---

* The proof of the Gronwall inequality in Chapter 6 is independent of the rest of that chapter.

Taking absolute values and using (7.7), we have

$$|\phi_2(t) - \phi_1(t)| \leq \left| \int_{t_0}^{t} |f(s, \phi_2(s)) - f(s, \phi_1(s))| \, ds \right|$$
$$\leq K \left| \int_{t_0}^{t} |\phi_2(s) - \phi_1(s)| \, ds \right| \qquad \text{(for } t \in J)$$

where $|(\partial f / \partial y)(t, y)| \leq K$ for all $(t, y) \in R$. Taking first the case $t \geq t_0$ and then $t \leq t_0$ the Gronwall inequality now implies for both cases that $|\phi_2(t) - \phi_1(t)| \leq 0$. Since $|\phi_2(t) - \phi_1(t)|$ is nonnegative, we have $|\phi_2(t) - \phi_1(t)| = 0$ for all t in J, or $\phi_2(t) = \phi_1(t)$ for t in J. Thus there cannot be two distinct solutions of (7.1), (7.2) on J, and this proves uniqueness. ∎

It is not necessary to assume as much as continuity of $\partial f / \partial y$ to ensure uniqueness. It is clear from the proof of Theorem 7.3 that the Lipschitz condition (7.7), which follows automatically from the continuity of $\partial f / \partial y$, could be used in the hypothesis of Theorem 7.3 instead of the continuity of $\partial f / \partial y$ without changing the proof. It is possible to prove uniqueness of solutions under considerably weaker hypotheses, but in most problems Theorem 7.3 is applicable and such more refined results are not needed.

• EXERCISE

1. State and prove a uniqueness theorem for solutions of the initial value problem

$$y'' + g(t, y) = 0 \qquad y(0) = y_0 \qquad y'(0) = z_0$$

where g is a given function defined on a rectangle R: $|t| \leq a$, $|y - y_0| \leq b$. Refer to Exercise 12, Section 7.1 (p. 324). [*Hint:* Under appropriate hypothesis if ϕ_1 and ϕ_2 are both solutions of the initial value problem existing on some interval $|t| \leq \alpha$, we have

$$\phi_k(t) = y_0 + z_0 t - \int_0^t (t - s) g(s, \phi_k(s)) \, ds \qquad (k = 1, 2)$$

for $|t| \leq \alpha$; subtract the two equations corresponding to $k = 1$ and $k = 2$, then use the Lipschitz condition (7.7), obtaining

$$|\phi_1(t)| - \phi_2(t)| \leq k \int_0^t (t - s)|\phi_1(s) - \phi_2(s)| \, ds \leq k\alpha \int_0^t |\phi_1(s) - \phi_2(s)| \, ds$$

and finally appeal to the Gronwall inequality.]

7.3 Dependence on Initial Conditions and Parameters

The third property that we desire of a mathematical model for a physical problem is that the solution should depend continuously on the initial conditions. A solution ϕ of the differential equation (7.1) passing through the point (t_0, y_0) depends not only on t, but also on the initial point (t_0, y_0). When we wish to emphasize this dependence, we may write the solution as $\phi(t, t_0, y_0)$. We will show that under suitable hypotheses ϕ depends continuously on the initial values, and in fact that ϕ is a continuous function of the triple (t, t_0, y_0). As in the previous sections of this chapter, we make no attempt to prove the most refined result of this type.

Theorem 7.4. *Suppose f and $\partial f / \partial y$ are continuous and bounded in a given region D. We assume that the bounds (7.6), (7.7) are satisfied on D (rather than on R). Let ϕ be the solution of the differential equation (7.1) passing through the point (t_0, y_0) and let ψ be the solution of (7.1) passing through the point $(\hat{t}_0, \hat{y}_0)$. Suppose that ϕ and ψ both exist on some interval $a < t < b$. Then to each $\epsilon > 0$ there corresponds $\delta > 0$ such that if $|t_0 - \hat{t}_0| < \delta$, and $|y_0 - \hat{y}_0| < \delta$, then*

$$|\phi(t) - \psi(t)| < \epsilon \qquad (a < t < b, a < \hat{t} < b) \tag{7.16}$$

Proof. Since ϕ is the solution of (7.1) through the point (t_0, y_0), we have for every t, $a < t < b$

$$\phi(t) = y_0 + \int_{t_0}^{t} f(s, \phi(s)) \, ds \tag{7.17}$$

Since ψ is the solution of (7.1) through the point $(\hat{t}_0, \hat{y}_0)$, we have for every $\hat{t}$, $a < \hat{t} < b$,

$$\psi(t) = \hat{y}_0 + \int_{\hat{t}_0}^{\hat{t}} f(s, \psi(s)) \, ds \tag{7.18}$$

Since

$$\int_{t_0}^{t} f(s, \phi(s)) \, ds = \int_{\hat{t}_0}^{t} f(s, \phi(s)) \, ds + \int_{t_0}^{\hat{t}_0} f(s, \phi(s)) \, ds$$

$$\int_{\hat{t}_0}^{\hat{t}} f(s, \psi(s)) \, ds = \int_{\hat{t}_0}^{t} f(s, \psi(s)) \, ds + \int_{t}^{\hat{t}} f(s, \psi(s)) \, ds$$

subtraction of (7.18) from (7.17) gives

$$\phi(t) - \psi(\hat{t}) = y_0 - \hat{y}_0 + \int_{\hat{t}_0}^{t} [f(s, \phi(s)) - f(s, \psi(s))] \, ds$$
$$+ \int_{t_0}^{\hat{t}_0} f(s, \phi(s)) \, ds - \int_{t}^{\hat{t}} f(s, \psi(s)) \, ds$$

and therefore

$$|\phi(t) - \psi(\hat{t})| \leq |y_0 - \hat{y}_0| + \left| \int_{\hat{t}_0}^{t} |f(s, \phi(s)) - f(s, \psi(s))| \, ds \right|$$
$$+ \left| \int_{t_0}^{\hat{t}_0} |f(s, \phi(s))| \, ds \right| + \left| \int_{t}^{\hat{t}} |f(s, \psi(s))| \, ds \right| \quad (7.19)$$

Using (7.6), (7.7) to estimate the right-hand side of (7.19), we obtain

$$|\phi(t) - \psi(\hat{t})| \leq |y_0 - \hat{y}_0| + K \left| \int_{\hat{t}_0}^{t} |\phi(s) - \psi(s)| \, ds \right|$$
$$+ M|\hat{t}_0 - t_0| + M|\hat{t} - t|$$

If $|t - \hat{t}| < \delta$, $|t_0 - \hat{t}_0| < \delta$, $|y_0 - \hat{y}_0| < \delta$, then we have

$$|\phi(t) - \psi(\hat{t})| \leq \delta + K \left| \int_{\hat{t}_0}^{t} |\phi(s) - \psi(s)| \, ds \right| + 2M\delta \quad (7.20)$$

The Gronwall inequality (Theorem 6.2, p. 252) applied to (7.20) gives

$$|\phi(t) - \psi(\hat{t})| \leq \delta(1 + 2M)e^{K|t - \hat{t}_0|} \leq \delta(1 + 2M)e^{K(b-a)}$$

using the fact that $|t - \hat{t}_0| < b - a$. Now, given $\epsilon > 0$, we need only choose $\delta < \epsilon e^{-K(b-a)}/(1 + 2M)$ to obtain (7.16) and thus complete the proof. ∎

Theorem 7.4 shows that the solution $\phi(t, t_0, y_0)$ of (7.1) passing through the point (t_0, y_0) is a continuous function of the triple (t, t_0, y_0). It is possible to show that if the initial point $(\hat{t}_0, \hat{y}_0)$ of ψ is sufficiently close to the graph of the solution ϕ, then there is a common interval on which both solutions ϕ and ψ exist.

We also remark that in practice the solutions ϕ and ψ are often known to remain in a closed bounded subset of D, so that the hypothesis that f and $\partial f/\partial y$ are bounded is automatically satisfied on this subset (which is all that is needed in the above proof), even though it may not hold on D.

Continuous dependence on initial conditions is true under considerably weaker hypotheses than those of Theorem 7.4.   In fact, it can be shown that uniqueness of solutions by itself implies the continuous dependence of solutions on initial conditions.   For a proof, see [5], Chapter 2, Theorem 4.1.

The technique used to prove Theorem 7.4 can be applied to establish the following result.

Theorem 7.5.   *Let f, g be defined in a domain D and satisfy the hypotheses of Theorem 7.4.   Let ϕ and ψ be solutions of $y' = f(t, y)$, $y' = g(t, y)$ respectively such that $\phi(t_0) = y_0$, $\psi(t_0) = \hat{y}_0$, existing on a common interval $a < t < b$.   Suppose*

$$|f(t, y) - g(t, y)| \leq \epsilon$$

for (t, y) in D.   Then the solutions ϕ, ψ satisfy the estimate

$$|\phi(t) - \psi(t)| \leq |y_0 - \hat{y}_0|e^{K|t-t_0|} + \epsilon(b - a)e^{K|t-t_0|}$$

for all t in $a < t < b$.

●**EXERCISE**

1. Prove Theorem 7.5.   [*Hint:* Write the integral equations satisfied by ϕ and ψ, and subtract to obtain

$$\phi(t) - \psi(t) = y_0 - \hat{y}_0 + \int_{t_0}^{t} \{f(s, \phi(s)) - f(s, \psi(s))\}\, ds$$
$$+ \int_{t_0}^{t} \{f(s, \psi(s)) - g(s, \psi(s))\}\, ds$$

Then take absolute values, and use (7.7), the hypotheses, and the Gronwall inequality to obtain the result.]

Theorem 7.5 says roughly that if two differential equations have their right-hand sides "close together," their solutions cannot differ by very much.   One immediate consequence of Theorem 7.5 is another proof of uniqueness (Theorem 7.3).   We simply take $g(t, y) = f(t, y)$, $y_0 = \hat{y}_0$. Then $\epsilon = 0$, and Theorem 7.5 gives $\phi(t) \equiv \psi(t)$.

Theorem 7.5 also gives a different type of continuity property.   Let $\{f_k(t, y)\}$ be a sequence of functions which converges to $f(t, y)$ in the sense that $|f(t, y) - f_k(t, y)| \leq \epsilon_k$ for all (t, y) in D, with $\epsilon_k \to 0$ as $k \to \infty$. Let $\{\hat{y}_k\}$ be a sequence of constants converging to y_0.

•EXERCISE

2. Let f and f_k satisfy the hypotheses of Theorem 7.5 and let $f_k \to f$ in the above sense. Let $\psi_k(t)$ be the solution of $y' = f_k(t, y)$ with $\psi_k(t_0) = \hat{y}_k$ ($k = 1, 2, \ldots$), existing on $a < t < b$, and let $\phi(t)$ be the solution of $y' = f(t, y)$ with $\phi(t_0) = y_0$, existing on $a < t < b$. Show that $\lim_{k \to \infty} \psi_k(t) = \phi(t)$ for $a < t < b$.

7.4   Existence Theory for Systems of First-Order Equations and Higher-Order Equations

We now wish to consider the extension of the results of Sections 7.1–7.3 to systems of first-order equations of the form

$$\mathbf{y}' = \mathbf{f}(t, \mathbf{y}) \tag{7.21}$$

where $\mathbf{y}$ and $\mathbf{f}$ are vectors with n components and where t is a scalar. Such systems were introduced in Chapter 6, and the reader is referred to Section 6.2 (pp. 243, 244) for the necessary background, basic definitions, and notation.   We are first of all concerned with the problem of existence and uniqueness of solutions of (7.21).   Such a result was stated as Theorem 6.1 (p. 251), but without proof.   Before proceeding, we remind the reader that because of the equivalence of single scalar differential equations of nth order and systems of first-order equations (established in Section 6.1), every result which is established for (7.21) has an immediate interpretation for an nth-order scalar equation, or for that matter a system of such equations of any order.

In what follows D will represent a region in $(n + 1)$ dimensions (recall that a region is a set in $(t, \mathbf{y})$ space with the property that given any point $(t_0, \boldsymbol{\eta})$ in D, the "box" $B = \{(t, \mathbf{y}) \mid |t - t_0| < a, \; |\mathbf{y} - \boldsymbol{\eta}| < b\}$ (where the second inequality uses the **norm** defined in Chapter 6, p. 245) lies in D, provided a and b are sufficiently small).   Let $\mathbf{f}$ be continuously differentiable with respect to t and the components of $\mathbf{y}$ at all points of D, which we denote by $\mathbf{f} \in C_1(D)$, and suppose that there exists a constant $K > 0$ such that the norms of $\partial \mathbf{f} / \partial y_j$ satisfy

$$\left| \frac{\partial \mathbf{f}}{\partial y_j} (t, \mathbf{y}) \right| \leq K \qquad (j = 1, \ldots, n) \tag{7.22}$$

for all $(t, \mathbf{y})$ in D.   As usually happens in practice, such an inequality is automatically satisfied if $\mathbf{f} \in C_1$, for example, on the closed "box"

$\bar{B} = \{(t, \mathbf{y}) \mid |t - t_0| \leq a, |\mathbf{y} - \boldsymbol{\eta}| \leq b\}$ for some fixed positive numbers a and b, or on any closed, bounded set in $(n + 1)$-dimensional space. It then follows that for any points $(t, \mathbf{y})$, $(t, \mathbf{z})$ in D we have the inequality

$$|\mathbf{f}(t, \mathbf{y}) - \mathbf{f}(t, \mathbf{z})| \leq K|\mathbf{y} - \mathbf{z}| \tag{7.23}$$

This may be seen by applying the mean value theorem to each variable separately and then using (7.22), or by the following, more elegant argument.   Define the function $\mathbf{G}$ by

$$\mathbf{G}(\sigma) = \mathbf{f}(t, \mathbf{z} + \sigma(\mathbf{y} - \mathbf{z})) \qquad (0 \leq \sigma \leq 1)$$

and consider $\mathbf{f}(t, \mathbf{y}) - \mathbf{f}(t, \mathbf{z})$.   We have

$$\mathbf{f}(t, \mathbf{y}) - \mathbf{f}(t, \mathbf{z}) = \mathbf{G}(1) - \mathbf{G}(0) = \int_0^1 \mathbf{G}'(\sigma)\, d\sigma$$

By the chain rule, letting $\mathbf{f}_{y_j} = \partial \mathbf{f} / \partial y_j$ $(j = 1, \ldots, n)$, we have

$$\mathbf{G}'(\sigma) = \mathbf{f}_{y_1}(t, \mathbf{z} + \sigma(\mathbf{y} - \mathbf{z}))(y_1 - z_1) + \mathbf{f}_{y_2}(t, \mathbf{z} + \sigma(\mathbf{y} - \mathbf{z}))(y_2 - z_2)$$
$$+ \cdots + \mathbf{f}_{y_n}(t, \mathbf{z} + \sigma(\mathbf{y} - \mathbf{z}))(y_n - z_n)$$

Using the bound (7.22), we find

$$|\mathbf{f}(t, \mathbf{y}) - \mathbf{f}(t, \mathbf{z})| \leq \int_0^1 |\mathbf{G}'(\sigma)|\, d\sigma \leq K\{|y_1 - z_1| + |y_2 - z_2| + \cdots$$
$$+ |y_n - z_n|\} = K|\mathbf{y} - \mathbf{z}|$$

which is (7.23).   A function $\mathbf{f}$ satisfying an inequality of the form (7.23) for any points $(t, \mathbf{y})$, $(t, \mathbf{z})$ in D is said to satisfy a **Lipschitz condition in D** with Lipschitz constant K.   A function $\mathbf{f}$ satisfying (7.23) need, of course, not be of the class C_1 and all the remarks made in the simple case of scalar functions apply here.

Just as we did earlier in this chapter for the scalar case, we prove Theorem 6.1 in a sequence of steps.   We begin with the problem of existence.

Theorem 7.6.   *Let $\mathbf{f}$ and $\partial \mathbf{f} / \partial y_j$ $(j = 1, \ldots, n)$ be continuous and bounded on the box $B = \{(t, \mathbf{y}) \mid |t - t_0| < a, |\mathbf{y} - \boldsymbol{\eta}| < b\}$, where a and b are positive numbers, and satisfying the bounds*

$$|\mathbf{f}(t, \mathbf{y})| \leq M \qquad \left| \frac{\partial \mathbf{f}(t, \mathbf{y})}{\partial y_j} \right| \leq K \qquad (j = 1, \ldots, n) \tag{7.24}$$

*for $(t, \mathbf{y})$ in B. Let α be the smaller of the numbers a and b/M and define
the successive approximations*

$$\phi_0(t) = \boldsymbol{\eta}$$

$$\phi_n(t) = \boldsymbol{\eta} + \int_{t_0}^{t} \mathbf{f}(s, \phi_{n-1}(s))\, ds \tag{7.25}$$

*Then the sequence $\{\phi_j\}$ of successive approximations converges (uniformly)
on the interval $|t - t_0| < \alpha$ to a solution $\phi(t)$ of (7.21) which satisfies the
initial condition $\phi(t_0) = \boldsymbol{\eta}$.*

We remark that if the hypothesis holds on the closed box $\bar{B} =
\{(t, \mathbf{y}) \mid |t - t_0| \leq a,\ |\mathbf{y} - \boldsymbol{\eta}| \leq b\}$, then (7.24) is automatically satisfied
and the conclusion holds on $|t - t_0| \leq \alpha$. The choice of α is suggested
by the same reasoning as in Theorem 7.1 (p. 320).

The proof is step by step and line by line the same as the proof of
Theorem 7.1 (p. 320), with the scalars f, ϕ, y_0 replaced by the vectors
$\mathbf{f}$, ϕ, $\boldsymbol{\eta}$, and in obvious places the absolute value is replaced by the norm.
We remind the reader that the first step is to establish the equivalence
of the initial value problem with the integral equation

$$\mathbf{y}(t) = \boldsymbol{\eta} + \int_{t_0}^{t} \mathbf{f}(s, \phi(s))\, ds \tag{7.26}$$

and then work with (7.26). This is the analogue of Lemma 7.1, p. 315.

•EXERCISES

1. Give a detailed proof of Theorem 7.6. (The reader is urged to carry out
this proof with care, in order to appreciate the usefulness of introducing
vectors.)

2. By writing the scalar equation $y^{(n)} = g(t, y, y', \ldots, y^{(n-1)})$ as a system
of n first-order equations (see Section 6.2, p. 242), apply Theorem 7.6 to deduce
an existence theorem for this scalar equation.

3. Given the system

$$y_1' = y_1{}^2 + y_2{}^2 + 1$$
$$y_2' = y_1{}^2 - y_2{}^2 - 1$$

Let $\mathbf{y} = \begin{pmatrix} y_1 \\ y_2 \end{pmatrix}$ and let B be the "box" $\{(t, \mathbf{y}) \mid |t| \leq 1,\ |\mathbf{y}| \leq 2\}$. Determine
the bounds M, K in (7.24) for $\mathbf{f}$ and $\partial \mathbf{f}/\partial y_j$ for this case. Determine α of
Theorem 7.6. Compute the first three successive approximations of the solu-
tion $\phi(t)$ satisfying the initial condition $\phi(0) = \mathbf{0}$, $\phi = \begin{pmatrix} \phi_1 \\ \phi_2 \end{pmatrix}$.

We remark that Theorem 7.2 also has an analogue which is easy to state. So far as uniqueness of solution of the system (7.21) is concerned we have the following analogue of Theorem 7.3.

Theorem 7.7. *Let the hypothesis of Theorem 7.6 be satisfied in the box B with center at (t_0, η). Then there exists at most one solution ϕ of (7.21) satisfying the initial condition $\phi(t_0) = \eta$.*

•EXERCISE

4. Prove Theorem 7.7. [*Hint:* Let ψ be another solution of the same initial value problem and suppose the solutions ϕ and ψ exist on some common interval J. Then ϕ and ψ both satisfy the integral equation (7.26). Using this and (7.23) show that

$$|\phi(t) - \psi(t)| \leq \left| K \int_{t_0}^{t} |\phi(s) - \psi(s)| ds \right| \qquad \text{for } t \text{ and } t_0 \text{ in } J$$

The conclusion now follows as in the scalar case (Theorem 7.3), by using the Gronwall inequality (p. 252).]

As far as continuous dependence of solutions of the system (7.21) on initial values and parameters is concerned, we have the following analogue for systems of Theorem 7.4 (p. 329).

Theorem 7.8. *Let $\mathbf{f}$ and $\partial f/\partial y_j$ $(j = 1, \ldots, n)$ be continuous in a region D and let the bounds (7.24) hold for (t, y) in D. Let ϕ be the solution of (7.21) which satisfies the initial condition $\phi(t_0) = \eta$, for any (t_0, η) in D. Let ψ be the solution of (7.21) which satisfies the initial condition $\psi(\hat{t}_0) = \hat{\eta}$, with $(\hat{t}_0, \hat{\eta})$ in D. Suppose that ϕ and ψ both exist on $a < t < b$. Then for every $\epsilon > 0$ there exists $\delta > 0$ such that if $|t - \hat{t}| < \delta$, $|t_0 - \hat{t}_0| < \delta$, and $|\eta - \hat{\eta}| < \delta$, then $|\phi(t) - \psi(\hat{t})| < \epsilon$, for $a < t, \hat{t} < b$.*

It is possible to show that if the solution ϕ exists on an interval I and if the initial point $(\hat{t}_0, \hat{\eta})$ of the solution ψ lies close enough to the graph of ϕ (that is, if $|\phi(\hat{t}_0) - \hat{\eta}|$ is sufficiently small), then the solution ψ also exists on I.

We remark that in practice the solutions ϕ, ψ often remain in a closed bounded subset S of D, in which case $\mathbf{f}$ and $\partial f/\partial y_j$ $(j = 1, \ldots, n)$ are automatically bounded on S (which is all that is needed in the proof), although they may not be bounded on the whole set D.

- **EXERCISES**

    5. Prove Theorem 7.8.

    6. State and prove the analogue of Theorem 7.5 (p. 331) for systems.

- **MISCELLANEOUS EXERCISES**

    1. Consider the differential equation $y' = y$, with the solution $\phi(t) = e^t$ satisfying the initial condition $\phi(0) = 1$. Let $p(t)$ be **any** polynomial in t and define

$$\phi_0(t) = p(t)$$
$$\phi_k(t) = 1 + \int_0^t \phi_{k-1}(s)\, ds \qquad (k = 1, 2, \ldots)$$

    (a) Is $\lim_{k \to \infty} \phi_k(t) = \phi(t)$? Prove your answer.

    (b) What general statement can you make concerning the initial "guess" $\phi_0(t)$ and the convergence of the successive approximations? What happens if the "1" in the definition of $\phi_k(t)$ for $k \geq 1$ is replaced by some other function, say $p(t)$?

    2. Consider the differential equation

$$y' = f(t, y)$$

where f and $\partial f / \partial y$ are continuous in a region D in the (t, y) plane, and let (t_0, y_0) be a point in D. Let G be a **bounded** subregion of D containing (t_0, y_0) and let $\bar{G}$ be the closure of G. Define

$$M = \max_{\bar{G}} |f(t, y)|$$

Through (t_0, y_0) construct the lines AB and CD of slope M and $-M$ respectively, as shown in Figure 7.3. Now, construct vertical lines HI, JK intersecting the t axis at α and β respectively, so that the isosceles triangles HOI, JOK are contained in G. Let $\phi_0(t)$ be any continuous function defined on $\alpha \leq t \leq \beta$ such that the set of points $\{(t, \phi_0(t)) \mid \alpha \leq t \leq \beta\}$ is contained in $\bar{G}$. Define

$$\phi_1(t) = y_0 + \int_{t_0}^t f(s, \phi_0(s))\, ds \qquad (\alpha \leq t \leq \beta)$$

and generally

$$\phi_k(t) = y_0 + \int_{t_0}^t f(s, \phi_{k-1}(s))\, ds \qquad (k = 1, 2, \ldots ; \alpha \leq t \leq \beta)$$

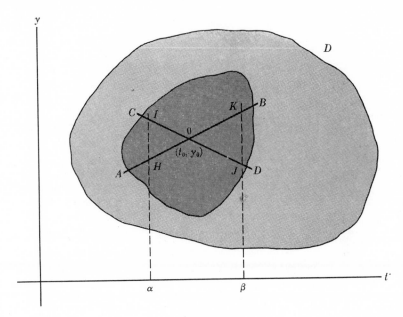

Figure 7.3

Prove that the successive approximations $\{\phi_k(t)\}$ converge (uniformly) to the (unique) solution $\phi(t)$ of $y' = f(t, y)$ with $\phi(t_0) = y_0$ on $\alpha \leq t \leq \beta$, and estimate the error $|\phi(t) - \phi_m(t)|$ on $\alpha \leq t \leq \beta$ in terms of

$$K_1 = \max_{\alpha \leq t \leq \beta} \{|\phi_0(t) + \phi_1(t)|\} \text{ for } m = 0$$

$$K_2 = \max_{\tilde{G}} \left| \frac{\partial f}{\partial y} (t, y) \right| \text{ for } m \geq 1$$

[*Hint:* Follow the proof of Theorem 7.1.]

(*Remark:* The same result holds if f satisfies a Lipschitz condition.)

3.   In the notation of Exercise 2, suppose that a function $\phi_0(t)$ has been found satisfying the hypotheses of Exercise 2, and also constants $k > 0$, $\delta \geq 0$ are known such that

$$|\phi_1(t) - \phi_0(t)| \leq K|t - t_0|^\delta \qquad (\alpha \leq t \leq \beta)$$

Show that

$$|\phi(t) - \phi_1(t)| \leq K|t - t_0|^{\delta+1} \left[\frac{K_2}{\delta + 1} + \frac{K_2{}^2}{(\delta + 1)(\delta + 2)} + \cdots \right]$$

$$(\alpha \leq t \leq \beta)$$

where K_2 is as in Exercise 2.   Can you generalize this result? [*Hint:* Assume an estimate for $|\phi_m(t) - \phi_{m-1}(t)|$ on $\alpha \leq t \leq \beta$ and compute an estimate for $|\phi(t) - \phi_m(t)|$ on $\alpha \leq t \leq \beta$.]

4.   Let $\phi(t)$ be the solution of $y' = t^2 + y^2$ on $0 \leq t \leq 1$, with $\phi(0) = 0$. Show that

$$\left| \phi(t) - \left(\frac{1}{3} t^3 + \frac{1}{63} t^7 \right) \right| \leq 0.0015 t^8 \qquad (0 \leq t \leq 1)$$

[*Hint:* In the notation of Exercise 3, let $\phi_0(t) = t^3/3$, and compute $\phi_1(t)$ and $|\phi_1(t) - \phi_0(t)|$.   Then apply the result of Exercise 3 to the differential equation $y' = t^2 + y^2$ on the closed rectangle $\{(t, y) \mid 0 \leq t \leq 1, |y| \leq A\}$ for some suitably chosen $A > 0$.   Such a choice is $A = 0.345$, and this gives $K_2 = 0.690$.]

5.   Prove the **Osgood uniqueness theorem:** Suppose that the function $f(t, y)$ satisfies the condition

$$|f(t, y_2) - f(t, y_1)| \leq h(|y_2 - y_1|)$$

for every pair of points (t, y_1), (t, y_2) in a region D.   Suppose that the function $h(u)$ is continuous for $0 < u \leq \alpha$ for some $\alpha > 0$, that $h(u) > 0$, and that

$$\lim_{\epsilon \to 0^+} \int_\epsilon^\alpha \frac{du}{h(u)} = \infty$$

Then through each point (t_0, y_0) in D there is at most one solution of the equation $y' = f(t, y)$.   [*Hint:* Suppose ϕ_1 and ϕ_2 are two solutions with $\phi_1(t_0) = \phi_2(t_0) = y_0$.   Define $\psi(t) = \phi_2(t) - \phi_1(t)$ and suppose $\psi(t) \not\equiv 0$. Then show that $|\psi'(t)| \leq h(|\psi(t)|) < 2h(|\psi(t)|)$.   Suppose $\psi(t_1) \neq 0$, for some $t_1 > t_0$ and let $u(t)$ be the solution of $u' = 2h(u)$ satisfying the initial condition $u(t_1) = |\psi(t_1)|$.   By Exercise 7 (p. 58) $u(t)$ is strictly positive for $t_0 \leq t \leq t_1$.   Show that $\psi'(t_1) < u'(t_1)$ and therefore $\psi(t) > u(t)$ on some interval to the left of t_1.   Then show that $\psi(t) > u(t)$ for $t_0 \leq t \leq t_1$ and obtain a contradiction.]

6.   Show that the functions $h(u) = Ku^\alpha$ $(\alpha \geq 1)$, $h(u) = Ku \log |u|$, $h(u) = Ku \log |u| \log |\log |u||$, and so on, satisfy the Osgood condition of 5 Exercise above.   (The case $h(u) = Ku$ is, of course, the Lipschitz condition.)

7.   Let $f(t, y)$ and $g(t, y)$ be continuous and satisfy a Lipschitz condition with respect to y in a region D.   Suppose $|f(t, y) - g(t, y)| < \epsilon$ in D for some $\epsilon > 0$.   Let $\phi_1(t)$ be a solution of $y' = f(t, y)$ and let $\phi_2(t)$ be a solution of $y' = g(t, y)$ such that $|\phi_2(t_0) - \phi_1(t_0)| < \delta$ for some t_0 and some $\delta > 0$.   Show that for all t for which $\phi_1(t)$ and $\phi_2(t)$ both exist,

$$|\phi_2(t) - \phi_1(t)| \leq \delta e^{K|t-t_0|} + \frac{\epsilon}{K} (e^{K|t-t_0|} - 1)$$

where K is the Lipschitz constant. [*Hint:* Show that $|\phi_2(t) - \phi_1(t)| \leq \delta + \int_{t_0}^{t} [K|\phi_2(s) - \phi_1(s)| + \epsilon]\, ds$ and complete the argument by a slight generalization of the Gronwall inequality.] Compare this result with Theorem 7.4 (p. 329), where a slightly weaker estimate is used.

8. Obtain the analogues of Exercises 2, 5, and 7 for systems of the form $\mathbf{y}' = \mathbf{f}(t, \mathbf{y})$, where $\mathbf{f}$ and $\mathbf{y}$ are vectors and where $\mathbf{f}$ satisfies suitable hypotheses.

9. Let $q(t)$ be a differentiable function on $0 \leq t \leq \pi$. Show that the differential equation

$$-y'' + q(t)y = \lambda y$$

has a solution $\phi_1(t, \lambda)$ on $0 \leq t \leq \pi$ such that

$$\phi_1(t, \lambda) = \frac{\sin \sqrt{\lambda}\, t}{\sqrt{\lambda}} + M_1$$

$$\phi_1'(t, \lambda) = \cos \sqrt{\lambda}\, t + M_2$$

where $|M_1| \leq K/\lambda$, $|M_2| \leq K/\sqrt{\lambda}$ on $0 \leq t \leq \pi$ for some constant K. [*Hint:* Consider the integral equation

$$\phi(t, \lambda) = \frac{\sin \sqrt{\lambda}\, t}{\sqrt{\lambda}} + \frac{1}{\sqrt{\lambda}} \int_0^t \sin \sqrt{\lambda}\, (t - s) q(s) \phi(s, \lambda)\, ds$$

and use successive approximations as in Exercise 13, Section 7.1 (p. 324) to prove the existence of a bounded solution $\phi_1(t, \lambda)$. Then estimate $M_1 = (1/\sqrt{\lambda}) \int_0^t \sin \sqrt{\lambda}\, (t - s) q(s) \phi_1(s, \lambda)\, ds$. Differentiate the integral equation to obtain the desired estimate for $\phi_1'(t, \lambda)$.]

10. Show that the differential equation considered in Exercise 9 has a solution $\phi_2(t, \lambda)$ on $0 \leq t \leq \pi$ such that

$$\phi_2(t, \lambda) = \cos \sqrt{\lambda}\, t + M_3$$

$$\phi_2'(t, \lambda) = -\sqrt{\lambda} \sin \sqrt{\lambda}\, t + \frac{1}{2} \cos \sqrt{\lambda}\, t \int_0^t q(s)\, ds + M_4$$

where $|M_3| \leq K/\sqrt{\lambda}$, $|M_4| \leq K/\sqrt{\lambda}$ on $0 \leq t \leq \pi$ for some constant K. [*Hint:* Proceed as in Exercise 9, using an appropriate integral equation.]

Remark: Exercises 9 and 10 above coupled with the Liouville transformation (Exercise 5, p. 234) are the starting points for the study of the asymptotic behavior of eigenvalues and eigenfunctions of general Sturm-Liouville boundary value problems; see for example [19], pp. 110–114.

Chapter 8

NUMERICAL METHODS OF SOLUTION

In many problems the only effective method for obtaining information about the solution of a differential equation is to use a numerical approximation procedure. We have studied one such procedure in Section 2.5 (p. 53), the **Euler method.** In this chapter we shall complete the study of the Euler method and discuss some other methods which are better suited to high-speed computation. As we can only give a brief introduction to this extensive subject, we refer the reader to other books, for example [8], [10], [13], [15], for a more complete discussion of many ideas.

8.1 The Euler Method

Let us begin by recalling the idea behind the Euler method. For simplicity, we confine ourselves here to problems involving a single first-order differential equation. In Section 8.6 we shall indicate how the methods of this chapter can be adapted to systems of differential equations and to differential equations of higher order.

We wish to find an approximation to the value of the solution ϕ at $t = t_0 + T$ of the differential equations

$$y' = f(t, y) \tag{8.1}$$

which satisfies the initial condition

$$\phi(t_0) = y_0 \tag{8.2}$$

Here (t_0, y_0) is a given initial point, T is a given positive number, and we assume for simplicity that $f(t, y)$ is continuous and has continuous first-order partial derivatives with respect to t and y for $t_0 \leq t \leq t_0 + T$ and all y. First, we observe that for $t_0 \leq t \leq t_0 + T$ the solution ϕ of (8.1), (8.2) satisfies the integral equation

$$\phi(t) = y_0 + \int_{t_0}^{t} f(s, \phi(s)) \, ds \tag{8.3}$$

(Lemma 7.1, p. 315).

It is an easy consequence of (8.3) that if t, τ are any two values in the interval $[t_0, t_0 + T]$, then

$$\begin{aligned}
\phi(t) &= y_0 + \int_{t_0}^{t} f(s, \phi(s)) \, ds \\
&= y_0 + \int_{t_0}^{\tau} f(s, \phi(s)) \, ds + \int_{\tau}^{t} f(s, \phi(s)) \, ds \\
&= \phi(\tau) + \int_{\tau}^{t} f(s, \phi(s)) \, ds
\end{aligned} \tag{8.4}$$

The next step is to divide the interval $[t_0, t_0 + T]$ into N subintervals by specifying intermediate points $t_0 < t_1 < t_2 < \cdots < t_N = t_0 + T$. In practice, these intermediate points are usually equally spaced, with spacing $h = T/N$. In fact, the question of the best choice of unequal spacing is a major unsolved practical problem. Now, because of (8.4), if we know $\phi(t_k)$ $(k = 1, \ldots, N)$, then $\phi(t_{k+1})$ is given (exactly) by

$$\phi(t_{k+1}) = \phi(t_k) + \int_{t_k}^{t_{k+1}} f(s. \phi(s)) \, ds \tag{8.5}$$

In the Euler method, we approximate the integral in (8.5) (see Figure 8.1) by the product of the length of the interval of integration and the value of

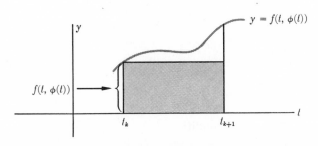

Figure 8.1

the integrand at the left-hand end point of the interval, that is, by $(t_{k+1} - t_k)f(t_k, \phi(t_k))$. In addition, since we do not know the exact value of $\phi(t_k)$, **we replace $\phi(t_k)$ by the approximation y_k obtained at the previous stage by considering the interval** (t_{k-1}, t_k). This yields an approximation y_{k+1} for $\phi(t_{k+1})$, given by

$$y_{k+1} = y_k + (t_{k+1} - t_k)f(t_k, y_k) \tag{8.6}$$

Since we are given the initial value $y_0 = \phi(t_0)$, we can use the formula (8.6) to calculate $y_1, y_2, \ldots, y_N$ in turn, and y_N is the desired approximation to $\phi(t_N) = \phi(t_0 + T)$. If we use equal subdivisions of the interval $[t_0, t_0 + T]$, so that $t_{k+1} - t_k = h = T/N$, then the formula (8.6) becomes

$$y_{k+1} = y_k + hf(t_k, y_k) \tag{8.7}$$

This is an example of a difference equation. The Euler method consists of using the difference equation (8.7) as an approximation to the differential equation (8.1).

In Section 2.5, we indicated that an approximation method, such as the Euler method, is subject to errors of two quite different kinds. One is the round-off error, caused by the fact that the values actually calculated are rounded off to a certain number of decimal places or to a certain number of significant figures, and are thus really approximations to the values given by the approximation method. The errors so introduced may accumulate as we proceed from one stage to the next. The analysis of round-off errors, being largely statistical in nature, is quite difficult. We shall not discuss it further at the moment, except to suggest that an approximation method, in order to be useful, ought to have the property that a smaller round-off error at each stage produces a smaller cumulative round-off error. Since we can reduce the round-off error at each stage by keeping more decimal places in the calculations, this property would give some control over the cumulative round-off error. It will turn out that we can check rather easily whether this property, called **stability of the numerical method,** holds for any given numerical method or not.

The other type of error is the truncation error, caused by the approximation in the method itself. For the Euler method, this arises in the use of $(t_{k+1} - t_k)f(t_k, \phi(t_k))$ as an approximation to the integral $\int_{t_k}^{t_{k+1}} f(s, \phi(s))\, ds$. We discussed the truncation error of the Euler method to some extent in Section 2.5 (p. 54). There we defined the local truncation error to be the error introduced in going from the value y_k at t_k to the value y_{k+1} at t_{k+1}, assuming the value y_k to be exact rather than an approximation. We also showed that the local truncation error of the Euler method (8.7) is no greater than $\frac{1}{2}Mh^2$. The constant M can be obtained from bounds for the function f and its first-order partial derivatives in the region under consideration.

In Section 2.5, we also indicated, without proof, that the **cumulative truncation error** of the Euler method is no greater than a constant multiplied by h. **The cumulative truncation error is defined to be the actual deviation of the approximation y_N from the true value** $\phi(t_0 + T) = \phi(t_N)$. (This tacitly assumes that all numbers can be computed without round-off error.) Let us now estimate this quantity. **We define**

$$E_k = |\phi(t_k) - y_k| \qquad (k = 1, \ldots, N)$$

the cumulative truncation error at the kth stage.

Theorem 8.1.   *If f is continuous and has continuous first-order partial derivatives with respect to t and y for $t_0 \leq t \leq t_0 + Nh$ and all y, then the cumulative truncation error of the Euler method with step length h is no greater than a constant multiple of h.*

Proof.   Since, by (8.4)

$$\phi(t_{k+1}) = \phi(t_k) + \int_{t_k}^{t_{k+1}} f(s, \phi(s))\, ds$$

and by (8.7)

$$y_{k+1} = y_k + hf(t_k, y_k)$$

we obtain

$$\phi(t_{k+1}) - y_{k+1} = \phi(t_k) - y_k + \int_{t_k}^{t_{k+1}} f(s, \phi(s))\, ds - hf(t_k, y_k)$$
$$= \phi(t_k) - y_k + \int_{t_k}^{t_{k+1}} f(s, \phi(s))\, ds - hf(t_k, \phi(t_k))$$
$$+ hf(t_k, \phi(t_k)) - hf(t_k, y_k)$$

Thus, taking absolute values, we obtain

$$|\phi(t_{k+1}) - y_{k+1}| \leq |\phi(t_k) - y_k| + \left| \int_{t_k}^{t_{k+1}} f(s, \phi(s))\, ds - hf(t_k, \phi(t_k)) \right|$$
$$+ h|f(t_k, \phi(t_k)) - f(t_k, y_k)|$$

Using the definition of E_k, we have

$$E_{k+1} \leq E_k + \left| \int_{t_k}^{t_{k+1}} f(s, \phi(s)) \, ds - hf(t_k, \phi(t_k)) \right|$$
$$+ h|f(t_k, \phi(t_k)) - f(t_k, y_k)| \qquad (8.8)$$

The local truncation error estimated in Section 2.5 is

$$\left| \int_{t_k}^{t_{k+1}} f(s, \phi(s)) \, ds - hf(t_k, \phi(t_k)) \right|$$

and we have shown that this is no greater than $\frac{1}{2}Mh^2$. Since we have assumed that f has a continuous partial derivative with respect to y, the mean value theorem for derivatives shows that there exists a constant L such that

$$|f(t_k, \phi(t_k)) - f(t_k, y_k)| \leq L|\phi(t_k) - y_k| = LE_k$$

(see Section 7.1, p. 318, for a similar calculation). When we use these estimates in (8.8), we see that

$$E_{k+1} \leq E_k + \frac{1}{2} Mh^2 + hLE_k = E_k(1 + hL) + \frac{1}{2} Mh^2$$
$$(k = 0, \ldots, N) \quad (8.9)$$

It is now easy to use induction to estimate E_k.

• **EXERCISE**

1. Show that the inequality (8.9) implies

$$E_k \leq \frac{(1 + hL)^k - 1}{hL} \cdot \frac{1}{2} Mh^2 \qquad (k = 0, 1, \ldots, N) \qquad (8.10)$$

(Note that $E_0 = 0$.)

To complete the argument, we require an elementary inequality.

Lemma 8.1. *If $p > 0$, $q > 0$, then $(1 + p)^q < e^{pq}$.*

Proof. For $p > 0$, $e^p > 1 + p$. Taking (natural) logarithms, we obtain $p > \log (1 + p)$. It follows that $pq > q \log (1 + p) = \log (1 + p)^q$, which implies $e^{pq} > (1 + p)^q$, as desired. ∎

Now, we apply this lemma to give $(1 + hL)^k < e^{Lkh}$, and then (8.10) yields

$$E_k \leq \frac{e^{Lkh} - 1}{hL} \cdot \frac{1}{2} Mh^2 \qquad (k = 0, 1, \ldots, N) \tag{8.11}$$

We wish to estimate E_N, and, since $Nh = T$, (8.11) gives

$$E_N \leq \frac{M(e^{LT} - 1)}{2L} h$$

If we define a new constant $M' = M(e^{LT} - 1)/2L$, this becomes

$$E_N \leq M'h$$

which completes the proof of Theorem 8.1. ∎

Since the cumulative truncation error of the Euler method is no greater than a constant multiplied by h, we can make this error as small as we wish by making the length h of the subintervals sufficiently small, that is, by making the number N of subintervals sufficiently large.   However, it is more efficient to use a more sophisticated approximation method whose cumulative truncation error is no greater than a constant multiplied by some higher power of h.   There is a balance to be sought here between the more involved computation of a more sophisticated method and the more rapid shrinking of the cumulative truncation error as h is decreased.   In the next two sections, we shall examine some refinements of the Euler method which are sufficiently simple for effective calculation, yet sufficiently accurate that a satisfactorily small error can usually be obtained with a reasonably small number of subintervals.   The reader should remember that a large number of subintervals means that a large number of separate calculations must be made, and a large number of simple calculations may take longer, either by hand or by computing machine, than a smaller number of more complicated calculations.   However, each problem and method must be examined with the particular computer available in mind.

The Euler method may be illustrated from the point of view of the computer by a flow diagram (Figure 8.2).   Such a diagram indicates the

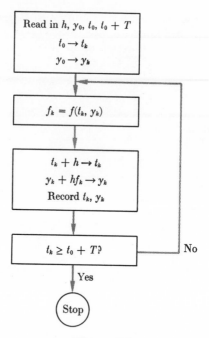

Figure 8.2

processes to be carried out by the computer. An instruction such as $t_k + h \to t_k$ means that the next step in the iterative procedure is started by replacement of $t_k + h$ by t_{k+1} (that is, $t_{k+1} = t_k + h$). The question $(t_k \geq t_0 + T?)$ is included in the flow diagram to show the process by which the computer decides when to stop iterating the procedure.

•EXERCISES

2. Use the Euler method, with $h = 0.1$, to approximate the value for $t = 1$ of the solution of the differential equation $y' = t + y$ passing through the origin.

3. Use the Euler method, first with $h = 0.2$, and then again with $h = 0.1$, to find an approximation to $\phi(1)$, where ϕ is the solution of $y' = 10(t^2 + y^2)$ such that $\phi(0) = 1$. Can you make any estimate of the accuracy of the answers?

4. The differential equation $y' = 3y^{2/3}$ has an infinite number of solutions through the origin, as we have seen in Sections 1.8 (p. 25) and 2.1 (p. 35). Suppose we try to use the Euler method to approximate one of these solutions, and repeat the process with a sequence of step sizes $\{h_n\}$ which decreases to zero. Does the sequence of approximations converge as $n \to \infty$? If so, to which solution does the sequence converge?

5. Use the Euler method, first with $h = 0.2$, and then again with $h = 0.1$, to approximate $\phi(1)$, where ϕ is the solution of $y' = ty^2 - y$ such that $\phi(0) = 1$. How small must h be chosen for the Euler method to give an approximation which is correct to two significant figures?

8.2   The Modified Euler Method

The Euler method, although easy to apply, has too large a truncation error to be of much use in the actual calculation of numerical approximations. This relatively large truncation error is due to the use of the crude approximation $hf(t_k, y_k)$ to the integral $\int_{t_k}^{t_{k+1}} f(s, \phi(s))\,ds$. By using a better approximation to this integral, we may expect to obtain a numerical method with a smaller truncation error. One obvious improvement is to approximate the integral by the length of the interval multiplied by the value of the integrand at the midpoint of the interval (see Figure 8.3),

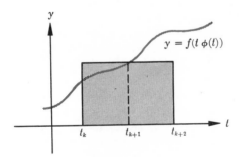

Figure 8.3

rather than by the length of the interval multiplied by the value of the integrand at one end of the interval. To do this, we integrate over two subintervals rather than divide each subinterval. Using (8.4), we write

$$\phi(t_{k+2}) = \phi(t_k) + \int_{t_k}^{t_{k+2}} f(s, \phi(s))\,ds \tag{8.12}$$

and we approximate the integral in (8.12) by $2hf(t_{k+1}, \phi(t_{k+1}))$. This leads to an approximation method given by the iterative formula

$$y_{k+2} = y_k + 2hf(t_{k+1}, y_{k+1}) \tag{8.13}$$

This method is called the **modified Euler method,** and the method of approximating the integral used in the modified Euler method is called **midpoint quadrature.** It is sometimes used in the numerical approximation of definite integrals. We shall see (Theorem 8.2 below) that the modified Euler method has a significantly smaller local truncation error than the Euler method.

The modified Euler method expresses y_{k+2} in terms of y_k and y_{k+1}. Since it involves two subintervals, it is called a **two-step method.** This introduces a difficulty which does not arise in the Euler method. In order to begin the approximation procedure by taking $k = 0$ in (8.13) to calculate y_2, we need not only the given initial value y_0 but also y_1. However, y_1 is not given by the initial conditions, and we must use some other approximation procedures, called a starting method, to calculate y_1.

One method of obtaining a value for y_1, which is frequently used if the function f is analytic, is to use a power series expansion about t_0 (see Section 4.1, p. 119). Power series expansions are not very useful for numerical approximations because their convergence near the ends of the interval of convergence may be very slow. However, if t_1 is close to t_0, a power series expansion may provide an accurate yet easily obtained approximation for y_1.

A second method of obtaining a value for y_1 is to use a one-step method, such as the Euler method. However, to improve the accuracy we subdivide the interval $[t_0, t_1]$ into smaller subintervals. Another approach, probably the most commonly used one, is to use a Runge-Kutta method. The basic idea of the Runge-Kutta methods is to obtain as small a truncation error as possible in an explicit one-step method. This requires subdivision of the interval $[t_0, t_1]$, and thus the Runge-Kutta methods may be regarded as refinements of the method suggested above, of subdividing the interval $[t_0, t_1]$ and using the Euler method. We shall discuss Runge-Kutta methods in Section 8.5; for the moment we wish only to point out the need for starting methods and to suggest some possibilities.

Example 1.   Let us estimate e by using the modified Euler method with $h = 0.1$ to approximate $\phi(1) = e$, where ϕ is the solution of $y' = y$ such that $\phi(0) = 1$. We begin by using a power series expansion to estimate $\phi(0.1) = 1 + 0.1 + \frac{1}{2}(0.1)^2 + \cdots$. This gives the value $y_1 = 1.105$, correct to three decimal places. Now, we can use the iterative formula (8.13). Using $h = 0.1$, $f(t, \hat{y}) = y$, in (8.13), we obtain

$$y_{k+2} = y_k + 0.2y_{k+1}$$

It is convenient to tabulate the calculations as follows.

t_k	y_k	y_{k+1}	$y_k + 0.2y_{k+1} = y_{k+2}$
0.0	1.000	1.105	1.221
0.1	1.105	1.221	1.349
0.2	1.221	1.349	1.491
0.3	1.349	1.491	1.647
0.4	1.491	1.647	1.820
0.5	1.647	1.820	2.011
0.6	1.820	2.011	2.222
0.7	2.011	2.222	2.455
0.8	2.222	2.455	2.713
0.9	2.455	2.713	
1.0	2.713		

We obtain the approximation 2.713 for e, which is considerably better than the approximation 2.593 obtained in Section 2.5 by the Euler method with the same number of mesh points.

We have suggested that the modified Euler method is more accurate than the Euler method for one particular problem. Let us prove that this is true in general by calculating the local truncation error of the modified Euler method.

Theorem 8.2.   *If f is continuous and has continuous partial derivatives with respect to t and y of the first and second orders for $t_0 \leq t \leq t_0 + Nh$ and for all y, then the local truncation error of the modified Euler method with step length h is no greater than a constant multiple of h^3.*

Proof.   Let ϕ be the solution of the equation (8.1) which satisfies the initial condition (8.2). Then, by (8.4),

$$\phi(t_{k+2}) = \phi(t_k) + \int_{t_k}^{t_{k+2}} f(s, \phi(s))\, ds \tag{8.14}$$

The approximations to this solution are defined by (8.13). The local truncation error T_k is defined to be $|\phi(t_{k+2}) - y_{k+2}|$, under the assumption that the approximate values at t_k and t_{k+1} are exact, that is, that $\phi(t_k) = y_k$ and that $\phi(t_{k+1}) = y_{k+1}$. Subtracting (8.13) from (8.14) and assuming that $\phi(t_k) = y_k$, $\phi(t_{k+1}) = y_{k+1}$, we see that

$$T_k = \left| \int_{t_k}^{t_{k+2}} f(s, \phi(s))\, ds - 2hf(t_{k+1}, \phi(t_{k+1})) \right|$$

For convenience of notation, we set $f(t, \phi(t)) = F(t)$. If F is twice differentiable, which is the case if f has continuous second-order partial derivatives with respect to t and y, we can use Taylor's theorem to write

$$F(s) = F(t_{k+1}) + (s - t_{k+1})F'(t_{k+1}) + \frac{(s - t_{k+1})^2}{2!} F''(\xi)$$

$$(t_k \leq s \leq t_{k+2}; t_k < \xi < t_{k+2})$$

Integration with respect to s from t_k to t_{k+2} gives

$$\int_{t_k}^{t_{k+2}} F(s)\ ds - 2hF(t_{k+1}) = \int_{t_k}^{t_{k+2}} (s - t_{k+1})F'(t_{k+1})\ ds$$

$$+ \int_{t_k}^{t_{k+2}} \frac{(s - t_{k+1})^2}{2} F''(\xi)\ ds$$

However,

$$\int_{t_k}^{t_{k+2}} (s - t_{k+1})F'(t_{k+1})\ ds = \frac{1}{2} F'(t_{k+1})[(t_{k+2} - t_{k+1})^2 - (t_k - t_{k+1})^2]$$

$$= \frac{1}{2} F'(t_{k+1})[h^2 - h^2] = 0$$

Thus the local truncation error T_k is

$$\left| \int_{t_k}^{t_{k+2}} \frac{(s - t_{k+1})^2}{2} F''(\xi)\ ds \right|$$

Suppose that $M = \max_{t_0 \leq t \leq t_0 + T} |F''(t)|$. There is such a constant M since the assumptions of the theorem imply that F has a continuous second derivative. Then

$$|T_k| \leq \frac{M}{2} \int_{t_k}^{t_{k+2}} (s - t_{k+1})^2\ ds = \frac{Mh^3}{3} \tag{8.15}$$

and Theorem 8.2 is proved. ∎

Theorem 8.2 suggests that if h is small, the modified Euler method represents an improvement in accuracy over the Euler method. This improvement, however, may be more apparent than real.   The constant M in (8.15), being a bound for $|F''(t)|$, involves bounds for the second-order partial derivatives of f, while the corresponding constant in the truncation error for the Euler method involves only bounds for the first-order partial derivatives of f.   This means that the constant in the bound for the truncation error for the modified Euler method may be considerably larger than the constant in the bound for the truncation error for the Euler method.   However, if h is sufficiently small, the additional factor h makes the modified Euler method more accurate than the Euler method.   The essential point is that the power of h is more important than the constant, **but only if h is small enough.**

The reader should note that we have not yet estimated the cumulative truncation error for the modified Euler method.   Rather than doing this now, we state the fact that this cumulative truncation error is no greater than a constant multiple of h^2, and defer the proof to the next section, where we shall indicate a general technique for passing from the local truncation error to the cumulative truncation error.

•EXERCISES

1. Use the modified Euler method, with $h = 0.2$, to approximate the value for $t = 1$ of the solution of the differential equation $y' = t + y$ passing through the origin.   Repeat the problem with $h = 0.1$, and compare the two results with the result obtained in Exercise 2, Section 8.1 (p. 346).

2. Use the modified Euler method, with $h = 0.1$, to find an approximation to $\phi(1)$, where ϕ is the solution of $y' = 10(t^2 + y^2)$ such that $\phi(0) = 1$.   Compare the result with the result obtained in Exercise 3, Section 8.1 (p. 346).

3. Use the modified Euler method with $h = 0.1$, to approximate the value $\phi(0.5)$ of the solution ϕ of $y' = y - t$ such that $\phi(0) = 0$.   Compare your answer with the one obtained by the Euler method with $h = 0.1$ and the one obtained by explicit solution of the differential equation.

4. Draw a flow diagram (analogous to Figure 8.2, p. 346), for the Euler method) for the modified Euler method.

Another possible approximation method is to use trapezoidal integration, that is, to approximate

$$\int_{t_k}^{t_{k+1}} f(s, \phi(s))\, ds \qquad \text{by } \frac{h}{2}\left[f(t_k, \phi(t_k)) + f(t_{k+1}, \phi(t_{k+1})) \right]$$

which is the area of the trapezoid bounded by the line segment joining $(t_k, f(t_k, \phi(t_k)))$ to $(t_{k+1}, f(t_{k+1}, \phi(t_{k+1})))$ and the three lines $y = 0$, $t = t_k$,

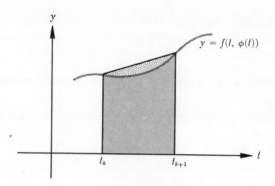

Figure 8.4

$t = t_{k+1}$; see Figure 8.4. This approximation leads to the iterative formula

$$y_{k+1} = y_k + \frac{h}{2}\left[f(t_k, y_k) + f(t_{k+1}, y_{k+1})\right] \tag{8.16}$$

This method, called the **improved Euler method,** gives y_{k+1} implicitly rather than explicitly. There are methods, as we shall soon indicate, for dealing with implicit formulas. For some problems the improved Euler method is useful.

8.3   The Milne Method

A more accurate approximation than the Euler and modified Euler methods is obtained by the use of Simpson's rule to approximate the integral $\int_{t_k}^{t_{k+2}} f(s, \phi(s))\, ds$. Simpson's rule gives the approximation

$$\frac{h}{3}\left[f(t_k, \phi(t_k)) + 4f(t_{k+1}, \phi(t_{k+1})) + f(t_{k+2}, \phi(t_{k+2}))\right] \tag{8.17}$$

for this integral and leads to the iterative formula

$$y_{k+2} = y_k + \frac{h}{3}\left[f(t_k, y_k) + 4f(t_{k+1}, y_{k+1}) + f(t_{k+2}, y_{k+2})\right] \tag{8.18}$$

known as the **Milne method** of approximation.

The use of the approximation (8.17) is suggested by an attempt to approximate the curve $y = f(t, \phi(t))$ by a parabola on the interval

$t_k \leq t \leq t_{k+2}$. As before, we write $F(t) = f(t, \phi(t))$ for convenience of notation.   Now, we determine the constants a, b, c so that the parabola

$$y = a + b(s - t_{k+1}) + c(s - t_{k+1})^2$$

with vertex at (t_{k+1}, a) and axis along the y axis passes through the three points $(t_k, F(t_k))$, $(t_{k+1}, F(t_{k+1}))$, $(t_{k+2}, F(t_{k+2}))$; see Figure 8.5.   Since

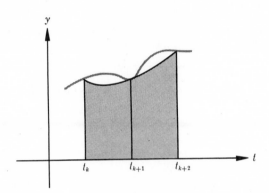

Figure 8.5

$t_{k+2} - t_{k+1} = t_{k+1} - t_k = h$, the conditions that these points lie on the parabola are

$$
\begin{aligned}
F(t_k) &= a - bh + ch^2 \\
F(t_{k+1}) &= a \\
F(t_{k+2}) &= a + bh + ch^2
\end{aligned}
\tag{8.19}
$$

We can solve the equations (8.19) for the three constants a, b, c, and then use

$$\int_{t_k}^{t_{k+2}} [a + b(s - t_{k+1}) + c(s - t_{k+1})^2] \, ds$$

as an approximation to $\int_{t_k}^{t_{k+2}} F(s) \, ds$.

Since

$$
\begin{aligned}
\int_{t_k}^{t_{k+2}} &[a + b(s - t_{k+1}) + c(s - t_{k+1})^2] \, ds \\
&= \left[as + \frac{b}{2}(s - t_{k+1})^2 + \frac{c}{3}(s - t_{k+1})^3 \right]_{t_k}^{t_{k+2}} = 2ah + \frac{2}{3}ch^3 \quad (8.20)
\end{aligned}
$$

we do not even need to solve (8.19) for b.   It is easy to obtain

$$a = F(t_{k+1}) \qquad c = \frac{F(t_{k+2}) - 2F(t_{k+1}) + F(t_k)}{2h^2}$$

and when we substitute these values in (8.20), we obtain (8.17) as an approximation for the integral $\int_{t_k}^{t_{k+2}} F(s) \, ds = \int_{t_k}^{t_{k+2}} f(s, \phi(s)) \, ds$.

Example 1.   Let us use the Milne method (8.18) with $h = 0.1$ to solve the same problem as the one discussed in Example 1, Section 8.2 (p. 348).   As before, we begin by using a power series expansion to obtain the approximation $y_1 = 1.105$.   Now, the formula (8.18), with $f(t, y) = y$, $h = 0.1$, becomes

$$y_{k+2} = y_k + \frac{1}{30} (y_k + 4y_{k+1} + y_{k+2})$$

We can solve this for y_{k+2}, obtaining

$$29y_{k+2} = 31y_k + 4y_{k+1}$$

Now, we can tabulate the calculations as follows:

t_k	y_k	y_{k+1}	$\frac{31}{29}y_k + \frac{4}{29}y_{k+1} = y_{k+2}$
0.0	1.000	1.105	$1.069 + 0.152 = 1.221$
0.1	1.105	1.221	$1.181 + 0.169 = 1.350$
0.2	1.221	1.350	$1.305 + 0.186 = 1.491$
0.3	1.350	1.491	$1.443 + 0.206 = 1.649$
0.4	1.491	1.649	$1.594 + 0.227 = 1.821$
0.5	1.649	1.821	$1.763 + 0.251 = 2.014$
0.6	1.821	2.014	$1.947 + 0.278 = 2.225$
0.7	2.014	2.225	$2.153 + 0.306 = 2.459$
0.8	2.225	2.459	$2.378 + 0.339 = 2.717$
0.9	2.459	2.717	
1.0	2.717		

The accuracy of this approximation, as compared to the accuracies of the approximations obtained earlier by the Euler method and the modified Euler method, suggests the usefulness of the Milne method in practice.

Although the Milne method is implicit (that is, the iterative formula (8.18) which defines the method expresses the approximation y_{k+2} which is being calculated implicitly in terms of y_k and y_{k+1}) this causes no difficulty because the differential equation $y' = y$ is linear, and this makes it possible to solve for y_{k+2} explicitly. However, the use of the Milne method for nonlinear differential equations requires some means of dealing with an implicit iterative formula.

The usual technique is to solve (8.18) by **another** iterative procedure at each step. One uses some other method to obtain a first approximation $\hat{y}_{k+2}$ to $\phi(t_{k+2})$ and then calculate a second approximation y_{k+2} from the formula

$$y_{k+2} = y_k + \frac{h}{3}\left[f(t_k, y_k) + 4f(t_{k+1}, y_{k+1}) + f(t_{k+2}, \hat{y}_{k+2})\right] \tag{8.21}$$

For more accuracy we may iterate this procedure, substituting y_{k+2} in the right-hand side of (8.21) and using (8.21) to calculate a third approximation, and continuing in the same way. It is possible to prove that if f is continuous and has continuous first-order partial derivatives with respect to t and y, then the approximations obtained in this way converge to a solution of the difference equation (8.18) for h sufficiently small. However, it is usually impractical to carry out this iteration procedure at each stage of the approximation method. Normally, the most efficient procedure is to calculate $\hat{y}_{k+2}$, called the **predictor,** by some explicit method, such as the Euler method or the modified Euler method, and then use (8.21), called a **predictor-corrector** formula, to calculate the **corrector** y_{k+2}. This value y_{k+2} is the one used in continuing to the next stage in the Milne method.

•EXERCISES

1.   Use the Milne method with $h = 0.2$ to approximate the value for $t = 1$ of the solution of the differential equation $y' = t + y$ passing through the origin. Repeat the problem with $h = 0.1$, and compare the two results with those obtained in Exercise 1, Section 8.2 (p. 351).

2.   Use the Milne method, with $h = 0.1$, to find an approximation to $\phi(1)$, where ϕ is the solution of $y' = 10(t^2 + y^2)$ such that $\phi(0) = 1$. Compare the result with that obtained in Exercise 2, Section 8.2 (p. 351).

3.   Draw a flow diagram (analogous to Figure 8.2, Section 8.1, p. 346) for the Euler method) for the Milne method.

4.   Use the Milne method with $h = 0.2$ to approximate $\phi(1)$, where ϕ is the solution of $y' = y - t$ such that $\phi(0) = 1$. Compare your answer with

that obtained by
   (a) using the Euler method with $h = 0.05$,
   (b) using the modified Euler method with $h = 0.1$,
   (c) finding the exact solution by the methods of Chapter 2.

5. Find an approximation to $\phi(0.5)$, where ϕ is the solution of $y' = y + y^2$ such that $\phi(0) = 1$, by using the Milne method with $h = 0.1$, and with the modified Euler method as predictor.

6. What value of h is needed to obtain an approximation correct to two significant figures, using each of the Euler, modified Euler, and Milne methods, for $\phi(1)$, where $\phi(t) = e^{-t^2}$ is the solution of $y' + 2ty = 0$ such that $\phi(0) = 1$?

The estimate of the local truncation error for the Milne method is considerably more difficult than the error estimates we have obtained previously. Obviously, the local truncation error depends on the accuracy of the predictor used. The simplest way to estimate this error is to split it into two parts. First, we estimate the local truncation error in the formula (8.21) under the assumption that the predictor $\hat{y}_{k+2}$ is exact. In addition, we assume as before that y_k and y_{k+1} are exact in our estimate. Then we calculate the additional error introduced in (8.21) by the error in the predictor. This, of course, will depend on the method used to obtain the predictor.

Let ϕ be the solution of the equation (8.1) which satisfies the initial condition (8.2). Then, by (8.4) (p. 341),

$$\phi(t_{k+2}) = \phi(t_k) + \int_{t_k}^{t_{k+2}} f(s, \phi(s))\, ds \tag{8.22}$$

The local truncation error of the Milne method is defined to be $T_k = |\phi(t_{k+2}) - y_{k+2}|$, calculated under the assumption that the values y_k and y_{k+1} in (8.21) are exact. Subtracting (8.21) from (8.22) and assuming $\phi(t_k) = y_k$, $\phi(t_{k+1}) = y_{k+1}$, we obtain

$$T_k = \left| \int_{t_k}^{t_{k+2}} f(s, \phi(s))\, ds - \frac{h}{3}\left[f(t_k, y_k) + 4f(t_{k+1}, y_{k+1}) + f(t_{k+2}, \hat{y}_{k+2}) \right] \right| \tag{8.23}$$

For convenience, we set $f(t, \phi(t)) = F(t)$, as before, and we split T_k into two parts U_k and V_k. The term U_k is calculated under the assumption that $\hat{y}_{k+2}$ is exact, that is, $\hat{y}_{k+2} = \phi(t_{k+2})$. Thus

$$U_k = \left| \int_{t_k}^{t_{k+2}} F(s)\, ds - \frac{h}{3}\left[F(t_k) + 4F(t_{k+1}) + F(t_{k+2}) \right] \right| \tag{8.24}$$

The term V_k is the additional error introduced by the assumption $\hat{y}_{k+2} = \phi(t_{k+2})$.   Thus

$$V_k = \frac{h}{3} |f(t_{k+2}, \phi(t_{k+2})) - f(t_{k+2}, \hat{y}_{k+2})| \qquad (8.25)$$

• **EXERCISE**

7. Show that $T_k \leq U_k + V_k$.

Let us estimate U_k; this is simply the truncation error in Simpson's rule. In doing this, **we must assume that $f(t, y)$ has continuous partial derivatives of all orders up to the fourth.**   We define $G(t) = \int_{t_k}^{t} F(s)\, ds$ on $[t_k, t_{k+2}]$, so that $G'(t) = F(t)$, and then we define the new function P on $[0, h]$ by

$$P(\tau) = G(t_{k+1} + \tau) - G(t_{k+1} - \tau) - \frac{\tau}{3} [F(t_{k+1} + \tau) + 4F(t_{k+1})$$
$$+ F(t_{k+1} - \tau)] \qquad (0 \leq \tau \leq h) \quad (8.26)$$

Comparing (8.24) and (8.26), we see that $U_k = |P(h)|$.   Differentiating (8.26) repeatedly, we obtain

$$P'(\tau) = F(t_{k+1} + \tau) - F(t_{k+1} - \tau) - \frac{1}{3} [F(t_{k+1} + \tau) + 4F(t_{k+1})$$
$$+ F(t_{k+1} - \tau)] - \frac{\tau}{3} [F'(t_{k+1} + \tau) - F'(t_{k+1} - \tau)]$$

$$P'(\tau) = \frac{2}{3} [F(t_{k+1} + \tau) - 2F(t_{k+1}) + F(t_{k+1} - \tau)]$$
$$- \frac{\tau}{3} [F'(t_{k+1} + \tau) - F'(t_{k+1} - \tau)] \qquad (8.27)$$

$$P''(\tau) = \frac{1}{3} [F'(t_{k+1} + \tau) - F'(t_{k+1} - \tau)] - \frac{\tau}{3} [F''(t_{k+1} + \tau)$$
$$+ F''(t_{k+1} - \tau)]$$

$$P'''(\tau) = -\frac{\tau}{3} [F'''(t_{k+1} + \tau) - F'''(t_{k+1} - \tau)]$$

By the mean value theorem, there exists ξ, $\overset{*}{t}_k \leq t_{k+1} - \tau < \xi < t_{k+1} + \tau \leq t_{k+2}$, such that

$$F'''(t_{k+1} + \tau) - F'''(t_{k+1} - \tau) = 2\tau F^{(4)}(\xi)$$

Thus

$$P'''(\tau) = -\frac{2}{3}\tau^2 F^{(4)}(\xi) \tag{8.28}$$

We observe from (8.26), (8.27) that $P(0) = P'(0) = P''(0) = 0$. Therefore,

$$P''(\tau) = \int_0^\tau P'''(\sigma)\,d\sigma \qquad P'(\tau) = \int_0^\tau P''(\sigma)\,d\sigma \qquad P(\tau) = \int_0^\tau P'(\sigma)\,d\sigma \tag{8.29}$$

Suppose that $M = \max\limits_{t_0 \le t \le t_0 + T} |F^{(4)}(t)|$. Then

$$-M \le F^{(4)}(\xi) \le M \tag{8.30}$$

From (8.28) and (8.30), we obtain

$$-\frac{2}{3}\tau^2 M \le P'''(\tau) \le \frac{2}{3}\tau^2 M$$

Integrating and using (8.29), we obtain

$$-\frac{2}{9}\tau^3 M \le P''(\tau) \le \frac{2}{9}\tau^3 M$$

Repeating the integration twice more, we obtain

$$-\frac{1}{18}\tau^4 M \le P'(\tau) \le \frac{1}{18}\tau^4 M$$

$$-\frac{1}{90}\tau^5 M \le P(\tau) \le \frac{1}{90}\tau^5 M$$

The final step in the calculation of U_k is the use of $U_k = |P(h)|$ to obtain

$$U_k \le \frac{1}{90}Mh^5 \tag{8.31}$$

This quantity is called **the local truncation error of the Milne method,** rather than T_k, even though T_k is the quantity which actually interests us.

To estimate V_k, we will only need to use the fact that $f(t, y)$ is continuous and has continuous first-order partial derivatives with respect to

t and y for $t_0 \leq t \leq t_0 + T$ and all y. This implies that there exists a constant L such that

$$|f(t, y) - f(t, \hat{y})| \leq L|y - \hat{y}| \tag{8.32}$$

for $t_0 \leq t \leq t_0 + T$ and all y. (See equation (7.7), p. 318.) Let us assume that the truncation error of the method used to calculate the predictor $\hat{y}_{k+2}$ is no greater than Ah^p for some positive integer p and some positive constant A. For example, if the Euler method is used, $p = 2$ and if the modified Euler method is used, $p = 3$. Then, using (8.25) and (8.32), we see that

$$V_k \leqq \frac{Lh}{3} |\phi(t_{k+2}) - \hat{y}_{k+2}|$$

Since $|\phi(t_{k+2}) - \hat{y}_{k+2}|$ is the truncation error of the method used to calculate $\hat{y}_{k+2}$, we have

$$V_k \leq \frac{Lh}{3} (Ah^p) \tag{8.33}$$

Since $T_k \leq U_k + V_k$, we obtain, using (8.31) and (8.33),

$$T_k \leq \frac{M}{90} h^5 + \frac{AL}{3} h^{p+1}$$

Then

$$T_k \leq \frac{M}{90} h^5 + \frac{AL}{3} h^{p+1} \tag{8.34}$$

If p is less than 4, the second term on the right side of (8.34) dominates for small h, while if p is greater than or equal to 4, the first term on the right side dominates. If we define q to be the smaller of the integers 5 and $p + 1$, then we can find a constant B such that

$$\frac{M}{90} h^5 + \frac{AL}{3} h^{p+1} \leq Bh^q$$

for small h, and thus

$$T_k \leq Bh^q$$

Notice that this error estimate is not improved by improving the method used to calculate the predictor beyond a certain point. If we can use a method with local truncation error no greater than a constant multiple of h^4, then T_k is no greater than a constant multiple of h^5.

In order to estimate the cumulative truncation error for the Milne method, we give a general method for passing from the local truncation error to the cumulative truncation error. We shall formulate this result only for one-step methods, but there is no serious difficulty in extending it to two-step methods such as the Milne method, provided f has sufficiently many continuous partial derivatives.

Theorem 8.3. *Suppose that f is continuous and has continuous first-order partial derivatives with respect to t and y for $t_0 \leq t \leq t_0 + T$ and all y. Suppose y_k $(k = 1, \ldots, N)$ are the approximations calculated by some one-step method with step-length h to the solution ϕ of (8.1), (8.2). Suppose that the local truncation error of the method is no greater than ϵ. Then the cumulative truncation error is no greater than a constant multiple of ϵ/h.*

Proof. For this proof it is convenient to define $\hat{\phi}_k$ to be the exact solution of the differential equation (8.1) such that

$$\hat{\phi}_k(t_k) = y_k \qquad (k = 0, 1, \ldots, N)$$

Thus, $\hat{\phi}_0$ is the solution ϕ which satisfies $\phi(t_0) = y_0$. In this notation, the local truncation error T_k is given by

$$T_k = |y_{k+1} - \hat{\phi}_k(t_{k+1})| = |\hat{\phi}_{k+1}(t_{k+1}) - \hat{\phi}_k(t_{k+1})|$$
$$(k = 0, 1, \ldots, N - 1) \quad (8.35)$$

(See Figure 8.6.)

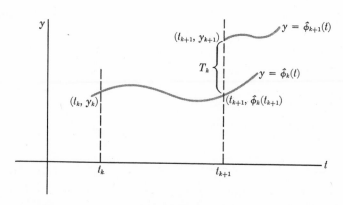

Figure 8.6

The cumulative truncation error is

$$E_N = |y_N - \phi(t_N)| = |\hat{\phi}_N(t_N) - \hat{\phi}_0(t_N)| \leq \sum_{k=1}^{N} |\hat{\phi}_k(t_N) - \hat{\phi}_{k-1}(t_N)| \quad (8.36)$$

We must estimate $|\hat{\phi}_k(t_N) - \hat{\phi}_{k-1}(t_N)|$. This quantity is the difference at t_N between two solutions of (8.1) whose difference at t_k is the local truncation error $T_{k-1} \leq \epsilon$, because of (8.35).   This difference can easily be estimated by means of the Gronwall inequality (Theorem 6.2, p. 252).   By (8.3), we can write

$$\hat{\phi}_k(t_N) = y_k + \int_{t_k}^{t_N} f(s, \hat{\phi}_k(s)) \, ds$$
$$\hat{\phi}_{k-1}(t_N) = \hat{\phi}_{k-1}(t_k) + \int_{t_k}^{t_N} f(s, \hat{\phi}_{k-1}(s)) \, ds \quad (k = 1, \ldots, N)$$

Subtracting and using (8.32) and (8.35), we obtain

$$|\hat{\phi}_k(t_N) - \hat{\phi}_{k-1}(t_N)| \leq |y_k - \hat{\phi}_{k-1}(t_k)| + \int_{t_k}^{t_N} |f(s, \hat{\phi}_k(s)) - f(s, \hat{\phi}_{k-1}(s))| \, ds$$
$$\leq T_{k-1} + L \int_{t_k}^{t_N} |\hat{\phi}_k(s) - \hat{\phi}_{k-1}(s)| \, ds$$
$$\leq \epsilon + L \int_{t_k}^{t_N} |\hat{\phi}_k(s) - \hat{\phi}_{k-1}(s)| \, ds \quad (k = 1, \ldots, N)$$

Now, the Gronwall inequality gives

$$|\hat{\phi}_k(t_N) - \hat{\phi}_{k-1}(t_N)| \leq \epsilon e^{L(t_N - t_k)} = \epsilon e^{L(N-k)h} \quad (k = 1, \ldots, N)$$

We substitute this into (8.36) and find

$$E_N \leq \epsilon \sum_{k=1}^{N} e^{L(N-k)h} = \epsilon e^{LNh} \sum_{k=1}^{N} e^{-kLh}$$

The geometric series $\sum_{k=1}^{N} e^{-kLh}$ with first term e^{-Lh} and ratio e^{-Lh} has sum

$$e^{-Lh} \cdot \frac{1 - e^{-NLh}}{1 - e^{-Lh}} = \frac{1 - e^{-NLh}}{e^{Lh} - 1}$$

Thus

$$E_N \leq \epsilon \frac{e^{LNh} - 1}{e^{Lh} - 1}$$

and since $e^{Lh} - 1 \geq Lh$, $Nh = T$, we obtain

$$E_N \leq \epsilon \frac{e^{LT} - 1}{Lh}$$

or

$$E_N \leq \frac{M\epsilon}{h}$$

where $M = ((e^{LT} - 1)/L)$. ∎

Theorem 8.3 shows that if the **local** truncation error of a one-step method is no greater than a constant multiple of h^p, then the **cumulative** truncation error is no greater than a constant multiple of h^{p-1}. As an analogous result can be proved for two-step methods (and for methods involving any finite number of steps), we now see that if f has sufficiently many continuous partial derivatives, the **cumulative** truncation error of the modified Euler method is no greater than a constant multiple of h^2, and the **cumulative** truncation error of the Milne method (with a predictor whose local truncation error is no greater than a constant multiple of h^4) is no greater than a constant multiple of h^4.

Obviously, the accuracy of approximation is improved if a method whose truncation error involves a higher power of h is used. On the other hand, to obtain this improvement in accuracy, a more complicated approximation procedure is required. The benefits of improved accuracy may be offset by the computational difficulties. For many problems, the Milne method represents a good compromise between accuracy of the formula and convenience of computation. The reader should remember that the truncation error depends on h, and can always be reduced by making h smaller.

The fact that the Milne method is implicit causes (as we have seen) some technical problems in its use and in the estimate of its error. There is another disadvantage, which we shall discuss in the next section. For some differential equations it is unsuitable because of difficulties arising from the round-off error, and other methods are more useful. One such method is the Adams method, which is obtained by the use of interpolating polynomials in approximating $\int_t^{t+h} f(s, \phi(s)) \, ds$ (see [8]). In implicit form this is given by

$$y_{k+3} = y_{k+2} + \frac{h}{24} [f(t_k, y_k) - 5f(t_{k+1}, y_{k+1}) + 19f(t_{k+2}, y_{k+2})]$$

$$+ 9f(t_{k+3}, y_{k+3})] \quad (8.37)$$

which has a local truncation error no greater than a constant multiple of h^5. An explicit Adams formula is

$$y_{k+3} = y_{k+2} + \frac{h}{12} [5f(t_k, y_k) - 16f(t_{k+1}, y_{k+1}) + 23f(t_{k+2}, y_{k+2})] \qquad (8.38)$$

whose local truncation error is no greater than a constant multiple of h^4. While the Adams methods are no more accurate than the Milne method, and are three-step methods (which require more computation), they are free from the disadvantages of the Milne method.

8.4 Stability, Consistency, and Convergence

When we use a numerical method to obtain an approximation to the solution of a differential equation, we are trying to find a set of numbers y_k $(k = 1, \ldots, N)$ defined by the method. However, we actually round off all numbers calculated to a specified number of decimal places, or to a specified number of significant figures, and thus we actually obtain a slightly different set of numbers z_k $(k = 1, \ldots, N)$. The difference $r_k = |z_k - y_k|$ is called the **round-off error.** If we retain more decimal places or significant figures, we obtain another set of numbers $\hat{z}_k$ $(k = 1, \ldots, n)$ with round-off error $\hat{r}_k = |\hat{z}_k - y_k|$. If $|z_N - \hat{z}_N|$ is small whenever all $|r_k - \hat{r}_k|$ $(k = 1, \ldots, N)$ are small, that is, if a small change in the round-off error at each stage produces only a small change in the final result, then the approximation method is said to be **computationally stable.** The property of stability depends on the approximation method and has nothing to do with the suitability of the method for a particular problem. For example, the formula $y_0 = 1$, $y_{k+1} = \frac{1}{2}y_k$ is a ridiculous attempt to approximate the solution ϕ of $y' = 0$ such that $\phi(0) = 1$, but it is stable in the sense just defined.

A numerical method is said to be **consistent** with a differential equation if the solution of the differential equation satisfies the approximation scheme except for terms which tend to zero as $h \to 0$. A numerical method is said to be **convergent** if the approximations tend to the actual solution as $h \to 0$. The reader will note that all methods presented above are convergent.

Example 1. Consider the Euler method as an approximation for the solution ϕ of the initial value problem, $y' = y$, $\phi(0) = 1$. We wish to show that it is both consistent and convergent. Consider the exact solution $\phi(t) = e^t$. At a mesh point $t_n = nh$, we have, from the Euler method,

$$y_{n+1} - (y_n + hy_n) = y_{n+1} - (1 + h)y_n$$

Substituting the exact solution, $\phi(t_n) = e^{nh}$, we have

$$\phi(t_{n+1}) - (1 + h)\phi(t_n) = e^{(n+1)h} - (1 + h)e^{nh}$$
$$= e^{nh}(e^h - 1 - h)$$

Since $nh = t$ we have $|e^{nh}| \leq K$, where K is a constant, for any finite t. Also, $|e^h - 1 - h| \leq Mh^2$ for some constant M. Therefore

$$|\phi(t_{n+1}) - (1 + h)\phi(t_n)| \leq K_1 h^2$$

for some constant $K_1 > 0$. Since $K_1 h^2$ tends to zero as $h \to 0$, the Euler method (for this problem) is consistent.

To show that the method is convergent, we solve the difference equation

$$y_{n+1} = (1 + h)y_n \qquad y_0 = 1$$

We obtain, by an easy induction, $y_n = (1 + h)^n$. Since $t = nh$, we consider $\lim_{h \to 0} (1 + h)^n = \lim_{h \to 0} (1 + h)^{t/h} = e^t$, which, of course, is the exact solution.

• EXERCISE

1. Show that the modified Euler method for the problem considered in Example 1 above is consistent and convergent.

Obviously, a method which is not convergent is useless for obtaining numerical approximations. It is possible to give conditions for stability and consistency of numerical methods which are easy to verify. Then the following result, for whose proof we refer the reader to more specialized works such as [8], is of great importance.

Theorem 8.4. *A stable, consistent finite difference approximation method is convergent.*

Of course, as we have seen in the preceding sections, the rate of convergence of the approximations to the actual solution as $h \to 0$ depends on the truncation error, and this must be estimated for each method.

To unify our previous considerations, we consider the difference equation

$$\sum_{i=0}^{p} \alpha_i y_{k+i} = h \sum_{i=0}^{p} \beta_i f(t_{k+i}, y_{k+i}) \tag{8.39}$$

with $\alpha_p \neq 0$, and with α_0 and β_0 not both zero. For example, in the Euler method (8.7), $p = 1$; $\alpha_1 = 1$, $\alpha_0 = -1$; $\beta_1 = 0$, $\beta_0 = 1$. The modified Euler method (8.13) is given by (8.39) with $p = 2$; $\alpha_2 = 1$, $\alpha_1 = 0$, $\alpha_0 = -1$; $\beta_2 = 0$, $\beta_1 = 2$, $\beta_0 = 0$. The Milne method (8.18) is given by (8.39) with $p = 2$; $\alpha_2 = 1$, $\alpha_1 = 0$, $\alpha_0 = -1$; $\beta_2 = \frac{1}{3}$, $\beta_1 = \frac{4}{3}$, $\beta_0 = \frac{1}{3}$. The implicit Adams method (8.37) is given by (8.39) with $p = 3$; $\alpha_3 = 1$, $\alpha_2 = -1$, $\alpha_1 = 0$, $\alpha_0 = 0$; $\beta_3 = 9/24$, $\beta_2 = 19/24$, $\beta_1 = -5/24$, $\beta_0 = 1/24$, while the explicit Adams method (8.38) is given by (8.39) with $p = 3$; $\alpha_3 = 1$, $\alpha_2 = -1$, $\alpha_1 = 0$, $\alpha_0 = 0$; $\beta_3 = 0$, $\beta_2 = 23/12$, $\beta_1 = -16/12$, $\beta_0 = 5/12$. The differnece equation (8.39) is said to define a **multi-step method.** The integer p is called the **rank** of the method. An explicit method is characterized by the condition $\beta_p = 0$.

It is convenient to define the two characteristic polynomials

$$\rho(\zeta) = \sum_{i=0}^{p} \alpha_i \zeta^i \qquad \sigma(\zeta) = \sum_{i=0}^{p} \beta_i \zeta^i$$

Thus, for the Euler method (8.7),

$$\rho(\zeta) = \zeta - 1 \qquad \sigma(\zeta) = 1$$

For the modified Euler method (8.13),

$$\rho(\zeta) = \zeta^2 - 1 \qquad \sigma(\zeta) = 2\zeta$$

For the Milne method (8.18),

$$\rho(\zeta) = \zeta^2 - 1 \qquad \sigma(\zeta) = \frac{1}{3}(\zeta^2 + 4\zeta + 1)$$

For the implicit Adams method (8.37),

$$\rho(\zeta) = \zeta^3 - \zeta^2 \qquad \sigma(\zeta) = \frac{1}{24}(9\zeta^3 + 19\zeta^2 - 5\zeta + 1)$$

For the explicit Adams method (8.38),

$$\rho(\zeta) = \zeta^3 - \zeta^2 \qquad \sigma(\zeta) = \frac{1}{12}(23\zeta^2 - 16\zeta + 5)$$

Two basic results, for whose proofs we again refer the reader to [8], are the following criteria for determining whether a method is stable and consistent.

Theorem 8.5.   *The multi-step method* (8.39) *is stable if and only if all roots of the polynomial equation* $\rho(\zeta) = 0$ *satisfy* $|\zeta| \leq 1$ *and those roots with absolute value* 1 *are simple roots.*

Theorem 8.6.   *The multi-step method* (8.39) *is consistent if and only if* $\rho(1) = 0$ (*that is,* 1 *is a root of* $\rho(\zeta) = 0$) *and* $\rho'(1) = \sigma(1)$.

•EXERCISES

2. Verify that the methods (8.7), (8.13), (8.18), (8.37), and (8.38) are all both stable and consistent.

3. Is the method (8.16) obtained by means of the trapezoidal rule stable and consistent?

If a method is both stable and consistent, then $\zeta = 1$ is a root of $\rho(\zeta) = 0$. If there are other roots of $\rho(\zeta) = 0$ with absolute value 1, as happens with the modified Euler and Milne methods but not with the Euler and Adams methods, then another error may appear. There may be an error in the initial value or starting value which tends to grow larger, and if the actual solution tends to zero as t becomes large, this error may eventually become large compared to the solution. This phenomenon is known as **numerical instability** or **conditional instability**. **The possibility of numerical instability is the reason why the Milne method is not always suitable, despite its small truncation error.** What may happen is that the Milne method, when applied to a differential equation such as $y'' = y$ one of whose solutions is a negative exponential, may give rise to a difference equation approximation whose solution includes a term which grows like a positive exponential. Then as the solution becomes small, the numerical approximation may grow.

We have devoted our attention mostly to the truncation error, and have given very little discussion of the round-off error. The study of the round-off error is largely statistical and quite difficult. We make no attempt to carry out such a study, but content ourselves with a few general remarks on the relationship between truncation error and round-off error.

We may reduce the truncation error in a given problem by using a more refined approximation method or by using a smaller step-length.   In either case, the number of computations becomes larger, and we must expect the round-off error to increase.   If the round-off error increases faster than the truncation error decreases, then the accuracy of the final result is not improved, and the additional effort is wasted.   In practice, the most efficient procedure is usually to choose the step-length so that the round-off error and truncation error are roughly the same size.

8.5   Runge-Kutta Methods

In Section 4.1 (p. 119) we considered the possibility of finding a power series expansion for a solution of a nonlinear differential equation.   At that time, we discarded this method because of computational difficulties and because of the difficulty of proving convergence of the series obtained. Now, however, let us return to this idea with a slightly different point of view.   Instead of seeking a power series expansion, we use the first few terms of the series expansion to obtain a numerical approximation.   Also, we divide the interval under consideration into subintervals of length h, just as we have done in developing finite difference methods in the preceding four sections.

Let ϕ be the solution of the differential equation

$$y' = f(t, y) \tag{8.1}$$

which satisfies the initial condition

$$\phi(t_0) = y_0 \tag{8.2}$$

If we assume that ϕ has a continuous second derivative on the interval $[t_0, t_0 + T]$, then we can use Taylor's theorem to write

$$\phi(t) = \phi(t_0) + (t - t_0)\phi'(t_0) + \frac{(t - t_0)^2}{2!} \phi''(\xi) \tag{8.40}$$

where $t_0 < \xi < t$.   If $t_1 = t_0 + h$, this becomes

$$\phi(t_1) = \phi(t_0) + h\phi'(t_0) + \frac{h^2}{2!} \phi''(\xi)$$

Using (8.1) and (8.2), we have

$$\phi(t_1) = y_0 + hf(t_0, y_0) + \frac{h^2}{2!}\phi''(\xi) \tag{8.41}$$

The idea behind our present approach is to obtain the approximation y_1 to $\phi(t_1)$ by neglecting the term $(h^2/2!)\phi''(\xi)$ in (8.41). Thus,

$$y_1 = y_0 + hf(t_0, y_0)$$

If we divide the interval $[t_0, t_0 + T]$ into N subintervals of length h by defining the partition points $t_k = t_0 + kh$ $(k = 0, 1, \ldots, N)$, we can use this procedure to obtain an iterative formula

$$y_{k+1} = y_k + hf(t_k, y_k) \tag{8.42}$$

with local truncation error $(h^2/2!)\phi''(\xi)$. The formula (8.42) is, of course, the Euler method which we have already studied in Sections 2.5 and 8.1.

Now let us use, instead of (8.40), Taylor's theorem with three terms plus an error term. Then

$$\phi(t) = \phi(t_0) + (t - t_0)\phi'(t_0) + \frac{(t - t_0)^2}{2!}\phi''(t_0) + \frac{(t - t_0)^3}{3!}\phi'''(\xi) \tag{8.43}$$

We can evaluate $\phi''(t_0)$ by differentiating

$$\phi'(t) = f(t, \phi(t))$$

obtaining

$$\phi''(t) = f_t(t, \phi(t)) + f_y(t, \phi(t))\phi'(t) = f_t(t, \phi(t)) + f_y(t, \phi(t))f(t, \phi(t))$$

Proceeding in the same way as above, we obtain the approximation formula

$$y_{k+1} = y_k + hf(t_k, y_k) + \frac{h^2}{2!}[f_t(t_k, y_k) + f_y(t_k, y_k)f(t_k, y_k)] \tag{8.44}$$

with local truncation error $(h^3/3!)\phi'''(\xi)$. The method (8.44) is a plausible means of obtaining numerical approximations. However, it suffers from the disadvantage that its use requires the calculation of derivatives of f.   We could develop analogous procedures using higher-order Taylor approximations, but these would require the calculation of higher-order derivatives of f.

The Runge-Kutta procedure is an attempt to obtain formulas equivalent to Taylor approximations which do not involve derivatives of f. The most frequently used Runge-Kutta formula is

$$y_{k+1} = y_k + \frac{h}{6} (p_1 + 2p_2 + 2p_3 + p_4) \tag{8.45}$$

where

$$p_1 = f(t_k, y_k) \qquad p_2 = f\left(t_k + \frac{h}{2}, y_k + \frac{hp_1}{2}\right)$$

$$p_3 = f\left(t_k + \frac{h}{2}, y_k + \frac{hp_2}{2}\right) \qquad p_4 = f(t_{k+1}, y_k + hp_3)$$

The term $\frac{1}{6}(p_1 + 2p_2 + 2p_3 + p_4)$ represents an "average" slope of ϕ over the interval $[t_k, t_{k+1}]$.   The term p_1 is the slope at t_k.   The term p_2 is an approximation to the slope at the midpoint of the interval obtained by means of the Euler method.   The term p_3 is a second approximation to the slope at the midpoint.   The term p_4 is an approximation to the slope at t_{k+1} obtained by means of the Euler method with slope p_3.   The formula (8.45) is an explicit one-step procedure, whose application does not require the calculation of any derivatives of f.   Since it requires an evaluation of f at four different points, it is still rather cumbersome. However, it is equivalent to a five-term Taylor formula, and can be shown to have local truncation error no greater than a constant multiple of h^5.   We omit the proof of this fact, because it is quite involved technically.   However, we shall suggest the idea behind the proof in Example 1 below, where we obtain a Runge-Kutta formula equivalent to a three-term Taylor formula.

Because the Runge-Kutta formula (8.45) is rather cumbersome, it is seldom used by itself.   Its chief value is as a starting method to obtain starting values before changing to a multi-step method such as the Milne method.   We recall that before we can use the Milne method (8.18), we need not only the given initial value y_0 but also the value y_1.   The determination of y_1 is usually carried out by a Runge-Kutta method.

The fact that the Runge-Kutta formula (8.45) is rather cumbersome may be illustrated by the complexity of its flow diagram (Figure 8.7). This diagram has even been simplified slightly by the suppression of

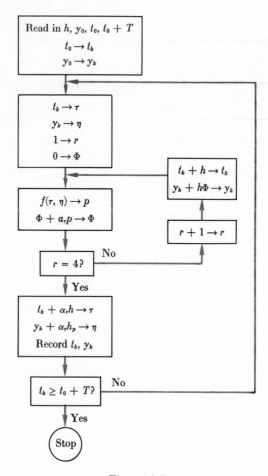

Figure 8.7

the notation $a_1 = \frac{1}{6}$, $a_2 = \frac{1}{3}$, $a_3 = \frac{1}{3}$, $a_4 = \frac{1}{6}$, $\alpha_1 = 0$, $\alpha_2 = \frac{1}{2}$, $\alpha_3 = \frac{1}{2}$, $\alpha_4 = 1$. In an actual calculation, this information would also have to be fed into the computer.

Example 1. Let us demonstrate how to obtain a Runge-Kutta formula equivalent to a three-term Taylor formula which agrees with the formula (8.44) except for a term no greater than a constant multiple of h^3. We are seeking a method of the form

$$y_{k+1} = y_k + h[af(t_k, y_k) + bf(t_k + \alpha h, y_k + \beta h f(t_k, y_k))] \tag{8.46}$$

where a, b, α, β are constants to be determined.   By Taylor's theorem for functions of two variables we may write

$$f(t_k + \alpha h, y_k + \beta h f(t_k, y_k)) = f(t_k, y_k) + \alpha h f_t(t_k, y_k)$$
$$+ \beta h f(t_k, y_k) f_y(t_k, y_k) + Rh^2 \qquad (8.47)$$

where R is a remainder term involving the second-order partial derivatives of f.   When we substitute (8.47) into (8.46) we obtain

$$y_{k+1} = y_k + h(a + b)f(t_k, y_k) + h^2[\alpha b f_t(t_k, y_k)$$
$$+ \beta b f(t_k, y_k) f_y(t_k, y_k)] + Rbh^3 \quad (8.48)$$

Comparing (8.48) with (8.44), we observe that if the constants a, b, α, β are chosen so that

$$a + b = 1 \qquad \alpha b = \frac{1}{2} \qquad \beta b = \frac{1}{2} \qquad (8.49)$$

then the approximations obtained by (8.44) and (8.48) differ only by the term Rbh^3.   Thus (8.46), with the constants satisfying (8.49), is a Runge-Kutta formula of the desired type.   For example, we may choose $a = \frac{1}{2}$, $b = \frac{1}{2}$, $\alpha = 1$, $\beta = 1$, to obtain

$$y_{k+1} = y_k + \frac{h}{2} [f(t_k, y_k) + f(t_{k+1}, y_k + h f(t_k, y_k))] \qquad (8.50)$$

as a Runge-Kutta method equivalent in accuracy to a three-term Taylor formula.   The reader should observe that (8.50) is equivalent to the improved Euler method (8.16) (p. 352), with the Euler method used as a predictor.

•EXERCISES

1.   Use the Runge-Kutta method (8.50) with $h = 0.2$ to approximate $\phi(1) = e$, where ϕ is the solution of $y' = y$ such that $\phi(0) = 1$.

2.   Use the Runge-Kutta method (8.45) with $h = 0.2$ to obtain an approximation to the same value $\phi(1) = e$ treated in Exercise 1.   Compare the accuracy and labor involved with those of previous attempts to solve the same problem: Example 1, Section 2.5 (Euler method) (p. 54), Example 1, Section 8.2 (modified Euler method) (p. 349), and Example 1, Section 8.3 (Milne method) (p. 354).

3. Use the Runge-Kutta method (8.45) to obtain a starting value $\phi(0.1)$ for the solution ϕ of the equation $y' = t + y^{1/2}$ with each of the following initial conditions
   (a) $\phi(0) = 0$.
   (b) $\phi(0) = 1$.
   (c) $\phi(0) = 10$.
   (d) $\phi(0) = 100$.

4. Obtain an approximation to $\phi(0.1)$, where ϕ is the solution e^t of $y' = y$ such that $\phi(0) = 1$ by using
   (a) the Runge-Kutta method (8.45),
   (b) the Runge-Kutta method (8.50).

How small must h be taken to obtain approximations of comparable accuracy by using the Euler method with a subdivision of the interval $0 \le t \le 0.1$?

8.6   Numerical Methods for Systems and Equations of Higher Order

Everything that we have done in this chapter has been for first-order equations, but the methods are equally suitable for systems of differential equations, although not entirely without difficulty. We can write a system

$$
\left.
\begin{aligned}
y'_1 &= f_1(t, y_1, \ldots, y_n) \\
y'_2 &= f_2(t, y_1, \ldots, y_n) \\
&\ \ \vdots \\
y'_n &= f_n(t, y_1, \ldots, y_n)
\end{aligned}
\right\}
\tag{8.51}
$$

in the form

$$
\mathbf{y}' = \mathbf{f}(t, \mathbf{y})
\tag{8.52}
$$

with $\mathbf{y}$ the column vector with components $(y_1, \ldots, y_n)$ and $\mathbf{f}(t, \mathbf{y})$ the column vector with components $(f_1(t, y_1, \ldots, y_n), f_2(t, y_1, \ldots, y_n), \ldots, f_n(t, y_1, \ldots, y_n))$ (see Section 6.2, p. 243). We can apply the approximation methods developed in this chapter to the system (8.51) by applying them to each component of the vector equation (8.52).

Example 1.   Consider the system

$$u' = v \qquad v' = g(t, u, v) \tag{8.53}$$

This can be written in the form (8.52) with

$$\mathbf{y} = \begin{pmatrix} u \\ v \end{pmatrix} \qquad \mathbf{f}(t, \mathbf{y}) = \begin{pmatrix} v \\ g(t, u, v) \end{pmatrix}$$

The Euler method applied to (8.53) leads to a pair of iterative formulas

$$\begin{aligned} u_{k+1} &= u_k + h v_k \\ v_{k+1} &= v_k + h g(t_k, u_k, v_k) \end{aligned} \tag{8.54}$$

For a system (8.53) we are given initial values u_0 and v_0, and once we have found both u_k and v_k, we can use (8.54) to compute u_{k+1} and v_{k+1}.

Example 1 illustrates how finite difference methods can be adapted to systems. Since an equation of order higher than the first can always be written as a system (Section 6.2, p. 242), such equations can also be treated numerically. Note, for example, that the system (8.53) is equivalent to the second-order equation $u'' = g(t, u, u')$. Every method and theorem presented for a single equation has an analogue for systems, though the analogue is not always obvious. For a complete discussion, we must again refer the reader to one of the more thorough treatments of the subject.

•EXERCISES

1. Find iterative formulas analogous to the modified Euler and Milne methods for the system (8.53).

2. Use the Euler method with $h = 0.1$ to approximate the value $\phi(\pi/2)$ of the solution ϕ of the second-order equation $y'' + y = 0$ such that $\phi(0) = 0$. (Note that $\phi(t) = \sin t$, so that the exact value of $\phi(\pi/2)$ is 1.)

3. Use the Euler method with $h = 0.1$ to estimate the smallest positive value τ at which the solution ψ of $y'' + y = 0$ such that $\psi(0) = 1$ vanishes. Use your answer to estimate a value of π, and suggest some ways of obtaining a more precise estimate. [*Hint:* Since $\psi(t) = \cos t$, the exact value of τ is $\pi/2$.]

4. Consider the solution ϕ of the differential equation $y'' + (g/L)y = 0$ such that $\phi(0) = \theta_0$, $\phi'(0) = 0$, where g, L, θ_0 are given positive constants. (This is one model for the simple pendulum obtained in Section 1.2, p. 12.) Use the Euler method with $h = 0.1$ to estimate the value of $\phi'(\tau)$, where τ is the first value of t for which $\phi(t) = 0$. Also estimate T, the first value of

$t > 0$ for which $\phi(t) = \theta_0$. Estimate the same quantities using the Milne method with $h = 0.1$.

5. Repeat the calculations of Exercise 4 using the more precise model $y'' + (g/L) \sin y = 0$.

•MISCELLANEOUS EXERCISES

1. For each of the following initial value problems obtain an approximate value of $\phi(1)$, where $\phi(t)$ is the (exact) solution, using steps size $h = 0.1$ by (i) the Euler method, (ii) the modified Euler method, (iii) the Milne method, using the Runge-Kutta method for starting values and predictor-corrector formulas, (iv) the Runge-Kutta method.

(a) $y' - 4y = 1 - t$ $\phi(0) = 1$.
(b) $y' = t^2 + y^2$ $\phi(0) = 0$ (compare Exercise 4, p. 338).
(c) $y' = e^y$ $\phi(0) = 0$.

[*Hint:* Use a table of exponentials.]

2. Repeat the calculations of Exercise 1, but with step size $h = 0.05$, and compare the results with those of Exercise 1. [*Suggestion:* Do not attempt this exercise unless you have a high-speed computer available or are unusually eager to do hard computing.]

3. Find iterative formulas analogous to the Euler, modified Euler, Milne, and Runge-Kutta methods for the system

$$y_1' = f_1(t, y_1, y_2)$$
$$y_2' = f_2(t, y_1, y_2)$$

4. Specialize the results of Exercise 3 to the linear system

$$y_1' = a_{11}(t)y_1 + a_{12}(t)y_2 + b_1(t)$$
$$y_2' = a_{21}(t)y_1 + a_{22}(t)y_2 + b_2(t)$$

5. Generalize the results of Exercises 3 and 4 to n-dimensional systems of the form

$$\mathbf{y}' = \mathbf{f}(t, \mathbf{y})$$

and

$$\mathbf{y}' = A(t)\mathbf{y} + \mathbf{b}(t)$$

6. For each of the following initial value problems obtain an approximate value of $\boldsymbol{\phi}(1) = (\phi_1(1), \phi_2(1))$, where $\boldsymbol{\phi}(t)$ is the (exact) solution, using step size $h = 0.1$ by (i) the Euler method, (ii) the modified Euler method, (iii) the Milne method, using the Runge-Kutta method for starting values and predictor-corrector formulas, (iv) the Runge-Kutta method.

(a) $y_1' = 2y_1 + ty_2$ $y_1(0) = 1$

     $y_2' = ty_1$ $y_2(0) = 0.$

(b) $y_1' = -y_1 + 2y_2 + 1$ $y_1(0) = 0$

     $y_2' = -2y_1 + 3y_2$ $y_2(0) = 1.$

7. For each of the following initial value problems, obtain an approximate value of $\phi(0.5)$, where $\phi(t)$ is the (exact) solution, using step size $h = 0.1$ by (i) the Euler method, (ii) the Runge-Kutta method

    (a) $y'' - 2y^3 = 0$ $\phi(0) = 1$ $\phi'(0) = -1.$

    (b) $y'' - 2y^3 = 0$ $\phi(0) = 1$ $\phi'(0) = -1.$

[*Hint:* Reduce to a system of two first-order equations and use the results of Exercise 3.]

9.1 Introduction

In this chapter we shall study a method of solving initial value problems for linear differential equations and linear systems of differential equations. This method does not enable us to solve any problems in differential equations which we could not solve by the methods already studied in Chapters 3, 4, and 6. It does, however, provide a simple and often employed technique for solving many problems which arise in applications, particularly those involving linear equations with constant coefficients. One reason for its usefulness is that it enables us to find the particular solution of the differential equation which satisfies the initial conditions directly, rather than first finding the general solution and then using the initial conditions to determine constants.

For every function $f(t)$ of a suitable class, we define the **Laplace transform** $F(s)$ by

$$F(s) = \int_0^\infty e^{-st} f(t) \, dt = \lim_{A \to \infty} \int_0^A e^{-st} f(t) \, dt \qquad (9.1)$$

where it is understood that we restrict our consideration to these values of the complex parameter s and to those functions f for which the above limit exists.

Example 1. To calculate the Laplace transform of the constant function 1, we evaluate

$$\int_0^\infty e^{-st} \, dt = \lim_{A \to \infty} \int_0^A e^{-st} \, dt = \lim_{A \to \infty} \left[\frac{1}{s} - \frac{e^{-sA}}{s} \right] = \frac{1}{s} \qquad (\Re s > 0)$$

$$(9.2)$$

Clearly, the integral does not converge for $\Re s \leq 0$.

376

Example 2.   We can calculate the Laplace transform of e^{zt} by almost exactly the same process as that used in Example 1.

$$\mathcal{L}(e^{zt}) = \int_0^\infty e^{-st} e^{zt} \, dt = \int_0^\infty e^{-(s-z)t} \, dt = \frac{1}{s-z} \qquad (\Re s > \Re z) \qquad (9.3)$$

Notice that the only difference between the integrals evaluated here and in Example 1 is that where there was an s in Example 1, there is an $(s - z)$ in Example 2.   This is an example of a general principle to which we shall return later.

The operator defined by (6.1) is linear in the sense of Chapter 3, that is, if $f_1(t)$ and $f_2(t)$ have Laplace transforms $F_1(s)$ and $F_2(s)$ respectively and if a and b are constants, then $af_1(t) + bf_2(t)$ has Laplace transform $aF_1(s) + bF_2(s)$.

The idea behind the Laplace transform method is very simple.   It will be shown that every solution of any linear homogeneous differential equation with constant coefficients has a Laplace transform.   In addition, the Laplace transform of the derivatives of f can be expressed in terms of the Laplace transform of f and the values of f and its derivatives at $t = 0$.   This then means that if ϕ is the solution of a linear differential equation with constant coefficients which satisfies some given initial conditions at $t = 0$, the Laplace transform of ϕ satisfies a **linear algebraic equation** rather than a differential equation.   When we have solved this algebraic equation, we need only find the function whose Laplace transform is the solution of this algebraic equation.   This may often be facilitated by tables of Laplace transforms.   Of course, in order to be sure that the function found by this procedure is the same as the function ϕ, we need a uniqueness theorem for Laplace transforms, to the effect that two different functions cannot have the same Laplace transform.

9.2   Basic Properties of the Laplace Transform

In defining the Laplace transform by the equation (9.1), we must impose some conditions on the function $f(t)$ to assure the convergence of the integral.   We consider functions $f(t)$ defined for $0 < t < \infty$ which grow sufficiently slowly near $t = 0$ to assure the convergence of the integral at zero (the integral may be improper); we also require that the function $f(t)$ grows sufficiently slowly for large t to assure the convergence of the infinite integral for some values of the complex parameter s; finally, we require $f(t)$ to be integrable over every closed subinterval of $0 < t < \infty$. This leads us to the following definition.

Definition. *A function f on $0 < t < \infty$ is said to be of exponential growth at infinity if it satisfies an inequality of the form*

$$|f(t)| \leq Me^{ct} \tag{9.4}$$

for some real constants $M > 0$ and c, for all sufficiently large t.

Now we define **the class Λ of functions on** $0 < t < \infty$ which are

  (i) absolutely integrable at zero,
  (ii) piecewise continuous on $0 < t < \infty$,
  (iii) of exponential growth at infinity.

This is the class of functions for which we wish to define the Laplace transform.   Clearly, the functions 1, t, t^n (n a positive integer), $\sin t$, $\cos t$, e^{zt} for any complex z are in the class Λ, but $\exp(t^2)$ is not.

Theorem 9.1. *If f is a function in the class Λ, the integral $\int_0^\infty e^{-st}f(t)\,dt$ converges absolutely for all complex numbers s with sufficiently large real part.*

Proof.   For small t, $|e^{-st}|$ is bounded, and therefore the assumption that f is absolutely integrable at zero implies the convergence of the integral $\int_0^\delta |e^{-st}f(t)|\,dt$ for every $\delta > 0$. If $\Re s = \sigma$, $|e^{-st}| = e^{-\sigma t}$, and then (9.4) yields

$$|e^{-st}f(t)| \leq Me^{-(\sigma-c)t}$$

for $t \geq T$, where T is some number greater than zero.   Therefore, if $\sigma > c$, the infinite integral $\int_T^\infty |e^{-st}f(t)|\,dt$ converges because its integrand decreases exponentially to zero, and we have

$$\left| \int_T^\infty e^{-st}f(t)\,dt \right| \leq \int_T^\infty |e^{-st}f(t)|\,dt \leq M \int_T^\infty e^{-(\sigma-c)t}\,dt = \frac{M}{\sigma-c}e^{-(\sigma-c)T}$$

Finally, because f is piecewise continuous on $\delta \leq t \leq T$, $\int_\delta^T |e^{-st}f(t)|\,dt$ exists, and this completes the proof of the theorem. ∎

The Laplace transform $F(s)$ of any function $f(t)$ in the class Λ is defined by the equation (9.1) for all complex s with sufficiently large real part; we will usually be concerned only with real values of s.   Sometimes we denote the Laplace transform by the symbol $\mathcal{L}$, to emphasize that the Laplace transform is an **operator,** which associates the function $F(s)$ with the function $f(t)$.   Thus we write

$$F(s) = \mathcal{L}\{f(t)\}$$

As already remarked, this operator is linear.

Example 1. If $f(t)$ is a complex-valued function of the class Λ, $f(t) = u(t) + iv(t)$, where u, v are real, we have

$$\mathcal{L}\{f(t)\} = \mathcal{L}\{u(t) + iv(t)\} = \mathcal{L}\{u(t)\} + i\mathcal{L}\{v(t)\}$$

From the definition, it is clear that the Laplace transform of a real-valued function is real for real s.   Thus $\mathcal{L}\{u(t)\}$ is the real part of $\mathcal{L}\{f(t)\}$ and $\mathcal{L}\{v(t)\}$ is the imaginary part of $\mathcal{L}\{f(t)\}$.   If $z = \alpha + i\beta$, and if $f(t) = e^{zt}$ we have

$$\mathcal{L}(e^{zt}) = \mathcal{L}\{e^{\alpha t}e^{i\beta t}\} = \mathcal{L}\{e^{\alpha t}\cos\beta t + ie^{\alpha t}\sin\beta t\} = \frac{1}{s - z}$$

$$= \frac{1}{s - \alpha - i\beta} = \frac{1}{s - \alpha - i\beta}\cdot\frac{s - \alpha + i\beta}{s - \alpha + i\beta} = \frac{s - \alpha + i\beta}{(s - \alpha)^2 + \beta^2} \quad (9.5)$$

When we take real and imaginary parts of (9.5) with s real, and then let s be complex again, we obtain

$$\mathcal{L}\{e^{\alpha t}\cos\beta\} = \frac{s - \alpha}{(s - \alpha)^2 + \beta^2}$$

$$\mathcal{L}\{e^{\alpha t}\sin\beta t\} = \frac{\beta}{(s - \alpha)^2 + \beta^2} \qquad (\Re s > \alpha) \qquad (9.6)$$

In particular, taking $\alpha = 0$ we obtain

$$\mathcal{L}\{\cos\beta t\} = \frac{s}{s^2 + \beta^2} \qquad \mathcal{L}\{\sin\beta t\} = \frac{\beta}{s^2 + \beta^2} \qquad (\Re s > 0) \qquad (9.7)$$

We could use the same direct approach to compute the Laplace transforms of other functions such as t^k and $t^k e^{zt}$, but we can calculate these transforms less laboriously by using some additional general properties of Laplace transforms.

Suppose f is in the class Λ. If we differentiate (9.1) with respect to s under the integral sign, we obtain formally

$$F'(s) = -\int_0^\infty te^{-st}f(t)\,dt \tag{9.8}$$

Since f is of exponential growth at infinity, satisfying (9.4),

$$|te^{-st}f(t)| \leq Mte^{-(\sigma-c)t}$$

where $\sigma = \Re s$, and the integral (9.8) converges absolutely for $\sigma > c$. From this we can prove that the relation (9.8) is valid if the real part of s is sufficiently large, that is, if $\Re s > c$. In fact, we can use the same argument to justify repeated differentiation under the integral sign, which gives the formula

$$F^{(k)}(s) = (-1)^k \int_0^\infty t^k e^{-st}f(t)\,dt \qquad (k = 1, 2, \ldots) \tag{9.9}$$

Comparing (9.9) with the definition of the Laplace transform, we see that we have sketched the proof of the following result. ·

Theorem 9.2. *The Laplace transform of a function f in the class Λ has derivatives of all orders and these derivatives are given by (9.9). If $f(t)$ belongs to the class Λ, then $t^k f(t)$ also belongs to the class Λ for every positive integer k, and its Laplace transform is given by*

$$\mathcal{L}\{t^k f(t)\} = (-1)^k \frac{d^k}{ds^k}\mathcal{L}\{f(t)\} \qquad (k = 1, 2, \ldots) \tag{9.10}$$

If we apply (9.10) with $f(t) = 1$ and use (9.2), we obtain

$$\mathcal{L}\{t^k\} = (-1)^k \frac{d^k}{ds^k}\left(\frac{1}{s}\right) = \frac{k!}{s^{k+1}} \qquad (\Re s > 0;\, k = 1, 2, \ldots) \tag{9.11}$$

If we apply (9.10) with $f(t) = e^{zt}$ and use (9.3), we obtain

$$\mathcal{L}\{t^k e^{zt}\} = (-1)^k \frac{d^k}{ds^k}\left(\frac{1}{s-z}\right) = \frac{k!}{(s-z)^{k+1}} \qquad (\Re s > \Re z;\, k = 1, 2, \ldots) \tag{9.12}$$

By letting $z = \alpha + i\beta$ and taking real and imaginary parts, we can obtain the formulas

$$\mathcal{L}\{t^k e^{\alpha t} \cos \beta t\} = \frac{k! \Re[(s - \alpha) + i\beta]^{k+1}}{[(s - \alpha)^2 + \beta^2]^{k+1}}$$

$$\mathcal{L}\{t^k e^{\alpha t} \sin \beta t\} = \frac{k! \Im[(s - \alpha) + i\beta]^{k+1}}{[(s - \alpha)^2 + \beta^2]^{k+1}} \tag{9.13}$$

$$\mathcal{L}\{t^k \cos \beta t\} = \frac{k! \Re(s + i\beta)^{k+1}}{(s^2 + \beta^2)^{k+1}} \qquad \mathcal{L}\{t^k \sin \beta t\} = \frac{k! \Im(s + i\beta)^{k+1}}{(s^2 + \beta^2)^{k+1}} \tag{9.14}$$

By evaluating the indicated real and imaginary parts in (9.13) and (9.14), we can obtain explicit expressions for these Laplace transforms.

• **EXERCISES**

1. Find the Laplace transforms of $t \cos \beta t$ and $t \sin \beta t$, using (9.14).

2. Find the Laplace transforms of $t \cos \beta t$ and $t \sin \beta t$ directly from the definition.

3. Calculate the Laplace transforms of
(a) $\cos^2 \beta t$.   [*Hint:* Use the half-angle formula.]
(b) $\sin \beta t \cos \beta t$.

4. Calculate the Laplace transform of the function f given by

$$f(t) = \begin{cases} 0 & (0 < t < 1) \\ t & (1 < t < 2) \\ 0 & (t > 2) \end{cases}$$

5. Calculate the Laplace transform of the function f given by

$$f(t) = \begin{cases} \sin 2t & (0 < t < \pi) \\ 0 & (t > \pi) \end{cases}$$

The relation between (9.2) and (9.3) suggests that multiplication of a function by an exponential does not affect its Laplace transform except for causing a translation of the independent variable.   This is in fact a general property.

Theorem 9.3.   *If the function f in the class* Λ *has Laplace transform F, then the Laplace transform of* $e^{at}f(t)$, *for any constant a (real or complex) is* $F(s - a)$.

Proof.   It is easy to verify that $e^{at}f(t)$ also belongs to the class Λ.   The only part of the verification which is not completely obvious is that $e^{at}f(t)$

is of exponential growth at infinity. If f satisfies (9.4), and if $\alpha = \Re a$, then

$$|e^{at}f(t)| \le e^{\alpha t}Me^{ct} = Me^{(\alpha+c)t}$$

and thus $e^{at}f(t)$ is of exponential growth at infinity and has a Laplace transform, which we may calculate directly. We obtain

$$\mathcal{L}\{e^{at}f(t)\} = \int_0^\infty e^{-st}e^{at}f(t)\,dt = \int_0^\infty e^{-(s-a)t}f(t)\,dt = F(s-a)$$

and the result is proved. ∎

•**EXERCISES**

6. Use Theorem 9.3 to derive (9.6) from (9.7).

7. Use Theorem 9.3 to derive (9.13) from (9.14).

8. Using the results of Exercise 1, find the Laplace transforms of $te^{\alpha t}\cos\beta t$ and $te^{\alpha t}\sin\beta t$.

9. Let $f(t) = \phi(t)$ for $0 < t < a$, and let f be periodic with period a, so that $f(t+a) = f(t)$ for $0 < t < \infty$. Show that

$$\mathcal{L}\{f(t)\} = \frac{\int_0^a e^{-st}\phi(t)\,dt}{1 - e^{-as}}. \qquad (\Re s > 0)$$

[*Hint:* Write

$$\mathcal{L}\{f(t)\} = \int_0^a e^{-st}f(t)\,dt + \int_a^{2a} e^{-st}f(t)\,dt + \cdots$$

and transform each integral so that the range of integration is $[0, a]$.]

10. Let f be the "square-wave function" given by $f(t) = 1$ $(0 < t < a/2)$, $f(t) = -1$ $(a/2 < t < a)$ with f periodic of period a. Sketch the graph and find the Laplace transform of f.

11. Let f be the "square-wave function" of Exercise 10 and let $g(t) = \int_0^t f(s)\,ds$. Sketch the graph and find the Laplace transform of g.

The usefulness of the Laplace transform in finding solutions of a differential equation depends on the fact that the Laplace transform of the derivative of a function can be expressed easily in terms of the Laplace transform of the function.

Theorem 9.4. *Let f be a differentiable function in the class Λ whose derivative also belongs to the class Λ, and let the Laplace transform of f be F.*

Then

$$\mathcal{L}\{f'(t)\} = sF(s) - f(0) \tag{9.15}$$

Proof. We simply apply the definition of the Laplace transform and integrate by parts.   This gives

$$\begin{aligned}
\mathcal{L}\{f'(t)\} &= \int_0^\infty e^{-st} f'(t)\, dt = \lim_{A \to \infty} \int_0^A e^{-st} f'(t)\, dt \\
&= \lim_{A \to \infty} \{e^{-st}f(t)]_0^A + \int_0^A se^{-st}f(t)\, dt\} \\
&= -f(0) + s \int_0^\infty e^{-st}f(t)\, dt = sF(s) - f(0)
\end{aligned}$$

where we have used the fact that $\lim_{A \to \infty} e^{-sA} f(A) = 0$ for $\Re s$ sufficiently large. ∎

The result of Theorem 9.4 can easily be extended to derivatives of higher order.   It is convenient to introduce some additional notation. For each positive integer k, **we define Λ^k to be the class of functions in Λ which have continuous derivatives up to order k on $(0, \infty)$ and whose derivatives up to order k also belong to Λ.**   Thus, the hypothesis of Theorem 9.4 is that f belongs to the class Λ^1.

Theorem 9.5.   *If f belongs to the class Λ^k for some positive integer k, and if F is the Laplace transform of f, then*

$$\mathcal{L}\{f^{(j)}(t)\} = s^j F(s) - s^{j-1}f(0) - s^{j-2}f'(0) - \cdots - sf^{(j-2)}(0) - f^{(j-1)}(0)$$
$$(j = 1, 2, \ldots, k) \quad (9.16)$$

Proof.   We can prove (9.16) most easily by induction on j for any fixed k, remembering that the induction procedure cannot be carried out for $j > k$ since the hypotheses do not guarantee the existence of the Laplace transforms of derivatives of order higher than k.   The case $j = 1$ of (9.16) was proved in Theorem 9.4.   If (9.16) has been established for $f^{(j)}(t)$, we can write $f^{(j+1)}(t)$ as the first derivative of $f^{(j)}(t)$ and apply Theorem 9.4.   We obtain

$$\begin{aligned}
\mathcal{L}\{f^{(j+1)}(t)\} &= s\mathcal{L}\{f^{(j)}(t)\} - f^{(j)}(0) \\
&= s[s^j F(s) - s^{j-1}f(0) - \cdots - f^{(j-1)}(0)] - f^{(j)}(0) \\
&= s^{j+1}F(s) - s^j f(0) - \cdots - sf^{(j-1)}(0) - f^{(j)}(0)
\end{aligned}$$

and this is the equation (9.16) with j replaced by $(j + 1)$. Thus, Theorem 9.5 is proved by induction. ∎

The formula (9.16) for calculating the Laplace transforms of the derivatives of a function is the key to the solution of linear differential equations by means of Laplace transforms. We shall study this subject in more detail in Sections 9.4 and 9.5. However, we give some simple examples here which we have already solved in Chapter 2 to illustrate the main idea.

Example 2.   Let us find the solution ϕ_0 of the familiar first-order differential equation

$$y' + ay = 0 \tag{9.17}$$

which satisfies the initial condition

$$\phi_0(0) = y_0 \tag{9.18}$$

where a and y_0 are given constants. From our previous solution in Section 2.2 (p. 41), we know that the solution ϕ_0 is in the class Λ'. Thus, we should be able to find ϕ_0 by Laplace transforms. Let $Y_0(s) = \mathcal{L}(\phi_0)$. Using (9.15), we may take the Laplace transform of every term in the equation

$$\phi_0'(t) + a\phi_0(t) = 0$$

satisfied by ϕ_0, and we obtain

$$sY_0(s) - \phi_0(0) + aY_0(s) = 0 \quad \text{or} \quad (s + a)Y_0(s) = y_0$$

using (9.18). This yields

$$Y_0(s) = \frac{y_0}{s + a}$$

and the only remaining problem is to find a function which has this expression as its Laplace transform. As we have seen in Example 2, Section 9.1 (p. 377), $y_0 e^{-at}$ is such a function. By direct verification and application of Theorem 1.1 (p. 24), we know that it is the only solution of the equation (9.17) satisfying (9.18). However, as motivation for more complicated problems, it is useful to look at this a little differently.

At this stage, we do not know that it is the only such function, but if we accept the truth of the statement that two different continuous functions cannot have the same Laplace transform, then we conclude that $\phi_0(t) = y_0 e^{-at}$. Since $y_0 e^{-at}$ does belong to the class Λ', our reasoning is valid, except for the uniqueness statement which will be stated precisely and justified in Section 9.3.

Example 3.   Now let us apply the same method to find the solution ϕ of the nonhomogeneous equation

$$y' + ay = f(t) \tag{9.19}$$

which satisfies the initial condition

$$\phi(0) = y_0 \tag{9.20}$$

Here f is a given function belonging to the class Λ.   The problem (9.19), (9.20) was solved in Section 2.2 (p. 41), and from the solution it is obvious that if f is in the class Λ, the solution ϕ is in the class Λ'.   We proceed as in Example 2; we may assume that ϕ belongs to the class Λ' and we let $Y(s)$ be the Laplace transform of ϕ and $F(s)$ the Laplace transform of f. Using (9.15) we take the Laplace transform of every term in the equation

$$\phi'(t) + a\phi(t) = f(t)$$

satisfied by ϕ, and we obtain

$$sY(s) - \phi(0) + aY(s) = F(s) \quad \text{or} \quad (s + a)Y(s) = y_0 + F(s)$$

using (9.20).   This yields

$$Y(s) = \frac{y_0}{s + a} + \frac{F(s)}{s + a}$$

We must now find a function which has this expression as its Laplace transform.   We have already seen in Example 2 that $y_0 e^{-at}$ has Laplace transform $y_0/(s + a)$, but we have no method as yet of finding a function whose Laplace transform is $(F(s)/(s + a))$.   This suggests that we will need a method of finding a function whose Laplace transform is the product of two given functions.   In this case the given functions are $F(s)$ and $1/(s + a)$, which are the Laplace transforms of $f(t)$ and e^{-at} respectively.   This problem will be studied in Section 9.3.   For the present, we remark that in Section 2.2 we have seen that

$$\phi(t) = y_0 e^{-at} + \int_0^t e^{-a(t-u)} f(u)\, du$$

and this suggests that $\int_0^t e^{-a(t-u)} f(u)\, du$ should have the Laplace transform $F(s)/(s+a)$.

Example 4. In Examples 2 and 3 we have used the Laplace transform to solve linear differential equations with constant coefficients. To show that the method is less useful for linear equations with variable coefficients, let us attempt to find the solution ψ of the equation

$$y' + 2ty = 0 \tag{9.21}$$

which satisfies the initial condition

$$\psi(0) = y_0 \tag{9.22}$$

In Section 2.2, Example 1 (p. 40) we found that $\psi(t) = y_0 e^{-t^2}$. When we try to obtain this solution by the use of Laplace transforms, we meet with serious difficulties. If we let $Z(s)$ be the Laplace transform of ψ and take the Laplace transform of every term in the equation

$$\psi'(t) + 2t\psi(t) = 0$$

satisfied by ψ, we apply (9.10) and (9.15) and we obtain

$$sZ(s) - \psi(0) - 2Z'(s) = 0 \tag{9.23}$$

While in Examples 2 and 3 we obtained an algebraic equation for the Laplace transform of the desired solution (and thus simplified the problem), here we have a differential equation for the transform of the solution which is no simpler than the original problem. **This example suggests that the usefulness of the Laplace transform method is limited mainly to equations with constant coefficients.**

9.3   The Inverse Transform

The examples of the previous section have indicated the need for finding a function with a given Laplace transform. The function $f(t)$ whose

Laplace transform is $F(s)$ is called the **inverse Laplace transform** of $F(s)$. The inverse Laplace transform is, as we shall prove later in this section, linear. We must consider the following questions:

(i) If we know that $F(s)$ is the Laplace transform of a function $f(t)$, how can we compute the inverse transform f from a knowledge of F?

(ii) Is the inverse transform of a given function F unique?

An answer to the first question can be given in a theoretical way by means of the so-called complex inversion formula (see, for example [18], p. 66). However, the derivation and application of this formula require a knowledge of real and complex analysis. Therefore, we confine ourselves to a more elementary approach which will enable us to find the inverse transforms of some functions commonly arising in applications.

We have seen in Example 3, Section 9.2 (p. 385) that it would be useful to have a general method of calculating the inverse Laplace transform of a product of two functions each of whose inverse Laplace transforms are known. Let us now determine whether there is a means for doing this.

We assume that we are given $F(s)$ and $G(s)$, and that we can find functions $f(t)$ and $g(t)$ in the class Λ whose Laplace transforms are $F(s)$ and $G(s)$ respectively; thus $F(s) = \mathcal{L}(f(t))$ and $G(s) = \mathcal{L}(g(t))$. **Our problem is to determine the function $h(t)$ whose Laplace transform is the product $F(s)G(s)$, if such a function exists.** If there is such a function, then

$$\mathcal{L}\{h(t)\} = \int_0^\infty e^{-st}h(t)\, dt$$
$$= F(s)G(s) = \int_0^\infty e^{-su}f(u)\, du \int_0^\infty e^{-sv}g(v)\, dv \qquad (9.24)$$

where $\Re s > \sigma$ for some real number σ. If $F(s) = \mathcal{L}\{f(t)\}$ for $\Re s > \alpha$, and $G(s) = \mathcal{L}\{g(t)\}$ for $\Re s > \beta$ (α, β real), then $\sigma = \max(\alpha, \beta)$. Since each integral converges absolutely for $\Re s > \sigma$, we may write the product of the two integrals on the right side of (9.24) as a double integral, obtaining

$$\int_0^\infty e^{-st}h(t)\, dt = \int_0^\infty \int_0^\infty e^{-s(u+v)}f(u)g(v)\, du\, dv \qquad (9.25)$$

for $\Re s > \sigma$.

We write this as an iterated integral,

$$\int_0^\infty e^{-st}h(t)\, dt = \int_0^\infty g(v)\left[\int_0^\infty e^{-s(u+v)}f(u)\, du\right]dv$$

this can be justified under our hypotheses because of the absolute convergence noted above. Making the change of variable $u + v = t$ in the inner integral, we obtain

$$\int_0^\infty e^{-st} h(t)\, dt = \int_0^\infty g(v) \left[\int_0^\infty e^{-st} f(t - v)\, dt \right] dv$$

$$= \int_0^\infty e^{-st} \left[\int_0^t f(t - v) g(v)\, dv \right] dt \qquad (\Re s > \sigma) \qquad (9.26)$$

where the interchange in the order of integration can again be justified.

•**EXERCISE**

1. Obtain the limits of integration in (9.26).   [*Hint:* Draw a sketch of the region of integration.]

The equation (9.26) says $\mathcal{L}\{h(t)\} = \mathcal{L}[\int_0^t f(t - v) g(v)\, dv]$, which suggests that the solution to our problem is

$$h(t) = \int_0^t f(t - v) g(v)\, dv \qquad (9.27)$$

By reversing the argument we have just completed, we may prove that the Laplace transform of the function $h(t)$ defined by (9.27) is $F(s)G(s)$, as desired.

•**EXERCISE**

2. Show that if f and g belong to the class Λ and h is defined by (9.27), then
$$\int_0^\infty e^{-st} h(t)\, dt = \int_0^\infty f(u) e^{-su}\, du \int_0^\infty g(v) e^{-sv}\, dv.$$

We may summarize what we have sketched above in the following theorem.

Theorem 9.6.   *Let $f(t)$, $g(t)$ belong to the class Λ and let $F(s) = \mathcal{L}\{f(t)\}$, $G(s) = \mathcal{L}\{g(t)\}$.   Then $\mathcal{L}\left[\int_0^t f(t - v) g(v)\, dv \right] = F(s)G(s)$.*

The function h is defined by (9.27) is called the **convolution of f and g**, and is sometimes denoted by $h = f * g$ to indicate that the convolution of two functions resembles a product in many ways.

•**EXERCISES**

3. Show that $f * g = g * f$ for any two functions f, g in the class Λ.

4. Show that $(f * g) * h = f * (g * h)$ for any three functions f, g, h in the class Λ.

5. Show that $f * 0 = 0$ for any function f in the class Λ.

6. Show that if f and g are defined for $-\infty < t < \infty$ but are both identically zero for $t < 0$, then their convolution $f * g$ can be written as $\int_{-\infty}^{\infty} f(t - v)g(v)\,dv$.

The convolution integral in Exercise 6 is sometimes used to define an operation analogous to multiplication for certain classes of functions. The reader should be careful not to carry the analogy too far; for example, it is not true that $f * 1 = f$.

The properties of the convolution make it possible for us to calculate some inverse Laplace transforms which would otherwise be difficult or impossible to find.

Example 1.   Find the inverse Laplace transform of $1/(s^2 - 1) = 1/((s - 1)(s + 1))$.   Since $\mathcal{L}^{-1}\{1/(s - 1)\} = e^t$, and $\mathcal{L}^{-1}\{1/(s + 1)\} = e^{-t}$, we see that

$$
\begin{aligned}
\mathcal{L}^{-1}\left\{\frac{1}{s^2 - 1}\right\} &= \int_0^t e^{t-u}e^{-u}\,du = e^t \int_0^t e^{-2u}\,du \\
&= e^t \left[\frac{e^{-2u}}{-2}\right]_0^t = \frac{1}{2}e^t(1 - e^{-2t}) = \frac{1}{2}(e^t - e^{-t})
\end{aligned}
$$

There is another way to calculate this particular inverse transform.   If we decompose $(1/(s^2 - 1))$ into partial fractions, we find

$$
\frac{1}{s^2 - 1} = \frac{1}{(s - 1)(s + 1)} = \frac{1}{2}\left(\frac{1}{s - 1} - \frac{1}{s + 1}\right)
$$

and thus, by the linearity of $\mathcal{L}^{-1}$ (for a proof see p. 393),

$$
\begin{aligned}
\mathcal{L}^{-1}\left\{\frac{1}{s^2 - 1}\right\} &= \frac{1}{2}\left[\mathcal{L}^{-1}\left(\frac{1}{s - 1}\right) - \mathcal{L}^{-1}\left(\frac{1}{s + 1}\right)\right] \\
&= \frac{1}{2}(e^t - e^{-t})
\end{aligned}
$$

Example 2.   Find the inverse Laplace transform of $(1/(s^2(s^2 + 1)))$. We have seen, in equation (9.11), that $\mathcal{L}^{-1}(1/(s^2)) = t$, and in equation (9.7), $\mathcal{L}^{-1}(1/(s^2 + 1)) = \sin t$.   Now, by Theorem 9.6, $\mathcal{L}^{-1}(1/(s^2(s^2 + 1)))$ is the convolution of t and $\sin t$, which is

$$
\begin{aligned}
\int_0^t (t - u)\sin u\,du &= t \int_0^t \sin u\,du - \int_0^t u \sin u\,du \\
&= t - t\cos t + t\cos t - \sin t \\
&= t - \sin t
\end{aligned}
$$

We may also obtain this result by partial fractions. For

$$\frac{1}{s^2(s^2+1)} = \frac{1}{s^2} - \frac{1}{s^2+1}$$

and hence

$$\mathcal{L}^{-1}\left(\frac{1}{s^2(s^2+1)}\right) = \mathcal{L}^{-1}\left(\frac{1}{s^2}\right) - \mathcal{L}^{-1}\left(\frac{1}{s^2+1}\right) = t - \sin t$$

The above examples suggest that if we wish to find the inverse transform of a rational function $N(s)/D(s)$, where N and D are polynomials with the degree of N less than the degree of D, then we can take advantage of partial functions to decompose $N(s)/D(s)$ into a sum of terms each of whose inverse transform is easily found.

•**EXERCISES**

7. Find the inverse Laplace transform of each of the following functions. (We indicate the partial fraction decomposition for the convenience of the reader.)

(a) $\dfrac{s^2-6}{s^3+4s^2+3s} = \dfrac{A}{s} + \dfrac{B}{s+1} + \dfrac{C}{s+3}$.

(b) $\dfrac{1}{s^2(s^2+1)} = \dfrac{A}{s} + \dfrac{B}{s^2} + \dfrac{Cs+D}{s^2+1}$.

(c) $\dfrac{16}{s(s^2+4)^2} = \dfrac{A}{s} + \dfrac{Bs+C}{s^2+4} + \dfrac{Ds+E}{(s^2+4)^2}$.

(d) $\dfrac{F(s)}{s+a}$, where $f(t)$ is in the class Λ and $\mathcal{L}\{f(t)\} = F(s)$.

(e) $\dfrac{F(s)}{s^2+1}$, where $f(t)$ is in the class Λ and $\mathcal{L}\{f(t)\} = F(s)$.

8. Find the solution ϕ of the integral equation

$$\phi(t) + \int_0^t (t-u)\phi(u)\,du = 1$$

[*Hint:* Take the Laplace transform of every term and use Theorem 9.6; then solve for $\mathcal{L}(\phi(t))$ and finally find ϕ.]

This is as far as we can go with systematic techniques for constructing inverse transforms, without using the inversion theorem. Beyond this the most useful aids in finding inverse transforms are a good table of

Laplace transforms (a brief one may be found at the end of the chapter), experience, and luck.

Let us now turn to question (ii), namely, the uniqueness of the inverse transform. The result which we shall prove depends on the following powerful theorem of analysis.

Weierstrass Approximation Theorem. *Let f be a continuous function on a closed bounded interval [a,b]. Then for every ε > 0 there exists a polynomial P such that*

$$|f(t) - P(t)| < \epsilon \qquad (a \leq t \leq b)$$

Since the proof would take us rather far afield, we refer the interested reader to another source, such as [14, pp. 146–148].

Now, we can prove that the only function in the class Λ whose Laplace transform is identically zero is the zero function. In fact, we do not even need to require the Laplace transform to vanish identically.

Theorem 9.7. *Let f be continuous on $0 \leq t < \infty$ and belong to the class Λ, and let its Laplace transform F(s) exist for $\Re s \geq \sigma$. If F(s) = 0 for $s = \sigma, \sigma + 1, \sigma + 2, \ldots$, then f is identically zero on $0 \leq t < \infty$.*

Proof. The hypothesis is

$$\int_0^\infty e^{-st}f(t)\, dt = 0 \qquad (s = \sigma, \sigma + 1, \sigma + 2, \ldots) \tag{9.28}$$

We define

$$g(t) = e^{-\sigma t}f(t) \qquad (0 \leq t < \infty)$$

We note that by the definition of the class Λ, this implies $\sigma > c$ in (9.4) (p. 378), and therefore $\lim_{t \to \infty} g(t) = 0$. Then (9.28) implies

$$\int_0^\infty e^{-nt}g(t)\, dt = 0 \qquad (n = 0, 1, 2, \ldots) \tag{9.29}$$

Making the change of variable $e^{-t} = u$, (9.29) becomes

$$\int_0^1 u^n g(-\log u)\, du = 0 \qquad (n = 0, 1, 2, \ldots) \tag{9.30}$$

We define

$$h(u) = g(-\log u) \qquad (0 \le u \le 1)$$

(note $h(0) = g(\infty) = 0$), so that (9.30) becomes

$$\int_0^1 u^n h(u)\, du = 0 \qquad (n = 0, 1, 2, \ldots) \tag{9.31}$$

We shall prove that (9.31) implies that the function h is identically zero. We first use the Weierstrass approximation theorem: For every $\epsilon > 0$ we find a polynomial P such that

$$|P(u) - \bar{h}(u)| < \epsilon \qquad (0 \le u \le 1) \tag{9.32}$$

where $\bar{h}(u)$ is the complex conjugate of $h(u)$. Since $P(u)$ is a polynomial, the equation (9.31) implies that $\int_0^1 h(u)P(u)\, du = 0$, and therefore

$$\int_0^1 |h(u)|^2\, du = \int_0^1 h(u)\bar{h}(u)\, du = \int_0^1 h(u)[\bar{h}(u) - P(u)]\, du$$

Because of (9.32),

$$\int_0^1 |h(u)|^2\, du \le \epsilon \int_0^1 |h(u)|\, du = K\epsilon$$

where $K = \int_0^1 |h(u)|\, du$ is a constant. Since this is true for every $\epsilon > 0$, we must have $\int_0^1 |h(u)|^2\, du = 0$, and this, together with the continuity of h implies that h is identically zero on $[0, 1]$. Thus, $g(-\log u) = 0$ for $0 \le u \le 1$, and since $t = -\log u$, $g(t) = 0$ for $0 \le t < \infty$. It follows immediately that f is identically zero on $0 \le t < \infty$. ∎

Corollary. *If f_1 and f_2 are functions in the class Λ which are continuous on $0 \le t < \infty$, whose Laplace transforms are both defined for $\Re s \ge \sigma$ and whose Laplace transforms are equal for $s = \sigma + n$ $(n = 0, 1, 2, \ldots)$, then $f_1(t) = f_2(t)$ $[0 \le t < \infty]$.*

Proof. We merely apply Theorem 9.7 to the difference $f_1(t) - f_2(t)$ and the result follows immediately. ∎

Theorem 9.7 and its corollary justify the method we have used in Examples 2 and 3, Section 9.2 (pp. 384, 385), where we found the Laplace transform of an unknown function and then found this unknown function by taking the inverse transform. If the inverse transform were not unique, we would not know that the process of taking the inverse transform returns us to the original unknown function.

Another consequence of Theorem 9.7 is **the linearity of the inverse Laplace transform:** If the continuous functions $f_1(t)$ and $f_2(t)$ in the class Λ are the inverse transforms of $F_1(s)$ and $F_2(s)$ respectively, and if a and b are constants, then the inverse transform of $aF_1(s) + bF_2(s)$ is $af_1(t) + bf_2(t)$. To prove this, we need only observe that $af_1(t) + bf_2(t)$ has Laplace transform $aF_1(s) + bF_2(s)$ and use the corollary to Theorem 9.7 to show that $af_1(t) + bf_2(t)$ is the only continuous function in the class Λ with Laplace transform $aF_1(s) + bF_2(s)$.

The problem of inversion of Laplace transforms presents many practical as well as mathematical problems. As a simple example, we give the following theorem which shows that not all functions $F(s)$ can be the Laplace transform of a function $f(t)$ in the class Λ.

Theorem 9.8.   *If f belongs to the class Λ and if $F(s)$ is its Laplace transform, then* $\lim\limits_{\Re s \to \infty} F(s) = 0$.

Proof.   Since f belongs to the class Λ, it satisfies an inequality of the form (9.4), (p. 378). Then, letting $\sigma = \Re s$, we have

$$
[F(s)] \leq M \int_0^\infty |e^{-st}| e^{ct}\, dt
$$

$$
= M \int_0^\infty e^{-\sigma t} e^{ct}\, dt = \frac{M}{\sigma - c} \qquad (\Re s > c)
$$

and it is clear that $\lim\limits_{\Re s \to \infty} F(s) = 0$. ∎

We have actually proved a little more than we claimed. Not only have we shown that $F(s)$ tends to zero as $s \to \infty$, but in fact that $|sF(s)|$ remains bounded as $\Re s \to \infty$.

The question of which functions are Laplace transforms is a difficult one, and we cannot in this brief treatment give a more precise answer. In practice, we only apply Laplace transforms when we can prove the existence of an inverse transform by finding it explicitly, but the question remains an important one because it is often impossible to find the inverse transform explicitly.

9.4   Applications to Linear Equations
with Constant Coefficients

Our main purpose in developing the Laplace transform has been to apply it to the solution of linear differential equations.   We have suggested how this may be done by examples in Section 9.2, where we considered first-order differential equations.   For equations of higher order, the general idea is the same, but there are some technical problems which arise when we try to find the inverse transform.   In this section we shall discuss these technical problems and the means of dealing with them by a collection of examples.   We shall concentrate on equations of the second order, but we shall also indicate the minor additional problems which arise for equations of higher order.

In each of the examples involving a second-order differential equation we shall be seeking the solution ϕ of an equation of the form

$$a_0 y'' + a_1 y' + a_2 y = f(t) \tag{9.33}$$

where a_0, a_1, a_2 are constants, which satisfies the initial conditions

$$\phi(0) = y_0 \qquad \phi'(0) = y_1 \tag{9.34}$$

Under suitable hypotheses on the function f, we may apply an existence theorem, such as Theorem 3.1 (p. 65), to conclude the existence of a unique solution ϕ of the equation (9.33) which satisfies the initial conditions (9.34).   When we attempt to find this solution by means of the Laplace transform, we can expect to obtain it only if it and its derivatives up to the second order are of exponential growth, that is, if it belongs to the class Λ^2.   Thus, to conclude the existence of a solution which can be found by means of the Laplace transform, we need a theorem on the growth of solutions of linear differential equations with constant coefficients.   Such a theorem has been proved in Chapter 6—Theorem 6.11 (p. 294) for systems and Exercise 5, Section 6.8 (p. 295) for equations of order n.   This theorem applied in the present context says that **every solution of a linear nonhomogeneous differential equation of order n with constant coefficients, whose nonhomogeneous term is in the class Λ, belongs to the class Λ^n.**

Example 1.   Let us use the Laplace transform to find the solution ϕ of the equation $y'' + y' + 2y = 0$ which satisfies the initial conditions $\phi(0) = 1$, $\phi'(0) = 1$.   We let Y be the Laplace transform of ϕ and take the Laplace transform of the equation

$$\phi''(t) + 3\phi'(t) + 2\phi(t) = 0$$

satisfied by ϕ. Using (9.16) (p. 383), we obtain

$$s^2 Y(s) - s\phi(0) - \phi'(0) + 3[sY(s) - \phi(0)] + 2Y(s) = 0$$

or

$$(s^2 + 3s + 2)Y(s) = (s + 3)\phi(0) + \phi'(0) = s + 4$$

Thus

$$Y(s) = \frac{s + 4}{s^2 + 3s + 2} = \frac{s + 4}{(s + 1)(s + 2)} \tag{9.35}$$

In order to take the inverse transform in (9.35), we must simplify the expression $(s + 4)/((s + 1)(s + 2))$. We use the method of partial fractions to accomplish this. Letting

$$\frac{s + 4}{(s + 1)(s + 2)} = \frac{A}{s + 1} + \frac{B}{s + 2}$$

for all s, we observe that

$$A = \lim_{s \to -1} \frac{s + 4}{(s + 1)(s + 2)} \cdot (s + 1) = \lim_{s \to -1} \frac{s + 4}{s + 2} = 3$$

$$B = \lim_{s \to -2} \frac{s + 4}{(s + 1)(s + 2)} \cdot (s + 2) = \lim_{s \to -2} \frac{s + 4}{s + 1} = -2$$

Thus,

$$Y(s) = \frac{s + 4}{(s + 1)(s + 2)} = \frac{3}{s + 1} - \frac{2}{s + 2}$$

Now, we may use (9.3) (p. 377) and the linearity of the inverse transform to find a function whose Laplace transform is $Y(s)$, and because of the uniqueness of the inverse transform (Theorem 9.7), this function must be the desired solution ϕ. We see that $\phi(t) = 3e^{-t} - 2e^{-2t}$. We could, of course, have obtained this solution by using the methods of Section 3.4 (p. 88), but this would have involved first finding the general solution of

(9.33) and then substituting the initial conditions (9.34) to determine the constants.   **The Laplace transform does not solve problems which would otherwise be unsolvable, but it does provide an easy, practical method of solution for many problems.**

•**EXERCISE**

   1. Verify the solution to Example 1 by direct substitution.

Example 2.   Let us now use the Laplace transform to find the solution ϕ of the equation $y'' + 4y' + 4y = f(t)$ which satisfies the initial conditions $\phi(0) = 1$, $\phi'(0) = 2$, where $f(t)$ belongs to the class Λ.   We let Y be the Laplace transform of ϕ, F the Laplace transform of f, and we take the Laplace transform of the equation

$$\phi''(t) + 4\phi'(t) + 4\phi(t) = f(t)$$

satisfied by ϕ.   Much as in Example 1, we obtain

$$s^2 Y(s) - s\phi(0) - \phi'(0) + 4[sY(s) - \phi(0)] + 4Y(s) = F(s)$$

or

$$\begin{aligned}
(s^2 + 4s + 4)Y(s) &= (s + 4)\phi(0) + \phi'(0) + F(s) \\
&= (s + 4) + 2 + F(s) = s + 6 + F(s)
\end{aligned}$$

Thus,

$$Y(s) = \frac{s + 6 + F(s)}{s^2 + 4s + 4} = \frac{s + 6}{(s + 2)^2} + \frac{F(s)}{(s + 2)^2}$$

Again, we use partial fractions to simplify this expression.   We must find constants A and B such that

$$\frac{s + 6}{(s + 2)^2} = \frac{A}{s + 2} + \frac{B}{(s + 2)^2}$$

We observe that

$$B = \lim_{s \to -2} \frac{s + 6}{(s + 2)^2} \cdot (s + 2)^2 = \lim_{s \to -2} (s + 6) = 4$$

and then

$$\frac{A}{s+2} = \frac{s+6}{(s+2)^2} - \frac{B}{(s+2)^2} = \frac{s+6}{(s+2)^2} - \frac{4}{(s+2)^2} = \frac{s+2}{(s+2)^2} = \frac{1}{s+2}$$

which implies $A = 1$. Now,

$$Y(s) = \frac{s+6}{(s+2)^2} = \frac{1}{s+2} + \frac{4}{(s+2)^2} + \frac{F(s)}{(s+2)^2}$$

and we may use (9.3) (p. 377), (9.12) (p. 380) and Theorem 9.6 (p. 388), to find the inverse transform. This yields the solution $\phi(t) = e^{-2t} + 4te^{-2t} + \int_0^t (t-u)e^{-2(t-u)}f(u)\,du$.

• EXERCISE

2. Verify the answer to Example 2 by direct substitution.

Examples 1 and 2 give us enough insight into the method to enable us to solve the general linear homogeneous equation of order n with constant coefficients. Let ϕ be the solution of the equation of order n,

$$L_n(y) = a_0 y^{(n)} + a_1 y^{(n-1)} + \cdots + a_n y = 0 \tag{9.36}$$

($a_0, a_1, \ldots, a_n$ constants) which satisfies the initial conditions

$$\phi(0) = y_0, \quad \phi'(0) = y_1, \quad \ldots, \quad \phi^{(n-1)}(0) = y_{n-1} \tag{9.37}$$

We let Y be the Laplace transform of ϕ and take the Laplace transform of the equation

$$a_0 \phi^{(n)}(t) + a_1 \phi^{(n-1)}(t) + \cdots + a_n \phi(t) = 0$$

We obtain

$$a_0[s^n Y(s) - s^{n-1}y_0 - s^{n-2}y_1 - \cdots - y_{n-1}]$$
$$+ a_1[s^{n-1} Y(s) - s^{n-2}y_0 - \cdots - y_{n-2}] + \cdots$$
$$+ a_{n-1}[s Y(s) - y_0] + a_n Y(s) = 0$$

or

$$p(s) Y(s) = a_0(s^{n-1}y_0 + s^{n-2}y_1 + \cdots + y_{n-1})$$
$$+ a_1(s^{n-2}y_0 + \cdots + y_{n-2}) + \cdots + a_{n-1}y_0 \tag{9.38}$$

where p is the characteristic polynomial of the linear operator L_n (see Section 3.5, p. 94),

$$p(s) = a_0 s^n + a_1 s^{n-1} + \cdots + a_n$$

We may write (9.38) in the form

$$p(s)Y(s) = q(s)$$

where q is a polynomial of degree at most $(n - 1)$ on the right-hand side of (9.38). (The degree could be less than $(n - 1)$ if the given initial value y_0 is zero.) This polynomial q is linear in $y_0, y_1, \ldots, y_{n-1}$. We now have

$$Y(s) = \frac{q(s)}{p(s)}$$

and the next step is to separate the rational function $q(s)/p(s)$ into partial fractions. If the roots of the polynomial p are $z_1, \ldots, z_k$. of multiplicities $m_1, \ldots, m_k$ respectively, then we can write

$$p(s) = a_0(s - z_1)^{m_1}(s - z_2)^{m_2} \cdots (s - z_k)^{m_k}$$

The process of separating into partial fractions gives

$$\frac{q(s)}{p(s)} = \frac{a_{11}}{s - z_1} + \cdots + \frac{a_{1,m_1}}{(s - z_1)^{m_1}} + \frac{a_{21}}{s - z_2} + \cdots + \frac{a_{2,m_2}}{(s - z_2)^{m_2}}$$
$$+ \cdots + \frac{a_{k1}}{s - z_k} + \cdots + \frac{a_{k,m_k}}{(s - z_k)^{m_k}}$$

where the constants $a_{11}, \ldots, a_{k,m_k}$ may be calculated. We may now take the inverse transform of $Y(s)$ using (9.3) (p. 377) and (9.12) (p. 380). We obtain the solution

$$\phi(t) = a_{11}e^{z_1 t} + \cdots + \frac{a_{1,m_1}}{(m_1 - 1)!} t^{m_1-1}e^{z_1 t} + \cdots + a_{k1}e^{z_k t}$$
$$+ \cdots + \frac{a_{k,m_k}}{(m_k - 1)!} t^{m_k-1}e^{z_k t}$$

which is, of course, the same as that obtained in Section 3.5. If some of the roots $z_1, \ldots, z_k$ are complex but the coefficients $a_0, \ldots, a_n$ of L

are real, then we may express the solutions in terms of real functions just as in Section 3.5 (p. 94).

We remark if in place of the equation (9.36) we consider the equation

$$L_n(y) = f(t)$$

where f belongs to the class Λ, we handle the additional term by using the convolution exactly as in Example 2 above.

The Laplace transform is used a great deal in the study of electrical circuits. We have already mentioned in Section 3.4 (p. 82) the linear electrical circuit consisting of a capacitance C, a resistance R, and an inductance L connected in series. The voltage $v(t)$ across the capacitance may be described by the equation

$$Lv'' + Rv' + \frac{1}{C}v = 0$$

Consider such a circuit with an external applied voltage $A \cos (kt + \alpha)$, such as might arise from connecting the circuit to a source of alternating current. Then the voltage $v(t)$ would be described by the equation

$$Lv'' + Rv'' + \frac{1}{C}v = A \cos (kt + \alpha) \tag{9.39}$$

In studying the equation (9.39), we find it convenient to write the non-homogeneous term as the real part of a complex exponential, solve the corresponding complex equation, and then take the real part of the solution, just as we suggested in Section 3.4, Exercise 6 (p. 86). To do this, we define the complex number

$$b = Ae^{i\alpha} \tag{9.40}$$

then

$$A \cos (kt + \alpha) = \Re[Ae^{i(kt+\alpha)}] = \Re(Ae^{i\alpha}e^{ikt})$$
$$= \Re be^{ikt}$$

Thus, instead of (9.39) we consider the complex equation

$$Ly'' + Ry' + \frac{1}{C}y = be^{ikt} \tag{9.41}$$

Let Y be the Laplace transform of the solution ϕ of (9.41) which satisfies the initial conditions $\phi(0) = y_0$, $\phi'(0) = y_1$. Then, using (9.3), p. 377, and (9.16), p. 383, we see that

$$L[s^2 Y(s) - sy_0 - y_1] + R[sY(s) - y_0] + \frac{1}{C}Y(s) = \frac{b}{s - ik}$$

or

$$\left(Ls^2 + Rs + \frac{1}{C}\right)Y(s) = \frac{b}{s - ik} + L(sy_0 + y_1) + Ry_0 \qquad (9.42)$$

Let z_1 and z_2 be the roots of the polynomial $p(s) = Ls^2 + Rs + 1/C$, so that $Ls^2 + Rs + 1/C = L(s - z_1)(s - z_2)$. Then we can write (9.42) as

$$Y(s) = \frac{b}{L(s - z_1)(s - z_2)(s - ik)} + \frac{L(sy_0 + y_1) + Ry_0}{L(s - z_1)(s - z_2)}$$

When we separate into partial fractions, we obtain

$$Y(s) = \frac{M}{s - ik} + \frac{N}{s - z_1} + \frac{P}{s - z_2}$$

with

$$M = \lim_{s \to ik} \frac{b}{L(s - z_1)(s - z_2)} = \frac{b}{p(ik)}$$

When we take the inverse transform, we obtain the solution of (9.41) in the form $\phi(t) = Me^{ikt} + Ne^{z_1 t} + Pe^{z_2 t}$. If L, C, R are all positive constants, a reasonable hypothesis in applications, then the roots z_1 and z_2 of the polynomial $p(s)$ have negative real part (Why?). We let $\phi_p(t) = Me^{ikt}$, $\phi_h(t) = Ne^{z_1 t} + Pe^{z_2 t}$. Then $\phi(t) = \phi_p(t) + \phi_h(t)$ and $\phi_h(t)$ tends to zero exponentially as $t \to \infty$. The term $\phi_h(t)$ is called a **transient,** because its effect dies out, and the term $\phi_p(t)$ is called **the steady state.** As we wish to concentrate on this steady state, we do not examine the transient term further. (For this reason we did not actually compute the constants N and P.) The steady state is $(b/p(ik))e^{ikt}$. To calculate the corresponding voltage $v_1(t)$, we must take the real part of this expression.   We define the **transfer function**

$$C(k) = \frac{1}{p(ik)}$$

Then

$$
\begin{aligned}
v_1(t) &= \Re[bC(k)e^{ikt}] = \Re[Ae^{i\alpha}|C(k)|e^{i \, \text{arg} \, C(k)}e^{ikt}] \\
&= \Re[A|C(k)|e^{i \, (kt+\alpha+ \, \text{arg} \, C(k))}] \\
&= A|C(k)| \cos \left[kt + \alpha + \text{arg} \, C(k) \right]
\end{aligned}
$$

When we compare this steady-state output voltage $v_1(t)$ with the input voltage $A \cos (kt + \alpha)$, we see that the effect of the circuit has been to multiply the amplitude by the **gain function** $|C(k)|$ and to introduce a **phase lag** arg $C(k)$.   Note that v_1 is independent of the initial conditions. The transfer function $C(k)$ is determined by the electrical circuit, but depends on the frequency of the input voltage.   The essential principle in tuning a radio is to adjust the circuit, usually by varying the capacitance C to maximize the gain function for a given k.   In other electrical applications, it is necessary to vary k to maximize the gain function for given values of L, R, and C.

The reader is warned that we have assumed that L, R, and C are constant and that the circuit is linear in the above discussion.   For time-dependent or nonlinear (vacuum tube) circuits, the resulting differential equations cannot, as a rule, be solved by means of the Laplace transform, and other methods must be developed.   It may still be reasonable to define a gain function and a phase lag, but these will no longer be given by a transfer function.

The Laplace transform is sometimes used to solve linear nonhomogeneous differential equations whose nonhomogeneous terms do not belong to the class Λ.   While the solutions obtained in those cases are then purely formal, it is possible to show that they are actual solutions in a more general sense.   The justification requires a more sophisticated approach, such as the theory of distributions.   (See, for example, [2].) Here, we shall only give an example to indicate the nature of the problem.

Let us again consider an electrical circuit consisting of a capacitance C, a resistance R, and an inductance L connected in series.   However, now let us attempt to determine the behavior of the circuit if a large external voltage is applied over a very short time interval.   Let this external voltage be defined by

$$
\delta_\sigma(t) = \begin{cases} 1/\sigma & (0 < t < \sigma) \\ 0 & (t > \sigma) \end{cases}
$$

Then the circuit is governed by the differential equation

$$Lv'' + Rv' + \frac{1}{C}v = \delta_\sigma(t) \tag{9.43}$$

Since $\delta_\sigma(t)$ is certainly in the class Λ, we can treat this equation by taking Laplace transforms, using

$$\mathcal{L}\{\delta_\sigma(t)\} = \int_0^\infty \delta_\sigma(t)e^{-st}\,dt = \int_0^\sigma \frac{1}{\sigma}e^{-st}\,dt$$
$$= \frac{1}{\sigma}\left[\frac{e^{-st}}{-s}\right]_{t=0}^{t=\sigma} = \frac{1}{\sigma s}(1 - e^{-\sigma s}) \tag{9.44}$$

• **EXERCISE**

3. Find the steady-state solution ϕ_p of the equation (9.43) satisfying the initial conditions $\phi(0) = y_0$, $\phi'(0) = y_1$. (By steady-state solution we mean, as above, the difference between the solution and those terms ϕ_h in the solution which (because L, R, C are positive constants) tend to zero as $t \to \infty$.)

It is of interest to consider the "limiting behavior" of this electrical circuit as $\sigma \to 0$. The applied voltage $\delta_\sigma(t)$ does not tend to a limiting function in the usual sense (see Figure 9.1 when $\sigma \to 0$), but we can think

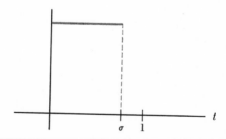

Figure 9.1

of the limit as an impulse at $t = 0$ whose integral is 1, and call this a "generalized function" $\delta(t)$ (also the Dirac delta function). This would lead to the differential equation

$$Lv'^h + Rv' + \frac{1}{C}v = \delta(t) \tag{9.45}$$

We treat this equation by Laplace transforms, proceeding as if we could write

$$\mathcal{L}\{\delta(t)\} = \lim_{\sigma \to 0} \mathcal{L}\{\delta_\sigma(t)\} = \lim_{c \to 0} \frac{1 - e^{-cs}}{cs} = 1 \tag{9.46}$$

The reader should compare (9.46) with Theorem 9.8 (p. 393), which says that for a function f in the class Λ, $\lim_{s \to \infty} \mathcal{L}\{f(t)\} = 0$, and should note that there is no contradiction here since δ does not belong to the class Λ, although δ_σ does.

If we let $Y(s)$ be the Laplace transform of the solution ϕ of (9.45) satisfying the initial conditions $\phi(0) = y_0$, $\phi'(0) = y_0$, we obtain, using (9.46) and writing $p(s) = Ls^2 + Rs + 1/C = L(s - z_1)(s - z_2)$ as before,

$$L[s^2 Y(s) - sy_0 - y_1] + R[sY(s) - y_0] + \frac{1}{C} Y(s) = 1$$

$$\left(Ls^2 + Rs + \frac{1}{C}\right) Y(s) = 1 + L(sy_0 + y_1) + Ry_0$$

$$Y(s) = \frac{1}{L(s - z_1)(s - z_2)} + \frac{L(sy_0 + y_1) + Ry_0}{L(s - z_1)(s - z_2)} \tag{9.47}$$

This can be separated into partial fractions in the form

$$Y(s) = \frac{A}{s - z_1} + \frac{B}{s - z_2}$$

which leads to the solution $\phi(t) = Ae^{z_1 t} + Be^{z_2 t}$. Observe that if L, R, C are all positive, so that z_1 and z_2 have negative real part, $\lim_{t \to \infty} \phi(t) = 0$. Observe also that the output voltage ϕ is a continuous function, even though the input voltage δ is not.

Since the method used in this example has not been justified, the answer obtained must be verified by direct substitution. Such a verification requires an understanding of the meaning of $\delta(t)$. Let us also point out that we could obtain the same solution without using the Laplace transform by means of variation of constants (see Section 3.8, p. 105). This would also involve the same nonrigorous calculations, and would also require verification by direct subsitution.

•EXERCISES

Find, using Laplace transforms, the solution ϕ of each of the following differential equations which satisfies the given initial conditions.

4. $y'' - y = 0,$ $\qquad\qquad\qquad$ $\phi(0) = 0,$ $\phi'(0) = 1.$

5. $y'' - 5y' + 6y = 0,$ $\qquad\quad$ $\phi(0) = 0,$ $\phi'(0) = 1.$

6. $y''' - 6y'' + 11y' - 6y = 0,$ $\quad$ $\phi(0) = \phi'(0) = 0,$ $\phi''(0) = 1.$

7. $y''' - 8y = e^{2t},$ $\qquad\qquad$ $\phi(0) = \phi'(0) = 0,$ $\phi''(0) = 1.$

8. $y'' - 9y = e^t,$ $\qquad\qquad$ $\phi(0) = 1,$ $\phi'(0) = 0.$

9. $y'' - 9y = \sin t,$ $\qquad\qquad$ $\phi(0) = 1,$ $\phi'(0) = 0.$

10. $y'' + 4y = \sin 2t,$ $\qquad\quad$ $\phi(0) = 1,$ $\phi'(0) = 1.$

11. $y'' - y = 0,$ $\qquad\qquad\qquad$ $\phi(1) = 0,$ $\phi'(1) = 1.$

[*Hint:* Begin by making the change of independent variable $\tau = t - 1$ to move the initial time to zero.]

12. $y'' - 9y = f(t),$ $\phi(0) = 1,$ $\phi'(0) = 0,$ where f is in the class $\Lambda.$ [*Hint:* Use the convolution.]

13. $y'' + 4y = f(t),$ $\phi(0) = 1,$ $\phi'(0) = 1,$ where f is in the class $\Lambda.$

14. Plot the gain and transfer functions of the linear differential operator defined by each of the following:

(a) $L(y) = y'' + 4y' + 3y.$

(b) $L(y) = y'' + 4y' + 4y.$

(c) $L(y) = y'' + y.$

15. Find the steady-state solution of the differential equation $y'' + 9y = e^{2t}.$

16. Find the steady-state voltage in an electrical circuit with $L = 1,$ $R = 10,$ $C = \frac{1}{9}$ with an applied voltage $9\delta(t).$

9.5   Applications to Linear Systems

The methods used in the previous section to obtain solutions of a linear differential equation with constant coefficients can be used with no essential change to obtain solutions of a linear system with constant coefficients. We shall not go into great detail in the solution of linear systems, but shall only give a few examples to illustrate the method. The applicability of the Laplace transform method to each of the systems considered follows from Theorem 6.11 (p. 294).

Example 1.   Find the solution $\phi = (\phi_1, \phi_2)$ of the system

$$y_1' = 2y_1 + y_2$$
$$y_2' = -y_1 + 4y_2$$

which satisfies the initial conditions $\phi_1(0) = 0$, $\phi_2(0) = 1$. Also find a fundamental matrix. We let $Y_1(s) = \mathcal{L}\{\phi_1(t)\}$, $Y_2(s) = \mathcal{L}\{\phi_2(t)\}$. When we take Laplace transforms in the equations satisfied by ϕ_1, ϕ_2, we obtain

$$sY_1(s) - \phi_1(0) = 2Y_1(s) + Y_2(s)$$
$$sY_2(s) - \phi_2(0) = -Y_1(s) + 4Y_2(s)$$

or

$$(s - 2)Y_1(s) - Y_2(s) = \phi_1(0) = 0$$
$$Y_1(s) + (s - 4)Y_2(s) = \phi_2(0) = 1$$

Solving for $Y_1(s)$ and $Y_2(s)$, we obtain

$$Y_1(s) = \frac{1}{(s - 3)^2} \qquad Y_2(s) = \frac{s - 2}{(s - 3)^2} = \frac{1}{s - 3} + \frac{1}{(s - 3)^2}$$

Taking the inverse transform, we obtain

$$\phi_1(t) = te^{3t} \qquad \phi_2(t) = e^{3t} + te^{3t}$$

To find a fundamental matrix we find the solution $\psi = (\psi_1, \psi_2)$ for which $\psi_1(0) = 1$, $\psi_2(0) = 0$. Proceeding as above we obtain

$$(s - 2)Y_1(s) - Y_2(s) = \psi_1(0) = 1$$
$$Y_1(s) + (s - 4)Y_2(s) = \psi_2(0) = 0$$

the solution of which is

$$Y_1(s) = \frac{s - 4}{(s - 3)^2} = \frac{1}{s - 3} - \frac{1}{(s - 3)^2}$$

$$Y_2(s) = \frac{-1}{(s - 3)^2}$$

Therefore, $\psi_1(t) = (1 - t)e^{3t}$, $\psi_2(t) = te^{3t}$, and by Theorems 6.5 (p. 266) and 6.6 (p. 268), a fundamental matrix is

$$\Phi(t) = (\phi(t), \psi(t)) = e^{3t}\begin{pmatrix} 1 - t & t \\ -t & 1 + t \end{pmatrix}$$

The reader should compare this solution with that of Example 5, Section 6.7 (p. 285), for the initial condition imposed here.

• EXERCISE

1. Verify the solution obtained in Example 1 above by direct subsitution.

By taking Laplace transform in Example 1, we reduce the problem of solving a system of differential equations to the problem of solving a linear system of algebraic equations. This is a substantial simplification, as algebraic systems can be solved explicitly by an easily carried-out procedure if the order of the system is not too large.

Another type of problem for which the Laplace transform is very useful is a system of linear differential equations with constant coefficients of order higher than the first. While such a system can be reduced to a system of first-order equations by the methods of Chapter 6, it can also be solved directly by means of the Laplace transform without the need for this reduction.

Example 2.   Find the solution (ϕ_1, ϕ_2) of the system

$$y_1'' - 2y_1' - y_2' + 2y_2 = 0$$
$$y_1' - 2y_1 + y_2' = -2e^{-t}$$

which satisfies the initial conditions $\phi_1(0) = 3$, $\phi_1'(0) = 2$, $\phi_2(0) = 0$. We let Y_1 and Y_2 be the Laplace transform of ϕ_1 and ϕ_2 respectively. When we take Laplace transforms in the equations satisfied by ϕ_1 and ϕ_2, we obtain

$$[s^2 Y_1(s) - 3s - 2] - 2[s Y_1(s) - 3] - s Y_2(s) + 2 Y_2(s) = 0$$

$$[s Y_1(s) - 3] - 2 Y_1(s) + s Y_2(s) = -\frac{2}{s+1}$$

or

$$(s^2 - 2s) Y_1(s) - (s - 2) Y_2(s) = 3s + 2 - 6 = 3s - 4$$

$$(s - 2) Y_1(s) + s Y_2(s) = -\frac{2}{s+1} + 3 = \frac{3s+1}{s+1} \tag{9.48}$$

Solving the system (9.48), we obtain

$$Y_1(s) = \frac{3s^2 - 4s - 1}{(s + 1)(s - 1)(s - 2)} = \frac{1}{s-1} + \frac{1}{s+1} + \frac{1}{s-2}$$

$$Y_2(s) = \frac{2}{(s + 1)(s - 1)} = \frac{1}{s-1} - \frac{1}{s+1} \tag{9.49}$$

We take inverse transforms of (9.49), to obtain the solution $\phi_1(t) = e^t + e^{-t} + e^{2t}$, $\phi_2(t) = e^t - e^{-t}$.

● **EXERCISE**

2. Verify the solution obtained in Example 2 by direct substitution.

To solve the problem of Example 2 we could proceed as follows. Transform the system to an equivalent system of 3 first-order equations, find a fundamental matrix for this system, and finally impose the initial conditions. It is clear that in most simple problems such as the one in Example 2, the use of Laplace transforms does give an answer more quickly.

Example 3.   Find the solution (ϕ_1, ϕ_2) of the system

$$y_1'' + 2y_1' + y_1 + y_2'' + y_2' = 0$$
$$y_1' + y_1 + y_2' = 0$$

which satisfies the initial conditions $\phi_1(0) = 1$, $\phi_1'(0) = 0$, $\phi_2(0) = 1$, $\phi_2'(0) = 0$. We let Y_1 and Y_2 be the Laplace transforms of ϕ_1 and ϕ_2 respectively. When we take Laplace transforms in the equations satisfied by ϕ_1 and ϕ_2, we obtain

$$[s^2Y_1(s) - s] + 2[sY_1(s) - 1] + Y_1(s) + [s^2Y_2(s) - s] + [sY_2(s) - 1] = 0$$
$$[sY_1(s) - 1] + Y_1(s) + [sY_2(s) - 1] = 0$$

or

$$(s^2 + 2s + 1)Y_1(s) + (s^2 + s)Y_2(s) = 2s + 3$$
$$(s + 1)Y_1(s) + sY_2(s) = 2 \tag{9.50}$$

When we attempt to solve the algebraic system (9.50), we find that it is inconsistent! Hence, there is no solution to the given system of equations which satisfies the initial conditions.

● **EXERCISES**

Find the solution (ϕ_1, ϕ_2) of each of the following systems of equations which satisfies the given initial conditions.

3. $y_1' + y_2' = 0$ $y_1' - y_2' = 1$
    $\phi_1(0) = 1$ $\phi_2(0) = 0$

4. $y_1' + 3y_2' = 0$ $y_1' - y_1 + 2y_2' = 0$
    $\phi_1(0) = 1$ $\phi_2(0) = -1$

5. $y_1'' + 3y_1' + 2y_1 + y_2' + y_2 = 0$ $y_1' + 2y_1 + y_2' - y_2 = 0$
 $\phi_1(0) = 1$ $\phi_1'(0) = -1$ $\phi_2(0) = 0$

6. $y_1'' - 3y_1' + 2y_1 + y_2'' - 2y_2' = 0$ $y_1' - y_1 + y_2' = 0$
 $\phi_1(0) = 1$ $\phi_1'(0) = 1$ $\phi_2(0) = 1$ $\phi_2'(0) = 0$

7. Solve the system (6.1), Section 6.1 (p. 238), assuming the spring constants are one, using the initial conditions $\phi_1(0) = 1$, $\phi_1'(0) = 0$, $\phi_2(0) = 0$, $\phi_2'(0) = 1$.

8. A mechanical system consisting of two coupled springs, assuming no friction and a periodic external force, is governed by a system of differential equations

$$m_1 y_1'' + k_1 y_1 - k_2(y_2 - y_1) = 0$$
$$m_2 y_2'' + k_2(y_2 - y_1) = A \cos \omega t$$

where m_1, m_2, k_1, k_2, A are positive constants. Find the motion of the system corresponding to the solution (ϕ_1, ϕ_2), where $\phi_1(0) = 1$, $\phi_1'(0) = 0$, $\phi_2(0) = 0$, $\phi_2'(0) = 0$.

9. For a system as in Exercise 7 with $k_1 = k_2 = k$, $A = 0$, define the kinetic energy $T = \frac{1}{2} m_1 y_1'^2 + \frac{1}{2} m_2 y_2'^2$ and the potential energy $V = (k/2(y_1^2 - 2y_1 y_2 + y_2^2))$. Show that the total energy $T + V$ is constant. [*Hint:* Show that $(d/dt\{T(t) + V(t)\}) = 0$, using the differential equations.]

10. Suggest a method, using the Laplace transform, for constructing a fundamental matrix for the system. $\mathbf{y}' = A\mathbf{y}$, where A is a constant $(n \times n)$ matrix. [*Hint:* See Example 1 above.]

11. Construct a fundamental matrix $\Phi(t)$ (for example, the one with $\Phi(0) = E$) for the system $\mathbf{y}' = A\mathbf{y}$, where

$$A = \begin{pmatrix} 3 & -1 & 1 \\ 2 & 0 & 1 \\ 1 & -1 & 2 \end{pmatrix}$$

Compare your result with Example 6, Section 6.7 (p. 288).

9.6   A Table of Laplace Transforms

We present here a brief table of Laplace transforms, with references to this chapter where the transforms listed are derived. It is understood that $F(s)$ denotes the Laplace transform of $f(t)$, that $G(s)$ denotes the Laplace transform of $g(t)$, and that in transforms involving an arbitrary function f or g, the functions involved belong to a suitable class to guarantee the existence of the transform.

Function	*Transform*	*Reference*
1	$\dfrac{1}{s}$	(9.2)
e^{zt}	$\dfrac{1}{s-z}$	(9.3)
$\cos \beta t$	$\dfrac{s}{s^2 + \beta^2}$	(9.7)
$\sin \beta t$	$\dfrac{\beta}{s^2 + \beta^2}$	(9.7)
$e^{\alpha t} \cos \beta t$	$\dfrac{s - \alpha}{(s - \alpha)^2 + \beta^2}$	(9.6)
$e^{\alpha t} \sin \beta t$	$\dfrac{\beta}{(s - \alpha)^2 + \beta^2}$	(9.6)
t^k	$\dfrac{k!}{s^{k+1}}$	(9.11)
$t^k e^{zt}$	$\dfrac{k!}{(s - z)^{k+1}}$	(9.12)
$t^k f(t)$	$(-1)^k F^{(k)}(s)$	(9.10)
$t^k \cos \beta t$	$\dfrac{k!\,\Re(s + i\beta)^{k+1}}{[(s - \alpha)^2 + \beta^2]^{k+1}}$ *	(9.14)
$t^k \sin \beta t$	$\dfrac{k!\,\Im(s + i\beta)^{k+1}}{[(s - \alpha)^2 + \beta^2]^{k+1}}$ *.	(9.14)
$t^k e^{\alpha t} \cos \beta t$	$\dfrac{k!\,\Re[(s - \alpha) + i\beta]^{k+1}}{[(s - \alpha)^2 + \beta^2]^{k+1}}$ *	(9.13)
$t^k e^{\alpha t} \sin \beta t$	$\dfrac{k!\,\Im[(s - \alpha) + i\beta]^{k+1}}{[(s - \alpha)^2 + \beta^2]^{k+1}}$ *	(9.13)
$e^{\alpha t} f(t)$	$F(s - a)$	Theorem 9.3
$f'(t)$	$sF(s) - f(0)$	(9.15)
$f^{(j)}(t)$	$s^j F(s) - s^{j-1} f(0) - \cdots - f^{(j-1)}(0)$	(9.16)
$\displaystyle\int_0^t f(t - u) g(u)\, du$	$F(s) G(s)$	Theorem 9.6

* For the purpose of carrying out this calculation, assume that s is real, and then let s be complex again after obtaining the answer.

•MISCELLANEOUS EXERCISES

1. Find the Laplace transform of each of the following functions

   (a) $f(t) = \begin{cases} \sin \omega t & 0 \le t \le \pi/\omega \\ 0 & \pi/\omega < t \le 2\pi/\omega \end{cases}$ and

   $f\left(t + \dfrac{2\pi}{\omega}\right) = f(t)$ for $0 \le t < \infty$.

   (b) $\displaystyle\int_0^t e^{-u} \sin(t - u)\, du$.

   (c) $t^{5/2}$.

   (d) $t^2 \sin \omega t$.

2. Find the solution of each of the following initial value problems by means of Laplace transforms.

   (a) $y'' - 4y' + 4y = 4 \cos 2t$, $y(0) = 2$, $y'(0) = 5$.

   (b) $y'' + \omega^2 y = f(t)$, where f is the function in Exercise 1(a) above, $y(0) = 0$, $y'(0) = 0$.

   (c) $y'' + y = H(t)$, where $H(t) = 3$ $(0 \le t \le 4)$, $H(t) = 2t - 5$ $(t \ge 4)$, $y(0) = 1$, $y'(0) = 0$.

   (d) $y'' + 2y' + y = 2 + (t - 3)U(t - 3)$, where U is the unit step function

   $$U(t) = \begin{cases} 0 & (t < 0) \\ 1 & (t \ge 0) \end{cases} \qquad y(0) = 2,\ y'(0) = 1.$$

3. (a) Show that if $f(t)$ belongs to the class Λ' and has Laplace transform $F(s)$, then $\displaystyle\lim_{s \to \infty} sF(s) = f(0)$. [*Hint:* Use Theorems 9.4 and 9.8.]

   (b) Generalize this to a result for functions in the class Λ^k by using Theorem 9.5.

4. (a) Show that if $\phi(t)$ is a solution of the Bessel equation of index zero,

   $$ty'' + y' + ty = 0$$

   then the Laplace transform $Y(s)$ of $\phi(t)$ satisfies the first-order differential equation

   $$(s^2 + 1)\frac{dY}{ds} + sY = 0$$

   regardless of the initial conditions prescribed.

   (b) Solve the equation obtained in part (a) and use Exercise 3 above to show that $Y(s) = \phi(0)/(s^2 + 1)^{1/2}$. Explain why $\phi'(0)$ cannot be prescribed.

   (c) By expanding $Y(s)$ in powers of $1/s$, show that

   $$Y(s) = \phi(0) \sum_{k=0}^{\infty} (-1)^k \frac{1 \cdot 3 \cdot 5 \cdots (2k - 1)}{2^k k!} \frac{1}{s^{2k+1}}$$

(d) Show that

$$\phi(t) = \phi(0) \sum_{k=0}^{\infty} (-1)^k \frac{t^{2k}}{2^{2k}(k!)^2}$$

Note that the step from (c) to (d) is purely formal. However (d) is a "rigorous" solution of the Bessel equation, as can be justified by direct substitution and theorems on power series (Section 4.2, p. 122).

5. Solve Exercise 1, p. 309, by Laplace transforms.

6. Solve Exercise 3, p. 309, by Laplace transforms.

7. Solve Exercises 8 and 9, pp. 310, 311, by Laplace transforms.

8. Each of the following equations defines a function $\phi(t)$. Find $\phi(t)$ by using Laplace transforms.*

(a) $\phi(t) = 4t^2 - \int_0^t \phi(t - \tau)e^{-\tau} \, d\tau.$

(b) $\phi(t) = t^3 + \int_0^t \phi(\tau) \sin(t - \tau) \, d\tau.$

(c) $\phi(t) = 1 + 2 \int_0^t \phi(t - \tau) \cos \tau \, d\tau.$

(d) $\phi'(t) = \sin t + \int_0^t \phi(t - \tau) \cos \tau \, d\tau, \; \phi(0) = 0.$

(e) $\phi'(t) = t + \int_0^t \phi(t - \tau) \cos \tau \, d\tau, \; \phi(0) = 4.$

(f) $\int_0^t \phi(t - \tau)e^{-\tau} \, d\tau = t.$

---

* Note that before one does this one should actually first prove that $\phi \in \Lambda$. This can, in fact, be done by estimating $|\phi(t)|$ and using the Gronwall inequality (Section 6.3, p. 252). Alternatively, one could just obtain the answer and then verify that it belongs to Λ.

Appendix 1 | DETERMINANTS AND LINEAR SYSTEMS

We consider the linear system in n equations and n unknowns w_1, $w_2, \ldots, w_n$:

$$
\begin{aligned}
a_{11}w_1 + a_{12}w_2 + \cdots + a_{1n}w_n &= c_1 \\
a_{21}w_1 + a_{22}w_2 + \cdots + a_{2n}w_n &= c_2 \\
&\ \ \vdots \\
a_{n1}w_1 + a_{n2}w_2 + \cdots + a_{nn}w_n &= c_n
\end{aligned}
\tag{A.1}
$$

where a_{ij} and c_i $(i, j = 1, \ldots, n)$ are given real or complex numbers. If $c_1 = c_2 = \cdots = c_n = 0$ we say that the system (A.1) is **linear homogeneous,** otherwise it is called **nonhomogeneous.** By a **solution** of the system (A.1) we mean a set of n numbers (real or complex) $\bar{w}_1, \ldots, \bar{w}_n$ with the property that if we replace w_i by $\bar{w}_i$ on the left-hand side of (A.1) for $i = 1, \ldots, n$, the left-hand side of the first equation will reduce to c_1, the second to $c_2, \ldots$, the last one to c_n. To discuss the solvability of the system (A.1) it is convenient to introduce the determinant Δ of coefficients denoted by

$$
\Delta = \begin{vmatrix}
a_{11} & a_{12} & \cdots & a_{1n} \\
a_{21} & a_{22} & \cdots & a_{2n} \\
\vdots & & & \vdots \\
a_{n1} & a_{n2} & \cdots & a_{nn}
\end{vmatrix}
$$

Here Δ is the number defined by

$$\Delta = \sum (\pm)\, a_{1i_1}, a_{2i_2}, \ldots, a_{ni_n}$$

where the sum is taken over all indices $i_1, \ldots, i_n$ such that $i_1, i_2, \ldots, i_n$ is a permutation of the numbers $1, 2, \ldots, n$ and where the $+$ sign is used if the permutation is even and the $-$ sign is used when the permutation is odd. Thus, if $n = 2$, $\Delta = a_{11}a_{22} - a_{12}a_{21}$, and if $n = 3$

$$\Delta = a_{11}a_{22}a_{33} - a_{11}a_{23}a_{32} + a_{12}a_{23}a_{31} - a_{12}a_{21}a_{33}$$
$$+ a_{13}a_{21}a_{32} - a_{13}a_{22}a_{31}$$

The first principal result concerning the system (A.1) is for the homogeneous system $(c_1 = c_2 = \cdots = c_n = 0)$.

Theorem A.1.   *If $c_1 = c_2 = \cdots = c_n = 0$ and if $\Delta = 0$, there exists a solution of* (A.1), *$\tilde{w}_1, \tilde{w}_2, \ldots, \tilde{w}_n$ such that not all $\tilde{w}_k$ are zero.*

Proof.   We prove the result only for $n = 2$; the general case is usually treated in courses in linear algebra. Thus, consider

$$a_{11}w_1 + a_{12}w_2 = 0$$
$$a_{21}w_1 + a_{22}w_2 = 0$$

with $\Delta = a_{11}a_{22} - a_{12}a_{21} = 0$. If $a_{11} \neq 0$ take $\tilde{w}_2 = 1$; then $\tilde{w}_1 = -a_{12}/a_{11}$ from the first equation. Moreover, substituting these values in the second equation, we obtain

$$a_{21}\left(-\frac{a_{12}}{a_{11}} + a_{22}\right) = \frac{1}{a_{11}}(a_{11}a_{22} - a_{21}a_{12}) = 0$$

Thus, if $a_{11} \neq 0$, $\tilde{w}_1 = -a_{12}/a_{11}$ and $\tilde{w}_2 = 1$ is a solution with $\tilde{w}_1, \tilde{w}_2$ not both zero.

Similarly if $a_{11} = 0$ and $a_{21} \neq 0$, $\tilde{w}_1 = -(a_{22}/a_{21})$, $\tilde{w}_2 = 1$ is a solution and if a_{11} and a_{21} are both zero $\tilde{w}_1 = 1$, $\tilde{w}_2 = 0$ is a solution which takes care of all the possibilities and completes the proof. ∎

We now turn to the full system (A.1). The basic result is the following.

Theorem A.2.   (Cramer's rule.)   *If the determinant Δ of coefficients of* (A.1) *is not zero then the system* (A.1) *has a unique solution $\tilde{w}_1$,*

. . . , $\tilde{w}_n$.   *This solution is given by*

$$\tilde{w}_k = \frac{\Delta_k}{\Delta} \quad (k = 1, \ldots, n)$$

where Δ_k is the determinant obtained by replacing the kth column of Δ (that is, $a_{1k}, a_{2k}, \ldots, a_{nk}$) by $c_1, c_2, \ldots, c_n$, and leaving the remaining columns unchanged. In particular, if $c_1 = c_2 = \cdots = c_n = 0$, then the only solution is $\tilde{w}_1 = \tilde{w}_2 = \cdots = \tilde{w}_n = 0$.

Proof.   We again give the proof for $n = 2$ only and we suppose first that there exist $\tilde{w}_1$, $\tilde{w}_2$ such that

$$\begin{aligned}
a_{11}\tilde{w}_1 + a_{12}\tilde{w}_2 &= c_1 \\
a_{21}\tilde{w}_1 + a_{22}\tilde{w}_2 &= c_2
\end{aligned} \tag{A.2}$$

Then we multiply the first equation by a_{22} and the second by $-a_{12}$ and add obtaining

$$\tilde{w}_1\Delta = c_1 a_{22} - a_{12}c_2 = \begin{vmatrix} c_1 & a_{12} \\ c_2 & a_{22} \end{vmatrix} = \Delta_1$$

Similarly, we multiply the first equation by $-a_{21}$, the second by a_{11} and add obtaining

$$\tilde{w}_2\Delta = -a_{21}c_1 + a_{11}c_2 = \begin{vmatrix} a_{11} & c_1 \\ a_{21} & c_2 \end{vmatrix} = \Delta_2$$

Since $\Delta \neq 0$ it must be the case that $\tilde{w}_1 = \Delta_1/\Delta$ and $\tilde{w}_2 = \Delta_2/\Delta$. If we now define the numbers $\tilde{w}_1$ and $\tilde{w}_2$ by these relations, we see by direct substitution that they satisfy (A.2).   This completes the proof. ∎

Combining Theorems A.1 and A.2, we easily obtain the following result.

Theorem A.3.   *The linear system (A.1) of n equations in n unknowns has a unique solution if and only if the determinant of coefficients Δ is not zero.*

Appendix 2 ‖ POLYNOMIAL EQUATIONS

Let

$$p_n(z) = a_0 z^n + a_1 z^{n-1} + \cdots + a_{n-1} z + z_n \qquad (A.3)$$

be a polynomial of degree $n \geq 1$ with real or complex coefficients. Let $z = b$ be a root of the equation $p_n(z) = 0$.

Theorem A.4. *If $z = b$ is a root of multiplicity k of the equation $p_n(z) = 0$, then*

$$p_n(b) = p_n'(b) = p_n''(b) = \cdots = p_n^{(k-1)}(b) = 0$$

but $p_n^{(k)}(b) \neq 0$.

Proof. Since $z = b$ is a root of multiplicity k

$$p_n(z) = a_0(z - b)^k q(z)$$

where $q(z)$ is a polynomial of degree $n - k$ with $q(b) \neq 0$; also, since b is a root, $p_n(b) = 0$. Differentiating $p_n(z)$ we have

$$p_n'(z) = a_0 k(z - b)^{k-1} q(z) + a_0(z - b)^k q'(z)$$

and thus if $k - 1 > 0$, $p_n'(b) = 0$. If, however, $k = 1$

$$p_n'(z) = a_0 q(z) + a_0(z - b)q'(z)$$

from which $p_n'(b) = a_0 q(b) \neq 0$. This proves the result for $k = 1$.

To establish the general case we recall the formula

$$(fg)^{(m)} = f^{(m)}g + mf^{(m-1)}g' + \frac{m(m-1)}{2!}f^{(m-2)}g'' + \cdots + fg^{(m)}$$

for finding the mth derivative of the product fg of two m times differentiable functions f and g. Applying this formula, using $f(z) = a_0(z - b)^k$, $g(z) = q(z)$, we obtain

$$p_n^{(j)}(z) = a_0[k(k - 1) \cdots (k - j + 1)(z - b)^{k-j}q(z)$$
$$+ \text{ terms which have higher powers of } z - b \text{ as factors}$$

Therefore, for any $k \geq 1$, letting j assume values $1, 2, \ldots, k - 1, k$, we find $p_n(b) = p_n'(b) = \cdots = p_n^{(k-1)}(b) = 0$, but $p_n^{(k)}(b) = k!a_0q(b) \neq 0$ and this completes the proof. ∎

Appendix 3

COMPLEX NUMBERS AND COMPLEX-VALUED FUNCTIONS

We assume that the reader is familiar with the definition of a complex number z as an ordered pair (x, y) of real numbers with the definitions of addition

$$(x_1, y_1) + (x_2, y_2) = (x_1 + x_2, y_1 + y_2)$$

and multiplication

$$(x_1, y_1) \cdot (x_2, y_2) = (x_1 x_2 - y_1 y_2, x_1 y_2 + x_2 y_1)$$

for any complex numbers $z_1 = (x_1, y_1)$ and $z_2 = (x_2, y_2)$, as well as the familiar associative, distributive, and commutative laws for addition and multiplication. It is customary to denote the complex number $(0, 0)$ by 0, and the complex number $(1, 0)$ by 1. Note that $z + 0 = z$ for every complex number z and $z \cdot 1 = z$. For $z = (x, y)$ we define $-z = (-x, -y)$ and $z^{-1} = (x/(x^2 + y^2), -y/(x^2 + y^2))$ if $z \neq 0$; then $z + (-z) = 0$ and $z \cdot z^{-1} = 1$. As is customary, we define $z_1 - z_2 = z_1 + (-z_2)$ and $z_1/z_2 = z_1 z_2^{-1}$ if $z_2 \neq 0$.

It is also customary to identify the complex number $(a, 0)$ with the real number a and to denote $(0, 1)$ by i. Then, using the rules of addition and multiplication, we have

$$z = (x, y) = x(1, 0) + y(0, 1) = x + iy$$

The number x is called **the real part** of z, written $x = \Re z$, and the number y is called **the imaginary part** of z, written $y = \Im z$. We also have

$$i^2 = (0, 1)(0, 1) = (-1, 0) = -1$$

418

We define $\bar{z}$, the complex conjugate of $z = x + iy$, by

$$\bar{z} = x - iy$$

The product $z\bar{z} = x^2 + y^2$, and we define the norm, or absolute value, of z as

$$|z| = (z\bar{z})^{1/2} = (x^2 + y^2)^{1/2}$$

The absolute value has the properties

(i) $|z| \geq 0$ and $|z| = 0$ if and only if $z = 0$.
(ii) $|-z| = |z| = |\bar{z}|$.
(iii) $|z_1 z_2| = |z_1| \cdot |z_2|$.
(iv) $|z_1 + z_2| \leq |z_1| + |z_2|$.
(v) $|z_1 - z_2| \geq \left| |z_1| - |z_2| \right|$.

It is often convenient to introduce polar coordinates for complex numbers as follows. Let $z = (x, y)$ be any complex number and let (r, θ) be the polar coordinates of the point (x, y) in the plane. Then $x = r \cos \theta$ and $y = r \sin \theta$, and we may write

$$z = x + iy = r(\cos \theta + i \sin \theta)$$

with

$$r = (x^2 + y^2)^{1/2} = |z| \qquad \theta = \arctan \frac{y}{x}$$

The reader can easily verify that if $z_1 = r_1 (\cos \theta_1 + i \cos \theta_2)$, $z_2 = r_2 (\cos \theta_2 + i \sin \theta_2)$, then, by the definition of $z_1 z_2$ and the trigonometric addition formulas,

$$z_1 z_2 = r_1 r_2 [\cos (\theta_1 + \theta_2) + i \sin (\theta_1 + \theta_2)]$$

Taking $z_1 = z_2 = z$ we obtain $z^2 = r^2 (\cos 2\theta + i \sin 2\theta)$, and by induction we see that $z^n = r^n (\cos n\theta + i \sin n\theta)$ for every positive integer n.

A complex function f (of the real variable t) defined on some real interval I is a rule (or correspondence) which assigns to each real number t and I exactly one complex number $f(t)$.

Example 1. Let z be a given complex number, $z = \alpha + i\beta$ (α, β real) and consider the function f given by $f(t) = e^{zt}$, $-\infty < t < \infty$. Thus to each real number t the correspondence f assigns the complex number $f(t) = e^{(\alpha + i\beta)t}$. (This function is discussed in the next paragraph.)

Each complex-valued function f defined on some interval I gives rise to two real functions, u, v each defined on I by the relations

$$u(t) = \mathfrak{R}[f(t)] \qquad v(t) = \mathfrak{I}[f(t)] \qquad (t \text{ in } I)$$

where $\mathfrak{R}[f(t)]$ is the real part of $f(t)$ and $\mathfrak{I}[f(t)]$ is the imaginary part of $f(t)$. Then we can write $f(t) = u(t) + iv(t)$. We sometimes write $u = \mathfrak{R}f$, $v = \mathfrak{I}f$. For example, if $f(t) = (t^2 - 1) + i \cos t$, t real, then $u(t) = \mathfrak{R}[(f(t))] = t^2 - 1$ and $v(t) = \mathfrak{I}[f(t)] = \cos t$. The function e^{zt}, $z = \alpha + i\beta$ plays an important role. For this function we have the important identity, due to Euler, which states that

$$f(t) = e^{zt} = e^{(\alpha + i\beta)t} = e^{\alpha t}(\cos \beta t + i \sin \beta t) \qquad (-\infty < t < \infty)$$

Thus, its real and imaginary parts are

$$u(t) = \mathfrak{R}[f(t)] = e^{\alpha t} \cos \beta t \qquad v(t) = \mathfrak{I}[f(t)] = e^{\alpha t} \sin \beta t$$

Any derivation of this formula requires some knowledge of complex analysis. It is, however, not incorrect from the logical point of view to take Euler's identity as a definition of e^{zt} when z is a complex number, and this is what is done here.

•EXERCISES

1. Using Euler's identity as a definition, prove that $e^{(z_1 + z_2)t} = e^{z_1 t} \cdot e^{z_2 t}$, where z_1, z_2 are given complex numbers.

2. For each of the following functions find the functions $u = \mathfrak{R}f$, $v = \mathfrak{I}f$:

(a) $f(t) = e^{2 + 3it}$, t real.

(b) $f(t) = \dfrac{1}{1 + it}$, t real.

(c) $f(t) = (2 + it)^2$, t real.

(d) $f(t) = \dfrac{1}{3 + it} + \dfrac{it}{3 - it}$, t real.

If f, g are complex-valued functions defined on some interval I, their sum $(f + g)$, product (fg), quotient $((f/g)(g(t) \neq 0))$ are defined respectively by the relations $(f + g)(t) = f(t) + g(t)$, $(fg)(t) = f(t) \cdot g(t)$, $((f/g)(t) = f(t)/g(t))$ exactly as in the real case. It should not come as a surprise that the definitions of limit, continuity, derivative, and integral for a complex-valued function f, and hence the calculus of such functions, is completely analogous to the real case. We shall summarize the appropriate definitions and properties.

Definition. *A function f is said to approach a (possibly complex) number L as t approaches some number t_0 (written $\lim\limits_{t \to t_0} f(t) = L$) if and only if* $\lim\limits_{t \to t_0} |f(t) - L| = 0$ (where $|f(t) - L|$ denotes absolute value).

•EXERCISE

3. Give an $\epsilon - \delta$ definition of the statement $\lim\limits_{t \to t_0} f(t) = L$.

It is clear that all properties of limits which hold in the real case hold in the present case as well. An important consequence of this definition is the following property which does not arise in the strictly real case, but which is very easy to prove:

Lemma. *Suppose f is a complex-valued function of the real variable t, with $u = \Re f$, $v = \Im f$. Then $\lim\limits_{t \to t_0} f(t) = L = \alpha + i\beta$ if and only if*

$$\lim_{t \to t_0} u(t) = \lim_{t \to t_0} \Re[f(t)] = \alpha \text{ and } \lim_{t \to t_0} v(t) = \lim_{t \to t_0} \Im[f(t)] = \beta$$

We say that a complex-valued function f defined on an interval I is differentiable at $t = t_0$ in I if and only if

$$\lim_{h \to 0} \frac{f(t_0 + h) - f(t_0)}{h} \qquad (h \text{ real})$$

exists. We define the value of this limit to be the derivative of f at $t = t_0$ and we denote the derivative of f at $t = t_0$ by $f'(t_0)$. More useful from the computational point of view is the following equivalent definition (the equivalence is established by the above lemma): f **is differentiable at $t = t_0$ if and only if the real functions $u = \Re f$, $v = \Im f$ are differentiable at $t = t_0$; the derivative of f at $t = t_0$ is given by**

$$f'(t) = u'(t_0) + iv'(t_0)$$

Example 2.   Prove that for every complex number $z = \alpha + i\beta$, and for all t, $(e^{zt})' = ze^{zt}$ (**same formula as in the real case**).

By Euler's formula $e^{zt} = e^{\alpha t} \cos \beta t + ie^{\alpha t} \sin \beta t$.   Since the real functions $e^{\alpha t} \cos \beta t$, $e^{\alpha t} \sin \beta t$ are differentiable for all t, we have by the above equivalent definition of derivative

$$
\begin{aligned}
(e^{zt})' &= (e^{\alpha t} \cos \beta t)' + i(e^{\alpha t} \sin \beta t)' \\
&= \alpha e^{\alpha t} \cos \beta t - \beta e^{\alpha t} \sin \beta t + i(\alpha e^{\alpha t} \sin \beta t + \beta e^{\alpha t} \cos \beta t) \\
&= (\alpha + i\beta)e^{\alpha t} \cos \beta t + (-\beta + i\alpha)e^{\alpha t} \sin \beta t \\
&= (\alpha + i\beta)[e^{\alpha t} \cos \beta t + ie^{\alpha t} \sin \beta t] = ze^{zt}
\end{aligned}
$$

It is clear that all properties and rules of differentiation familiar from the study of real functions hold in the case of complex-valued functions. This includes, of course, derivatives of higher order.

Finally, we say that a complex function f, whose domain is the real interval $a \leq t \leq b$ is **integrable** on $[a,b]$ if and only if both real functions on $u = \Re f$, $v = \Im f$ are integrable on $[a,b]$, and in this case we define

$$
\int_a^b f(t)\, dt = \int_a^b u(t)\, dt + i \int_a^b v(t)\, dt
$$

This definition gives all the usual rules of integration.

Example 3.

$$
\begin{aligned}
\int_0^{\pi/2} e^{it}\, dt &= \int_0^{\pi/2} \cos t\, dt + i \int_0^{\pi/2} \sin t\, dt \\
&= \sin t \Big|_{t=0}^{t=\pi/2} - i \cos t \Big|_{t=0}^{t=\pi/2} \\
&= 1 + i
\end{aligned}
$$

CANONICAL FORMS OF 2×2 MATRICES

We consider a 2×2 matrix A, which we regard as the coefficient matrix of a two-dimensional linear system with constant coefficients $\mathbf{y}' = A\mathbf{y}$. The change of variable $\mathbf{y} = T\mathbf{z}$, where T is a nonsingular matrix, transforms this to the system $\mathbf{z}' = T^{-1}AT\mathbf{z}$. Our object is to choose T in such a way as to make the coefficient matrix $T^{-1}AT$ as simple as possible. A simplification is always possible, as shown in the following result, which incidentally is entirely independent of differential equations and is purely algebraic.

Theorem A.5. *Let A be a 2×2 matrix. Then there exists a nonsingular 2×2 matrix T such that $T^{-1}AT$ is one of the following:*

(i) $\begin{pmatrix} \lambda & 0 \\ 0 & \mu \end{pmatrix}$ $(\lambda \neq \mu)$.

(ii) $\begin{pmatrix} \lambda & 0 \\ 0 & \lambda \end{pmatrix}$.

(iii) $\begin{pmatrix} \lambda & 1 \\ 0 & \lambda \end{pmatrix}$.

Proof. Case (i). Suppose A has distinct eigenvalues λ, μ. Let $\mathbf{x} \neq \mathbf{0}$ be an eigenvector corresponding to λ and let $\mathbf{y} \neq \mathbf{0}$ be an eigenvector corresponding to μ; that is, $\mathbf{x}$ is a nonzero vector such that $A\mathbf{x} = \lambda\mathbf{x}$ and $\mathbf{y}$ is a nonzero vector such that $A\mathbf{y} = \mu\mathbf{y}$.

We define the 2×2 matrix T whose columns are the (column) vectors $\mathbf{x}$ and $\mathbf{y}$, which we write

$$T = (\mathbf{x}, \mathbf{y}) = \begin{pmatrix} x_1 & y_1 \\ x_1 & y_2 \end{pmatrix}$$

In order to show that T is nonsingular, we must prove that $\mathbf{x}$ and $\mathbf{y}$ are linearly independent. Suppose not; then there exist constants c_1, c_2 such that

$$c_1\mathbf{x} + c_2\mathbf{y} = 0$$

Since $\mathbf{x}$ and $\mathbf{y}$ are both different from zero, both c_1 and c_2 are different from zero. Thus, we may write

$$\mathbf{x} = -\frac{c_2}{c_1}\mathbf{y}$$

multiplying both sides on the left by A and using $A\mathbf{x} = \lambda\mathbf{x}$, $A\mathbf{y} = \mu\mathbf{y}$, we obtain

$$\lambda\mathbf{x} = A\mathbf{x} = -\frac{c_2}{c_1}A\mathbf{y} = -\frac{c_2}{c_1}\mu\mathbf{y}$$

Since $\lambda\mathbf{x} = -(c_2/c_1)\lambda\mathbf{y}$, this becomes

$$-\frac{c_2}{c_1}\lambda\mathbf{y} = -\frac{c_2}{c_1}\mu\mathbf{y}$$

This is impossible unless either $c_2 = 0$ or $\lambda = \mu$, both of which are false. Therefore, $\mathbf{x}$ and $\mathbf{y}$ are linearly independent, and T is nonsingular.

It is easy to verify that

$$T^{-1} = \frac{1}{x_1y_2 - x_2y_1}\begin{pmatrix} y_2 & -y_1 \\ -x_2 & x_1 \end{pmatrix}$$

Thus,

$$T^{-1}AT = T^{-1}(A\mathbf{x}, A\mathbf{y}) = T^{-1}(\lambda\mathbf{x}, \mu\mathbf{y})$$

$$= \frac{1}{x_1y_2 - x_2y_1}\begin{pmatrix} y_2 & -y_1 \\ -x_2 & x_1 \end{pmatrix}\begin{pmatrix} \lambda x_1 & \mu y_1 \\ \lambda x_2 & \mu y_2 \end{pmatrix} = \begin{pmatrix} \lambda & 0 \\ 0 & \mu \end{pmatrix}$$

This completes the proof in Case (i).

Case (ii). Suppose A has a double eigenvalue λ for which there are two linearly independent eigenvectors $\mathbf{x}$ and $\mathbf{y}$. Then defining T exactly as in Case (i), we see that T is nonsingular because its columns are given linearly independent. The same calculation as in Case (i) (but with μ

replaced by λ) shows that

$$T^{-1}AT = \begin{pmatrix} \lambda & 0 \\ 0 & \lambda \end{pmatrix}$$

Case (*iii*).   Suppose A has a double eigenvalue λ but any two eigenvectors are linearly dependent (that is, the space of eigenvectors has dimension 1).   Let $\mathbf{v}$ be a nonzero vector which is not an eigenvector of A and let

$$\mathbf{u} = (A - \lambda E)\mathbf{v}$$

Since $\mathbf{v}$ is not an eigenvector, and $A - \lambda E$ is not the zero matrix, $\mathbf{u} \neq 0$; we will show that $\mathbf{u}$ is an eigenvector.

We assert that the vectors $\mathbf{u}$ and $\mathbf{v}$ are linearly independent.   Suppose not; then there exist constants c_1, c_2 such that

$$c_1\mathbf{u} + c_2\mathbf{v} = 0$$

Since $\mathbf{u}$ and $\mathbf{v}$ are both different from zero, both c_1 and c_2 are different from zero.   Using the definition of $\mathbf{u}$ and the fact that $c_1 \neq 0$, we may rewrite this as

$$c_1(A - \lambda E)\mathbf{v} + c_2\mathbf{v} = 0$$

or

$$c_1\left[\left(A - \lambda E + \frac{c_2}{c_1}E\right)\mathbf{v}\right] = 0$$

This says that $\lambda - c_2/c_1$ is an eigenvalue of A.   Since λ is the only eigenvalue, $c_2 \neq 0$, which is a contradiction.   Thus, $\mathbf{u}$ and $\mathbf{v}$ are linearly independent and span the space E_2.

Let $\mathbf{x}$ be any eigenvector of A; we may therefore write

$$\mathbf{x} = a\mathbf{u} + b\mathbf{v}$$

If $a = 0$, then $\mathbf{x}$ is a multiple of $\mathbf{v}$, and therefore $\mathbf{v}$ is an eigenvector (but by hypothesis it is not); thus $a \neq 0$.   Now,

$$0 = (A - \lambda E)\mathbf{x} = a(A - \lambda E)\mathbf{u} + b(A - \lambda E)\mathbf{v}$$
$$= a(A - \lambda E)\mathbf{u} + b\mathbf{u} = a\left[\left(A - \lambda E + \frac{b}{a}E\right)\mathbf{u}\right]$$

This says that $\lambda - b/a$ is an eigenvalue, and since λ is the only eigenvalue $b = 0$. Therefore, **x** is a nonzero multiple of **u**, and **u** must be an eigenvector.

Now, we define

$$T = (\mathbf{u}, \mathbf{v}) = \begin{pmatrix} u_1 & v_1 \\ u_2 & v_2 \end{pmatrix}$$

As in Case (i),

$$T^{-1} = \frac{1}{u_1 v_2 - u_2 v_1} \begin{pmatrix} v_2 & -v_1 \\ -u_2 & u_1 \end{pmatrix}$$

We have, using $(A - \lambda E)\mathbf{v} = A\mathbf{v} - \lambda\mathbf{v}$,

$$
\begin{aligned}
T^{-1}AT &= T^{-1}(A\mathbf{u}, A\mathbf{v}) \\
&= T^{-1}(\lambda\mathbf{u}, \mathbf{u} + \lambda\mathbf{v}) \\
&= T^{-1}(\lambda\mathbf{u}, \lambda\mathbf{v}) + T^{-1}(0, \mathbf{u}) \\
&= \lambda T^{-1}T + \frac{1}{u_1 v_2 - u_2 v_1} \begin{pmatrix} v_2 & -v_1 \\ -u_2 & u_1 \end{pmatrix} \begin{pmatrix} 0 & u_1 \\ 0 & u_2 \end{pmatrix} \\
&= \lambda E + \begin{pmatrix} 0 & 1 \\ 0 & 0 \end{pmatrix} = \begin{pmatrix} \lambda & 1 \\ 0 & \lambda \end{pmatrix}
\end{aligned}
$$

This completes the proof of the theorem. With reference to the above proof, the reader should note that in showing that $\mathbf{u} = (A - \lambda E)\mathbf{v}$ is an eigenvector we have actually shown that $(A - \lambda E)^2\mathbf{w} = \mathbf{0}$ for every vector **w** in E_2. For this reason we say that $A - \lambda E$ is **nilpotent** on E_2. ∎

We remark that if A is a real matrix and if its eigenvalues are real, then the matrix T constructed in each of the three cases above is real. However, if A is real but has complex eigenvalues (necessarily complex conjugates), the matrix T will not be real and it is of interest to learn the simplest form of $T^{-1}AT$ which can be achieved with a **real** matrix T. The answer lies in the following result.

Theorem A.6. *Let A be a real 2×2 matrix with complex conjugate eigenvalues $\alpha \pm i\beta$ then there exists a real nonsingular matrix T such that*

$$T^{-1}AT = \begin{pmatrix} \alpha & \beta \\ -\beta & \alpha \end{pmatrix}$$

Proof. Let $\mathbf{u} + i\mathbf{v}$ be an eigenvector corresponding to the eigenvalue $\alpha + i\beta$, where $\mathbf{u}$ and $\mathbf{v}$ are real. If $\mathbf{v} = \mathbf{0}$, so that this eigenvector is real,

$$A\mathbf{u} = (\alpha + i\beta)\mathbf{u}$$

the left side of which is real and the right side of which is not real. Thus, $\mathbf{v} \neq \mathbf{0}$, and a similar argument shows that $\mathbf{u} \neq \mathbf{0}$.

We define the matrix T with columns $\mathbf{u}$ and $\mathbf{v}$,

$$T = (\mathbf{u}, \mathbf{v}) = \begin{pmatrix} u_1 & v_1 \\ u_2 & v_2 \end{pmatrix}$$

In order to show that T is nonsingular, we must show that $\mathbf{u}$ and $\mathbf{v}$ are linearly independent. Suppose not; then there exist real constants c_1, c_2 both different from zero such that

$$c_1\mathbf{u} + c_2\mathbf{v} = \mathbf{0}$$

Since $c_1 \neq 0$, and $A(\mathbf{u} + i\mathbf{v}) = (\alpha + i\beta)(\mathbf{u} + i\mathbf{v})$, we have $A(\mathbf{u} + i\mathbf{v}) = A\left(-\dfrac{c_2}{c_1}\mathbf{v} + i\mathbf{v}\right) = (\alpha + i\beta)\left(-\dfrac{c_2}{c_1} + i\right)\mathbf{v}$; thus

$$A\mathbf{v} = (\alpha + i\beta)\mathbf{v}$$

Then $\mathbf{v}$ is a real eigenvector, and as remarked above this is impossible. Thus $\mathbf{u}$ and $\mathbf{v}$ are linearly independent and T is nonsingular.

Taking real and imaginary parts in the equation

$$A(\mathbf{u} + i\mathbf{v}) = (\alpha + i\beta)(\mathbf{u} + i\mathbf{v})$$

we obtain

$$A\mathbf{u} = \alpha\mathbf{u} - \beta\mathbf{v} \qquad A\mathbf{v} = \beta\mathbf{u} + \alpha\mathbf{v}$$

Therefore,

$$AT = (A\mathbf{u}, A\mathbf{v}) = (\alpha\mathbf{u} - \beta\mathbf{v}, \beta\mathbf{u} + \alpha\mathbf{v})$$

and

$$T^{-1}AT = \frac{1}{u_1v_2 - u_2v_1}\begin{pmatrix} v_2 & -v_1 \\ -u_2 & u_1 \end{pmatrix}\begin{pmatrix} \alpha u_1 - \beta v_1 & \beta u_1 + \alpha v_1 \\ \alpha u_2 - \beta v_2 & \beta u_2 + \alpha v_2 \end{pmatrix}$$

$$= \begin{pmatrix} \alpha & \beta \\ -\beta & \alpha \end{pmatrix}$$

This completes the proof of the theorem. ∎

BIBLIOGRAPHY

1. G. Birkhoff and G. C. Rota, *Ordinary Differential Equations* (Ginn, Boston, 1962).
2. H. Bremermann, *Distributions, Complex Variables, and Fourier Transforms* (Addison-Wesley, Reading, Mass., 1965).
3. N. de Bruijn, *Asymptotic Methods in Analysis* (North Holland, Amsterdam, 1958).
4. R. C. Buck and E. F. Buck, *Advanced Calculus*, 2nd ed. (McGraw-Hill, New York, 1965).
5. E. A. Coddington and N. Levinson, *Theory of Ordinary Differential Equations* (McGraw-Hill, New York, 1955).
6. A. Erdélyi, *Asymptotic Expansions* (Dover, New York, 1956).
7. P. R. Halmos, *Finite-Dimensional Vector Spaces*, 2nd ed. (Van Nostrand, Princeton, N. J., 1958).
8. P. Henrici, *Discrete Variable Methods in Ordinary Differential Equations* (Wiley, New York, 1962).
9. F. B. Hildebrand, *Advanced Calculus for Applications* (Prentice-Hall, Englewood Cliffs, N. J., 1962).
10. F. B. Hildebrand, *Introduction to Numerical Analysis* (McGraw-Hill, New York, 1956).
11. E. Jahnke and F. Emde, *Tables of Functions with Formulae and Curves* (translation) (Dover, New York, 1945).
12. W. Magnus and F. Oberhettinger, *Formulas and Theorems for the Special Functions of Mathematical Physics*, 3rd ed. (translation) (Springer, Berlin, 1966).
13. B. Noble, *Numerical Methods*, Vol. 2: *Differences, Integration, and Differential Equations* (Oliver & Boyd, Edinburgh, 1964).
14. W. Rudin, *Principles of Mathematical Analysis*, 2nd ed. (McGraw-Hill, New York, 1964).
15. J. Todd, *A Survey of Numerical Analysis* (McGraw-Hill, New York, 1962).
16. W. Wasow, *Asymptotic Expansions for Ordinary Differential Equations* (Wiley, New York, 1966).

17. E. T. Whittaker and G. N. Watson, *A Course of Modern Analysis*, 4th ed. (Cambridge Univ. Press, Cambridge, 1927).
18. D. V. Widder, *The Laplace Transform* (Princeton Univ. Press, Princeton, N. J., 1946).
19. K. Yosida, *Lectures on Differential and Integral Equations* (Wiley [Interscience], New York, 1960).

ANSWERS TO SELECTED EXERCISES

• CHAPTER 1

SECTION 1.1.
3. $y(t) = -\frac{1}{2}gt^2 + v_0 t + y_0$.
5. $x(t) = [v_0 \cos \theta]t + y_0$, $y(t) = -\frac{1}{2}gt^2 + [v_0 \sin \theta]t + y_0$.

SECTION 1.6.
1. (i) $\phi(t) \equiv 0$. (ii) $\phi(t) \equiv 0$. (iii) $\phi(t) = 2e^{2(t+1)}$.

SECTION 1.7.
5. $\phi(t) = \sin 2t + 4 \cos 2t$.

SECTION 1.8.
2. (a), (c), (d) are regions, (b) is not because the boundary $y = -2$ is in the set.
5. $\phi(t) \equiv 0$ is the only solution through $(1, 0)$.
7. Yes.

MISCELLANEOUS.
2. (b) $\{(t, y) \mid t^2 + y^2 < 2\}$.
(h) There are really two differential equations; for each the regions are $\{(t, y) \mid t^2 > y^2\}$.
3. (b) $\{(t, y, y') \mid y'^2 < 4\}$.
(c) $\{(t, y, y') \mid y^2 + y'^2 < 4\}$.
(e) $\{(t, y, y') \mid t > 0\}$.
5. (i) No, (ii) Yes, (iii) No, (iv) No.
6. $f(t_0, y_0) = 0$; maximum if $(\partial f/\partial t)(t_0, y_0) + (\partial f/\partial y)(t_0, y_0)f(t_0, y_0) < 0$ and minimum if this inequality is reversed.
9. $f(t) \equiv 0$; $f(t) = \begin{cases} 0 & t \le c \\ \frac{1}{2}(t - c) & t > c \end{cases}$ $(c \ge 0)$.

• CHAPTER 2

SECTION 2.1.
8. $(0, -1)$.
15. $\phi(t) = -\left(\dfrac{1}{y_0{}^2} + t_0{}^2 - t^2\right)^{-1/2}$, $|t| < c$.
17. $\phi(t) \equiv 0$.
19. $\phi(t) = -(y_0{}^2 - t_0{}^2 + t^2)^{1/2}$, $t^2 > (t_0{}^2 - y_0{}^2)$.
21. $\phi(t) \equiv 1$.
23. $\phi(t) \equiv -2$.

SECTION 2.2.
3. $\phi(t) = \frac{1}{3}e^t + \frac{2}{3}e^{-2t}$.
5. $[\phi(t)]^{1-k} = y_0{}^{1-k}e^{-P(t)} + (1 - k)e^{-P(t)}\displaystyle\int_{t_0}^{t} e^{P(s)}b(s)\,ds$,
where $P(t) = (1 - k)\displaystyle\int_{t_0}^{t} a(s)\,ds$, $(k \ne 1)$.

7. All solutions tend to zero if $\lambda < 0$; all solutions are constants if $\lambda = 0$; all solutions grow exponentially if $\lambda > 0$.

SECTION 2.3.   4. $\phi(t) = \theta_0 \cos \left(\dfrac{g}{L}\right)^{1/2} t.$

5. (e) Escape velocity is $(2gR)^{1/2}$ in proper units.

MISCELLANEOUS.   1. (a) $\tan\left(t + \dfrac{\pi}{4}\right).$ (c) $\phi(t) \equiv 0.$

(e) $\arcsin \left(\tfrac{1}{2} \sec t\right).$ (f) $-\dfrac{2}{t^2 + 1}.$ (g) $\dfrac{t}{3} - 1 + e^{-3t}.$

(h) $t^2 - 1 + e^{-t^2}.$ (i) $\dfrac{1}{\log |1 - t|}.$ (l) $\sin\left(t^2 + \dfrac{\pi}{2}\right).$

3. (a) $ae^{-t} + e^{-t} \displaystyle\int_0^t \dfrac{e^{2s}}{s + 1}\, ds,\ t > -1.$

(c) $(a + 1)e^t - 1.$

4. (a) $e^{-t}.$ (b) $1 - t.$ (c) $(1 - t)^{-1/3}.$

10. Solution is $t^{-a} \displaystyle\int_0^t s^{a-1} f(s)\, ds,$ limit is $b/a.$

11. (a) $y = cx.$ (b) $y^2 = x + c.$ (c) $2x^2 + y^2 = c^2.$
(d) $y^2 = 4cx.$

12. $y = cx^2 + \dfrac{2a^2}{x}$ (c a constant).

13. $\dfrac{30 \log 100}{\log 2}$ days (these are natural logarithms).

15. $\phi(t) = \dfrac{2Ae^{kAt}}{(A - 2) + 2e^{kAt}},\ \lim\limits_{t \to \infty} \phi(t) = A.$

16. $3 - 3/e \approx 1.9$ kg.

•CHAPTER 3

SECTION 3.3.   7. (a) 1.   (b) $-2.$ (c) 0.   (d) 0.

16.   (a) $\tfrac{3}{4}e^{2t} + \tfrac{5}{4}e^{-2t}.$

(b) $e^{-t/2}\left(\cos\dfrac{\sqrt{3}}{2}t + \dfrac{7}{\sqrt{3}}\sin\dfrac{\sqrt{3}}{2}t\right).$

(c) 0.   (d) $-3e^{(t-1)} + 2te^{(t-1)}.$

(e) $2 + \displaystyle\sum_{m=1}^{\infty} \dfrac{2t^{3m+1}}{3 \cdot 4 \cdot 6 \cdot 7 \cdots (3m)(3m + 1)}.$

(f) $\tfrac{3}{2}e^t + \tfrac{1}{2}\cos t - \tfrac{5}{2}\sin t.$

SECTION 3.4.   2. (a) $\tfrac{1}{2}e^t - \tfrac{1}{2}e^{-t}.$ (b) $e^{3t} - e^{2t}.$ (c) $\tfrac{1}{2}e^t - e^{2t} + \tfrac{1}{2}e^{3t}.$
3. Condition is $p^2 > 4q$, and all solutions tend to zero.
9. (a) $\sin t + \cos t.$ (b) $e^{2t}\left(\cos 3t - \tfrac{1}{3}\sin 3t\right).$
(c) $\cos 2t + \tfrac{1}{2}\sin 2t.$ (d) $e^{-t}(\cos t + 2\sin t).$

10. Condition is $p^2 < 4q$, and all solutions tend to zero.

11. (a) $c_1 \sin 3t + c_2 \cos 3t$.   (b) $c_1 e^{2t} + c_2 e^{3t}$.

     (d) $c_1 \exp[(-1 + \sqrt{2})it] + c_2 \exp[(-1 - \sqrt{2})it]$.

     (f) $e^{-5t/2}\left(c_1 \cos \dfrac{\sqrt{15}}{2}\, t + c_2 \sin \dfrac{\sqrt{15}}{2}\, t \right)$.

     (g) $c_1 \exp\left(\dfrac{-1 + (1 - \epsilon)^{1/2}}{\epsilon} \right) t$

$$+ \, c_2 \exp\left(\frac{-1 - (1 - \epsilon)^{1/2}}{\epsilon} \right) t.$$

     (h) $(c_1 + c_2 t)e^{-t/2}$.

13. (i) (a), (c), (d), (f), (g), (h).

     (ii) (a), (d).

15. (a) $A \sin (\sqrt{2}\, t + \alpha)$.

     (b) Solution is $\dfrac{\sqrt{13}}{3} \sin\left(3t + \arcsin \dfrac{3}{\sqrt{13}} \right)$.

SECTION 3.5.

1. (a) $c_1 e^{3t} + \left(c_2 \cos \dfrac{3\sqrt{3}}{2}\, t \right.$

$$\left. + \, c_3 \sin \frac{3\sqrt{3}}{2}\, t \right) \exp\left(-\frac{3t}{2} \right).$$

     (b) $c_1 e^{2t} + c_2 e^{-2t} + c_3 \cos 2t + c_4 \sin 2t$.

     (c) $(c_1 + c_2 t)\cos t + (c_3 + c_4 t)\sin t$.

     (d) $c_1 \sin t + c_2 \cos t + c_3 \sin 2t + c_4 \cos 2t$.

     (e) $c_1 \sin t + c_2 \cos t$

$$+ \exp\left(\frac{\sqrt{3}}{2}\, t \right)\left(c_3 \sin \frac{t}{2} + c_4 \cos \frac{t}{2} \right)$$

$$+ \exp\left(-\frac{\sqrt{3}}{2}\, t \right)\left(c_5 \sin \frac{t}{2} + c_6 \cos \frac{t}{2} \right).$$

3. (i) $c_1 + c_2 t + c_3 t^2 + c_4 t^3$.

     (ii) $\left(c_1 \sin \dfrac{\sqrt[4]{\lambda}}{\sqrt{2}}\, t + c_2 \cos \dfrac{\sqrt[4]{\lambda}}{\sqrt{2}}\, t \right) \exp \dfrac{\sqrt[4]{\lambda}}{\sqrt{2}}\, t$

$$+ \left(c_3 \sin \frac{\sqrt[4]{\lambda}}{\sqrt{2}}\, t + c_4 \cos \frac{\sqrt[4]{\lambda}}{\sqrt{2}}\, t \right) \exp - \frac{\sqrt[4]{\lambda}}{\sqrt{2}}\, t.$$

     (iii) $c_1 \exp \sqrt[4]{-\lambda}\, t + c_2 \exp - \sqrt[4]{-\lambda}\, t$

$$+ \, c_3 \cos \sqrt[4]{-\lambda}\, t + c_4 \sin \sqrt[4]{-\lambda}\, t.$$

SECTION 3.6.

2. (a) $c_1|t|^2 + c_2|t|^{-3}$.   (b) $c_1|t|^{2i} + c_2|t|^{-2i}$.

     (c) $c_1|t|^{1/2} + c_2|t|^{-1}$.   (d) $c_1|t|^3 + c_2|t|^i$.

     (e) $c_1|t| + c_2|t| \log |t| + c_3|t|^{-1}$.

SECTION 3.7.

2. (a) $1/t$.   (b) te^{t^2}.   (c) $\dfrac{t}{2}\log\left|\dfrac{t+1}{t-1}\right| - 1$.

(d) $-(t+1)$.

4. General solution $c_1 t + c_2 t^3 + c_3 t^{-1}$ $(t > 0)$.

SECTION 3.8.

4. (a) $(\cos t)(\log|\cos t|) + t\sin t + c_1\cos t + c_2\sin t$.

(c) $c_1\cos 2t + c_2\sin 2t - \tfrac{1}{2}\cos 2t\displaystyle\int_{t_0}^{t} f(s)\sin 2s\,ds$
$+ \tfrac{1}{2}\sin 2t\displaystyle\int_{t_0}^{t}\cos 2s\,f(s)\,ds$.

(e) $c_1|t|^i + c_2|t|^{-i} + \tfrac{1}{10}t^3$.

9. (i) $e^{-t}(c_1\cos\sqrt{3}\,t + c_2\sin\sqrt{3}\,t) + c_3 e^{2t} + \tfrac{1}{12}te^{2t}$.

11. $c_1 e^{3t} + c_2 e^{-3t} + e^{-3t}(-\tfrac{1}{216}t - \tfrac{1}{72}t^2 - \tfrac{1}{36}t^3 - \tfrac{1}{24}t^4)$.

13. (a) $c_1\cos 2t + c_2\sin 2t - \tfrac{1}{4}t\cos 2t$.

(c) $c_1 e^{-t} + c_2 t e^{-t} + c_3 t^2 e^{-t} + t^2 - 6t + 12 - \tfrac{1}{6}t^3 e^{-t}$.

(e) $c_1 e^{2t} + c_2 e^{-2t} + \tfrac{1}{8}t^2 e^{2t} - \tfrac{1}{16}te^{2t}$.

SECTION 3.9.

3. $\dfrac{A(k_0{}^2 - k^2)}{(k_0{}^2 - k^2)^2 + a^2 k^2}\cos kt + \dfrac{akA}{(k_0{}^2 - k^2)^2 + a^2 k^2}\sin kt$.

4. Amplitude is $A[(k_0{}^2 - k^2)^2 + a^2 k^2]^{-1/2}$.

MISCELLANEOUS.

6. (a) $c_1\cos t + c_2\sin t - t\sin t - \cos t\log|\sin t|$.

(b) $c_1\cos(2\log|t|) + c_2\sin(2\log|t|) + \tfrac{1}{3}\sin\log|t|$.

(d) $c_1 e^{3t} + c_2 t e^{3t} + \tfrac{1}{4}e^t$.

(f) $c_1 t^2 + c_2 t^2\log|t| + \tfrac{1}{4}\log|t| + \tfrac{1}{4}$.

(h) $c_1 t[\cos\log|t| + i\sin\log|t|]$
$+ c_2 t^{-1}[\cos\log|t| - i\sin\log|t|]$.

(j) $-\log|\cos t| - \sin\log|\sec t + \tan t| + c_1\cos t$
$+ c_2\sin t + c_3$.

9. $u'' + \left(1 - \dfrac{n^2 - \tfrac{1}{4}}{t^2}\right)u = 0$.

11. $2\pi/7\sqrt{10}$.

21. $\dfrac{\alpha E_0}{L(\omega^2 - \alpha^2)}(\cos\alpha t - \cos\omega t)$, where $\omega^2 = \dfrac{1}{LC}$,
provided that $\omega \neq \alpha$.

●**CHAPTER 4**

SECTION 4.1.

3. $\phi(t) = (t-1) + (t-1)^2 + \displaystyle\sum_{k=3}^{\infty}\dfrac{(t-1)^k}{k}$.

SECTION 4.3.

5. $1 \pm \displaystyle\sum^{\infty}\dfrac{1\cdot3\cdot5\cdots(2k-3)}{(2k)!}t^{2k}$.

7. $\dfrac{2(-1)^m(2m+1)!}{m!}\overset{k=1}{\Bigg[}\,t\,+$

$$\sum_{k=1}^{\infty}\frac{(1-4m)(6-4m)\,\cdots\,(4(k-m+4))}{(2k+1)!}\,t^{2k+1}\Bigg].$$

9. $\phi(t) = 1 - \alpha(\alpha+1)\dfrac{t^2}{2!}$

$$+\,\alpha(\alpha+1)(\alpha+2)(\alpha+3)\dfrac{t^4}{4!}\cdots.$$

11. $P_0(t) = 1, P_1(t) = t, P_2(t) = -\frac{1}{2}(1 - 3t^2),$
$P_3(t) = -\frac{3}{2}(t - \frac{5}{3}t^2), P_4(t) = \frac{3}{8}(1 - 10t^2 + \frac{3\cdot 5}{3}t^4).$

13. $2, \frac{2}{3}, \frac{2}{5}.$

19. $\phi(t) = \displaystyle\sum_{k=0}^{\infty} c_k t^k,$ where $c_0 = 1,\ c_1 = 2,$

$$c_{k+2} = -\frac{1+k(k-1)}{(k+2)(k+1)}\,c_k \qquad \text{if } k \geq 0.$$

SECTION 4.5.

4. $t = 0$ irregular singular point.
5. $t = \pm 1$ regular singular points.
6. $t = 0$ regular singular point.
7. $t = 0, \pm 1$ regular singular points.
8. $t = 0$ regular singular point.
9. $t = 0, -1$ regular singular points.
10. $t = 0, 1$ regular singular points.
11. $t = 0, -2$ regular singular points.
12. $t = 0$ regular singular point; $t = \pm 1$ irregular singular points.

SECTION 4.6.

9. $c_1\phi_1(t) + c_2\phi_2(t),$ where

$$\phi_1(t) = 1 + \sum_{k=1}^{\infty}\frac{(-1)^k}{1\cdot\frac{3}{2}\cdots k(k+\frac{1}{2})}\,t^k,$$

$$\phi_2(t) = |t|^{-1/2}\left[1 + \sum_{k=1}^{\infty}\frac{(-1)^k}{\frac{1}{2}\cdot 1\cdots(k-\frac{1}{2})k}\,t^k\right]$$

valid on $-\infty < t < 0$ or $0 < t < \infty.$

13. $\phi_j(t) = |t|^{z_j}\displaystyle\sum_{k=0}^{\infty} c_k(z_j)t^k \ (j = 1, 2),$ where

$$z_1 = -\frac{1}{2} + \frac{\sqrt{3}}{2}\,i,\ z_2 = -\frac{1}{2} - \frac{\sqrt{3}}{2}\,i,$$

$$c_k(z_j) = \frac{2(k - 1 + z_j)}{f(z_j + k)} \cdot c_{k-1}(z_j),$$

with $f(z) = z^2 + z + 1$, valid on $0 < |t| < \infty$.

15. $\phi(t) = |t| \sum_{k=0}^{\infty} c_k t^k$, where $c_k = -\dfrac{kc_{k-1}}{f(k + 1)}$, $f(z) =$

$z^2 - 1$, valid on $0 < |t| < \infty$.

17. None, as $t = 0$ is an irregular singular point.

SECTION 4.7.·

3. (a) Two solutions valid for $0 < |t| < \infty$; the one corresponding to the root $z = 0$ of the indicial equation is analytic at $t = 0$.

(c) One solution, analytic for all t.

(e) If 2γ is not an integer or zero, two solutions valid for $0 < |t| < \infty$; if 2γ is an integer or zero, one solution valid for $0 < |t| < \infty$, and if $\gamma = 0$ or γ is an integer this solution is analytic at $t = 0$.

(g) Two solutions valid for $0 < |t| < \infty$, neither of which is analytic at $t = 0$.

4. (a) $\phi(t) = |t|^{1/2} \sum_{k=0}^{\infty} c_k t^k$, where $c_0 = 1$, $c_1 = 0$,

$$c_k = -\frac{c_{k-2}}{f(k + \frac{1}{2})}, \quad f(z) = z^2 - \tfrac{1}{4}.$$

(c) $\phi(t) = \sum_{k=0}^{\infty} c_k t^k$, where $c_0 = 1$, $c_{k+1} = \dfrac{k - \gamma}{f(k)} c_k$,

$f(z) = z^2$.

(f) If c is not a negative integer or zero,

$$\phi(t) = 1 + \frac{a \cdot b}{1 \cdot c} t + \frac{a(a + 1)b(b + 1)}{1 \cdot 2 \cdot c \cdot (c + 1)} t^2 + \cdots$$

$$= F(a, b, c; t) \text{ for } |t| < 1.$$

If c is not a positive integer, there is a second solution $|t|^{1-c} F(a - c + 1, b - c + 1, 2 - c; t)$, also valid for $0 < |t| < 1$. Thus, if c is not zero or an integer the general solution is $AF(a, b, c; t) + B|t|^{1-c} F(a - c + 1, b - c + 1, 2 - c; t)$

5. 1 in each case.

SECTION 4.8.

11. (a) $\phi_j(t) = |t|^{z_i} \sum_{k=0}^{\infty} c_k(z_j) t^k$ with $j = 1, 2$, $z_1 = \frac{1}{2}$,

$$z_2 = 0, \quad c_{k+1}(z_j) = \frac{-\frac{1}{4} c_k(z_j)}{f(z_j + 1 + k)}, \quad f(z) = z^2 - \frac{z}{2}.$$

(b) $\phi_1(t) = \sum_{k=0}^{\infty} c_k t^k$, with $c_k = \dfrac{c_{k-1}}{k^2}$,

$$\phi_2(t) = |t| \sum_{k=0}^{\infty} b_k t^k + \phi_1(t) \log |t|, \text{with } b_0 = 2c_0,$$

$$b_k = \frac{b_{k-1} - 2(k+1)c_{k+1}}{(k+1)^2} \text{ for } k \geq 1.$$

(c) $\phi_j(t) = |t|^{z_j} \sum_{k=0}^{\infty} c_k(z_j) t^k$ with $j = 1, 2,$

$$z_1 = \frac{1}{2} + \frac{\sqrt{5}}{2}, \; z_2 = \frac{1}{2} - \frac{\sqrt{5}}{2},$$

$$c_k(z_j) = -\frac{(k - 1 + z_j)c_{k-1}(z_j)}{f(k + z_j)},$$

$$f(z) = z^2 - z - 2.$$

(d) $\phi_1(t) = |t|^{-1} \sum_{k=0}^{\infty} c_k t^k$ with $c_1 = 0, c_k = \dfrac{c_{k-2}}{f(k-1)}$,

$$(k \geq 2), \; f(z) = z^2 + 4z + 3.$$

$$\phi_2(t) = |t|^{-3} \sum_{k=0}^{\infty} b_k t^k + a\phi_1(t) \log |t|, \text{ with}$$

$$b_0 = 1, \; a = \frac{1}{2c_0}, \; b_{k+3} = \frac{b_{k+1} - a(2k+4)c_{k+1}}{f(k)},$$

$$b_1 = b_3 = \cdots = 0.$$

SECTION 4.9. 23. $c_1 J_p(kt) + c_2 J_{-p}(kt)$ if p is not an integer or zero; $c_1 J_p(kt) + c_2 Y_p(kt)$ if p is an integer or zero.

SECTION 4.10. 6. $p(\infty) = 0, p'(\infty) = 2, q(\infty) = q'(\infty) = q''(\infty) = q'''(\infty) = 0.$

MISCELLANEOUS. 3. (a) $\phi_1(t) = |t|^{1/2} \sum_{k=0}^{\infty} \dfrac{2^k}{(2k+1)!} t^k$,

$$\phi_2(t) = \sum_{k=0}^{\infty} \frac{2^k}{(2k)!} t^k.$$

(c) $\phi_1(t) = |t|, \; \phi_2(t) = |t|^{1/3} \left[1 + \dfrac{2t}{9} \right.$

$$\left. - 2 \sum_{k=2}^{\infty} \frac{(-1)^k 1 \cdot 4 \cdot 7 \cdots (3k-5)}{9^k k!} t^k \right].$$

(d) $\phi_1(t) = 1 + t + t^2$, $\phi_2(t) = \dfrac{|t|^3}{1-t}$ $(|t| < 1)$.

(g) $\phi_1(t) = \displaystyle\sum_{k=0}^{\infty} \dfrac{(-1)^k t^k}{(k+1)!k!}$, $\phi_2(t) = -\phi_1(t) \log |t|$

$$+ |t|^{-1}\left[1 + \sum_{k=1}^{\infty} \dfrac{H_k + H_{k-1}}{k!(k-1)!}(-1)^k t^k \right],$$

where $H_k = 1 + \dfrac{1}{2} + \cdots + \dfrac{1}{k}$.

(i) $\phi_1(t) = |t|(1+t)$, $\phi_2(t) = \phi_1(t) \log |t| - 2|t|^2$

$$\times \left[1 + \sum_{k=2}^{\infty} \dfrac{(-1)^k}{2k(k-1)} t^{k-1} \right].$$

(k) $\phi_1(t) = |t|e^t$, $\phi_2(t) = \phi_1(t) \log |t|$

$$+ 1 - \sum_{k=2}^{\infty} \dfrac{H_k}{(k-1)!} t^k,$$

where $H_k = 1 + \dfrac{1}{2} + \cdots + \dfrac{1}{k}$.

(m) $\phi_1(t) = J_2(t)$, $\phi_2(t) = Y_2(t)$.

4. (c) $\phi_1(t) = |t-1|^{1/2}[1 - \frac{7}{12}(t-1)$
$+ \frac{43}{480}(t-1)^2 + \cdots]$.

5. (d) $c_1 \displaystyle\sum_{k=0}^{\infty} \dfrac{(2k)!}{2^{2k}k!(k+1)!} t^{-2k-1} + c_2 t$, $|t| > 1$.

6. (a) $\phi_1(t) \sim \dfrac{e^t}{\sqrt{t}} \left[1 + \dfrac{1^2}{1!8t} + \dfrac{1^2 3^2}{2!(8t)^2} + \cdots \right]$,

$\phi_2(t) \sim \dfrac{e^{-t}}{\sqrt{t}} \left[1 - \dfrac{1^2}{1!8t} + \dfrac{1^2 3^2}{2!(8t)^2} - \cdots \right]$.

7. (a) $c_1 I_1(t) + c_2 K_1(t)$.

(b) $c_1 t^2 J_2(t) + c_2 t^2 Y_2(t)$.

(c) $c_1 I_{1/2}(t) + c_2 I_{-1/2}(t) = c_1 t^{-1/2} \cosh t$
$+ c_2 t^{-1/2} \sinh t$.

(d) $c_1 t J_{1/2}(t^2) + c_2 t J_{-1/2}(t^2) = c_1 \cos t^2 + c_2 \sin t^2$,
where $I_p(t) = i^{-p}J_p(it)$, $K_1(t) =$
$-\dfrac{\pi}{2}[J_1(it) + iY_1(it)]$.

•CHAPTER 5

SECTION 5.2.   4. $c_1 + c_2 t$.

9. $\sqrt{\lambda_n} = (n + \frac{1}{2})$, $\phi_n(t) = A_n \sin (n + \frac{1}{2})t$
($n = 0, 1, 2, \ldots$).

23. $\sqrt{\lambda_n} = \dfrac{n\pi}{(b - a)}$, $\phi_n(t) = A_n \sin \dfrac{n\pi(t - a)}{b - a}$
($n = 1, 2, \ldots$), where $b > a$.

SECTION 5.3.   11. $\dfrac{(1 + \cos \pi \sqrt{2}) \sin \sqrt{2}\, t}{\sin \pi \sqrt{2}} - \dfrac{1}{2} \cos \sqrt{2}\, t + \dfrac{1}{2}$.

SECTION 5.4.   4. $\alpha\delta - \beta\gamma = 1$.

SECTION 5.5.   4. $p(\pi)(\alpha\delta - \beta\gamma) = p(0)$.

MISCELLANEOUS.   1. (a) $\lambda_n = (n + \frac{1}{2})^2$, $\phi_n(t) = A_n \sin (n + \frac{1}{2})t$,
$n = 0, 1, \ldots$

(c) $\phi_n(t) = \sin \sqrt{\lambda_n}\, t$, where λ_n is a root of
$\sqrt{\lambda} = -\tan \sqrt{\lambda}\, \pi$.

(d) $\lambda_n = n^2$, $\phi_n(t) = A_n e^{-t} \sin nt$,   ($n \geq 1$).

(e) No real eigenvalues.

(f) $\lambda = 0$, $\phi_0(t) = t - 1$.

7. $\sqrt{\lambda_n} = 4n$,
$$\phi_n(t) = \begin{cases} A_n \sin 8nt & 0 \leq t \leq \pi/2 \\ A_n \sin 4n(\pi - t) & \pi/2 < t \leq \pi \end{cases}$$
($n = 1, 2, \ldots$).

12. (a) $\lambda_n = n^2\pi^2$, $\phi_n(t) = e^t \sin n\pi t$, ($n = 1, 2, \ldots$).

(b) $\sqrt{\lambda_n} = 2 \tan \sqrt{\lambda_n} L$, $\phi_n(t) = e^{-2t} \sin \sqrt{\lambda_n}\, t$,
($n = 1, 2, \ldots$).
If $L = \frac{1}{2}$, $\lambda_0 = 0$ is an eigenvalue,
$\phi_0(t) = A_0 t e^{-t}$.
If $L \neq \frac{1}{2}$, $\lambda = 0$ is not an eigenvalue.
If $L < \frac{1}{2}$ there are no negative eigenvalues,
while if $L > \frac{1}{2}$ there is one negative eigen-
value.

13. (a) $\lambda_n = \left(\dfrac{n\pi}{L}\right)^4$, $\phi_n(t) = A_n \sin \dfrac{n\pi t}{L}$,
($n = 1, 2, \ldots$).

(b) $\sin \sqrt[4]{\lambda_n} L \cosh \sqrt[4]{\lambda_n} L$
$- \cos \sqrt[4]{\lambda_n} L \sinh \sqrt[4]{\lambda_n} L = 0,$

$$\phi_n(t) = \frac{A_n}{\sinh \sqrt[4]{\lambda_n} L} [\sin \sqrt[4]{\lambda_n} t \sinh \sqrt[4]{\lambda_n} L$$
$$- \sin \sqrt[4]{\lambda_n} L \sinh \sqrt[4]{\lambda_n} t].$$

14. (a) $\dfrac{\cos \sqrt{\lambda} \sin \sqrt{\lambda} t + \sin \sqrt{\lambda} \cos \sqrt{\lambda} t}{\sin 2 \sqrt{\lambda}}$

if $\sin 2 \sqrt{\lambda} \neq 0$.

(c) $e^{-2t} \left[\dfrac{\sqrt{\lambda} \sin \sqrt{\lambda} L + 2 \cos \sqrt{\lambda} L}{\sqrt{\lambda} \cos \sqrt{\lambda} L - 2 \sin \sqrt{\lambda} L} \sin \sqrt{\lambda} t \right.$
$\left. + \cos \sqrt{\lambda} t \right]$

if $\sqrt{\lambda} \cos \sqrt{\lambda} L - 2 \sin \sqrt{\lambda} L \neq 0$.

(f) No solution.

(g) $c \cos 2t + \frac{1}{3} \cos t$, c arbitrary.

(i) $\dfrac{(\cos 1) - 1}{\sin 1} \sin t - \cos t + 1$.

•CHAPTER 6

SECTION 6.1.

3. $m_3 x_3'' + k_3(x_3 - x_2 - x_1) = F(t),$
$m_2 x_2'' + k_2(x_2 - x_1) - k_3(x_3 - x_2 - x_1) = 0,$
$m_1 x_1'' + k_1 x_1 - k_2(x_2 - x_1) = 0,$
$x_1(0) = x_2(0) = x_3(0) = 0,$
$x_1'(0) = x_2'(0) = x_3'(0) = 0.$

4. $L_1 i_1' + R_1 i_1 - R_1 i_2 = 0,$ $L_1 i_1' + L_2 i_2' + R_2 i_2 = 0.$

SECTION 6.2.

6. $y_1' = 3y_1^2 - 2y_1 y_2 + 3y_2^2,$
$y_2' = -2y_1^2 + 2y_1 y_2 - 2y_2^2.$

13. $\psi(t) = c(e^{-t}, e^{-t})$, c any nonzero constant.

14. $\phi(t) = (2e^{-t}, 2e^t - e^{-t})$, $-\infty < t < \infty$.

15. $\phi(t) =$
$$\left(2e^{-t}, e^{t^2/2} \left\{ 1 + 2 \int_0^t \exp \left(-u - \frac{u^2}{2} \right) du \right\} \right).$$

17. $\phi(t) = \left(\int_0^t [g(u) + f(u)] \, du, \int_0^t g(u) \, du \right)$, where
$$g(u) = e^{2u} \int_0^u e^{-2s} f(s) \, ds.$$

SECTION 6.3.

2. $f(t) \equiv 0.$

SECTION 6.4.   2.

$$A(t) = \begin{pmatrix} 0 & 1 & 0 & \cdots & & 0 \\ 0 & 0 & 1 & \cdots & & 0 \\ \cdot & \cdot & \cdot & & & \cdot \\ \cdot & \cdot & \cdot & & & \cdot \\ \cdot & \cdot & \cdot & & & \cdot \\ 0 & 0 & 0 & \cdots & \cdots & 1 \\ -a_n(t) & a_{n-1}(t) & -a_{n-2}(t) & \cdots & -a_1(t) & \end{pmatrix}, \quad g(t) = \begin{pmatrix} 0 \\ \cdot \\ \cdot \\ \cdot \\ 0 \\ b(t) \end{pmatrix}.$$

5. The system has a solution if and only if the rank of the coefficient matrix is equal to the rank of the augmented matrix.

8. $(\Phi^{-1})' = -\Phi^{-1}\Phi'\Phi^{-1}$.

11. $|\phi(t)| \le \left(|\phi(t_0)| \right.$

$$\left. + \int_{-\infty}^{\infty} |g(t)| \, dt \right) \exp\left(\int_{-\infty}^{\infty} |A(t)| \, dt \right).$$

SECTION 6.5.   18. $c = \tilde{\Phi}^{-1}(t_0)\mathbf{d}$.

27. (b) No, because $A(t)$ is not continuous at $t = 0$.

SECTION 6.6.   3. $\phi(t) = (-\frac{2}{25} \cos t - \frac{14}{25} \sin t + \frac{3}{5}e^{2t}(t-1),$
$-\frac{2}{5} \cos t + \frac{1}{5} \sin t - \frac{3}{5}e^{2t})$.

SECTION 6.7.   8. $\Phi(t) = e^{-2t} \begin{pmatrix} 1 & t & t^2/2 \\ 0 & 1 & t \\ 0 & 0 & 1 \end{pmatrix}$.

9. $\Phi(t) = \begin{pmatrix} 1 & t & \frac{t^2}{2} & \cdots & & \frac{t^{n-1}}{(n-1)!} \\ & 0 & 1 & t & \cdots & \\ & 0 & 0 & 1 & & \\ & \cdot & \cdot & \cdot & & \cdot \\ & \cdot & \cdot & & & \cdot \\ & \cdot & \cdot & & & \cdot \\ 0 & 0 & 0 & & 0 & 1 \end{pmatrix}$.

13. $\phi(t) = (2e^{5t} + e^{-t}, 4e^{5t} - e^{-t})$.

15. Fundamental matrix is

$$\Phi(t) = \begin{pmatrix} e^{-3t} & e^{(2+\sqrt{7})t} & e^{(2-\sqrt{7})t} \\ -\frac{7}{3}e^{-3t} & \dfrac{-5 + 4\sqrt{7}}{3}e^{(2+\sqrt{7})t} & \dfrac{-5 - 4\sqrt{7}}{3}e^{(2-\sqrt{7})t} \\ -\frac{4}{3}e^{-3t} & \dfrac{1 + \sqrt{7}}{3}e^{(2+\sqrt{7})t} & \dfrac{1 - \sqrt{7}}{3}e^{(2-\sqrt{7})t} \end{pmatrix}.$$

17. $(-\frac{1}{5} \sin t - \frac{3}{5} \cos t + \frac{19}{15}e^{2t} + \frac{1}{3}e^t,$
$-\frac{1}{5} \sin t + \frac{2}{5} \cos t + \frac{19}{15}e^{2t} - \frac{2}{3}e^{-t})$.

SECTION 6.8.   3. $K \geq K_1|\mathbf{c}| + \dfrac{1 - e^{-\sigma T}}{\sigma} K_1K_2 + \dfrac{K_1M}{|a - \sigma|} e^{aT}.$

4. $|\phi'(t)| \leq e^{bt}[K|A| + M].$

SECTION 6.9.   1. $\phi(t) = (\eta_1 e^{2t}, \eta_2 e^{3t})$

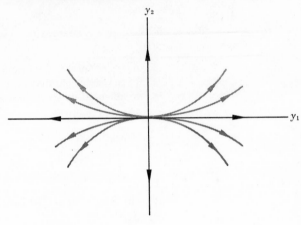

3. $\phi(t) = (\eta_1 e^{2t}, \eta_2 e^{-3t}).$

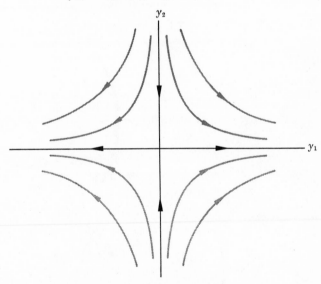

15. Node, not an attractor.
17. Saddle point, not an attractor.
19. Node, attractor.
21. Saddle point, not an attractor.

MISCELLANEOUS.   1. (a) $\begin{pmatrix} e^t & e^{5t} \\ -e^t & 3e^{5t} \end{pmatrix}$.

(c) $\begin{pmatrix} e^{2t}\cos t & e^{2t}\sin t \\ e^{2t}(\cos t - \sin t) & e^{2t}(\cos t + \sin t) \end{pmatrix}$.

(g) $\begin{pmatrix} e^t & 0 & e^{-t} \\ e^t & e^{2t} & 0 \\ 0 & 2e^{2t} & -e^{-t} \end{pmatrix}$.

(k) $\begin{pmatrix} 1 & t & 4e^{3t} \\ -2 & 1-2t & 4e^{3t} \\ 1 & -1+t & e^{3t} \end{pmatrix}$.

(m) $e^{2t}\begin{pmatrix} 1 & t & t^2 \\ 2 & -1+2t & -2t+2t^2 \\ 1 & -1+t & 2-2t+t^2 \end{pmatrix}$.

3. (a) $\begin{pmatrix} e^t & e^{-t} \\ e^t & -e^{-t} \end{pmatrix}\mathbf{c} + \begin{pmatrix} te^t - t^2 - 2 \\ (t-1)e^t - 2t \end{pmatrix}$.

(c) $\begin{pmatrix} e^t & 3e^{2t} \\ e^t & 2e^{2t} \end{pmatrix}\mathbf{c} + \begin{pmatrix} \cos t - 2\sin t \\ 2(\cos t - \sin t) \end{pmatrix}$.

4. $\mathbf{p} = -(A - mE)^{-1}\mathbf{c}$.

7. $t^A\mathbf{c} + t^A \int_{t_0}^t s^{-A}\mathbf{b}(s)\, ds$, where either $t_0 > 0, t > 0$.

or $t_0 < 0,\ t < 0$.

8. (d) $y_1(t) = \frac{1}{2} - 2e^t + \frac{3}{2}e^{2t}$, $y_2(t) = 1 - e^t$.

•CHAPTER 7

SECTION 7.1.   1. $y(t) = 1 + \int_1^t \{s^2 + [y(s)]^4\}\, ds$.

6. (a) $K \geq 48$.   (b) $K \geq \max\limits_{-100 \leq t \leq 100} |p(t)|$

$+ \max\limits_{-100 \leq t \leq 100} |q(t)|$.

(c) $K \geq (2/e)^{1/2}$.

9. $\phi_0(t) = 1$, $\phi_1(t) = \sum\limits_{j=1}^k \dfrac{t^j}{j!}$.

11. $\phi_0(t) = 0$, $\phi_1(t) = t$, $\phi_2(t) = \sin t$,

$\phi_3(t) = \int_0^t \cos(\sin s)\, ds$.

14. Yes, to $\phi(t) \equiv 0$.

15. Yes, to $\phi_1(t)$.

MISCELLANEOUS.   2. $|\phi(t) - \phi_m(t)|$

$\leq K_1 K_2{}^m |t - t_0|^m \left\{ \dfrac{1}{m!} + \dfrac{K_2|t - t_0|}{(m+1)!} + \cdots \right\}$.

•CHAPTER 8

SECTION 8.1.	4. Yes, $\phi(t) \equiv 0$.
SECTION 8.4.	3. Yes.
SECTION 8.6.	1. See answer to Exercise 3 in Miscellaneous Exercises below.
MISCELLANEOUS.	1. (a) (i) $\phi(1) \approx 34.411$.

                (ii) $\phi(1) \approx 59.938$.

               (iii) $\phi(1) \approx 64.858$.

               (Exact value is 64.898.)

      (c) Exact value is infinite—for which methods, if any, does the numerical approximation suggest this?

    3. (a) $y_{1,n+1} = y_{1,n} + hf_1(t_n, y_{1,n}, y_{2,n})$

          $y_{2,n+1} = y_{2,n} + hf_2(t_n, y_{1,n}, y_{2,n})$.

    7. (a) True value is $\frac{2}{3}$.

•CHAPTER 9

SECTION 9.2.

    3. (a) $\dfrac{s^2 + 2\beta^2}{s(s^2 + 4\beta^2)}$ $\Re s > 0$.

      (b) $\dfrac{\beta}{s^2 + 4\beta^2}$ $\Re s > 0$.

    5. $\dfrac{2(1 - e^{-\pi s})}{s^2 + 4}$ $(\Re s > 0)$.

   11. $\dfrac{1}{s^2}\dfrac{1 - e^{-as/2}}{1 + e^{-as/2}}$ $(\Re s > 0)$.

SECTION 9.3.

    7. (a) $-2 + \frac{5}{2}e^{-t} + \frac{1}{2}e^{-3t}$.

      (c) $1 - \cos 2t - t \sin 2t$.

      (e) $\displaystyle\int_0^t \sin(t - u)f(u)\,du$.

SECTION 9.4.

    3. $\dfrac{1}{\sigma(z_2 - z_1)}\left(e^{-z_1(t-\sigma)} - e^{-z_2(t-\sigma)} + e^{-z_2 t} - e^{-z_1 t}\right)$.

    5. $e^{3t} - e^{2t}$.

    7. $\frac{1}{24}e^{2t} - \frac{1}{24}e^{-t}\left(\cos\sqrt{3}\,t + \dfrac{5\sqrt{3}}{3}\sin\sqrt{3}\,t\right) + \dfrac{t}{12}e^{2t}$.

    9. $\frac{1}{48}(25e^{3t} + 23e^{-3t}) - \frac{1}{8}\sin t$.

   11. $\frac{1}{2}(e^{(t-1)} - e^{-(t-1)})$.

   13. $\cos 2t + \frac{1}{2}\sin 2t + \frac{1}{2}\displaystyle\int_0^t \sin 2(t - x)f(x)\,dx$.

   15. $\frac{1}{13}e^{2t} + \alpha\cos 3t + \beta\sin 3t$.

SECTION 9.5.

    3. $\phi_1(t) = \dfrac{t}{2} + 1$, $\phi_2(t) = -\dfrac{t}{2}$.

    5. $\phi_1(t) = \frac{1}{4}e^{-2t} + \frac{2}{3}e^{-t} + \frac{1}{12}e^{2t}$, $\phi_2(t) = \frac{1}{3}(e^{-t} - e^{2t})$.

6. $\phi_2(t)$ is any function for which $\phi_2(0) = 1$, $\phi_2'(0)$
   $= 0$, $\phi_1(t) = e^t - \int_0^t e^{(t-u)}\phi_2'(s)\,ds$.

MISCELLANEOUS. 1. (a) $\dfrac{\omega}{s^2 + \omega^2} \dfrac{1}{1 - e^{-\pi s/\omega}}$.

    (b) $\dfrac{1}{(s^2 + 1)(s + 1)}$.

    (c) $\dfrac{15}{8s^3}\left(\dfrac{\pi}{s}\right)^{1/2}$ $(\Re s > 0)$.

    (d) $\dfrac{2\omega(3s^2 - \omega^2)}{(s^2 + \omega^2)^3}$ $(\Re s > 0)$.

2. (a) $2e^{2t}(1 + t) - \frac{1}{2}\sin 2t$.

  (c) $3 - 2\cos t + 2[t - 4\sin (t - 4)]U(t - 4)$,
     where $U(t)$ is the unit step function (p. 410).

8. (a) $-1 + 2t + 2t^2 + e^{-2t}$.

  (b) $t^3 + \frac{1}{20}t^5$.

  (c) $1 + 2te^t$.

  (d) $\frac{1}{2}t^2$.

  (e) $4 + \frac{5}{2}t^2 + \frac{1}{24}t^4$.

INDEX